On a Steel Horse I Ride

A History of the MH-53 Pave Low Helicopters in War and Peace

Darrel D. Whitcomb

Air University Press
Air Force Research Institute
Maxwell Air Force Base, Alabama

September 2012

Library of Congress Cataloging-in-Publication Data

Whitcomb, Darrel D., 1947–
    On a steel horse I ride : a history of the MH-53 Pave Low helicopters in
    war and peace / Darrel D. Whitcomb.
        p. cm.
    Includes bibliographical references and index.
    ISBN 978-1-58566-220-3
1. Sikorsky H-53 (Military transport helicopter)—History. 2. United States. Air
Force—Search and rescue operations—History. 3. United States. Air Force—History.
I. Title. II. Title: History of the MH-53 Pave Low helicopters in war and peace.
    UG1232.T72W55 2012
    358.4—dc23

                                                                    2012022142

Cover photo of MH-53M #68-10357 courtesy of Air Force Special Operations Command
Public Affairs

Disclaimer

AIR FORCE RESEARCH INSTITUTE

Air University Press
Air Force Research Institute
155 North Twining Street
Maxwell AFB, AL 36112-6026
http://aupress.au.af.mil

*Dedicated to
the Airmen of Pave Low who conceptualized it,
created it, operated it, maintained it, lived it, loved it,
and, yes, sometimes cursed it. It was your creation—
your Steel Horse—and you rode it well. You were
the "quiet professionals," the reality of the motto
Any Time, Any Place, and yours were the collective
"hearts of man" that made it all work.*

Contents

PART II

FROM CONCEPT TO CAPABILITY

PART IV

INTO THE MILLENNIUM

Illustrations

Figures

Photos

xvii

CONTENTS

Foreword

It is my honor to contribute to this book—a tribute to the Pave Low weapon system and its place in our nation's proud heritage of military aviation. The passing of time since the Pave Low was retired in September 2008 has given the community of those who were involved with these venerable aircraft—including those who still serve in Air Force special operations forces (SOF), very often in harm's way—an opportunity to reflect on this milestone and its significance to the US Air Force and the US Special Operations Command (USSOCOM). This volume is a thoughtful retrospective not only for Pave Low veterans but also for those who have never had the privilege of working on or with this historic aircraft.

The "quiet professionals" of the Air Force Special Operations Command (AFSOC) make up a close-knit community—one that takes great pride in holding to its traditions and in helping to provide for our nation's security, often through unique and game-changing contributions, and with little fanfare. Along with its joint comrades-in-arms in USSOCOM, this community of Airmen has embraced, over the decades, a handful of principles that came to be known as the SOF Truths. The first of these precepts—"Humans are more important than hardware"—captures the essence of what sets SOF apart: the *people* of SOF, not necessarily the equipment. SOF personnel believe that the right people, when properly trained and working as a team, can accomplish the mission with the appropriate equipment, and that no level of technology can compensate for the lack of properly trained, experienced people in creating SOF effects. This is especially true at H-hour, when mission execution is at hand.

But this does not alleviate the need for very capable equipment to complement our people when they are called upon to act. Hard-fought experience also informs us of the critical need to invest in equipment that has been designed for the most demanding missions—a lesson that our nation has learned in the aftermath of both operational successes and disappointments. This lesson led to the development of the first CH-53s to meet requirements that were established nearly five decades ago by the US Marine Corps, just as the lessons learned in Vietnam and beyond led to the development of a series of Pave Low modifications for the US Air Force's C/HH-53 variants, enhancing their capabilities considerably. The Pave Low became a critical component of AFSOC, whose largest subordinate unit, the 1st Special

Operations Wing, proudly maintains the motto Any Time, Any Place. The Pave Low was a key enabler of that promise.

In its era—which spanned some three decades—the Pave Low, along with crews and support personnel, deployed to combat and humanitarian operations in hot spots across the globe, such as Panama, Kuwait, Haiti, Bosnia, Serbia, the Horn of Africa, Afghanistan, and Iraq. Of the original 72 C/HH-53 aircraft that were built for the Air Force, only 30 made it to retirement—a testament to the perilous environments and dangerous times in which they flew.

Ultimately, the story of Pave Low bears out the first SOF Truth: Pave Low proved to be a highly capable and impressive aircraft, but more significantly, the people behind Pave Low, and those who served with it, were, and always will be, even more impressive. The Pave Low family spans the decades, beginning with the veterans of conflict in Southeast Asia who conceptualized the Pave Low, tested it, made it operational, and served as the initial cadre of leaders of units equipped with Pave Low. Those who followed cut their teeth in action during the 1990s and served as leaders of operations in the aftermath of 9/11. More recently, the young troops and crew members who came into their own during the demanding missions in Afghanistan and Iraq have acquitted themselves admirably, tirelessly maintaining and flying these aging but storied aircraft through the last years of Pave Low's operational service life. We must also remember the members of this family who have passed during the Pave Low era, including those who gave their lives in selfless service to our nation. The story of Pave Low is the story of all who envisioned, created, modified, maintained, and operated Pave Low throughout its service life, and to them goes the credit for the remarkable contributions of this unique aircraft and the red scarves that adorned her cabins.

NORTON A. SCHWARTZ
General, USAF
Chief of Staff

About the Author

Darrel Whitcomb is a career aviator. A 1969 graduate of the US Air Force Academy, he served three tours in Southeast Asia as a cargo pilot and forward air controller (FAC), including duty as a Raven FAC. After a tour as a T-38 instructor pilot, he transferred to the Air Force Reserve, where he flew A-37s and A-10s. He attended the Army Command and Staff College and the National War College and also served on the Air Staff and Joint Staff and at the Air Force Doctrine Center, retiring as a colonel in 1999.

The author was also a career airline pilot for Delta Airlines and retired as an international captain in 2003.

A noted writer on aviation history, personnel recovery, and combat search and rescue, he has published numerous articles in several magazines and periodicals. His first book, *The Rescue of Bat 21*, was published in 1998; his second book, *Combat Search and Rescue in Desert Storm*, in 2006; and his third book, *Call-Sign Dustoff: A History of U.S. Army Aeromedical Evacuation from Conception to Hurricane Katrina*, in 2011. Still active in aviation, he served a tour as a contract pilot in Iraq in 2004.

Acknowledgments

This work has afforded me an opportunity to meet an eclectic group of individuals who have facilitated its creation. I acknowledge their support and enthusiasm and state openly that I could not have done this without them. I began this project with a trip to Hurlburt AFB, Florida. There I met with Mr. Herb Mason, the AFSOC historian. He and his office mates, Tim Brown, Randy Bergeron, and Cindy Scharf, helped me complete all of the administrative processing necessary to gain the accesses I required to start my work. Through my successive visits, they were absolutely selfless in helping me research and find the story.

The 1st Special Operations Wing, also located at Hurlburt, is the premier AFSOC unit and has adopted as its motto Any Time, Any Place. It has had Pave Low helicopters assigned to it since 1980, and its historian, Keith Alexander, opened the unit's voluminous files for my use.

While on that initial visit to Hurlburt, I also attended the Air Commando Association annual reunion and began to meet veterans from the Pave Low community. The next week, I was able to attend the bittersweet ceremonies held to mark the retirement of the fleet of the Pave Low aircraft.

I was also able to meet with Lt Gen Donny Wurster, the commander of AFSOC. He graciously gave me an illuminating interview and his thoughts and guidance on this project.

Those events gave me an opportunity to conduct interviews with several Pave Low crew members. My first was with Col Gary Weikel, USAF, retired, a consummate warrior who truly lived the early years of Pave Low and, in his own way, helped to infuse into the community an earnest desire to fly and utilize the machines to their very limits in support of the special forces teams that they carry. I made the acquaintance of John Grove, another retired Air Force officer and Pave Low veteran. After his flying days ended, he maintained a strong affiliation with the Pave Low community and, de facto, became its "historian." It immediately became abundantly clear to me that I could not find or follow the Pave Low story without his help. Early on, he sat with me for an interview, provided many critical "vectors" for this journey, and helped me contact many others so critical to the telling of the story. Unfortunately, John passed away quite suddenly and unexpectedly just two months later. The powerful and moving response of the Pave Low community to his passing was vivid testimony to its love and respect for this man.

Hurlburt has a well-stocked base library, and I was able to accomplish initial basic research in their facility. I gratefully acknowledge the generous support provided by the librarians there. The Air Commando Association also opened its library to me, and its leader, Felix Sambogna, and office support personnel were most helpful in obtaining some great historical data.

I had an opportunity to travel to Stratford, Connecticut, to visit the Sikorsky Aircraft Corporation. While there, I spent several hours in its archives and, with the assistance of the archives' director, Mr. Dan Libertino, was able to find quite a bit of information on the initial production of the Air Force HH- and CH-53 helicopters. I was also able to have a long and interesting discussion with Mr. Tom Lawrence, a 31-year Sikorsky veteran, who explained the initial evolution of the Pave Low program from Sikorsky's perspective.

The Pentagon is a rich source of information, and I was able to do some significant research there, graciously supported by Col Henry Sanders and the Airmen in the AFSOC Liaison Office, located in the Air Force section of the building.

A few weeks later, I traveled to Wright-Patterson AFB, Ohio, to visit with Ms. Diana Cornelisse, the historian for the Aeronautical Systems Center of the Air Force Materiel Command. She shared with me a wealth of documents pertaining to the conceptualization and initial development of Pave Low. I also visited with Col Ron Thurlow, USAF, retired. He has collected an extensive history of the Pave Low aircraft by specific tail number and generously reviewed his collection with me. Dr. Jeff Greenwood hosted me for a quick visit to the Research Division of the National Museum of the US Air Force. There Brett Stolle and his assistant, Christina Douglass, helped me find documents and photographs in their collections.

From there, I went to Maxwell AFB, Alabama, to visit the Air Force Historical Research Agency (AFHRA), where I was greeted by Dr. Forrest Marion. He, Joe Caver, and Joe's two able assistants, Sylvester Jackson and Juan Rackley, helped me find a trove of documents and histories. Many were still marked as classified or otherwise restricted, and Archie Difante and Anne O'Connor were able to review and release most of them. All of the AFHRA staff members were absolutely selfless in their support of my efforts as I made several subsequent visits to their facility.

I made a research trip to Fort Rucker, Alabama, the home of US Army Aviation, to visit the Aviation Technical Library. Jill Redington, Beata Totten, and their team helped me collect a great deal of data concerning Pave Low operations in conjunction with various Army aviation units, especially the famed 160th Special Operations Aviation Regiment—the Night Stalkers.

Traveling to MacDill AFB, Florida, I visited the Special Operations Command History Office. Lt Col Mike Simpson and Ms. Gaea Levy generously supported me as I reviewed historical documents pertaining to the creation of that command and specific items relating to Pave Low.

One of the unsung heroes in the Pave Low saga is former congressman Earl Hutto. From 1979 to 1995, he represented the 1st Congressional District of Florida, which includes Hurlburt AFB and Pensacola. He played a key role in supporting the Pave Low program in its formative years. His congressional papers are now held in the special collection section of the John C. Pace Library at the University of West Florida in Pensacola. I visited the facility, and the curator, Mr. Dean DeBolt, graciously allowed me to peruse the collection and copy several key documents pertaining to the congressman's involvement with Pave Low.

Kirtland AFB and Cannon AFB, New Mexico, were my next stops. At Kirtland, I was able to do some great research in the historical files at the Air Force Operational Test and Evaluation Center, generously facilitated by its historian, Dr. Barren Oder, and his assistant, Stephen Watson. I also conducted interviews with numerous Pave Low crew members now serving in the 71st SOS and 58th SOW, as well as with retired veterans in the area. At Cannon AFB, I interviewed Pave Low veterans now stationed there with the 27th SOW. Returning to Kirtland, I was also able to procure documents concerning CH/HH/MH-53 crashes from Mr. Louie Alley at the Air Force Safety Center. I also visited the 377th Air Base Wing, where the unit public affairs director, Jillian Speake, helped me conduct research in the historical files of its base newspaper.

Throughout my research, I made many trips to Hurlburt. So many helped me collect data at many locations on the base and in the Fort Walton Beach area. Lt Col Kent Landreth at the 18th Flight Test Squadron allowed me to spend a day with his archivist, Anissa Rush, who provided me the opportunity to dig through the squadron's test files on Pave Low. Lt Col Gene Becker, the last 20th SOS commander, and TSgt Vince DePersio are the local keepers of the Pave Low lore and helped me find and review a trove of historical "stuff" collected by that unit over the years, including some formal histories, after action reports, photos, and personal vignettes containing rich portions of the story of Pave Low. Ms. Linda Murchison is the archivist for the *Northwest Daily News* in Fort Walton Beach. She graciously helped me recover numerous articles from the newspaper tracing the history of Pave Low and the 20th SOS. I was also able to visit the offices of the *Hurlburt Patriot,* where Ms. Deborah Tipton helped me collect several articles that had been done on the Pave Lows and their Airmen. While visiting Robins AFB, Georgia, I was able to have a long background conversation with Mr. Steve Sherburne, Mr. Walt Seefeld, and Mr. Scott Stringer, who all provided me with a tutorial on the logistical history of the Pave Low helicopters.

I must also recognize the unwavering support of my key partner in this endeavor—my wife, Chris. She has been with me throughout this journey, working transcriptions, reviewing my writing, and providing me with the critical guidance so necessary to bring a project like this to maturity. She is the sweetness in my life.

Throughout the project, though, I have labored with one formidable limitation. A great deal of the Pave Low story is classified, and must remain so for a long time, if not forever. This has made the research process challenging and, at times, frustrating, as I am unable to use key parts of the story. That immutable fact precludes a full telling of the tales in this effort. So it must be.

I offer a sincere thank you and salute to all of the men and women whom I interviewed for the work. My mythical goal was to interview all who ever flew or were associated with these aircraft. Practically, though, that was unachievable. However, I amassed quite a list of potential interviewees, nominated to me by the participants themselves. I subsequently interviewed a broad cross-section of the community, enabling me to capture the essence—but certainly not all—of the story. However, no book can tell it all.

I have done my best to accurately record and use their words and hold in deepest confidence all of those background discussions so necessary to the understanding of the larger story. To all I interviewed I say, your words are the heart of the tale; they are the heart of man.

I honor, too, those who did not want to be interviewed. I understand that. So much of this story is about war. That searing experience touches its participants in different ways. Some troops love it; some troops hate it; all are changed in so many unpredictable ways by the experience.

To all—I offer a sharp and humble hand salute!

Introduction

Any Time, Any Place

—1st Special Operations Wing motto

The Conjure

Pave Low. The term itself generates an image: a dark, wispy night; a low, pulsating rumble approaching from the distance. The rumble becomes a presence, a large helicopter that settles onto the ground amidst the deep darkness. Earnest men of determination spew forth from it. Heavily armed, they quickly set up to collect intelligence, kill enemy troops, rescue downed or isolated friendly personnel, or otherwise conduct a direct action mission.

Mission complete, they just as quickly reassemble, reboard the aircraft, and then disappear into the consuming darkness. It is a powerful image—a conjure, if you will—that strikes fear into any enemy of the United States.

But the conjure is real. It is a helicopter called the MH-53J/M. That machine is the end result of the evolution of state-of-the-art avionics, communication, and navigation equipment crewed by highly motivated, enthusiastic, and smart young operators well steeped in the principles, heritage, and credo of special operations. It is the classic combination of men and machine.

Those aircraft and Airmen were assigned to the US Air Force Special Operations Command (AFSOC), "America's specialized airpower . . . a step ahead in a changing world, delivering special operations power anytime, anywhere."[1] AFSOC controls a mixed fleet of both rotary- and fixed-wing aircraft to facilitate the fulfillment of that mission. However, the single aircraft that, in its day, has best epitomized that role is the Pave Low helicopter. It, perhaps more than any other aircraft, allowed the AFSOC to realize its purpose.

But it was not always so. The aircraft themselves were revolutionary combinations of new, more powerful turbine engines with rotary-wing aircraft to produce vastly increased lifting power. Conceptualized, built, and designated for simpler missions, they were immediately swept up into the long war in Southeast Asia. There they proved the efficacy of the aircraft for dangerous rescue missions, for the initiation of a whole new generation of developing avionics and navigation technology, for providing challenging direct support to small special forces teams and indigenous forces inserted behind enemy lines, and for a myriad of other things that heavy-lift helicopters could be assigned to do. In accomplishing all of that, they also trained a whole generation of men who learned of combat along the Ho Chi Minh Trail in Laos and at other places like Quang Tri, South Vietnam; Son Tay, North Vietnam; and Koh Tang Island, Cambodia.

After that conflict, those aircraft and men were returned to peacetime locations and duties, and much was forgotten of those dangerous times and missions. However, a cadre of dedicated combat aviators and commanders felt that the aircraft and community of Airmen had much more to give. Foreseeing an ever-dangerous world, they harnessed those aircraft to a series of evolving new technologies that vastly improved the aircraft by giving them the ability to traverse airspace in any weather conditions, day and night, and to avoid enemy threats. That concept was validated in operations in Panama, Kuwait, Iraq, Serbia, Afghanistan, and many more smaller and quieter operations in between. The men and aircraft also showed the larger utilitarian value of the aircraft as, over the years, they were called out many times to provide natural disaster and humanitarian relief from Africa to New Orleans, Louisiana.

As good as the new technology was, though, that validation was the end result of the hard work and sweat equity of a small but driven cadre of officers and enlisted Airmen who took the concepts and promises of the engineers and technicians and made it all work. The second commander of AFSOC, Maj Gen Bruce Fister, explained this critical relationship when he stated, "In order for Air Force special operations forces (AFSOF) to fight and win, only one factor is more important than technology—its people. This is not to underestimate the importance of technological superiority. However, no technology supporting AFSOF has or will ever count unless its people are superior as well."[2]

That combination of the right technology with the right aviators was the essence—the very heart—of what Pave Low became. This was an attribute long understood by military commanders and historians. In the mid-1800s, the noted French commander and theorist Charles Ardant du Picq conducted detailed and exhaustive studies into this relationship. Studying conflict over eons and leavening his work with his own observations in several conflicts, he noted presciently, "The art of war is subject to many modifications by industrial and scientific progress. However, there is truly one constant, and that is the heart of man."[3]

It is doubtful that many Pave Low crew members were students of du Picq. It is certain, though, that this identified essence was clearly understood and passed down from generation to generation through the Pave Low community. The aircraft were ultimately retired but not the spirit and values that were instilled in its personnel. That power still exists and has been spread throughout the AFSOC and Air Force as they continue to serve this great nation today.

But Pave Low was never exclusively about work; there were light moments, too. When the young Airmen had the opportunity to party, they enjoyed those times with just as much verve and enthusiasm, accompanied by the calling card of youth—ever-present loud music. Long ago, one of the young Airmen heard a vibrant tune that seemed to capture their spirit. That song, "Wanted Dead or Alive" (performed by the American rock band Bon Jovi), proclaims:

> I'm a cowboy, on a steel horse I ride
> I'm wanted dead or alive
> Wanted dead or alive . . .
> I play for keeps, 'cause I might not make it back.[4]

The men of Pave Low stole that song as their anthem. When the Pave Low guys sang it, they sang it loud and enthusiastically. It's a Pave Low thing.

Notes

1. "Air Force Special Operations Command," USAF fact sheet.
2. "Quotes," permanent file, box 253, AFSOC/HO.
3. Jacobs, "Human Element of Battle," 36.
4. Waller, *Commandos*, 172.

PART I

A Rich Heritage

Chapter 1

From End to Beginning

It wasn't just a job; it was a brotherhood.

—TSgt Corey Fossbender
20th Expeditionary Special
Operations Squadron

Last Mission

27 September 2008, Southwest Asia

It was almost 2 a.m. when the six helicopters from the 20th Expeditionary Special Operations Squadron (ESOS) approached the airfield in formation. The pilots of the MH-53 aircraft, using the call signs Cowboy 21 through 26 and led by their squadron commander, Lt Col Gene Becker, called the control tower for landing instructions. Pro forma, they were directed to land in their designated parking area on the crowded west side of the huge complex.

It had been a relatively routine night for the crews. Unlike most other evenings, the Pave Low crews were not involved in any direct action missions against enemy forces. Maj Brian Roberts, the designated flight lead, had initially planned and led the mission that night, with Capt Dan Florence—the most junior Pave Low pilot—as his co-pilot. Colonel Becker rode in the back. After a six-ship takeoff, Roberts directed the formation to split into three two-ship elements to deliver supplies and personnel to multiple safe houses and forward operating locations (FOL) to further facilitate taking the fight to the enemy.

Toward the end of the evening, Roberts reassembled the formation at an airfield about 15 minutes from the crews' home base for gas and an impromptu rally with other squadron personnel assigned there to work with the Iraqi air force. After the last element of Pave Lows landed and refueled, Colonel Becker took Roberts's place. Captain Florence assumed that he would be the pilot to give up his seat. Instead, Becker made it clear that he wanted to fly with Florence so that the senior and junior Pave Low pilots present would fly together on this last mission to lead the formation back to their assigned base. Florence was deeply appreciative of the gesture.[1]

The approaches and landings were uneventful. As the aircraft reached their designated parking spots, the crew chiefs signaled to the aircrews to shut down their engines. Becker had briefed that they would shut down together and explained, "Once all of the crews were ready to shut down the engines, we announced on radio, '3, 2, 1, throttles off now,' and then a few seconds later, '3, 2, 1, rotor brake now.' All six aircraft's rotors stopped together."[2]

It was with a heavy heart that the flight engineers pulled the throttles to shut off, engaged the rotor brake, and listened, for the last time, to the sound of the engines and rotors slowly spinning to a halt. For not only were the missions complete for the night, the lifetime mission for the last active MH-53 Pave Low aircraft was also at its end. These six aircraft were the last of the entire Pave Low fleet to fly. All of their sister aircraft had been decommissioned over the previous two years. Said career flight engineer SMSgt Mark Pryor, as he stepped off of his aircraft, "When I grabbed those throttles and pulled them off for the last time and realized that this is the last time I will fly on the Pave Low and work with this group of guys, it was bittersweet."[3] Some of the aircraft had "extra" crew members on board. The Air Force Special Operations Command (AFSOC) commander, Lt Gen Donald Wurster, himself a former Pave Low pilot, made a quick trip

Courtesy US Special Operations Command Public Affairs

Pave Lows taking off from Balad AB, Iraq, on their last sorties

to the theater to mark the occasion. He wanted to share the memories and risk of that last mission with his young air commandos and jumped aboard the lead aircraft.

Col Scott Howell also flew along on the last aircraft, or "Chalk six," as it was officially designated. He had previously commanded the 20th Special Operations Squadron (SOS) and also wanted to share the ride with his troops. The aircraft commander was also a volunteer of sorts. Capt Phil Cooper specifically asked to be put on the flight in the last aircraft. His request was granted, and as his aircraft crossed over the airfield boundary for landing as the tail-end Pave Low, he remarked on the aircraft intercom that he was proud to know that he was the last Pave Low guy in combat. His remark was intended to identify himself as the last pilot. However, before he could refine his statement, his tail gunner, SSgt Shawn Lewis, corrected him by pointing out that it was in reality he who—by the nature of his position at the tail of the aircraft—was the last one.[4]

Created to fly in combat and a vital weapon in the war on terror, these aircraft had reached the end of their usefulness and, like all of their cohorts, were being decommissioned. Within days, all six would be packaged up and flown by cargo aircraft back to the United States. Some would be put in the massive aircraft storage area just south of Tucson, Arizona. Others would be put on permanent static display at bases and locations across the country, quiet reminders of the valiant service that they had provided for the nation. Colonel Becker, noting the poignancy of the moment, said, "We really feel like we are standing on the shoulders of giants. . . . As the Pave Low goes on to retire from combat today, she goes out as she came in—the very best." Planeside, the Airmen held an impromptu celebration as the unit troops and visitors chatted and reminisced. Captain Florence remembers that "we were all smiles, and some tears . . . all hugging and shaking hands in the back of the helicopter as we collected our gear."[5] General Wurster shook hands with everyone. Slowly, though, everybody drifted away. Wurster lingered a bit and cast a last look at the aircraft. They were dirty and grimy but now eternally quiet as the maintenance troops began to disassemble them for shipment home. In that peaceful moment, as the first hint of dawn began to appear, he was reminded of the sweet words of Paul the Apostle when he wrote, "I have fought the good fight, I have finished the race, I have kept the faith." To him, it was a perfect epitaph for the final flight of these

"Steel Horses."[6] However, there was much more to the story because those last six sorties were about six decades in the making.

The Beginning

It all began with the United States Marine Corps (USMC). Hard lessons learned on the bloody beaches of the Pacific and the development of nuclear weapons convinced post–World War II USMC commanders that amphibious landings like those carried out at Normandy or Iwo Jima, which required the concentration of large, ponderous forces into relatively narrow approach zones, were no longer plausible. Future operations would have to be conducted with mobile forces able to rapidly concentrate to seize critical objectives and then just as quickly disperse for survival. Several vehicular alternatives were considered, but recent successes with helicopters seemed to offer the most promise. Mr. Igor Sikorsky of the Sikorsky Aircraft Corporation—considered the "gentle genius" of the helicopter community—even suggested that helicopters capable of hauling as many as 40 troops in a single lift were possible. Based upon this premise, the USMC commandant, Gen Alexander Vandergrift, accepted the concept in principle and in 1947 took a series of actions that wed the USMC to a

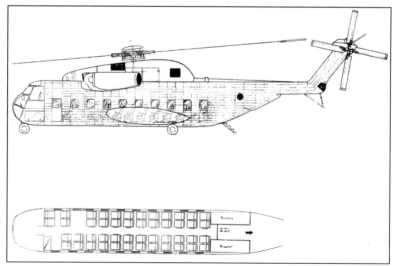

Initial Sikorsky plan for an H-53

new doctrine: the vertical assault concept for amphibious operations. Vandergrift noted in the report that "on the premise that the helicopter offers a valuable means of accelerating ship-to-shore movement, it is recognized that . . . it would appear necessary that there be designed . . . large helicopters capable of lifting divisional loads."[7] Field tests with the handful of helicopters then owned by the Marines showed that the concept was indeed feasible, and within two years, the USMC submitted a request for a large, multiengine assault helicopter capable of carrying 20 combat-equipped troops. This was consolidated with a larger US Navy (USN) request for more powerful helicopters for fleet operations.

Subsequent combat operations in the Korean conflict afforded the USMC an opportunity to further develop and refine its helicopter tactics and procedures. At the same time, Sikorsky Aircraft developed a prototype to meet the combined service request. That aircraft was the Sikorsky model S-56, designated the HR2S by the USMC but more commonly known as the H-37. The aircraft had the classic single five-bladed main rotor and four-bladed antitorque rotor on the tail. Two 4,200-horsepower Pratt and Whitney R-2800-54 piston engines mounted above the spacious cabin powered the aircraft. Impressive on paper, the aircraft was actually underpowered and hard to maintain. The H-37 never reached its expected potential, and the USMC purchased only 55 of the originally intended order of 180 aircraft.[8]

As turbine engines were refined and came into more general use, production companies began to match them to helicopters. Manufacturers immediately noted that turbines created more lift per engine pound, thus providing a larger useful load or lift capacity. This was always the fundamental challenge of helicopter design. Sikorsky built the first functional helicopter in 1909 but abandoned it when he could not find an engine that could produce enough lift to carry a useful load. This began to change in the 1950s with turbine-engine development. A series of helicopters was produced by several companies, culminating in the Sikorsky model S-64. Known in the military as the CH-54 Tarhe, it was essentially a bare-bones flying crane that could lift up to 25,000 pounds.[9]

Aware of this trend, in 1961 the USMC solicited a new turbine-powered assault helicopter to replace the HR2S. In August 1962, Sikorsky Aircraft Corporation won the competition with a proposal for its model S-65, essentially an S-64 with a full cargo/passenger cabin. Given the Department of Defense (DOD) designation of CH-

53A, it would be equipped with new General Electric T64-GE-6 engines, each producing 2,850 shaft horsepower (shp).[10]

Sikorsky built two YCH-53A prototype aircraft, which began flying in October 1964. Initial design gross weight was 33,490 pounds, allowing for a maximum useful load of 8,000 pounds carried to a range of 100 nautical miles. The internal cabin was 30 feet long, seven-and-a-half feet wide, and six-and-a-half feet high. It could carry 37 combat troops or 24 stretchers for casualties and attending medics. Aft clamshell doors and a moveable ramp allowed the loading of vehicles and even a 105-millimeter (mm) howitzer. The aircraft was equipped with a newly designed automatic flight control system (AFCS) incorporating a stability augmentation system (SAS) and an autopilot. It was also outfitted with aluminum main rotor blades mounted on pressurized spars, monitored for integrity by a blade inspection method system. Although the aircraft was initially unarmed, provisions were made to mount machine guns on both sides.[11]

The CH-53As were certified for use in 1966 and put into general production. In early 1967, they deployed with Marine Heavy Helicopter Squadron 463 (HMH-463) to South Vietnam for combat duty as our nation steadily built up its participation in that conflict. Quickly embraced by the commanders there, the heavy-lift helicopters were heavily tasked. In 1968 they were integral to supporting the surrounded USMC forces at Khe Sanh, where the first CH-53As delivered over one million pounds of cargo. During one particularly trying period, HMH-463 logged 1,252 sorties in one week. By the end of 1968, the USMC had taken delivery of over 100 CH-53A aircraft, and they were being dispatched for duty with Marine units all over the globe.[12]

The USMC also explored modifying the CH-53As for use at low altitude in all weather and visibility conditions. USMC personnel worked with Sikorsky to incorporate a terrain-following radar (TFR) and integrated helicopter avionics system (IHAS) in conjunction with the AFCS and SAS systems. The TFR and IHAS could also be combined with an automatic station-keeping radar, allowing the CH-53As to fly in formation in such conditions. Sikorsky explained that

the IHAS avionics package will permit the CH-53A to realize its full mission performance potential under the most demanding conditions—including zero or low visibility, controlled proximity to other aircraft and high airspeeds and low altitudes. . . . The terrain following radar permits the CH-53A to fly at extremely low levels. The pilot is provided with a vertical display showing a complete picture of the terrain contours ahead of the aircraft. The terrain following radar also has a ground-mapping display as an added navigational aid.[13]

Over the next year, a prototype aircraft was equipped with the components and flown through several scenarios. The TFR designed by the Norden Division of the United Aircraft Corporation scanned forward five miles. Its radar return was presented on a visual display with three-dimensional cueing that calculated a flight path to maintain terrain clearance and combined with other symbology displaying airspeed, altitude, pitch and roll, and vertical velocity. The test series provided Sikorsky and the Marines valuable performance information, and the overall concept seemed feasible. The USMC, however, chose not to bring the concept to fruition for its fleet of aircraft. The Sikorsky engineers filed the data away for future use.[14]

☆ ☆ ☆ ☆ ☆

"Necessity," stated the great Greek philosopher Plato, "is the mother of invention." The horror of another Normandy or Iwo Jima drove the USMC to create an alternative strategy based upon vertical envelopment to replace large amphibious landings. That created a need for a heavy-lift helicopter that American industry provided as the H-53. Observing the success of that aircraft, other services would also purchase the aircraft for more esoteric uses well beyond its initial conceived purpose.

Notes

(All notes appear in shortened form. For full details, see the appropriate entry in the bibliography.)

1. Florence, interview.
2. Becker, interview; and Becker to the author, e-mail, 6 Aug 2009.
3. Pryor, interview.
4. Cooper to the author, e-mail; and Howell, interview.
5. Florence, interview.
6. Michael Hoffman, "MH-53s Fly Final Combat Mission," *Air Force Times*, 13 Oct 2008, 16; Thacker, "MH-53s' Final Mission," 35; Florence and Wurster, interviews; and Lt Gen Donald Wurster, comments, Pave Low inactivation dinner, Hurlburt Field, FL, 16 Oct 2008.
7. Barich, "History of Heavy Lift?," 2.
8. Ibid., 29.

9. Lawrence, "Design and Development of the Sikorsky S-65 Helicopter," 2.
10. Ibid.; and *Jane's All the World's Aircraft 1963–64*, 279.
11. Lawrence, "Design and Development of the Sikorsky S-65 Helicopter," 2.
12. *Sikorsky News*, Feb 1968, 3.
13. Ibid., Apr 1967, 4.
14. Ibid., June 1968, 4.

Chapter 2

Of Jolly Greens . . .

*An integrated system to enable the . . . helicopters to perform
the essential elements of search and rescue [SAR] under
conditions of total darkness and/or low visibility.*

—SEA Operational Requirement #114

Air Force Use

Officers within the US Air Force also watched the development of
the H-53. As USAF involvement in the Vietnam War continued to
rise, an increasing number of aircraft were being shot down, and ever
more aircrews were being killed and captured. Additionally, USAF
aircraft and crews were involved throughout the Southeast Asia
(SEA) region, not just in South Vietnam. Consequently, they were far
away from US field units that could provide immediate ad hoc rescue.
For such contingencies, the USAF had a rescue force—the Air Rescue
Service (ARS)—assigned to the Military Air Transport Service
(MATS). This was a worldwide organization with both rotary- and
fixed-wing aircraft and crews on call for recovery duty.

However, the ARS was focused on noncombat rescue and optimized for the recovery of B-52 crews lost after strategic strikes on the
Soviet Union. As the fighting ratcheted up in SEA, though, the USAF
dispatched rescue forces to the region. In the spring of 1964, the first
aircraft and personnel deployed to the growing USAF air bases at Da
Nang on the coast in northern South Vietnam and Udorn in northern
Thailand. All rescue forces were under the command of the 38th Air
Rescue Squadron (ARSq). However, their Korean-era SU-16 aircraft
and unarmed, short-range HH-43 helicopters were not adequate for
rescue in the deep jungles and vast expanses over which USAF and
other service personnel flew in both Vietnams, Laos, and Cambodia.[1]

As an interim solution, in July 1965 these aircraft were reinforced
with two new CH-3E aircraft recently purchased from Sikorsky Aircraft and dispatched TDY to a newly built air base in northeast Thailand, Nakhon Phanom (NKP). This base was 110 miles east of Udorn,

just four miles from the Mekong River separating Thailand from Laos. Mu Gia Pass, one of the key entry points for the Ho Chi Minh Trail (fig. 1) that North Vietnamese forces were using to move supplies and troops to the battlefields in South Vietnam, was just 90 miles farther east. These aircraft were stronger and faster than the HH-43s, with a longer range and some armor protection. Additionally, they could fly higher to avoid the ever-increasing enemy antiaircraft guns. Adorned in a mottled coat of camouflage paint, the aircraft were quickly dubbed the "Jolly Green Giants" after the characters used to advertise canned vegetables back in the United States.

Two months later, two new HH-3E helicopters arrived and assumed rescue duties at Udorn. The CH-3s from NKP then consolidated there with them. The HH-3E aircraft were specifically optimized for rescue.

Figure 1. Southeast Asia. (Copyright Darrel Whitcomb, 2010.)

They had external fuel tanks and an added internal tank for extended range, 1,000 pounds of armor plating arrayed around critical parts of the aircraft, shatterproof canopies, a hydraulic hoist with 240-foot steel cable for pulling personnel up out of the dense and sometimes triple-canopy jungle, and more powerful engines that allowed the helicopters to climb up to 12,000 feet to avoid antiaircraft guns.[2]

On 1 January 1966, MATS was renamed the Military Airlift Command (MAC), and the ARS was renamed the Aerospace Rescue and Recovery Service (ARRS). The name change was necessary to reflect a larger global mission because the ARRS was also assigned responsibility for recovery of space hardware for the National Aeronautics and Space Administration (NASA). In subordinate fashion, its individual units would change their designations from Air Rescue to Aerospace Rescue and Recovery.

As the rescue force in SEA grew, the USAF, in early 1966, assigned the 3d Aerospace Rescue and Recovery Group (ARRG) to deploy to Saigon, South Vietnam, and command and control all USAF rescue units and operations in the theater. It would still be administratively aligned under the ARRS, but under the operational control (OPCON) of the Seventh Air Force. Concurrently, the 37th Aerospace Rescue and Recovery Squadron (ARRSq) was activated at Da Nang, with the HH-3s at Udorn assigned as a detachment. The recovery forces continued to receive more HH-3E aircraft, building to a force of 32 of the newer aircraft to be split between Da Nang and Udorn to replace the Korean-era machines.

The HH-3Es were also in-flight refuelable. This was an exciting development and the end result of some hard work and intense lobbying by a group of engineers and Maj Harry Dunn, an experienced helicopter pilot at Wright-Patterson AFB, Ohio. The ARS had earlier published a worldwide operational requirement for in-flight refueling for helicopters. Dunn felt that the standard USAF KC-97s and newly arriving KC-135s had to refuel at too high an airspeed to be compatible with helicopters. He and the test engineers developed a test plan with USMC KC-130 tanker aircraft that seemed much more capable of refueling the helicopters. The tests were successful. They then briefed their findings to commanders at every level. Consequently, new HH-3s coming off the production line were modified with in-flight refueling probes, and all crews were trained in the procedures. The USAF allocated funds to modify 11 C-130 aircraft to serve as the initial cadre of HC-130 tankers.[3]

However, accumulating rescue after action reports were suggesting that the new HH-3s needed more onboard firepower and better hover capability at the higher elevations in the mountainous areas of Laos. Such reports generated deep concern among the rescue commanders that the HH-3 was not up to the evolving task in SEA. Maj Baylor Haynes, the detachment commander at Udorn, noted in a comprehensive field study that even though the HH-3 was the best recovery aircraft then available, it still had its shortcomings. While in-flight refueling gave it the range it needed, the steady increase of enemy antiaircraft guns put the aircraft at high risk in increasingly more areas. Additionally, studies showed that reaction time to aircraft shootdowns was critical. The longer an Airman was on the ground, the worse were his odds of being rescued. In this business, speed was life. A faster, more heavily protected and armed helicopter was needed.

Haynes also suggested that a night rescue capability would be extremely useful. Some night rescues had been attempted. But they really consisted of helicopters and fixed-wing escort aircraft dropping flares so that the crews could execute daylight procedures for a recovery. Haynes was aware of some developmental work being done with infrared sensors, low-light-level TV, and light-intensification systems and suggested that those technologies could possibly be useful in addressing the challenge. However, until such developmental breakthroughs existed, the only option extant was to plan for a sunrise recovery effort, further exposing the survivor(s) to capture.[4]

Combat Aircrew Recovery Aircraft

Air Force rescue commanders and planners agreed that a new rescue helicopter was needed to replace the HH-3. The 3d ARRG commander, Col Albert Lovelady, directed his staff to analyze rescue operations in SEA to date. Maj John McLeaish and Maj John Silvis carried out the project. Completed on 22 May 1967, that detailed and exhaustive report was chockablock full of data and analysis substantiating ARRS's lack of preparation for or capability to conduct combat recovery as opposed to worldwide SAR. It included a requirement for a new combat aircrew recovery aircraft (CARA).

However, the document had a larger purpose. It noted that the increasingly sophisticated and heavy antiaircraft defensive arrays being steadily deployed around Hanoi, at the coastal regions of North Vietnam, and near the demilitarized zone (DMZ) in the south seriously challenged rescue in those areas. Repeating that all requirements had been detailed in validated Requirements Action Directive (RAD) 7-39-1, dated 31 January 1967, it declared,

> The single most important parameter to successful combat aircrew recovery is to minimize the time from bailout to recovery, i.e., speed of reaction. CARA must be able to penetrate the most highly defended areas day or night, since this is where most aircrew are downed. Lastly, CARA must be able to survive in [the] pickup area.
>
> The pie-shaped area north of Hanoi between the Red River, from Hanoi northwest to the Chinese border, and the railroad complex from Hanoi northeast to Langson is presently denied to SAR forces. . . . [It] denied 79 Airmen a SAR effort. Twenty-two Airmen downed along the Gulf of Tonkin coast were denied rescue because of the heavily defended coastline.[5]

To address these challenges, the report suggested that CARA needed to have several specific capabilities. One of these was the ability to utilize developing electronic countermeasures (ECM) to facilitate penetration and operation in high-threat areas. However, the single biggest threat was visually aimed antiaircraft guns. To answer this threat, the report suggested a need for a ground fire-detection system, better aircraft armor, and heavier onboard weaponry for fighting the close-in fight, usually encountered in the hover recovery phase.

The aircraft also needed to be multiengined for redundancy and safety and to operate effectively at slow speed and while hovering over heavily sloped and jungle terrain. It had to be capable of carrying auxiliary fuel tanks and refueling in flight for maximum mission planning and performance flexibility. CARA also required onboard advanced integrated avionics packages having secure communications capability with all SAR participants, including the survivor(s) if possible, and advanced navigational systems allowing precision navigation over a vast area.

Perhaps most evolutionarily, the report suggested a need for operations at night and in low-visibility conditions. The explicitly stated reason was to provide quick recovery response under all conditions. Implicit, though, was the belief that night and low-visibility operations would also negate the capability of visually aimed weapons to shoot down low and slow helicopters. The report specified that

> an integrated night and low visibility system will provide the CARA another tactic to penetrate "hot" areas under the cover of darkness at low level utiliz-

ing terrain avoidance radar. The system must solve navigation to the search area, establish [the] pinpoint location of the downed airman, provide for terrain/obstacle avoidance, program an automatic approach to the high (250') hover mode, maintain the hover mode over all terrain environments, permit visual acquisition of the downed airman . . . and emit neither [infrared] nor electronic signals that would compromise the survivor, the air rescue crew, or the CARA.[6]

Seventh Air Force validated RAD 7-39-1 and submitted it to the Air Staff. The requirement for the night and low-visibility capability was submitted as a standalone requirement as SEA Operational Requirement (SEAOR #114) dated 3 April 1967. It called for "an integrated system to enable helicopters to perform the essential elements of search and rescue under conditions of total darkness and/or low visibility." Those essential elements were to

(1) navigate to and establish a pinpoint location at the search area,

(2) avoid hills and obstacles,

(3) program an approach to a 250-foot hover and maintain it over land or water,

(4) enter into both an automatic approach and hover mode at a selected altitude and maneuver precisely,

(5) locate a downed Airman from approximately five miles,

(6) "see" with instruments when lighting was equivalent to a moonless, starlit night,

(7) obtain information, not necessarily from the same source, through display instruments at both the pilot and pararescueman positions, and

(8) conduct operations in such a manner that the location of neither the downed Airman nor the rescue helicopter crew would be given away.[7]

The Pacific Air Forces (PACAF) commander, Gen John Ryan, concurred and in a separate message to MAC and the chief of staff of the Air Force (CSAF) pointed out that "the lack of [a] reliable night SAR capability was seriously impairing SAR effectiveness" and demanded that "interim measures" be taken to increase its capability to meet its current operational tasks.[8] Air Staff planners, though, concluded that the procurement of CARA would have necessitated a long and costly development and certification process. They also rejected any consideration for converting the HH-3s for this mission, determining that the HH-3s were already performing at maximum capability.[9] Having seen the success that the USMC was having with the CH-53As, the Air Staff concluded that this machine could be procured as an off-the-shelf replacement and modified for the rescue mission as opposed to designing and developing the CARA. Furthermore, it believed that the performance and load capability of a modified CH-53 variant was such that the airframe could meet most of the specifications for fuel flexibility and in-flight refueling, added armor, weaponry, and upgraded avionics—particularly to include the avionics developed to enable night and all-weather recovery operations, thus satisfying the requirements of SEAOR #114.[10]

Courtesy National Museum of the US Air Force

One of the USMC CH-53As loaned to the USAF for initial testing

When the USAF contracted to buy an initial batch of eight HH-53B aircraft for rescue duties, Sikorsky loaned two CH-53As built for the USMC to the USAF and delivered them to the 48th ARRSq at Eglin AFB, Florida, for initial operational test and evaluation (IOT&E) and to train the first cadre of aircrews. Over the next eight years, the USAF would procure a total of 52 HH-53B/C aircraft and, collaterally, 20 CH-53C helicopters for special operations use.[11]

To Southeast Asia

In June 1967, the ARRS took delivery of the first HH-53B. It was picked up at the Sikorsky plant by Lt Col James Dixon, Capt Fredric Donohue, and other Airmen from Detachment 2 of the 37th ARRSq at Udorn AB, Thailand. En route to Eglin AFB, they stopped in Washington, DC, to display the aircraft for senior government and military leaders. They then continued on to Eglin and earnestly began training initial crews for SEA. Two months later that aircraft and the second production model were loaded aboard the USS *Card*, an old escort aircraft carrier, for transport to Vietnam. When the aircraft arrived at the port of Vung Tau a month later, Sikorsky technicians assembled them, and they were ferried to Udorn. The following table provides a comparison of the HH-3E capabilities with those of the HH-53B/C.

Table. Comparison of the HH-3E and HH-53B/C

	HH-3E	HH-53B/C
Gross weight (pounds) with crew and ammo	18,000	37,193/36,000
Useful load (pounds)	3,000	13,000
Engine(s) shp (each)	2/T-58-GE-5 1,250	2/T-64-GE-7 3,080/3,925
Speed (knots) cruise/maximum	120/143	140/190+
Altitude (ft. max.)	12,000	18,550/16,000
Range (ft. max.) (unlimited with in-flight refueling)	310	290
Hover altitude (ft. max.)	4,000	6,500
Crew	4	4–6
Armament	2XM-60 .30 cal	3XGAU-2B 7.62 mm
Hoist (feet)	240	240

Adapted from Earl H. Tilford, *Search and Rescue in Southeast Asia* (Washington, DC: Center for Air Force History, 1992), 91; John W. R. Taylor, ed., *Jane's All the World's Aircraft 1969–70* (London: Jane's Yearbooks, 1969), 436; and Walter F. Lynch, *USAF Search and Rescue in Southeast Asia (1 July 1969–31 December 1970),* Project CHECO Report (Hickam AFB, HI: Headquarters Pacific Air Forces, 1971), 43, K717.0414-1, Air Force Historical Research Agency.

Arriving at Udorn, Colonel Dixon was designated the HH-53B detachment commander. He certified that the first crews were ready for combat, and the HH-53Bs began to augment the HH-3s sitting alert for rescue missions. Their initial use was limited, as maintenance crews had to work through some preliminary equipment challenges, and several aircrew members needed to qualify for in-flight refueling. Immediately, though, all participants could see that the HH-53 was indeed a major advancement over the HH-3. However, larger issues concerning capability still needed to be addressed. As one commander noted in a mission report,

> desperately needed in the Southeast Asia rescue effort are more HH-53s, equipped with an integrated night and low visibility system. In the hours of darkness or low visibility, rescue helicopters are, for the most part, ineffective for rescue and recovery, especially in mountainous terrain. A number of factors enter into the problem, such as navigation to the search area, terrain avoidance, as in rugged or mountainous areas, the descent to a hover mode, positioning the rescue craft over the downed airman, and finally, the establishment of a hover not to exceed a wander of five to seven feet laterally nor altitude deviations of greater than five feet.[12]

As the USAF was accepting completed aircraft, it dispatched four more HH-53Bs of the initial buy to Udorn. Colonel Dixon put HH-53s and crews on alert at Udorn and NKP and even dispatched them to secure remote locations in northern Laos, such as Lima Site 98 near the Plain of Jars. In an evolutionary development, Dixon also put the HH-53Bs into orbits with newly received HC-130 tankers where they could periodically refuel for several hours, remaining instantly on call for a recovery so that reaction and recovery times could be reduced as much as possible.

When the aircraft arrived, an impromptu debate took place among the aircrews as to a proper nickname for the aircraft. The HH-43s were called "Pedros" and the HH-3s, "Jolly Greens"; on missions crews used those designators with an individual numerical suffix as their call signs. Initially, the HH-53s were called "Buffs," which stood for big, ugly, fat fellows (with lots of variations for the last two words). Operationally, the crews also adopted the Jolly Green radio call sign and, de facto, came to be known as the "Super Jolly Greens."[13]

The rescue forces at Udorn and NKP were responsible for the northern two-thirds of Laos and all of North Vietnam, a huge area indeed. On 23 October 1967, a Udorn HH-53B commanded by Capt Russ Cayler was scrambled to recover an F-105 pilot who had bailed

Courtesy Air Force Historical Research Agency

One of the first HH-53Bs arriving in Southeast Asia in 1968

out over Thailand after a midair collision. One month and two days later, the HH-53s logged their first combat rescue with a Udorn HH-53B when Cayler and his crew scrambled off of the alert pad at Lima Site 98 in northern Laos to help rescue the crew of an Air America H-34 that had gone down 50 miles northeast of their location.[14]

In January 1968, two HH-53s commanded by Cayler and Maj John Allison supported a rescue operation in North Vietnam for the six-man crew of a downed EB-66. As they were en route, an HH-3 already there was also shot down. Reaching the area, Allison recovered three members of the EB-66 crew but could not find the others. Cayler and crew picked up the HH-3 crew, but their aircraft was damaged by ground fire and was leaking fuel. As they were climbing out of the area, both engines failed. Cayler and his crew were able to get one engine restarted and then proceeded to an emergency field nearby for a safe landing. Six days later, an emergency beeper was heard in the vicinity of the three missing crewmen. Major Allison and crew launched again with an escort of A-1 aircraft to search for and possibly recover the three remaining EB-66 crew members. Arriving overhead, they and the escort A-1s could hear the beacon and also saw several pen-gun flares. As the helicopter flew low and slow over the trees, it began to take heavy antiaircraft fire from several different locations. The crew answered the enemy with sustained minigun fire as Allison pulled his aircraft out of the area. The aircraft had suffered 23 hits; fortunately, none were serious. Allison and his crew had been lured into a classic trap, something the North Vietnamese were increasingly attempting to do. The HH-53 crews were now fully initiated into the risks and rewards of combat recovery.

40th Aerospace Rescue and Recovery Squadron

On 18 March 1968, the 40th ARRSq was activated at Udorn and assumed control of the six HH-53Bs there and at NKP. Its assigned mission was to "search for, locate, and recover distressed personnel engaged in combat operations in Southeast Asia."[15] Lt Col Jim Dixon was assigned as the commander. He focused on training for his crews and support personnel and was notified that within the year, the unit would be receiving at least three newer HH-53C aircraft with more powerful engines. A month later, he directed the 40th to establish an FOL at Ubon AB in southeast Thailand for possible use in southern Laos.

Although dispatched to SEA for SAR duties, the HH-53s could perform just about any basic lift mission. Given its load capability, the 40th began to get calls to recover downed aircraft, such as UH-1s, A-1s, and C-123s, or even to move heavy gear, such as generators and whole 25,000-pound tactical air navigation (TACAN) system units, between bases. It also got calls to support civil affairs efforts in Thailand, transport medical teams, and provide medical evacuation for local Thais in remote areas. On another occasion, four HH-53Bs were dispatched to evacuate 59 indigenous personnel and their American advisors who were under direct attack at an FOL in Laos. This was not rescue per se but direct support of ongoing operations by special operations–type units. As time passed, the Buffs would get an ever-increasing number of requests to perform such missions. The aircrews were also busy, as personnel turnover dictated a continuous training and upgrade program. On several occasions, aircrews traveled to other bases to brief aircrew personnel on SAR procedures.[16]

During the year, unit crews participated in rescue or recovery operations for an F-111 crew capsule, the crew and passengers of an Air America Porter aircraft, an F-105 pilot and a pararescue jumper (PJ) inserted to care for him, an Air American H-34 helicopter, several F-4 crews, the crew of a US Navy P2V, and on and on, while USAF and allied aircraft continuously attacked enemy targets throughout the 40th Squadron's area of responsibility (AOR). Many of these rescue operations took place in hostile areas, and on several occasions the helicopters were damaged by enemy guns. The unit was rapidly becoming a highly combat-experienced squadron. The crews and their ever-present escort A-1 "Sandys," support tankers, command and control aircraft, and even forward air controllers (FAC) were melding into a cohesive team.

HH-53 crews conducted two rescue operations at night. These were, by necessity, more limited and conducted in an ad hoc fashion. One after action report states that "tactics were developed during the rescue by the crews taking part. . . . Such operations are considered hazardous except under favorable circumstances, i.e., no hostile activity, terrain which is fairly level, good weather conditions, and a flare drop crew [in support]." The crews also realized that they could do the recoveries at night but were limited by the difficulties of trying to coordinate the actions of supporting A-1s to suppress enemy ground fire.[17]

In early June 1968, crews from the 40th responded with unit H-3s to the shootdown of a USN A-7, call sign Streetcar 304. The pilot was alive and located a few miles southwest of Tchepone on the Ho Chi Minh Trail in central Laos. For 40 hours an armada of helicopters and support aircraft made several attempts to rescue the survivor. In the melee, an A-1 was shot down and that pilot taken prisoner. The effort became a battle, as successive shifts of recovery and support aircraft tried to get the A-7 pilot out. They were supported by 44 F-4s and 42 F-105s that relentlessly pummeled the enemy guns with an estimated 86 tons of bombs and rockets. Almost mind-boggling at the time, that mission would soon be dwarfed many times over as the number of SAR missions continued to increase and the enemy fought tenaciously to oppose them. Many would become much more than SAR. They were horrific battles, dances of death for the purposes of facilitating a rescue. No quarter was asked, and no quarter was given.[18]

Being the first and, so far, only HH-53 unit in the war, the 40th received many distinguished visitors, such as the Honorable Dr. Harold Brown, secretary of the Air Force. Keenly interested in the squadron and its operations, he spent an entire day there. He later wrote of rescue operations that "the extent of the operation, the danger involved, and the dedication on an everyday basis month after month make these rescue operations something unique in our military history. These men are all heroes. . . . Certainly, the ARRS people deserve their immortality."[19]

As 1968 ended, commanders took stock of their accomplishments. Blessedly, no HH-53s had been shot down; however, many had been damaged by the enemy guns. Their efforts had led to the recovery of 100 personnel, 79 in noncombat conditions and 21 in combat. The HH-53s were performing well, although they were power limited at the higher elevations. All recognized, too, the need for a true night and all-weather capability that could be used in combat conditions as specified in SEAOR #114, subsequently changed to Seventh Air Force Combat Required Operational Capability 11-70 (CROC 11-70). Those commanders had also been apprised that efforts were under way with Sikorsky Aircraft Corporation to develop just such a capability.[20]

Pave Star

In 1967 Sikorsky Aircraft Corporation was awarded a contract to develop onboard avionics with off-the-shelf technology to satisfy CROC 11-70. The project was named Pave Star, and USAF engineers estimated that eight HH-53s could be equipped with a fully tested system by early 1969.[21]

Building on its fundamental work with the IHAS initiative, Sikorsky engineers, working with the Norden Division of United Aircraft Corporation, developed a prototype kit that would provide the HH-53 with a night operations system (NOS). The NOS would have two subsystems. First, a night-vision subsystem would provide terrain cues during low-level flight and detect a strobe light displayed by the survivor. Additionally, it would provide the necessary visual references for the pilots to maintain overall situational awareness during the critical approach and hover operations under very low light levels. Second, an approach and hover coupler subsystem would be integrated with the aircraft's automatic flight control and stability augmentation systems. Reflecting almost 15 years of developmental work, this system would "allow the pilot to automatically transition from search altitude and cruise speed to hover and automatically maintain the hover with almost no assistance from the pilot. The equipment that provides this capability consists of new components and modifications to some of the existing components already installed on the aircraft."[22]

The new systems would rely on the onboard TACAN and Doppler navigational systems for overall navigation and could conceptually be supplemented with TFR. Through 1968 and 1969, Sikorsky engineers and test pilots and flight personnel from MAC and the ARRS flew numerous test missions with the intent of delivering an operationally usable system by the end of 1969. The program, while closely monitored by MAC, was plagued with problems. It was not developing as desired or within projected time or cost constraints. Increasingly, it became clear that the program would require quite a bit of elemental development work because the Pave Star system would require over 60 new components and 200-plus electronic interfaces and basic modifications to the HH-53. In May 1970, Lt Gen Otto Glasser, the Air Force deputy chief of staff (DCS) for research and development, and Lt Gen James Sherrill, the vice-commander of MAC, conducted a program review. Based upon their findings and budgetary constraints, the chief of staff of the Air Force, General Ryan, directed that the program be terminated and all remaining funds be redirected to the Aeronautical Systems Division of the Air Force Systems Command that was concurrently developing a limited night recovery system (LNRS) under the program "Pave Imp."

However, MAC did not intend to give up on the overall concept and in July 1970 published MAC Required Operational Capability (ROC) 19-70, which specified, "A requirement exists for an integrated system to enable a rescue vehicle to perform search and rescue under conditions of total darkness and/or adverse weather in all geographical areas including mountainous terrain. Additionally, the rescue vehicle must have a low level capability to penetrate hostile territory against radar directed weapons in the above stated environmental conditions."[23] Regretfully, the Sikorsky engineers terminated their efforts. A summation report, however, captured an interesting conclusion:

> Considerable experience and expertise have been gained in the field of integrated radar and displays by the Sikorsky and Norden Divisons as the prime and/or subcontractors in the Integrated Helicopter Avionics and Pavestar programs. . . . [The] night recovery mission is the primary mission for which

the NOS has been designed; however, during the extensive flight testing of the NOS and its subsystems, it was found that the system enabled the aircraft to perform a wide variety of night operations. Low speed maneuvering over all types of terrain could be accomplished under semi-automatic control.[24]

These concepts being pursued had potential far beyond their critical but relatively limited use specifically for SAR.

40th and 37th Aerospace Rescue and Recovery Squadrons

The last of the HH-53Bs and then the improved HH-53Cs continued to flow into the theater through 1969 and 1970 until the 40th had received a total of six Bs and eight Cs. The 37th ARRSq at Da Nang was also equipped with C models, receiving eight. Both squadrons relinquished their HH-3s as the larger Buffs—as they were now semi-officially called—arrived. With a bombing halt in effect over North Vietnam, most combat SARs were now occurring in Laos and the western regions of South Vietnam. As the North Vietnamese continued to bring an increasing number of guns down from the north along the Ho Chi Minh Trail, ever more areas became high threat, and the scope of the rescue efforts continued to grow. On 17 January 1969, an F-4 Fast FAC, Stormy 02, was shot down in the dangerous Tchepone area of central Laos. For three days, rescue forces including HH-3s and HH-53s made several attempts to recover the surviving backseater as he lay badly wounded. Hundreds of strike aircraft pummeled the enemy guns as they battled to control the area long enough for one of the helicopters to slip in and grab the wounded Airman. In the melee, a supporting A-1 was shot down and the pilot eventually rescued by one of the helicopters. But deteriorating weather and darkness precluded a pickup.

The next day the battle resumed, and another A-1 was shot down with no survivor. Regardless, the battle went on. Sensing an opportunity, Jolly Green 68, an HH-53B, was cleared in to pick up the F-4 backseater. Hovering over the survivor for 22 minutes as a PJ went down the hoist to help the badly injured survivor, the pilot had to keep the aircraft below the tops of the trees because of an active 37 mm gun one kilometer to the south. As soon as the survivor and PJ were inside the aircraft, the pilot turned to the egress heading and departed the area.

Next, Jolly Green 67, another one of the 40th Squadron HH-53s, was cleared in to pick up the downed A-1 pilot. The crew rapidly moved in and recovered him. On departure, though, the aircraft was hit by several rounds of 37 mm fire. The damage was severe, and the pilots put their aircraft on the ground. Quickly, the escort helicopter, Jolly Green 70, another HH-53, dashed in and recovered the crew of Jolly 67 and the survivor. Since the area was too dangerous for a recovery operation for the damaged aircraft, a flight of F-4s destroyed the wreckage. HH-53B #66-14430 was the first of its breed lost in combat.

But the battle was not yet over. Just as this action was ending, an O-2 FAC aircraft from Da Nang was shot down about 15 miles to the south, also along the Ho Chi Minh Trail. Once again, the rescue forces mounted up and prepared to duel with the guns to facilitate another rescue for the two O-2 pilots. It took another 24 hours of intense action before the two survivors were finally pulled out by two different helicopters, the second man recovered by an HH-53B from the 40th.

The effort for Stormy 02 and the others dwarfed any rescue to date. The almost three-day event involved 264 aircraft, all playing their critical roles to bring out the downed Airmen. The amount of weapons tonnage expended was staggering. In-flight refueling, now almost routine, played a key role as the helicopters logged 14 refuelings, taking a total of 40,200 pounds of fuel from the HC 130s.[25]

Weather and darkness, too, played a negative role in the effort. But did they always have to be adverse factors? Aware of technological developments in the CONUS, one anonymous participant wrote during this time period that "weather and darkness can become assets rather than liabilities if and when systems are developed which permit effective rescue operations in these environments." To those who had to face the massed guns at places like Tchepone or Mu Gia Pass, it was a beguiling thought. But one had to wonder if the lack of aiming capability at night for the enemy gunners would be worth the obvious loss of direct support from the escort A-1 crews, who could not dare to expend munitions without being able to clearly see the Jolly Greens.[26]

For the rescue units, as the year 1969 progressed, the battle pace remained steady; missions of desperation and, sometimes, life or death shattered endless periods of tedious alert. Additionally, the HH-53s were continuously called upon to perform military and civil medevacs, heavy lifts, and civic actions operations. Occasionally, the units would get more calls to move indigenous forces. Above and beyond their primary mission, they were in constant demand. For the year, the HH-53s logged 48 combat saves and 164 other "saves."[27]

The new year started ominously for the rescue forces when, on 28 January 1970, an HH-53B and crew from the 40th ARRSq were lost in North Vietnam. It was one of four helicopters launched to recover an F-105G crew of two shot down north of Mu Gia Pass in North Vietnam while escorting an RF-4C. Two of the helicopters were in an orbit over Laos refueling from an HC-130 when two MiG-21s attacked HH-53B #66-14434—flying as Jolly Green 71—and its wingman and escort A-1s. No MiG combat air patrol (MiGCAP) USAF fighters were available, and a heat-seeking missile from one of the MiG-21s hit and destroyed the Jolly Green. There were no survivors, mute testimony that vulnerable aircraft like rescue helicopters and HC-130 tankers could not operate without air superiority. It was a tragic and egregious mistake.[28]

On 30 June, an OV-10 from the 23d Tactical Air Support Squadron (TASS) based at NKP was shot down while supporting a US Army (USA) special forces team in southern Laos. Only the backseater, an Army sergeant, survived. Two HH-53s from the 40th ARRSq at Udorn responded. While flying over the area to locate the survivor, HH-53C #68-8283 was engaged by multiple enemy guns of varying calibers and blown out of the sky. A second helicopter recovered the original survivor, but there were no survivors from the stricken Jolly Green.[29]

To readily locate and communicate with isolated personnel, the HH-53s were equipped with ultrahigh frequency (UHF) radios that could be tuned to the same frequencies programmed into the survival radios. The helicopter radios were also equipped with a "direction finder" capability that allowed them to receive steering guidance from voice or beeper communication from the survivor's radio. However, these auxiliary systems were notoriously finicky and too often unreliable. In November the 3d ARRG forwarded an operational requirement to MAC for an "electronic location finder" (ELF) to replace this built-in device. MAC published MAC ROC #27-70 to address this requirement on a worldwide basis because the capability would be useful anywhere. The ROC specified a "capability to locate and expeditiously maneuver to a hover over a survivor in a combat environment." That generated a requirement for an ELF that would provide a terminal location to within 10 feet at close ranges, operate covertly and under jungle canopies without significant degradation, function effectively day and night and in all weather conditions, work with developing night recovery systems and with issued personal survival equipment, and be transportable on rescue helicopters. Cubic Corporation received the contract and went to work to develop and test the system on a priority basis.[30]

Not all of the HH-53s produced for the USAF were deployed to the war in SEA. Several were based at various locations in the United States, Europe, and Asia for more routine SAR duties. To highlight their versatility for missions on a more global scale, in August two HH-53Cs were flown to SEA. The trip took nine days. The helicopters were accompanied by 2 HC-130N tankers, enabling them to fly nonstop legs up to almost 13 hours. In flying the almost 9,000 miles from Eglin AFB to Da Nang AB, South Vietnam, the aircraft and crews logged 69 hours and 42 minutes of flight time on eight legs. "The entire mission went much better than we had anticipated," said the mission commander, Maj Larry Butera. "This first flight of an HH-53 across the Pacific was a near flawless mission."[31]

In-flight refueling for helicopters, critical for long-range and long-duration operations, was developed during the Vietnam War.

The Son Tay Raid

In mid-November, the 40th received an unusual order to stand down for a few days, ostensibly to spend additional time doing maintenance on the hard-flown helicopters. However, the directive also stipulated that the unit would have five aircraft ready to go on 20 November. Late that evening, several C-130s arrived from Takhli AB, Thailand. They disgorged a small force of US Army and Air Force personnel, who then transferred to the ready HH-53s and also an HH-3. That force and several accompanying HC-130 tankers took off just a few minutes before midnight and turned northeast. They were headed for a POW camp in North Vietnam near the village of Son Tay, about 30 miles northwest of Hanoi, and would combine with other elements departing other airfields and even aircraft carriers in the Gulf of Tonkin in an effort to recover the estimated 75 US and allied POWs being held there.

Planning for the mission had begun the previous August when Brig Gen Leroy Manor, then serving as commander of the USAF special operations force headquartered at Eglin, was called to the Pentagon for a meeting with the chairman of the Joint Chiefs of Staff (CJCS), Adm Thomas Moorer. The chief asked Manor and US Army colonel Arthur "Bull" Simons if they would be interested in studying the feasibility of conducting the mission and then executing it if it appeared doable. Both men answered affirmatively. Moorer appointed Manor as the commander of a joint task force (JTF) with Simons as his deputy and gave them broad authority to recruit personnel for the operation, buttressed with the priorities necessary to obtain materiel, facilities, and exercise areas to begin training their force.

Manor and Simons immediately established a joint planning group of 26 experts from all services to consider the effort from all aspects, especially operational security, as any unusual movement of equipment or troops could be spotted and possibly compromise the element of surprise, so important to such a small operation. The planning determined that the best approach would be by helicopter. A small contingent of Army special forces would be inserted to conduct the ground operation. The USAF would provide the air element.[32]

Given the ranges and loads involved, the only USAF helicopter lift option was the air-refuelable HH-53s of the 37th and 40th ARRSqs already located in SEA. Additionally, their onboard miniguns could be used to suppress any enemy reaction, and personnel aboard could also be equipped with Starlight scopes for improved night vision. Consequently, the ARRS commander, Brig Gen Frank Everest, was approached for his advice and support. He assigned a top-notch HH-53 pilot, Lt Col Warner Britton, the chief of training at the Air Rescue and Recovery Training Center (ARRTC) at Eglin, to the planning staff. Britton's initial analysis was straightforward: "From the outset it was clear that Rescue participation would be vital to the operation, because it possessed the properly-configured helicopters, the only tankers to refuel them, and the essential technical expertise which the mission required."[33] Subsequently, he and 18 other officers and enlisted Airmen from the ARRTC, three from the 37th ARRSq, and six from the 40th ARRSq would be selected to serve as the HH-53 aircrews on the mission.[34]

Since Udorn AB in northern Thailand would be a perfect launch point, the 40th was furtively directed to supply the HH-53s. The planners determined that the mission would have the best chance of success if it were conducted at night. The HH-53s still did not have any optimized night recovery capability. Additionally, this was not a classic rescue mission per se. The intent of the mission was to directly attack a well-guarded enemy facility for the purposes of rescuing as many as 75 unarmed and probably weakened individuals. It would require a significant force of support aircraft to provide night illumination and direct fire support. Accordingly, several MC-130s and A-1s were included in the task force.[35]

Manor and Simons collected their force at Eglin AFB. There they could train on the large land ranges without drawing any attention. All participants were volunteers, especially sought out for their recognized expertise and recent SEA experience. Of all the rescue crews interviewed for the operation, only one refused to join the effort. The task force trained diligently through September. Planners also added an HH-3 to the operation; it would be used to insert a small strike team of 13 Soldiers directly into the prison, thereby achieving immediate surprise. However, the aircraft would be destroyed in the process.[36]

Working with various governmental and military intelligence agencies, Manor and Simons determined that the operation was feasible, with an acceptable element of risk, and so briefed Admiral Moorer and the secretary of defense (SecDef), the Honorable Melvin Laird. Having considered the lunar and predicted weather patterns, Manor also recommended that the operation occur on 21 October.

Moorer and Laird agreed. Pres. Richard Nixon then gave his approval but not in time to allow the operation on 21 October. The new date would be 21–22 November.[37]

In early November, Manor and Simons made arrangements to move all of the mission aircrews to Thailand. The two flew to Hawaii to brief the US Pacific Command (USPACOM) commander, Adm John McCain, and then to Saigon to brief the Military Assistance Command, Vietnam (MACV), commander, Gen Creighton Abrams, and his air deputy, Gen Lucius Clay Jr., Seventh Air Force commander. Clay's forces would provide vital F-105s for surface-to-air missile (SAM) suppression and F-4s for MiG suppression if the North Vietnamese chose to respond. Manor and Simons then met with Adm Fred Bardshar, the commander of Task Force 77, the aircraft carrier force in the Gulf of Tonkin. He agreed to support the operation with an air strike force launched to draw the attention of the North Vietnamese air defense forces, as the task force would slip in quietly over the mountains from Laos.

General Manor oversaw the arrival of his forces in Thailand and watched them make their last preparations. He decided to move the operation forward 24 hours, though, when his team weathermen determined that a developing typhoon near the Philippines could disrupt the operation on 22 November. With all preparations finalized, he proceeded to Da Nang to monitor the operation from a major command center there.

The 40th ARRSq had the five HH-53s for the mission ready to go plus five spares. The selected HH-53s and the one HH-3 lifted off exactly on schedule from Udorn, followed almost immediately by an HC-130 tanker and two MC-130 Talons for navigation and flare support. A few minutes later, a flight of five A-1s took off from NKP and rendezvoused with one of the MC-130s. The weather was clear in the helicopter refueling area, and all six took on fuel without incident. The tanker then proceeded back to Udorn for more fuel, which the helicopters would need after the raid. Above, the fighter force of F-4s and F-105s approached the Son Tay area, and the large USN strike package drew away the attention of the North Vietnamese air defenders.

Arriving over the prison camp, the HH-3 and first two HH-53s landed and unloaded their assault troops as the MC-130s filled the sky with flares and the F-105s dueled with the now fully alerted North Vietnamese SAM sites. While orbiting and awaiting the signal to land and pick up the raiders and freed POWs, the HH-53 crews used their miniguns to decimate watchtowers around the camp. Firefights broke out in the compound as enemy troops began to respond. Hurriedly, the American Soldiers searched through the prison, systematically going from cell to cell. But their efforts were for naught; the prisoners were gone. They had been moved a few weeks earlier, probably because of flooding of the local area caused by heavy rains. After 29 minutes on the ground, all of the assault troops were reloaded and accounted for; the helicopters lifted off, and the task force turned southwest for the long flight back to Thailand. The force sustained no losses and only two injuries—a sprained ankle and a minor bullet wound. One F-105G was damaged by a SAM. The crew made it well into Laos before it bailed out and was then rescued by one of the HH-53s.

Overall, the mission was a failure in that it did not bring back any POWs. However, it did force the North Vietnamese to collect all prisoners into larger groups, where they received better care. This improved morale, as did the prisoners' inevitable discovery of the effort. Remembered Jay Jayroe, one of the Son Tay prisoners, "We were not forgotten; our country cared. During the hard times ahead, our renewed faith in God and Country served us well."[38]

Tactically, however, from an HH-53 perspective, the mission was quite successful. The helicopters and crews performed magnificently. This was not a rescue mission so much as it was a special operations mission. With their heavy-lift helicopters, though, and without any equipment that optimized them for night operations, the crews were able to enter enemy airspace and operate without any losses for 29 minutes just 30 miles from the North Vietnamese capital of Hanoi. Maybe there were tactical advantages to operating at night doing rescue or whatever else those heavy-lift helicopters were needed to do.

The Son Tay mission did have one more unintended consequence. It helped one young Air Force Academy cadet decide that he wanted to fly rescue helicopters. Just a few months prior to the raid, Cadet 3d Class Rich Comer got to take a ride on an HH-53 when his cadet class visited Norton AFB, California, as part of its summer training. He sat on the back ramp of the aircraft as his pilot, Maj Frederic Donohue, took him and several others on a low-level tour of southern California. Sitting next to him was a young USAF PJ, SSgt Stu Stanaland, who bragged that Donohue was "the greatest helicopter pilot in the world!" Four months later, when the news of the Son Tay mission broke, Comer read everything he could find about the mission. And when he discovered that Donahue had flown one of the HH-53s, he decided that he would ask to fly rescue helicopters when he was commissioned. His request would be honored, and four and one-half years later, he would fly on a mission just as dramatic and desperate. With him on that mission would be Stanaland, now a tech sergeant.[39]

All and all, though, except for the two terrible losses, SAR activity in 1970 was much less intense than in previous years. For the year, the HH-53s logged 54 combat and 23 noncombat saves.[40]

The new year, 1971, started as several before it had in SEA. Third ARRG helicopters sat on alert at Da Nang, Udorn, NKP, Ubon, Bien Hoa (South Vietnam), and intermittently at Dong Ha and Pleiku in South Vietnam and several sites in Laos depending on operational requirements. Most alert aircraft were now HH-53s, as the Buffs were steadily replacing the HH-3s. Jollys also maintained orbits over Laos and occasionally off the coast of North Vietnam when reconnaissance aircraft were operating there. Most helicopters and crews were ready from first light to last light. Unit aircraft were launched for several SARs in Laos, with the majority occurring near Tchepone, Laos, where South Vietnamese forces tried to cut the Ho Chi Minh Trail in February and March.[41]

On 21 July, Jolly Green 54, HH-53C #68-8285, was dispatched into northwest Laos to recover some "aerospace hardware." The PJ was hoisted down to attach a sling to the equipment. As he did so, he heard ground fire and called for extraction. As the hoist was descending down to him, the load began to slip down the hill, pulling the helicopter down into the trees. The aircraft commander jettisoned the load and auxiliary tanks. Regardless, the aircraft settled into the trees, crashed to the ground, and rolled several times. The crew members were able to escape, but several were seriously injured. They were recovered by a civilian aircraft. The area was considered insecure, and the aircraft and load were destroyed. In response to this debacle, the squadron initiated an intensive sling-load training and qualification program.[42]

Over the next several days, the 40th ARRSq moved to NKP and absorbed its Detachment 1. This allowed the unit to consolidate its operation at one base and placed it 90 miles closer to the Ho Chi Minh Trail, the arena of most of its rescues. The unit also shipped its two oldest HH-53Bs, #66-14431 and #66-14432, back to Hill AFB, Utah, for use as trainer aircraft.[43]

Pave Imp

With the demise of the Pave Star program in 1970, remaining hopes for a night and adverse-weather recovery system to satisfy the original SEAOR #114 requirement rested with the LNRS, now called Pave Imp. Two HH-53Bs in the states and six HH-53Cs scheduled to be shipped to Thailand would be modified for field testing. However, one of the aircraft was lost in combat.

The aircraft were modified with the latest iteration of avionics and AFCS modifications comprised of low-light-level television, infrared illuminators, a direct viewing device, a television monitor, an automatic approach coupler, an automatic hover coupler, and a hover trim controller. MAC and the ARRS conducted the initial testing at Eglin AFB in late 1970. The aircraft in Thailand would be tested after they arrived. All participants realized that this would only partially fulfill the requirement initially stated in SEAOR #114.[44]

Testing at Eglin identified numerous problems with onboard systems interface and larger logistical support challenges. The field test was conducted by the crews of the 40th and extended into early 1971. When enough statistical data were collected, the commander, Lt Col John Morse, wrote up a final report. It pronounced,

> The present configuration of the Pave Imp, HH-53 helicopter will not support the theater commander's requirement for a night, all weather rescue vehicle. . . . The extremely limited terrain avoidance feature that presently exists on the Pave Imp aircraft could not provide necessary clearance in most areas.
>
> In reviewing all the factors involved it does not appear justified for commitment of the Pave Imp rescue vehicle to an unrestricted operational status at this time. However, the system should continue to be utilized to the fullest extent possible within the limits of capabilities. Engineering improvements and a terrain avoidance system should be provided as quickly as possible. Protection, ECM and fire support concepts and requirements should also continue to receive priority consideration.[45]

General Clay concurred with the finding that Pave Imp did not satisfy CROC 11-70. However, he did not concur with the recommendation to keep it in-theater and recommended that all Pave Imp aircraft be returned to the United States and replaced with otherwise combat-ready machines.

MAC responded with an almost plaintive message requesting reconsideration. It pointed out that the MAC ROC 19-70 recommended modifying the Pave Imp aircraft with terrain following/terrain avoid-

ance (TF/TA) radar and stated that an LNRS HH-53 was scheduled
to be tested with such a radar in January 1972. It further persisted,

> The Pave Imp system represents the only [existing] night combat rescue capa-
> bility. The system is operational within the limits of VFR [visual flight rules],
> permissive environment, and open area. The increased capability provides an
> option to effect night rescues on a selective basis with no degradation of the
> SAR posture or capability. More importantly, continuing operational experi-
> ence is essential to the development of a system satisfying the total require-
> ment. Reconsideration of your recommendation to de-modify the aircraft and
> PACAF support of the MAC recovery program . . . is requested.[46]

Seventh Air Force, in reviewing all the messages, concurred with
retention in-theater of the Pave Imp configuration. However, the approval came with a few "recommendations." For instance, all equipment modifications should be fully tested prior to deployment to the
theater, and all aircrews should receive their mission training in the
CONUS. Also, in-theater testing would be restricted only to the development of tactics and procedures. The bottom line, though, was
that Pave Imp aircraft—as limited as they were—would remain in
SEA and be used where and when they could as the best technology
available. Two HH-53Cs equipped with the LNRS would stand ready
on 45-minute alert at NKP or Ubon.[47] However, all parties realized
clearly now that for the LNRS to become a fully capable system, it had
to have an improved navigational system tied to a flight director and
computer interface system, TF/TA radar that allowed "blind" flying
to defeat enemy threats while also circumnavigating terrain, and a
terminal location device to swiftly locate a survivor so that the helicopter could quickly be brought to a hover over his position.[48]

Building upon the lessons learned in both Pave Star and Pave Imp,
the Aeronautical Systems Division at Wright-Patterson awarded a
contract to the Norden Division of United Aircraft Corporation and
Sikorsky in early 1972 to design, build, and install a terrain-following
radar on an HH-53B at Edwards AFB, California. Norden procured
an APQ-141 radar from the US Army and optimized it for the HH-53
while Sikorsky technicians installed it on the aircraft and modified
cockpit displays for its use. The Air Force then tested and evaluated
its use as a night, all-weather rescue vehicle. The new project was
named Pave Low.[49]

40th and 37th Aerospace Rescue
and Recovery Squadrons

The commander of the 3d ARRG, Col Warner Britton, was also concerned about the increasing enemy threat posed by radar-controlled SAMs and antiaircraft guns. In November he forwarded a request to Seventh Air Force for radar homing and warning (RHAW) systems for the HH-53s so that the crews would receive visual and aural warnings when enemy radars were painting (detecting and tracking) or targeting them. Seventh Air Force approved the request and forwarded it to MAC as CROC 15-71. In May 1972, the first conversion kits arrived, and by September all HH-53s in SEA had working RHAW gear.[50]

During the year, the 37th ARRSq at Da Nang supported the FOL at Bien Hoa AB, just north of Saigon, with helicopters and crews for possible use in the southern regions of the theater. On 25 November 1971, Jolly Greens 70 and 73 launched to recover the crew and passengers of a US Navy CH-46 shot down 90 miles to the south with 21 people on board. Proceeding to the area at low level to stay out of the weather, they joined other US Army and Navy helicopters to recover the survivors. Jolly Green 70 landed at the crash site and recovered 14 persons. The Jolly Greens then proceeded to Binh Thuy AB to drop them off. While there, the crews of both aircraft inspected their machines and discovered several small arms hits, none serious. The two crews then relaunched and headed back to Bien Hoa. En route Jolly Green 70, HH-53C #68-10366, was shot down by enemy fire. Jolly Green 73 immediately overflew the crash site and recovered one of the PJs. A Navy helicopter recovered another enlisted crew member, but the rest of the crew had been killed.[51]

In December, 40th crews at NKP were scrambled to rescue an F-105G crew (Ashcan 01) and F-4 crew (Gunfighter 82) downed near Mu Gia Pass and an F-4 crew (Falcon 74) downed in northeastern Laos. All missions were long, involved, and dangerous and tasked the crews and machines to the limit. As a result of their efforts and the efforts of supporting A-1s and FACs, one man from the F-105 and both members of each of the F-4s were recovered and sent home.

However, those successes were not just blind luck. They were the result of some other improvements made to rescue forces in general in the theater. When the 40th was moved to NKP, it was then based

Courtesy Air Force Historical Research Agency

Satisfied customer. 1st Lt Woody Bergeron after being rescued from Mu Gia Pass, Laos, in December 1969.

with several other key and developing components of the overall SAR force. The 1st Special Operations Squadron (SOS), the remaining USAF A-1 unit, was also stationed there. Its primary mission was SAR support, and it kept several aircraft on alert at all times for SAR tasking.

The 3d ARRG had a command and control center there, call sign Joker, which provided critical command and control and liaison for the various SAR forces. Joker had an intelligence section, and during 1971, it established a critical intelligence link to Task Force Alpha (TFA), also located at NKP. TFA commanded and controlled all of the sensors implanted along the Ho Chi Minh Trail and other areas of SEA. The data that it was collecting could be very useful in real time for SAR missions. As missions occurred, Joker began asking TFA for data, which it then began passing out to the rescue and support squadrons and/or briefing directly to the crews as they prepared for their missions. Additionally, Joker procured secure radios, giving TFA the capability to pass intelligence by voice via secure communications to the aircrews in their aircraft, which had compatible equipment. This node was in full bloom for the December SARs.

Also stationed at NKP was the 23d TASS. This FAC unit currently flew the OV-10 and patrolled over large sections of Laos and Cambodia. Like all FAC units, its pilots were able to initiate and support SARs as a basic skill. Recently, though, 15 of its OV-10s had been highly modified with some new and exciting technology. The aircraft were equipped with the Pave Spot, an optical system that the weapons systems operator (WSO) in the backseat ran. It was designed to provide magnification for better visual reconnaissance along the Ho Chi Minh Trail. Built into the Pave Spot was a laser designation system that allowed the WSO to illuminate a target with an energy beam so that a laser-guided bomb (LGB) could track the beam to the designated target. This system was proving to be extremely useful against trucks and supplies along the trail. It was also effective for destroying antiaircraft guns, something of great use in SARs.[52]

Additionally, the 15 OV-10s were equipped with a long-range aid to navigation (LORAN) system, a precise (for its day) navigational device integrated into the Pave Spot system. When a target was designated on the ground with a laser beam, the crew would get a LORAN readout on its exact location, which could be expressed in either a military grid system or geographical coordinates. Those coordinates could be passed to another LORAN-equipped aircraft. That aircraft could then be flown to that point to drop bombs or cluster bomb units (CBU) on the position through the weather with reasonable accuracy. These CBUs could also be area-denial ordnance that could protect the survivor for a period of time until the rescue forces could arrive.

If the delivering aircraft was dropping a bomb capable of being guided by the laser beam from the OV-10, the LGB could be dropped through the weather and then guided to the target by the laser designator on the "Pave Nail" OV-10s, as they came to be called. The use of a laser/LORAN combined system proved an effective way to deliver bombs through the weather, even for precision delivery, and to destroy antiaircraft guns.

Beyond this, though, it did not take the crews long to realize the value of the laser/LORAN combination not only in SAR situations for finding and pinpointing survivors but also for leading non-LORAN-equipped aircraft at least to the area of the survivor, where they could then use their own limited navigational systems. Effectively, this meant that the Pave Nail could provide the precision navigation that was lacking on the LNRS aircraft. While not the optimum solution, certainly, this capability was a definite battlefield expedient until the HH-53s could be equipped with LORAN or some other long-range precision navigational device.[53]

Very soon, young officers from the various squadrons at NKP were holding informal conferences to compare tactics and to explore how these new technological advances could be used in the SAR arena. Such extemporaneous meetings led to many "bar-napkin agreements" among the participants as they jotted down their ideas in the various unit "hootch bars." The Nails proposed that the Pave Nail aircraft should be called in early in any SAR situation to quickly determine the exact survivor position. They even developed a procedure whereby in bad weather that prevented visual search, they could use a collection of automatic-direction-finding cuts taken from a survivor's radio using precisely recorded LORAN positions to calculate a location within 1,000 meters—accurate enough to enable SAR operations in instrument flight rule (IFR) conditions. The crews then used three-dimensional tactical maps of the area and literally planned a best approach to the survivor's location through the weather, which could then be used by the Jolly Green crew in a Pave Imp–equipped aircraft.

The after action report written for the Ashcan 01 SAR mission explained how this procedure was accomplished to recover the one survivor:

> The SAR [task force] arrived back at the scene at [5:45 a.m.] . . . and awaited first light. Major [Ken] Ernest's crew in Jolly Green 30 (Jolly Low) secured a Doppler fix [determined by a Pave Nail] from over the survivor's position to aid in returning to him and . . . descended through a hole in the clouds and began searching. Beginning his run-in to Ashcan 01[A] from about two miles southwest, Major Ernest was IFR, and required assistance in locating the survivor. The assistance was provided by a Sandy [A-1] and Pave-Nail.[54]

The Jolly crew members spotted the body of the F-105G WSO, but he was clearly dead. No recovery attempt was made. Instead, they overflew him to get the pilot. The report continued to say that "the coordination between the Jolly, the Pave-Nail, and the Sandy resumed as Jolly Green 30 continued to inch its way toward the [pilot] until a hover was established over [the pilot]. Approximately one hour had been spent in mostly IFR weather." The survivor then spotted them. He recalled, "I could see the penetrator with the PJs coming down, and I could see the bottom of the helicopter, but the top of it was in the clouds. I thought that the chopper pilot must be having one helluva tough time trying to hover there, with the gusty wind, and him just about IFR. Anyway, they got me on the penetrator and pulled me aboard."[55]

These new procedures were used in varying combination a week later to recover the crews from Gunfighter 82 and Falcon 74. Drawing upon intelligence provided through Joker, the laser/LORAN combination on the Pave Nails was used effectively to pummel enemy forces in IFR conditions. Then the precision navigation capability of the system was used to help steer the SAR task forces to the SAR areas and establish the necessary Doppler reference for the HH-53 to find and recover the survivors. This was truly unexpected value added to the SAR team. It was also testimony to the inventiveness and creativity of young aircrews from the various squadrons who were able to take new technology designed for specific purposes and then use it in innovative ways. For the HH-53 crews, these missions showed that the LNRS system, while clearly recognized as a limited tool, could still be used in unforeseen ways to effect successful recoveries, even when facing stiff enemy opposition. The combination of the powerful H-53 heavy-lift helicopter and evolving technology was a potentially potent mix, especially if it was further combined with eager and smart young operators who would push the technology well beyond intended uses and limits.

All of this was captured by the NKP wing commander, Col Jack Robinson, who wrote directly to the Seventh Air Force commander, now Gen John Lavelle, of these amazing events:

> Recent introduction of sophisticated navigation and ordnance delivery systems designed for IFR conditions . . . have major implications for USAF rescue capabilities.
>
> . . . The PAVENAIL can lead the helicopter directly over the survivor and provide a zero reference for the Jolly's Doppler navigation system. This technique permitted the rescue of Ashcan 01[A] . . . in IFR conditions, and the PAVE IMP instrumentation proved invaluable in this situation.
>
> . . . TFA sensor monitoring provided real-time targeting of traffic attempting to move through the route structure into the survivor's location.[56]

As the year ended, the 3d ARRG announced plans to reduce the 40th ARRSq from 10 to eight aircraft and the 37th from eight to five as part of the overall withdrawal of USAF assets from SEA. For the year, 3d ARRG crews conducted 149 combat saves and 109 noncombat saves. The numbers were no longer presented by aircraft type.

Several of the noncombat events were medevac missions conducted with the Pave Imp aircraft in remote locations.[57]

Just a few days into the new year, 1st Lt Steve Connelly reported to the 40th as a new copilot. After graduating from the Air Force Academy in June 1970, he attended undergraduate helicopter training (UHT) with the US Army at Fort Wolters, Texas. This was a new program designed to address the overall USAF shortage of helicopter pilots caused by the steady attrition of now eight years of continuous combat in SEA. Heretofore, all USAF helicopter pilots attended the standard fixed-wing undergraduate pilot training and then, at some later point, were transitioned to rotary-wing assignments. As an expedient, the USAF decided to direct young officers through the US Army UHT program, and Connelly was one of the first.

Courtesy Col Steve Connelly, USAF, Retired

Capt Ben Orrell and 1st Lt Steve Connelly with the 40th ARRSq at Nakhon Phanom AB, Thailand, in 1972

After completing his training at Fort Wolters, Connelly reported to the 1550th Aircrew Training and Test Wing (ATTW) at Hill AFB, where he received some Air Force–specific training and his pilot wings. Then he entered the HH-53 qualification course for eventual assignment to the 40th ARRSq at NKP. His "stick buddy"—the fellow student he was paired with—was Capt Mark Schibler.

Schibler was a highly experienced helicopter pilot. He had been commissioned in 1962 through the Reserve Officer Training Corps (ROTC) program at the University of Oregon. After pilot training at Williams AFB, near Phoenix, Arizona, he was assigned to helicopters and flew the H-43 at several locations including Bien Hoa AB and Clark AB, the Philippines, before receiving his orders to the HH-53 and a second combat tour.[58]

Partway through the course, maintenance problems limited available training sorties. The two pilots and an instructor pilot (IP) were farmed out to Hamilton AFB, California, to accomplish a portion of their training with the 41st ARRSq. In late December, though, the 40th ARRSq needed pilots, and the 1550th ATTW was directed to send its two NKP-bound students who were furthest through the course on to NKP to complete their training there with the 40th. Connelly and Schibler packed their bags and caught MAC flights to NKP.

Arriving there a few days later, Connelly was a bit overwhelmed. With barely 30 hours in the aircraft and still learning the systems and basic flight characteristics of the aircraft, he was paired with Capt Dave Pannabecker, an experienced IP, and placed on the flight schedule. He also tried to learn all he could from the "older" experienced pilots. He remembers, "I was pretty clueless; I was still learning the 53 and understanding how that whole package worked. . . . The Nails and the Sandys . . . the guys like [Dale] Stovall and Ben Orrell and Lou Grant were all captains [and] just seemed to me like they knew everything, while I was struggling to find my way to first base."[59]

He also encountered a bias for which he was not prepared. He, 1st Lt Jim Casey, and 1st Lt Brian McDowell—the first UHT graduates to arrive at NKP—immediately sensed resentment that they were somehow not "real" pilots but products of inferior Army training. The three of them became very protective of each other and formed an informal copilots union for mutual support. Connelly recalls that "the copilots union was the low-life, bottom-feeding vermin that hadn't been to pilot training. . . . They were undergraduate helicopter Army-trained guys who knew how to hover but weren't real pilots. We were all second-class citizens. . . . We were the first ones over there. . . . And we turned out to be pretty good copilots, and over time, it was dispelled, but [initially] we were clearly second class."[60]

Regardless, they were there and learned about combat flying within the maelstrom of what would turn out to be some of the heaviest fighting of the entire war.

Captain Schibler arrived a few days after Connelly. His "welcome" was also rather rushed, and within a week, he was in the combat upgrade program, flying with Capt Ken Ernest, an old friend from a previous H-43 assignment. The 40th launched sorties each day to cover two orbits, strategically placed so that the HH-53s could more rapidly respond to shot-down aircraft. The northern one was along the Laos–North Vietnam border southeast of Hanoi, and the southern one was over lower Laos, near the Ho Chi Minh Trail. Schibler was dispatched to both and also sat alert at NKP and the FOL at Ubon. He easily qualified as a rescue crew commander and entered upgrade to IP and then flight examiner.[61]

By early 1972, development of and CONUS testing on the ELF system specified in MAC ROC #27-70 were completed. In March, the 40th received the first kit to modify one of its LNRS aircraft, which would help locate survivors quickly and provide terminal guidance to expedite recoveries. At the same time the new commander of the 3d ARRG, Col Cy Muirhead, forwarded to Seventh Air Force a request for ECM equipment for the HH-53s. This request was based upon the increasing sophistication and proliferation of radar-guided antiaircraft guns and SAMs being steadily brought south by the North Vietnamese. The aircrews needed equipment that gave them the ability to jam or counteract them. Seventh Air Force supported the request and published it as CROC 6-72. Headquarters (HQ) PACAF demurred, pointing out several problems concerning weight tradeoff on board the HH-53s and the physical size of a jammer capable of overcoming the large radar cross-section generated by the main rotor. MAC otherwise concurred with the request and began testing to answer PACAF's concerns.[62]

On 27 March, Joker at NKP launched Jolly Greens 52 and 62 when it received a report of a downed Jolly Green aircraft in northeastern Cambodia. Jolly Greens 60 and 61 had departed NKP earlier to rendezvous with Jolly Green 64, which had departed Da Nang and was en route to NKP via Cambodia. At one point, the other two crews lost sight of Jolly Green 61. When the Jolly 61 crew did not respond to a radio check, the two crews began a visual search and spotted a large fire with black smoke. They swiftly realized that it was Jolly Green 61, HH-53C #68-10359. The crews of Jolly Green 60 and 64 tried to hover

over the wreckage but were driven away by enemy ground fire. Both sustained damage to their aircraft. When Jolly Greens 52 and 62 arrived and could find no survivors, they escorted 60 and 64 to friendly fields and then returned to the crash site. Eventually, a PJ was able to descend to the crash site but was unable to search it in any detail because of the lingering fire. When a search was finally conducted, no survivors or remains were found. Instead, the searcher discovered that the cockpit and cabin had been reduced to ashes.[63]

The reason for the ECM upgrade request became brutally clear the next night when a radar-guided SA-2 missile hit and destroyed an AC-130 Spectre gunship operating along the Ho Chi Minh Trail southwest of Tchepone. There were no survivors, and there was no SAR. Two nights after that, several rounds of radar-controlled 57 mm fire hit and severely damaged another AC-130, call sign Spectre 22, also working along the trail but farther south. One wing was on fire. The aircraft commander, Capt Waylon Fulk, ordered the crew to bail out. Two members did so immediately. However, since the aircraft was still somewhat controllable, the rest of the crew elected to stay on board to try to save it. Fulk declared an emergency and turned toward their home base at Ubon. En route, though, the wing fire continued, and the aircraft steadily lost controllability. Fulk again ordered the crew to bail out, and the remaining 13 Airmen did so into the cold Laotian night.

Other Spectre aircraft and several Pave Nail FACs swarmed into the area and began to locate the survivors using their onboard sensor/laser systems. The area where most survivors were located was relatively benign and mostly flat, and Joker considered launching the LNRS HH-53 out of NKP for the pickups. However, dawn was just an hour away; instead, Joker used the time to organize for a first-light maximum effort to recover all the survivors at once. An Air America helicopter recovered the first two Airmen to bail out and flew them to Pakse. HH-53s from both the 37th and 40th recovered the other 13. Maj Ken Ernest commanded one crew, with Capt Mark Schibler as copilot; Capt Dale Stovall and copilot 1st Lt Steve Connelly led another crew; and Capt Ben Orrell commanded a third.[64]

That same month, SSgt Rick Simmon reported to NKP for duty as a flight mechanic with the 40th. The son of a career USAF navigator, he had enlisted in the USAF in 1966 and, after basic training, served as a crew chief on UH-1F helicopters at Malmstrom AFB, Montana. Two years later, Simmon was selected to serve as an initial cadre crew chief on the new HH-53Bs and went through aircraft maintenance training at the Sikorsky plant at Stratford, Connecticut. He then joined the 40th ARRSq at Udorn AB and served a one-year tour. Returning to the CONUS in 1969, he reported to Edwards AFB, where he served as a UH-1 flight mechanic and flew local base rescue support. In the summer of 1971, he received orders to Hill AFB to qualify as an HH-53 flight mechanic and then proceed to the 40th ARRSq, now at NKP, for a second combat tour. Arriving as a highly experienced crew member, he was quickly put on the flight schedule and began to fly his share of combat rescue missions. He also became involved in training the younger Airmen assigned to the aircrews, stressing to them the critical job that the flight mechanic performed as an integral part of the aircrew.[65]

As rescuers were conducting the Spectre 22 SAR, the entire war in SEA was changing dramatically. The previous day, a multidivision force of North Vietnamese regulars invaded South Vietnam across the DMZ separating the two countries and from Laos. Even though US ground forces were being pulled out of South Vietnam, USAF and USN combat power was abundant, and at once swarms of fighter and attack aircraft sprang into action against the invading divisions. The next nine months would be some of the most dramatic, and for the rescue crews, some of the most dangerous of the war, as aircraft fell from the sky almost every day.

On 2 April 1972, as B-52s were bombing North Vietnamese armored and infantry units just south of the DMZ, a SAM shot down an accompanying EB-66, call sign Bat 21. Only one man of six, the navigator, was able to eject. He landed amidst 30,000 enemy troops. For the next 24 hours, several US Army helicopters and two HH-53s from the 37th ARRSq unsuccessfully tried to rescue the survivor. All were badly damaged or shot down. In the process, a supporting OV-10 was also shot down. The pilot was captured, and the backseater was evading. The Air Force launched hundreds of supporting air strikes against the enemy units in an attempt to beat down the enemy guns. Three days later, Jolly Green 67, an HH-53C #68-10365, was shot down while trying to pick up the two men. All six men on board were killed. Captain Schibler was flying a backup aircraft on that mission and watched Jolly Green 67 go down. The message presented was obvious—even heavily armored helicopters would have a hard time surviving during daylight operations over massed and heavily armed enemy formations. Increasingly, as the North Vietnamese brought more antiaircraft guns and now even SAMs farther south, there were ever more places where helicopters could not go.

Watching this debacle, the MACV commander, Gen Creighton Abrams, decreed that there would be no more helicopter rescue attempts for the men. Five days later, a small team consisting of a USMC lieutenant colonel, a US Navy SEAL, and seven South Vietnamese commandos extricated the two men in daring night surface recoveries.[66]

Courtesy Gary Ferentchek

Jolly Green 67, HH-53C #68-10365. On a mission to rescue two downed Americans in South Vietnam on 6 April 1972, the helicopter was shot down and destroyed, killing all six Airmen aboard.

On 13 April, in a battle almost as epic, a Jolly Green crew from the 40th ARRSq, led by Capt Ben Orrell, flew into central Laos to recover a USMC A-6 pilot shot down while bombing enemy trucks and supplies on the Ho Chi Minh Trail destined for the major battles raging farther south. Again braving the massed enemy gunners along the now infamous trail, Orrell and his crew of the "low" bird reached a hover over Maj Clyde Smith. As the supporting A-1s laid down torrents of suppressive fire, Orrell held the aircraft steady long enough to get the pilot on board. Watching from above, Captain Stovall and his crew stood ready as the backup or "high" bird just in case the low bird needed assistance or had to abort. That day, though, their services were not needed, and they joined up with Orrell and flew back to NKP. For his efforts that day, Captain Orrell, described as "unpretentious, rock solid, steady, cool, and fearless," was awarded the Air Force Cross.[67]

Three weeks after the loss of Jolly Green 67, the 37th was called out for a different type of rescue. The attacking North Vietnamese Army (NVA) forces had steadily pushed back the defending South Vietnamese Army (ARVN) forces and tried to envelop them as the ARVN struggled to defend the city of Quang Tri. The ARVN forces had their headquarters in an old French citadel in the center of the city. As the NVA pressed its attack, it slowly surrounded the citadel and threatened to capture the US Army, Air Force, and Marine advisors assigned to the headquarters staff. To evacuate them under fire, the 37th dispatched five HH-53s with several A-1 escorts. Arriving as an attack was in progress, the first three Jollys landed one at a time and evacuated all 129 Americans as the A-1s provided perimeter defensive suppression. The fourth Jolly Green also landed in the citadel but left empty when the crew discovered that all of the Americans had already gotten out. Rescues came in all shapes and sizes.[68]

After the Jolly Greens exited the battle cauldron around Quang Tri, though, several USAF aircraft were shot down in the area over the next 24 hours. All were hit by the newly introduced SA-7 heatseeking missile. Capable of being carried and fired by one man, these weapons could be very effective against low-flying aircraft like helicopters. Consequently, decoy flare dispensers were rapidly installed on all HH-53s. No missile warning system was available. Detection had to be visual, and response had to be immediate. Consequently, the systems were configured so that any crew member could expend flares. Additionally, all crews carried flare guns that could also fool the missiles. As a result of these quick actions, no HH-53s were shot down by SA-7s in SEA.[69]

In response to the enemy offensive, the US military once again unleashed its airpower against North Vietnam. Strike packages headed for northern targets launched from air bases in Thailand and South Vietnam and from USN aircraft carriers. Accordingly, the Jollys began to get calls to fly farther north for recoveries.

Missions increased dramatically for the Jollys. Captain Stovall was on alert on 1 June when crews were scrambled to rescue an F-4 WSO, Capt Roger Locher. He had been shot down 23 days earlier northwest of Hanoi and had been evading. Launching with escort A-1s, Stovall and crew and their wingman proceeded north. As they crossed into

North Vietnam, MiGs challenged their flight. The slow-moving HH-53s and A-1s had to take wild, evasive action to keep from being shot down. Their actions depleted their fuel, and they had to return empty-handed. Planning began immediately for a much larger effort the next day. Fully aware of the enemy threat so near Hanoi, the Seventh Air Force commander, Gen John Vogt, authorized a huge package of 119 aircraft to provide support such as MiGCAP, SAM suppression, and tankers. Launching the next morning, Stovall and his crew were Jolly Green 30. His wingman was Jolly Green 60, commanded by Capt Jerry Shipman. This time, the Jolly/Sandy task force was able to reach the survivor. Stovall was flying one of the HH-53s with the newly installed ELF. It picked up Locher's radio signal from 40 miles away and gave excellent guidance directly to him. Stovall brought his helicopter to a hover over Locher and swiftly hoisted him aboard as the escort A-1s attacked enemy guns in the area. The force then turned south and headed back to Thailand. En route, the A-1 pilots spotted an enemy train full of supplies and heavily damaged it. This was the deepest penetration of a rescue task force into North Vietnam in the entire war. Subsequently, all HH-53s in Thailand received the ELF system.[70]

On 20 May, Capt Mark Schibler led a crew that flew to within 35 miles of Hanoi to recover the crew of an F-4 shot down in an air-to-air engagement. They were able to recover the pilot, Capt John Markle, but could not reach the WSO before he was captured. Schibler received the Silver Star for that mission.[71]

On 27 June, Capt Dale Stovall and crew, including SSgt Rick Simmon, again proceeded deep into North Vietnam to pick up another downed F-4 crew member located 70 miles west of Hanoi, near the Red River. Coming to a hover as ground fire had already driven away another Jolly Green, Stovall held the aircraft steady as Simmon lowered the penetrator to the survivor and a PJ whom the other Jolly Green had inserted to help with the recovery. With escort A-1s attacking enemy forces and laying down smoke screens, the onboard PJs firing their miniguns, and enemy rounds striking the aircraft, Simmon stood in the open door and steadily raised the survivor and pararescueman into the aircraft. As they reached the cabin door, he dragged them into the aircraft and called for Stovall to depart the area. Simmon then instantly began applying first aid to another crew member who had been wounded while they held their hover. For their actions that day, all crew members were highly decorated. Sergeant Simmon was awarded the Silver Star.[72]

As part of the enemy offensive, small teams of Viet Cong routinely attacked the huge US air bases in South Vietnam. On 18 August, they bombarded the Da Nang airfield with a barrage of 122 mm rockets. One of them slammed into the Jolly Green alert area and severely damaged HH-53C #68-10361. Unfortunately, that proud veteran of the Son Tay raid was destroyed by the ensuing fire.[73]

The missions continued through the rest of the year as an average of two US and allied aircraft were being shot down a day. There were so many that it seemed as if they all ran together. As part of the continuing drawdown of US forces in Vietnam, the 37th ARRSq was inactivated on 30 November 1972. All remaining personnel, aircraft, and equipment were transferred to the 40th ARRSq at NKP. It would remain as the sole rescue unit in SEA and provide top cover for the residual USAF forces in Thailand. The 40th continued to maintain an FOL at Da Nang and Saigon.[74]

In late December, Captain Shipman and his crew were sitting on night alert with one of the LNRS aircraft when they received an alert for a possible recovery mission. Another AC-130 gunship, Spectre 17, had been shot down, again along the Ho Chi Minh Trail southeast of the deadly Saravane area in Laos. Only two of the crew members had gotten out. The vicinity was considered acceptable for use of the LNRS, and Shipman and crew as Jolly Green 32 took off. Using the LNRS, Shipman was able to fly directly to the first survivor and hover the big helicopter directly over him. Shipman then sent one of his PJs down on the hoist. He easily found the man and brought him back up. The system worked perfectly. Shipman then flew to the second survivor. He was in some dense brush and took longer to recover because the helicopter rotor downwash caused the brush to move, affecting the sensors for the Doppler navigation system and, at one point, causing Shipman and his crew to lose sight of the survivor. Fortunately, another Spectre was orbiting above and monitoring the recovery. Its crew used its sensors to vector the Jolly back around to him and pick him up. With both men then on board, the crew of Jolly Green 32 hovered around the area to insure that no other crew members were alive. Satisfied that they had the only survivors, they returned to NKP and logged the first successful LNRS rescue.

Shipman was impressed. Even though they had been right along a portion of the Ho Chi Minh Trail, they had encountered only minor ground fire. To all involved, the tactical benefits of operating at night were obvious. As Shipman later summed up, "The ability to go in there blacked out at night gives you a definite advantage because the gunners just can't see you." Shipman was also impressed with the role played by the Spectre crew, stating in his mission report that "the combination of the NRS [night recovery system] equipped HH-53 and the AC-130 could play an increased role for night rescue operations if a limited training program could be developed."[75]

Another dramatic rescue attempt occurred in December. While supporting the massive Linebacker II bombing operations against North Vietnam, an F-111, call sign Jackel 33, was shot down about 50 miles west of Hanoi in the early morning hours of the 23d. The two pilots, Capt Robert Sponeybarger and 1st Lt Bill Wilson, evaded for three days before Sponeybarger was captured. A rescue task force of Jolly Greens and A-7s, now performing the Sandy mission, tried to get into the area but was blocked by the poor weather and thunderstorms. Wilson continued to dodge the enemy search teams, and on the 27th, four Jolly Greens from the 40th, led by Capt Rick Shapiro in Jolly Green 01 and supported by a task force of 13 A-7Ds, two HC-130s, and 32 F-4s, flew in to pick him up.

Entering the survivor's area, the A-7s laid down a smoke screen and began to attack enemy targets as Shapiro went for the survivor, drawing enemy fire as he did. The flight mechanic, Sgt Chuck Rouhier, spotted Wilson and began to lower the penetrator. Wilson ran for the penetrator and was almost on when he slipped and fell down a steep incline. As Shapiro tried to reposition for another attempt, his copilot was hit in the arm and bleeding badly. Given this development and the steadily increasing and accurate ground fire, Shapiro decided to pull out without the Airman.

Struggling with the now badly damaged aircraft, Shapiro rendezvoused with an HC-130 tanker over northeastern Laos because he did not have enough fuel to get back to any base in Thailand. Unfortunately, the enemy fire had also damaged the aircraft's refueling probe, and it could not take on any fuel. Facing fuel starvation, Shapiro put the helicopter down in a benign area, and his wingman picked up Shapiro and his crew. However, the area was not secure, so the escorting A-7Ds had to destroy HH-53C #69-5788. Wilson evaded for several more days as other efforts were mounted to support him with supply drops. While evading, though, he stumbled into enemy troops and was captured.[76]

When the 37th ARRSq inactivated, most of its helicopters and a number of its personnel were moved to the 40th at NKP. This caused an overage of rescue crews in the 40th, and some personnel were allowed to curtail their tours and return home. Lieutenant Connelly had been flying as an aircraft commander since his upgrade in September and decided to take the early return. His 11 months at NKP had been eventful. He had flown on several significant missions, amassed a wealth of combat flight experience, and had 15 saves to his credit. He transferred to the 41st ARRSq at Hamilton AFB.[77]

Courtesy Air Force Historical Research Agency

Rescue forces were proud of their saves.

US military forces stopped all combat operations in South and North Vietnam on 28 January 1973, in accordance with the peace treaty signed in Paris between the United States, South Vietnam, and North Vietnam. The 40th terminated operations at its FOLs at Da Nang and Saigon. Combat operations in Laos ended one month later. But direct military operations did continue in Cambodia as well as support operations throughout the theater. To assist these operations, the 40th still had 11 aircraft, of which five were Pave

Imp–modified. The unit kept two HH-53s on alert at NKP and two at Ubon AB for daytime rescue operations and one LNRS aircraft on alert at NKP at night.

Finishing his tour with the 40th ARRSq in March, Sergeant Simmon returned to Hill AFB. His tour had been fruitful. He learned to use the first generation of NVGs and had upgraded to flight mechanic instructor. He had flown on several intense SAR missions in Laos and North Vietnam. For his individual actions, Simmon had been awarded two Silver Stars, two Distinguished Flying Crosses, and numerous air medals and campaign ribbons, quite an accomplishment for an enlisted man. At Hill, he would train new HH-53 flight mechanics and pass along to them the intricacies of the fine art of the integral crew coordination so critical to the safe and effective operation of the HH-53.[78]

In March an HH-53 flew to a US Navy ship off of Saigon to deliver a doctor and medical supplies to care for a critically sick Sailor. Two months later, a USAF A-7D went down in the Tonle Sap Lake in central Cambodia, killing the pilot. A 40th crew recovered the body. The next day, the Ubon HH-53s were launched to successfully rescue the pilot and WSO of an F-4 that went down in northeast Cambodia. The unit also began to get increased calls from units and bases within Thailand to perform medevac missions.

Tragically, on 14 June 1973, Jolly Green 64, HH 53C #68-10362, experienced an undetermined flight control malfunction and crashed in the Tonle Sap Lake. Three crew members were killed. The two PJs were able to bail out and were successfully recovered. On 15 August 1973, per US congressional mandate, all combat operations ceased in Cambodia. The Ubon FOL was then terminated and all 40th operations consolidated at NKP. As of that date, USAF rescue forces were credited with 2,683 combat and 1,290 noncombat saves in SEA. More importantly, the rescue forces helped to maintain the morale of the aircrews who had to fly in every corner of the war. Stated General Vogt, the Seventh Air Force commander in 1972 and 1973, rescue was "absolutely essential for the morale of the combat crews. The guy had to have a feeling that he had some chance if he were shot down. . . . It did instill in the combat crews a feeling that they had a fighting chance."[79]

Notes

1. Anderson, *United States Air Force Search and Rescue in Southeast Asia* [hereafter referred to as *USAF SAR in SEA* for all editions], *1961–66*, Project CHECO (Contemporary Historical Examination of Current Operations) Report, 16.

2. Ibid., 42.

3. Tilford, *Search and Rescue in Southeast Asia*, 84.

4. Ibid.; and Anderson, *USAF SAR in SEA, 1961–66*, Project CHECO Report, 76.

5. McLeaish and Silvis, "Southeast Asia Operational Analysis," 3d ARRG study, 6, 10.

6. Ibid., 12–18.

7. History of the Aerospace Rescue and Recovery Service (hereafter referred to as History of ARRS), 1 July 1970–30 June 1971, vol. 1, 191.

8. Ibid., 190.

9. Ibid., 191.

10. McLeaish and Silvis, "Southeast Asia Operational Analysis," 3d ARRG study, 12.

11. Tilford, *Search and Rescue in Southeast Asia*, 90, app. A.

12. Durkee, *USAF SAR in SEA, July 1966–November 1967*, Project CHECO Report, 17.

13. LaPointe, *PJs in Vietnam*, 356.

14. Ibid.; and Galdorisi and Phillips, *Leave No Man Behind*, 326.

15. History of the 40th Aerospace Rescue and Recovery Squadron (hereafter referred to as History of 40th ARRSq), Detachment 1, 1 Jan–31 Mar 1968, 1.

16. Ibid., 9; and Overton, *USAF SAR in SEA, November 1967–June 1969*, Project CHECO Report, 21.

17. History of 40th ARRSq, Detachment 1, 1 Jan–31 Mar 1968, 3.

18. Overton, *USAF SAR in SEA, November 1967–June 1969*, Project CHECO Report, 39. Kenny Fields, the A-7 pilot, eloquently tells this story in his book, *The Rescue of Streetcar 304: A Navy Pilot's Forty Hours on the Run in Laos*, published in 2007.

19. Overton, *USAF SAR in SEA, November 1967–June 1969*, Project CHECO Report, 69.

20. Ibid., 54.

21. History of ARRS, 1 July 1970–30 June 1971, vol. 1, 194.

22. "H-53 Night Operation," *Sikorsky News*, May 1972, 4–9.

23. Gambone, *Pave Low III: That Others May Live*, 5, 25; Overton, *USAF SAR in SEA, November 1967–June 1969*, Project CHECO Report, 54–57; History of ARRS, 1 July 1970–30 June 1971, vol. 1, 194; message, 191331Z MAY 70, CSAF to MAC, subject: Pave Star Night Recovery System; message, 212209Z MAY 70, CSAF to AFSC, MAC et al., subject: Pave Star, 21 May 1970; and message, 251620Z AUG 71, MAC to CINCPACAF et al., subject: Pave Imp Combat Eval.

24. "H-53 Night Operation," May 1972, 4, 13.

25. Overton, *USAF SAR in SEA, November 1967–June 1969*, Project CHECO Report, 42–46, app. A.

26. Lynch, *USAF SAR in SEA, 1 July 1969– 31 December 1970*, Project CHECO Report, 7.

27. Ibid., table 1.

28. History of the 3d Aerospace Rescue and Recovery Group (hereafter referred to as History of 3d ARRG), 1 Jan–31 Mar 1970, 17.

29. Ibid., 1 Apr–30 June 1970, 18.

30. Lowe, *USAF SAR in SEA, 1 January 1971–31 March 1972*, Project CHECO Report, 27.

31. "Pilots Praise HH-53C in Pacific Run," *Sikorsky News*, Sept 1970, 5.

32. Manor, "Son Tay Raid," 8.

33. History of ARRS, 1 July 1970–30 June 1971, vols. 1, 2.

34. Ibid., viii.

35. Manor, "Son Tay Raid," 8.

36. Ibid.

37. Ibid.

38. Ibid.

39. Comer, interviews.

40. Lynch, *USAF SAR in SEA, 1 July 1969–31 December 1970*, Project CHECO Report, table 3.

41. History of 3d ARRG, 1 Apr–30 June 1971, 13.

42. History of 40th ARRSq, 1 July–30 Sept 1971, 24.

43. History of 3d ARRG, 1 July–30 Sept 1971, 13, 24.

44. Lynch, *USAF SAR in SEA, 1 July 1969–31 December 1970*, Project CHECO Report, 16–18; and History of the 3d ARRG, 1 Apr–30 June 1971, 16.

45. Lt Col John H. Morse, "Final Evaluation Pave Imp Operational Test Order 6-6-71, HH-53," 9 July 1971; message, 120900Z AUG 71, Headquarters (HQ) 7AF TSN AFLD RVN to PACAF and various, subject: Pave Imp; message, 251620Z AUG 71, MAC to PACAF et al., subject: Pave Imp Combat Eval; and message, 130800Z SEP 71, HQ 7AF TSN AFLD RVN to CINCPACAF/DO, subject: Pave Imp. See also History of 3d ARRG, 1 Oct–31 Dec 1971, vol. 1, 14.

46. Ibid.

47. Ibid.

48. History of ARRS, 1 July 1971–30 June 1972, vol. 1, 139.

49. "HH-53B Modified for PAVE LOW," *Sikorsky News*, June 1972, 8.

50. Francis and Nelson, *USAF SAR in SEA, 1 April 1972–30 June 1973*, Project CHECO Report, 17.

51. History of the 37th Aerospace Rescue and Recovery Squadron (hereafter referred to as History of 37th ARRSq), 1 Oct–31 Dec 1971, 15.

52. History of the 23d Tactical Air Support Squadron, 1 July–30 Sept 1971, in History of the 504th Tactical Air Support Group, vol. 3, 3–6.

53. Ibid.

54. Ernest, "Craziest SAR I've Ever Seen."

55. Ibid.

56. Col Jack Robinson, 56 SOW commander, to 7AF/CC, subject: Improvements in Search and Rescue (SAR) Capabilities, letter, 30 Dec 1971, in History of the 56th Special Operations Wing (hereafter referred to as History of 56th SOW), 1 Oct–31 Dec 1971, vol. 2.

57. History of 3d ARRG, 1 Oct–31 Dec 1971, vols. 1, 9, 15.

58. Schibler, interview.

59. Connelly, interview.

60. Ibid.

61. Schibler, interview.

62. Lowe, *USAF SAR in SEA, 1 January 1971–31 March 1972*, Project CHECO Report, 31.

63. Ibid., 71; History of 40th ARRSq, 1 Jan–31 Mar 1972, mission narrative; and Morse to the author, e-mail.

64. Lowe, *USAF SAR in SEA, 1 January 1971–31 March 1972*, Project CHECO Report, 70; History of 40th ARRSq, 1 Jan–31 Mar 1972, mission narrative; and Connelly, interview.

65. Simmon, interview.

66. This event is fully explained in Whitcomb's book *The Rescue of Bat 21.*

67. Whitcomb, *Combat Search and Rescue in Desert Storm*, 1–5.

68. History of 3d ARRG, 1 Apr–30 June 1972, 17.

69. Francis and Nelson, *USAF SAR in SEA, 1 April 1972–30 June 1973*, Project CHECO Report, 17.

70. History of 40th ARRSq, 1 Apr–30 June 1972, mission narrative; and Stovall, interview.

71. Schibler, interview.

72. Simmon, interview.

73. History of 3d ARRG, 1 July–30 Sept 1972, 5-1.

74. Francis and Nelson, *USAF SAR in SEA, 1 April 1972–30 June 1973*, Project CHECO Report, 10.

75. Ibid.; Shipman, interview; and Hobson, *Vietnam Air Losses*, 244.

76. History of 3d ARRG, 1 Oct 1972–31 Dec 1972; Hobson, *Vietnam Air Losses,* 244; Francis and Nelson, *USAF SAR in SEA, 1 April 1972–30 June 1973*, Project CHECO Report, 48; and Rouhier to the author, e-mail.

77. Connelly, interview.

78. Simmon, interview.

79. History of 40th ARRSq, 1 Jan–31 Mar 1973, 102; ibid., 1 Apr–30 June 1973, 152; History of 3d ARRG, 1 July–30 Sept 1973, 1; and Gen John Vogt, USAF oral history interview, transcript, 197, Air Force Historical Research Agency (AFHRA).

Chapter 3

. . . and Knives

*The distinguished work of the . . . 21st [SOS] in Southeast
Asia strengthened the Air Force's entitlement to future special
air operations roles.*

—Col Ray Bowers

21st Special Operations Squadron

As part of the acquisition contract for the H-53, the Air Force
ordered 12 CH-53C cargo helicopters in 1968 for special operations
use. This was in response to a Headquarters Seventh/Thirteenth Air
Force and MACV direct request. Increasingly, the joint headquarters
had to call for heavy-lift helicopter support from units in South Vietnam for a variety of missions, such as aircraft recovery, artillery
movement for indigenous forces, and the general transport of large or
heavy equipment items. US Army CH-54s or USMC CH-53As were
dispatched to fulfill the missions, but the transit times consumed
large amounts of flying time and created serious logistical challenges.
When the Seventh/Thirteenth Air Force requested the permanent
assignment of a detachment of CH-54s in northern Thailand, MACV
demurred and instead requested that the USAF acquire its own
heavy-lift helicopters. On 20 April 1968, the Honorable Clark Clifford,
secretary of defense, approved the initial buy of the 12 CH-53Cs, with
later options for eight more.[1]

These aircraft were similar to the HH-53B/Cs, lacking only the
in-flight refueling capability and some onboard armor protection.
Interestingly, the acquisition did include one refueling kit and armor
kit per two aircraft for later assignment flexibility. The first aircraft
were destined for shipment to SEA for duty with the 21st SOS at NKP,
Thailand. They would join a squadron highly experienced in all aspects
of "special air warfare."[2]

The 21st SOS derived from the 21st Helicopter Squadron (HS) and
has a long heritage reaching back to its initial activation as a pursuit
(fighter) squadron in 1936. Inactivated in 1946, the 21st SOS was

briefly reactivated from 1956 to 1957 as a helicopter squadron. It was again reactivated as a helicopter squadron at Shaw AFB, South Carolina, on 15 July 1967. Initially commanded by Lt Col Harry Hauser, the squadron formed 10 crews as personnel arrived and then trained them as much as the short time allowed. The squadron's eight assigned CH-3 aircraft and 157 of its troops deployed to NKP in December. Arriving there, the 21st HS received another four CH-3s from the 20th HS based in South Vietnam but serving throughout the theater, and it prepared to begin operational missions.

At NKP the unit was assigned to the 56th Air Commando Wing (ACW), commanded by Col Heinie Aderholt. The wing had recently been formed at NKP to prosecute increased air operations against the Ho Chi Minh Trail as the North Vietnamese developed and increasingly used it to move their supplies and troops to the battlefields in South Vietnam and Cambodia. Under the operation Muscle Shoals, the trail area would be seeded with a variety of electronic sensors to detect enemy forces and vehicles. The 21st would directly support that operation. Its assigned missions were to "(1) implement and support designated portions of Muscle Shoals by airlifting personnel and/or sonic or seismic detection devices to designated targets; (2) conduct intra- and intertheater airlift as required for self-support to provide faster reaction time of unit aircraft; (3) maintain a search and rescue capability; [and] (4) sustain a flare drop capability in support of local base defense and nearby Special Forces defense." Precise placement of the sensors was critical. They had to be delivered to specific known locations to provide valid data for vehicle and troop movement analysis. Strike aircraft could then use the information as targeting data. Preliminary testing at Shaw AFB showed that this was a challenging task for the CH-3 crews, and it initiated an intense training program to bring the crews up to proficiency.[3]

By early January 1968, the crews were trained, and the unit was ready to execute its assigned mission. Using the call sign of Dusty and a numbered suffix, the aircraft would always fly in formations of two for mutual support and immediate rescue, if necessary. Within the next 60 days, the crews implanted 239 sensors along the trail and another 78 devices around the encircled USMC forces at the Khe Sanh forward base in South Vietnam. On 30 March, the 21st HS's first aircraft was shot down on an insertion mission. The escort aircraft recovered all crew members. Once the crews were proficient at their primary task, they began to get secondary missions such as night base-perimeter surveillance and purely administrative and logistics runs to other bases.

To better determine the sensor locations, a special camera was mounted on the aft of the aircraft to visually record the implant position. The squadron also began flying missions to insert or extract small allied special forces teams for surveillance purposes. Unfortunately, the gross weight of the aircraft in full combat dress limited its hover capability to 1,500 feet, a serious limitation since much of the Ho Chi Minh Trail was in terrain above that elevation.

On 23 May 1968, Dusty 51, the leader of a three-ship mission to deliver sensors around Khe Sanh, had to abort the mission because of bad weather. The three helicopters scattered and tried to climb above the clouds. For unknown reasons, Dusty 52 crashed into the top of a pinnacle. Continued bad weather and enemy forces in the area precluded a ground search, and the five crew members and a combat cameraman on board were reported as missing in action.

As the squadron became known in the theater, it received more calls for missions. Several times, squadron members were directed to move heavy ground equipment such as aircraft engines, TACAN, or radar sites. They also received taskings to insert small teams into or extract them from North Vietnam, thus becoming adept at tactical mission planning, threat analysis, map reading, and working with FACs, A-1s, A-26s, and T-28s. In July a Dusty crew recovered the crew of a FAC O-2 that made an emergency landing at a small field in central Laos. The next day, another Dusty returned to the site and recovered the aircraft. That same month, the squadron was temporarily redesignated from a helicopter squadron to an air commando squadron. On 1 August 1968, per an order from PACAF, all air commando units were to change their designation to special operations units. The 56th ACW became the 56th Special Operations Wing (SOW). In parallel, the 21st also changed. However, its transition was a bit more notable because in a period of 31 days, the 21st went from being a helicopter squadron, to an air commando squadron, to the 21st SOS.

The 21st gradually reduced its sensor-placing missions as other platforms, especially LORAN-equipped F-4s, arrived in the theater to drop the sensors. However, it did see a corresponding increase in insertion and extraction missions, especially in Laos. Frequently, it was called upon to augment the 20th SOS, which had those as its primary missions throughout the theater and used primarily CH-3s to do them. This role was formalized when the 21st's mission statement was modified to include infiltration/exfiltration as a secondary mission. The unit began conducting these assignments, called X-ray missions, for special operations personnel into northern Laos. It also began to support the Military Assistance Command Vietnam Studies and Observation Group (MACVSOG), which, under Operation Prairie Fire (PF), involved working with covert US Army teams in Laos. Many of the unit members had worked with these teams before in a variety of ways and were much more comfortable with this mission as opposed to the sensor mission. It was what classic air commandos—now special operations forces—did.

On 11 December, an RF-4 was shot down in central Laos. An H-3 Jolly Green from Udorn picked up the pilot but did not recover the WSO. The next day, Seventh Air Force directed the 21st to conduct an infiltration/search mission to find the missing man. The squadron launched three aircraft that delivered an indigenous team. It searched diligently but to no avail. Even though the mission was unsuccessful, the crews had to overcome some difficult challenges to get in and out of the landing zones. It further sharpened their skills and reinforced their confidence that they could handle the more demanding special operations missions. They flew five more PF missions that month. As 1968 was ending, the squadron commander, Lt Col Harold Welch, wrote,

> The most significant event during this quarter was the Squadron involvement in Operation PRAIRIE FIRE. The impact of this operation reached every operating level and required a complete and immediate reappraisal of tactics, procedures, and training. Flight line activities increased manyfold in configuring the aircraft to meet the new mission. All flight crews and operations supervisors responded to the commitment and in minimum time re-shaped our entire operational concept to assure the least possible exposure to enemy fire. This mission falls more in the role of the helicopter than did our previous mission.[4]

Unfortunately, events early in the new year would bring into question the ability of the CH-3 to accomplish these ever more arduous missions in this terrain, against this enemy. On 15 January 1969, Knife 52 (the new squadron call sign) and Knife 53 were en route from Dong Ha, South Vietnam, to NKP when they were contacted by a FAC who needed them to extract a small MACVSOG team that was in trouble. The two helicopters descended through the weather and rendezvoused with the FAC. As they were orbiting in preparation for the extraction, several rounds of 12.7mm fire hit Knife 52, rendering it uncontrollable and causing it to crash through 30-foot trees. Fortunately, the crew survived, and Knife 53 was able to extract all members.

A second aircraft was lost a month later on a sensor drop mission. Ground fire shot out one engine. The aircraft was flyable but could not climb high enough to clear the surrounding terrain. The pilot put the aircraft down in a controlled landing, and the wingman scooped in to pick up the crew. All missions were now flown as a minimum two-ship, and that policy was certainly saving lives.

A third aircraft was lost a few nights later while performing night reconnaissance duties. This was not in combat and was attributed to pilot error. However, the accident did highlight the dangers of disorientation when flying at night and away from lighted fields and structures.

All of these incidents reflected poorly on the CH-3. Additionally, 21st SOS officers attending a PF planning conference in January had to explain to their Army counterparts that the aircraft was severely hover-limited at the higher elevations the teams needed for increased mission effectiveness. They confirmed that the CH-3s had to be limited to landing zones at a maximum of 3,000 feet above mean sea level. Even with these constraints, though, the Knives inserted 72 sensors and 147 special mines along the Ho Chi Minh Trail and hauled 1,087 passengers and 51,885 pounds of cargo in the first quarter of the year.[5]

Over the summer, the 21st steadily reduced its sensor implant missions. Also, a detachment of CH-3s from the 20th SOS stationed at Udorn was reassigned to the 21st, increasing the squadron's aircraft to 14. While the squadron kept some aircraft on call for more PF missions, their crews began to receive more taskings to work with indigenous forces in Laos and to support remote TACAN sites. In September Knife crews were dispatched into northern Laos to move 95 troops from a Laotian special guerilla unit (SGU) into an ongoing battle where the Soldiers were inserted under fire. The next week, those same aircraft flew to central Laos to move 756 refugees from Moung Phine to Moung Phalane. Eight helicopters made the move in one day, along with 11,460 pounds of cargo, to include live pigs. They replicated this mission three days later by moving another 660 personnel. Then the Knives were tasked to support Hmong forces in the Plain of Jars area of northern Laos. On another support mission for the Hmong, five CH-3s sling-loaded 183,500 pounds of equipment in two days of lifts.[6]

The Knives were now in high demand. One daily log entry from this period captures the diversity of their efforts:

On 3 October, Major Arnau, Lt Col Hartman, TSgt Stagers, and TSgt Ramsey were low bird in a flight of three CH-3s on an emergency exfiltration of a forward reconnaissance team. The team had been under hostile fire, but Spads [A-1s] suppressed it before the helicopters went in to make the pickup and the aircraft received no hits. On the same day, six Knife helicopters transported 201 Laotian troops and 13,500 pounds of cargo from the SGU camp to Muong Phine.

The unit and its crews were becoming inextricably linked into the clandestine "out country" operations that were the "secret" part of the larger conflict in SEA. As the year was ending, the intelligence section of the 21st gave its Airmen an ominous warning. Tracking the number of antiaircraft guns being moved out along the Ho Chi Minh Trail by the North Vietnamese, it estimated that the number of firings against aircraft would triple in the next four months. Already, the HH-3s were having difficulty flying high enough to skirt the guns now available. This portended challenging times ahead.[7]

As 1970 began, the 21st crews continued to support indigenous forces in Laos. Early in January, they launched 13 aircraft and joined with several HH-53s from the 40th ARRSq to move Hmong tribes in response to an attack by NVA forces. Over a period of 10 days, they carried 232,000 pounds of cargo and 4,291 personnel while dealing almost continuously with low ceilings and visibility.

Prairie Fire and X-ray missions continued as Knife crews responded to increasing calls for infiltration and exfiltration missions. When an A-1 unit was ordered to move from Udorn to NKP, the Knives flew several sorties to haul shipping containers full of unit equipment. At one point, they were asked to recover an A-1 that had crashed on the Plain of Jars. The load was too heavy for a CH-3, and the Knives escorted a US Army H-54 that deployed from South Vietnam to do it. The 21st also continued to receive calls to perform various civic action and medevac missions around the local area. Everybody had something for the helicopters to do. Then, in late February, the unit was informed that it would begin to receive new CH-53s projected to arrive at a rate of two per month starting in August. It would be better able to handle the steadily increasing enemy antiaircraft guns now along all sections of the Ho Chi Minh Trail. All CH-3s would be returned to the CONUS.[8]

In March 1970, Lt Col Wilbur Huff from the USAF Tactical Air Command (TAC) took delivery of CH-53C #68-10922. The first of 12 ordered, it would be flown to Shaw AFB, where the first crews were training for duty in SEA with the 21st SOS.[9]

On 8 August, the 21st SOS received its first CH-53C. A week later, the aircraft began initial training missions for the newly arriving crews. By early September, it began to replace the CH-3s on tactical missions and easily carried passenger and cargo loads three times larger than the CH-3s could hold. Its first combat mission was to support the insertion of indigenous troops into southern Laos to cut a portion of the Ho Chi Minh Trail. That same month, the unit received a new mission statement. All references to sensor delivery were removed. Now the unit was ordered to provide

1. airlift and limited defensive firepower in support of MACVSOG and . . . (controlled American source) operations;

2. mass evacuation of troops, dependents, and refugees from remote areas;

3. helicopter support for remote TACAN sites;

4. night reconnaissance support for air base defense;

5. airlift of personnel and equipment to and from remote areas in case of aircraft crash, explosive ordnance disposal, and emergency medical evacuation;

6. unit aircrew training;

7. search and rescue as back up for the ARRS;

8. airlift for civic action in Thailand;

9. airlift for VIPs; [and]

10. other mission support as directed by higher headquarters.[10]

The unit continued to receive taskings for all of these missions as more CH-53s arrived. By the end of the year, seven CH-53Cs were on hand and flying missions in all areas under this more focused and specialized mission directive.[11]

As 1971 began, the 21st received two more CH-53s. The unit increasingly began to fly the more demanding combat missions as the CH-3s were pulled back for use on the logistics, administrative, and civic missions. The CH-53s were now used for X-ray missions and PF operations and began to suffer battle damage. Since the new aircraft and their pilots were new to these missions, the CH-53 crew spent a great deal of time listening to the "old heads" as they shared with them their accumulated knowledge of the theater and its weather patterns, how best to conduct tactical missions, and the overall heritage and legacy of these special operations missions. Steadily, too, they developed the skills to make steep, high-speed approaches and departures from remote landing zones while under fire and supported by an assortment of FACs and fighter escorts, especially the venerable A-1s from NKP.[12]

New personnel also arrived to fly the CH-53s. One was Capt John Grove. He had been commissioned in 1965 and sent directly to pilot training. With his shiny new pilot wings, he flew C-141 transports until 1969, when he was sent to helicopter transition and then switched to flying H-3s—known as "Banana Boats"—at Patrick AFB, Florida, where his unit provided launch support for the Apollo space program. While there, he was asked if he would like to go to Southeast Asia to fly the new CH-53. He took the assignment. That fall he was at the transition course at Shaw and reported to the 21st at NKP in December 1970. As an experienced fixed-wing and helicopter pilot, he quickly upgraded to aircraft commander, then IP, and eventually flight examiner for the unit. Additionally, he was qualified to do functional check flights (FCF) for aircraft after they had received intensive maintenance and flew the acceptance flight for several of the new CH-53s as they arrived in Thailand.

Grove also began flying the full gamut of missions that the Knives flew, especially support for the "Heavy Hook" MACVSOG operations. In mid-May1971, he flew the lead aircraft in a major POW recovery effort for a USAF OV-10 FAC shot down near Tchepone on the Ho Chi Minh Trail. The young pilot, 1st Lt Jack Butcher, had been shot down and captured by NVA forces a month prior. However, he had escaped, and intelligence sources indicated that he was evading near Tchepone. The Joint Personnel Recovery Center within MACVSOG headquarters in Saigon mounted a "Bright Light" recovery effort. Grove led the four CH-53s dispatched with a Heavy Hook team to recover him. Unfortunately, Butcher had already been captured, and enemy forces were waiting for the MACVSOG team. The Soldiers were attacked as they were unloading at the infiltration site. FACs overhead directed supporting A-1s against the enemy forces as the Soldiers broke contact, and Grove and his wingmen extracted all of the troops with several wounded.[13]

Reporting to the 21st SOS at about the same time was SSgt Tom Green. He had enlisted in the USAF in 1965 and trained as a crew chief on B-52s. In 1969 he volunteered for duty in Southeast Asia, trained as a helicopter crew chief, and then reported to the 40th ARRSq at Udorn AB to serve as a crew chief on the new HH-53s.

Courtesy Air Force Historical Research Agency

CH-53C #68-10933 and wingman, serving with the 21st SOS, inserting indigenous forces in Laos in 1971. It was destroyed on 13 May 1975 when it crashed 37 miles south of Nakhon Phanom, killing its crew of five and the 18 security police Airmen on board.

When that tour ended, he returned to Patrick AFB but soon volunteered for duty as a CH-53 flight mechanic and subsequently reported to the 21st SOS at NKP, Thailand. Quickly combat qualified, he flew the full gamut of missions common to the unit, especially several big missions to move large formations of Laotian troops into remote locations and infiltration and extraction missions in support of the MACVSOG teams. Green also flew many of the humanitarian missions that the unit was called upon to perform within Thailand.[14]

The 21st SOS lost its first CH-53 on 18 February 1971, when #68-10929 encountered heavy antiaircraft fire while inserting a PF team in Laos. The accurate enemy fire destroyed the tail rotor just as the pilot, Capt Roger Korenberg, was flaring for landing. The resulting hard landing broke the tail pylon, destroying the aircraft. Fortunately, there was no fire. The crew was able to get out safely, although one crew member sustained a leg wound.[15]

The squadron lost its second CH-53 11 days later when #68-10931 was hit by multiple rounds of enemy fire as it crossed a ridgeline in northern Laos and descended into a tight landing zone. The enemy rounds hit and damaged the left engine. With the loss of the engine, the pilot, Maj Milton Ramsey, did not have enough power to properly flare and land the aircraft. The helicopter hit hard, began to break up, and caught fire. The two pilots, Ramsey and copilot Capt Albert Tijerina, were killed. The flight mechanic and gunners were able to escape, as were all passengers, although three were badly burned. Later in the month, Knife crews performed two rescues. The first was accomplished by a crew on a tactical mission in Laos when it picked up the crew of an Air America Pilatus Porter that lost its engine near the Ho Chi Minh Trail. The second occurred when a CH-53 crew on base defense recovered the crew of an AC-119 that bailed out 10 miles north of NKP.[16]

New CH-53s continued to arrive as the CH-3s were slowly withdrawn. By the end of the year, all CH-3s were gone, and 11 CH-53s were in the squadron. The squadron's overall experience level steadily dropped as the initial cadre of CH-53 pilots began to rotate home. Additionally, the unit pilot training load increased when an ever higher percentage of the new arrival pilots were individuals who had cross-trained from fixed-wing aircraft or were recent graduates of helicopter pilot training. Capt John Grove spent the second half of his tour with the Knives instructing the new aircrews or administering check rides. He left the 21st in December 1971 for duty at Shaw as an H-3 IP.[17]

As Sergeant Green's tour with the 21st SOS was ending in early 1972, he realized that he had come to enjoy life in Thailand. Young and still single, he decided to volunteer for another combat tour, this time as a flight mechanic on HH-53s with the 40th ARRSq also there at NKP. His request was approved, and he just changed squadron patches. The flight mechanic duties for the two aircraft were almost identical; Green just had to be certified for in-flight refueling, which he accomplished on a local training mission. He adjusted easily, noting, though, that the two units had different work tempos. The 21st crews, most of the time, had a predictable flight schedule. They rarely maintained aircraft on alert anymore for immediate response. This made life at the 21st fairly routine. However, the 40th ARRSq always had aircraft and crews on alert for SAR duties. Life in this unit was much more reactive and much less predictable. The change took some adjustment. Green remembered of the two units, "At the 21st it was 'you call—we haul.' At the 40th, it was 'you crash—we dash.' " Green's timing was fortuitous. He subsequently flew in many of the large SARs that occurred during that halcyon year. He was on one of the Jolly Greens that flew in the Jackel 33 recovery effort. When Captain

Shapiro had to land his Jolly Green at a remote site in Laos because he could not refuel, Green's aircraft commander, Capt Roger Bradley, landed near the downed aircraft. Green and one of the PJs aboard his aircraft ran to the other aircraft and collected several high-value and classified items before it was destroyed. After serving his three combat tours on both the CH-53 and HH-53, he finally left the 40th ARRSq in 1973 and was reassigned to the HH-53-equipped 76th ARRSq at Hickam AFB, Hawaii.[18]

When the North Vietnamese invaded South Vietnam in late March 1972, numerous Thailand-based USAF units began supporting the South Vietnamese Army. The 21st SOS was not so tasked. Instead, it continued to conduct its standard assigned missions, with a decrease in controlled American source support flights and an increase in training sorties and night base-protection missions around NKP, to include working with local Thai police and river patrols on the Mekong River. These night sorties always carried two security policemen using starlight scopes for night vision. The unit also received a steady increase in requests for logistical and administrative sorties between the USAF bases in Thailand as all units stepped up operations against the enemy offensive.[19]

In September, 2d Lt Lorren "Rus" Stiles joined the unit. He had been commissioned out of the Air Force Academy in 1971 and had gone through helicopter flight school with the US Army. After finishing the HH/CH-53 course at Hill AFB, he reported to the 21st to find a unit full of mostly young officers and enlisted troops who were full of spirit and perhaps too much experience for their age. Within a few weeks, he was fully trained and combat ready and took his place on the flying schedule. His timing was fortuitous, for in October combat activity picked up for the 21st SOS when the squadron was tasked to support Laotian troops counterattacking NVA forces near Saravane in southern Laos as part of Operation Black Lion III. For several days, eight unit aircraft ferried 1,904 troops, several artillery pieces, and over 40,000 pounds of combat cargo in support of the successful effort to take control of the strategic town. Stiles participated in those operations and rapidly accumulated combat hours and an ability to read and navigate from military maps, especially at the low altitudes at which they had to fly to avoid the SA-7 heat-seeking missiles carried by the NVA troops. He also flew his share of TACAN site replenishment missions and civic action flights in Thailand.[20]

On 22 November, Knife 30 joined two HH-53s and an HH-43 from the 40th ARRSq to recover six crew members from a USAF B-52 that went down 12 miles southwest of NKP. One of the Jolly Green crews served as the on-scene commander as the Knife picked up four of the survivors and the HH-53 recovered the other two.[21]

The 21st SOS also continued to fly the base security mission each night over and around NKP. On the night of 18–19 December, a B-52, badly damaged on a Linebacker mission over North Vietnam, attempted to fly back into Thailand before the crew had to bail out. Rus Stiles was flying base security when the damaged aircraft flew near NKP, and he and his crew watched the B-52 crew eject. As the Airmen floated to the ground, a crew member on board using a starlight scope spotted the survivors, and Stiles and his crew rescued several. At one point, the base command center called them and asked if the alert NRS HH-53 should be launched. Stiles and his crew rejected the help and completed the mission.

The last assault mission for the 21st SOS in Laos took place on 20 January 1973, when seven of its aircraft teamed up with two Air America CH-47s to insert 1,166 Laotian troops to reopen a major road from Vientiane on the Mekong River to Luang Prabang in the north. Under the cover of USAF FACs and many air strikes, the operation was successful; however, ground fire damaged four of the Knife aircraft to varying degrees. Just 33 days later, though, the Knives, along with all other USAF forces in Thailand, were prohibited from entering Laotian airspace per a side agreement to the Paris Peace Accords that ended the Vietnam War. The Laotian and Hmong forces that we had supported since 1964 were now on their own.[22] With the major reduction of missions, the 21st was soon tasked to provide night reconnaissance around the other major US air bases at Udorn, Ubon, and U-Tapao. This appeared to be a long-term commitment.

In February a new organization arrived at NKP. The Joint Casualty Resolution Center (JCRC) took up tenancy and began preparing teams to carry on the challenging task of finding and recovering the bodies of Americans who had been reported missing in the conflict. The 21st SOS was well known for its ability to transport teams of varying sizes to remote locations, and it received the mission to provide tactical transport to the JCRC.

However, combat operations were still ongoing in Cambodia. Receiving orders from the United States Support Activities Group (USSAG)—the new headquarters set up at NKP as a detachment of

Seventh Air Force—the Knives began flying logistics support missions to the Cambodian capital of Phnom Penh and also positioned aircraft at Ubon AB for possible emergency evacuation duty for American and designated allied personnel in Cambodia under Operation Eagle Pull. This requirement necessitated the cancellation of the night reconnaissance missions at the other bases. Unit crews also began flying training missions with the JCRC. In June Knife crews were called upon to recover the wreckages of an F-111 that crashed in central Cambodia and a Jolly Green 64 that crashed in the Ton Le Sap Lake. Stiles flew on those missions.[23]

The 21st received a new mission statement in June. It was to provide heavy-lift helicopter capability and defensive firepower for missions as directed by USSAG. This could include support for controlled American sources, TACAN site support, refugee evacuation, explosive ordnance disposal, civic actions, Security Service site support, general USAF support, and support for the JCRC. Training plans were designed accordingly and stepped up as newly arriving personnel replaced the experienced departing veterans. The next month, the Knives supported their first JCRC mission when they airlifted a team of 86 personnel led by Capt Chuck Hightower and 10,600 pounds of cargo to a site near Nha Trang, South Vietnam, to look for the remains of seven US Soldiers killed in the crash of a UH-1H in 1969. The mission was successful.

The Knives flew logistics missions into Cambodia until all military activity there ceased on 15 August 1973. Their focus then shifted to maintaining the Eagle Pull alert at Ubon and conducting a panoply of missions throughout Thailand that utilized their heavy-lift capabilities. However, with the cessation of combat activity, flying hours were reduced, and the Thai government closed two key training areas and firing ranges. Training suffered until flight hours could be increased. That summer the unit was assigned the following CH-53C aircraft: #68-10925, -10926, -10927, -10928, -10930, -10932, -10933, #70-1625, -1626, -1627, and -1628.[24]

In the latter half of the year, the 21st SOS maintained its alert posture at Ubon and worked to establish a full-spectrum training program to instruct the newly arriving personnel, to include live fire on a gunnery range for its gunners. It also flew several missions to recover aircrew who bailed out in Thailand and to provide medevac to local civilians. The 21st was also tasked to maintain the ability to launch sorties to evacuate American and selected allied personnel from several sites in Laos under Operation Talon Blade.

CH-53C #70-1628 serving with the 21st SOS. The CH-53s were called upon to perform all manner of utility operations.

The squadron received an increase in flying hours as 1974 began. The JCRC requested its support on several training events as it prepared for more recovery missions. Working with crews from the 40th ARRSq, FACs, A-7s from Korat Royal Thai AB, and HC-130 "King" aircraft, the 21st initiated and staged a large SAR event just southwest of NKP. In May two Knife aircraft, again led by Captain Hightower, supported a United Nations team at Chiang Mai, Thailand, as it conducted operations to disrupt the production of opium. In this mission, the Knives hauled 295 passengers and moved 83,600 pounds of cargo. Another team flew to Phitsanulok, Thailand, to support a combined airborne exercise with US and Thai troops. Knife crews were also called upon to assume SAR alert several times to support the 40th ARRSq and to recover reconnaissance drones that went down in Thailand. As the unit adapted to a peacetime regimen, it was busier than ever supporting a true diversity of missions. At the same time, the older heads like Stiles were rotating out and being replaced by mostly inexperienced younger Airmen. But such was the process. Stiles departed, though, well satisfied with his tour. He had amassed over 1,000 hours of solid tactical flying and had upgraded to aircraft commander and IP. He also felt that he had been given an extraordinary amount of responsibility for a new pilot on first assignment.[25]

As the year was ending, the unit was alerted for possible execution of Operation Talon Blade as communist elements threatened two areas in Laos where American diplomatic personnel were located. The mission was cancelled, though, when the Laotian government interceded and protected those threatened. Reflecting this overall increase in activity, the squadron commander, Lt Col Carl Crews, wrote that "the morale of the 21st [SOS] is at an all time high. Increased flying and the diversity of the missions flown contributed to this state. . . . The 'can-do/will-do' capability of the 21st [SOS] has been most apparent to the 56 SOW, USSAG/7AF and JCRC."[26]

40th Aerospace Rescue and Recovery Squadron

After the cessation of hostilities in Cambodia, the rest of 1973 was a quiet period for the 40th ARRSq. The Airmen who flew the heavy missions in 1971 and 1972 had all rotated home. With the drawdown, too, many more were given early returns and transferred to rescue units elsewhere in Asia, Europe, or the CONUS. Many had converted to helicopters for this tour and returned to assignments flying C-141s, C-130s, and so forth. The experience level in the squadron rapidly dropped. Consequently, the operational focus shifted to training and planning. Aircraft were kept on alert both day and night for inevitable calls for taskings such as intra-Thailand rescues, medevacs, and civic action responses. However, the unit mission remained as before; that is, the squadron had to be prepared to "search for, locate, and recover distressed personnel in combat operations in Southeast Asia." Like the Knives, though, 40th crew members could also be called for medevac and heavy equipment movement within Thailand. The squadron planned and initiated training exercises to keep the aircrews qualified for all taskings.[27]

In October the 3d ARRG tasked the unit to reopen its FOL at Ubon and maintain aircraft there on alert status. This was in support of a contingency plan that dealt with the reinitiation of military operations in Cambodia. Along with the Knives, the unit was specifically to be ready to support Operation Eagle Pull—the evacuation of remaining Americans and select indigenous personnel from Phnom Penh.[28]

In early 1974, the unit was also tasked to be ready to support Operation Talon Blade—an operational contingency to evacuate Americans and selected indigenous personnel from Vientiane, Laos. A series of local training exercises utilizing FACs from the 23d TASS, also still at NKP, and the A-7s based at Korat AFB was designed to practice the necessary command and control procedures and tactics, techniques, and procedures (TTP) necessary for this and Eagle Pull. Such training was also necessary to train the constant influx of new personnel, most of whom arrived with no combat experience.

One of those was 1st Lt Gary Weikel. Growing up in Ohio and graduating from the University of Cincinnati in the summer of 1970, he initially tried to join the Ohio Air National Guard (ANG) to fly F-100s. Problems with his flight physical, however, delayed his entry, and he was drafted. He subsequently enlisted in the Air Force and attended basic training at Lackland AFB, Texas. Graduating from that course, he was immediately selected for a commission and then walked across the street to attend Officer Training School. He graduated from that program as a distinguished graduate and requested pilot training with a desire to fly A-1s. Unfortunately, though, the A-1s were slowly being retired, and a slot in fixed-wing pilot training would not be available for possibly 14 months. However, a slot was available in the next helicopter training course, and Weikel took it. He then attended training with the US Army at Fort Wolters, Texas, and Fort Rucker, Alabama, and graduated at the top of his class. At both locations, he flew with older USAF officer instructors who had logged many hours of combat in SEA. Weikel was especially taken with their skills and wisdom, and they convinced him that he wanted to fly with the 20th SOS still in South Vietnam. He subsequently attended USAF helicopter top-off training at Hill AFB and then received an assignment to fly the UH-1P gunship with the 20th SOS.

The UH-1P qualification course was also taught by MAC at Hill AFB, and Weikel flew with several IPs who had more combat experience, like Maj Herb Cullers and Maj Mike Douglas, who reinforced his desire to get into the 20th. By the time his course was complete, though, the USAF had begun reequipping the 20th SOS with UH-1N aircraft, and Weikel was diverted to Luke AFB, Arizona, a TAC base, where he did fly the UH-1P with returning 20th SOS veterans in the base support flight. He and Lieutenants Bill Hudspeth, Ron Vickroy, and Mike

Williams flew a great deal, soaked up a tremendous amount of tactical sense from the old heads, and upgraded to aircraft commander before Weikel received an assignment to HH-53s with the 40th ARRS at NKP, reporting in November 1974.

In late spring of 1974, Weikel once again reported to Hill AFB, this time for qualification on the HH-53. While there, he learned to fly the much larger aircraft from instructors like Steve Connelly, Mark Schibler, and Ben Orrell. Weikel initially chafed at the program because MAC was much more regulations-oriented than TAC. Regardless, the instructors suffused him with another dose of hard-learned combat knowledge, to include NRS training, before sending him on his way to NKP.[29]

Right behind Weikel was 2d Lt Rich Comer. He graduated from the Air Force Academy in June 1973, one of 25 new lieutenants in his class who decided to go to helicopter pilot training (2d Lt Donny Wurster was also in that class). A month later, he reported to Fort Rucker, Alabama, to attend basic helicopter training with the US Army. There he trained on TH-55 and UH-1H helicopters. He did well in his class and was able to select an assignment to HH-53s with the 40th ARRSq at NKP. Then he proceeded to Hill AFB for his HH-53 class date in August 1974. In his class of eight students, all were heading for the two squadrons at NKP. His flying partner was 1st Lt Dick Brims, going over to fly the CH-53. Also in the class was Lt Col John Denham, initially assigned to the 40th. While at Hill, though, Denham was reassigned to take command of the 21st SOS. One of his IPs was Captain Connelly, who qualified Comer in the NRS aircraft. Finishing the course in October, Comer then took some leave before departing for Southeast Asia, arriving at NKP on Christmas Eve. Within a week, he was on the flying schedule, quickly qualified as a combat copilot, and crewed with Capt Barry Walls. Then he and his crew sat alert periods at NKP and also rotated down to Ubon AB for the same duty.[30]

Realizing that the fighter aircraft were steadily being reduced in Thailand, the 40th squadron training and tactics personnel reviewed mission reports from the later combat years and designed a series of exercises to work with AC-130s to refine night recovery procedures. They tested using an X-band beacon on top of the helicopter that would allow the AC-130 to view it with its side-looking radar. Such a capability would allow the AC-130 then to provide immediate precision navigation assistance or direct fire support.[31]

1975 Southeast Asia Endgame

As the new year began, the US Air Force still had a considerable presence in Thailand. Located at the Udorn, Korat, and NKP Air Bases were six fighter squadrons with F-4s and A-7s, a reconnaissance squadron with RF-4Cs, a gunship squadron with 17 AC-130s, a FAC squadron with 40 OV-10s, and the two helicopter units—the 21st SOS and 40th ARRSq at NKP—with 10 and nine aircraft, respectively. Both were providing top cover for their brother units and were involved in a variety of missions utilizing their unique capabilities and the skills of their crews.

The 21st SOS had aircraft and crews engaged in a variety of missions across Thailand. The US Army Advisory Group / Seventh Air Force (USAAG/7AF) accepted a request from the Southeast Asia Treaty Organization to dispatch two CH-53s to support a multinational medical team operating throughout Thailand. Later in the month, two more aircraft were dispatched to southern Thailand at the request of the king of Thailand to provide disaster relief after a typhoon devastated the area. The squadron suffered a terrible loss on 24 January when CH-53C #70-1628 crashed while on an FCF. The crew and a maintenance specialist were killed.

Communist forces in Cambodia continued to mount threats against the central government, and the security of Americans still in that country was increasingly in doubt. The next month, USSAG/7AF tasked the squadron to conduct a rehearsal of Eagle Pull. Eight aircraft were launched and arrived at their designated landing zones on time. Additionally, unit aircraft started working with AC-130 gunships as they developed procedures for vectoring the helicopter onto landing zones and then providing protective fire. The daytime procedures worked well, but the use of lasers on board the AC-130s during night operations was disorienting to the Knife pilots and was not accepted as a valid tactic. As events continued to deteriorate in Cambodia, the 21st received ever more explicit instructions for pending operations and, by the end of March, was maintaining crews on six-hour alert.[32]

The 40th ARRSq became steadily more interlinked with the 21st SOS as it also dispatched helicopters to help with the typhoon flooding in southern Thailand and then responded to the CH-53 crash in January. In March the unit was ordered to move its FOL from Ubon to Korat. As conditions continued to deteriorate in Cambodia—and the US ambassador, the Honorable John Gunther Dean, ordered the initiation of phased evacuation operations under Operation Eagle Pull—the 40th was also placed on alert for that operation, and the two squadrons began to coordinate their actions. Both units began to receive increased direct logistical support from the Air Force Logistics Command (AFLC) under a project called Pacer Topaz, which dramatically increased their aircraft in-commission rates.

The Evacuations

On 11 April, both squadrons were ordered to launch aircraft to Ubon for their first potential combat action in over 20 months. The 21st launched nine CH-53C aircraft. Arriving at Ubon, three went immediately on 30-minute alert and the rest on one-hour alert. The 40th launched seven HH-53Cs, also to Ubon. The next day, USAAG/7AF ordered the complete evacuation of all American and selected allied personnel from Phnom Penh. Two 40th HH-53s launched with combat control teams (CCT) on board. First Lts Don Backlund and Gary Weikel flew the lead aircraft. As they descended into the designated landing zone, a large bird smashed into the windscreen, smearing its entrails all over it and severely obstructing forward vision. The windshield washers were able to clear away enough of it so the pilots could continue the mission. They and their second aircraft inserted the teams into the designated landing zones around Phnom Penh and then departed. The teams directed the flow of helicopters in and out. The 21st launched all nine of its aircraft to holding points north of the city. However, the evacuees were all taken out by USMC CH-53s and CH-46s operating off of the aircraft carrier USS *Midway,* located in the Gulf of Thailand.

The Knives returned to Ubon without evacuating any personnel. As the USMC helicopters finished evacuating 276 persons, the two Jolly Greens returned to the landing zones to recover the CCTs and then proceeded back to Ubon. Both aircraft sustained battle damage for their efforts.[33] Both squadrons returned to NKP the next day, only to be notified that communist forces were threatening Saigon, South Vietnam, and that both units were now to begin detailed planning for Operation Frequent Wind, the evacuation of American and designated allied personnel from that city.

When the US ambassador to South Vietnam, the Honorable Graham Martin, directed that evacuation operations should begin, the 21st

SOS received an execution order and on 19 April deployed eight aircraft to U-Tapao AB in southern Thailand, while the 40th followed with seven aircraft. Both contingents took extra crews and maintenance support. The next morning, six CH-53s and four HH-53s departed U-Tapao and flew to the USS *Midway*, located in the South China Sea, 50 miles southeast of Saigon. They joined the fleet of USMC CH-53s and CH-46s that had flown the Phonm Penh mission. Two days later, the 40th was ordered to return two aircraft to U-Tapao, and two more Knives were dispatched to take their place, leaving eight CH-53s and two HH-53s. All HH-53s were then moved to Ubon AB to assume SAR alert for the pending operation.

Collaterally, the 40th received another recovery mission. On the morning of the 29th, the unit was directed to launch two HH-53s to recover a Sailor with a broken back off of a ship in the Gulf of Thailand. The two crews made the 2,000-mile round-trip with no difficulties.

That same afternoon at 3 p.m., USSAG/7AF directed that Operation Frequent Wind be executed. Immediately, the collected CH-53s of both services, HH-53s, and CH-46s lifted in a coordinated fashion to begin the evacuation. For the next 13 and a half hours, they shuttled

Courtesy Air Force Historical Research Agency

An HH-53 and two CH-53s operating off the USS *Midway* during the evacuation of Saigon

back and forth from the ship to several landing zones in the city. None of the aircraft from the two squadrons suffered any damage from enemy fire, although the crews observed a great deal of it. One CH-53, #68-10928, had a serious mechanical problem and could not fly. It provided parts to the other aircraft. Another CH-53 had a complete electrical failure while flying at night. Quick action by the crew recovered one generator, and it was able to safely land aboard the aircraft carrier.

After departing Saigon for the last time the next morning, the helicopters shuttled evacuees between various ships. The next day, the Knives were alerted to make one more run into Saigon, but that directive was subsequently cancelled. Both the Knives and Jolly Greens were alerted to fly an evacuation mission to Con Son Island off the coast of South Vietnam. But that mission, too, was cancelled.

On 2 May, the 21st and 40th aircraft and crews departed the *Midway* for U-Tapao, carrying with them 97 American evacuees from Saigon. The next day, the Jolly Greens returned to NKP. However, the Knives received another mission at U-Tapao. During the evacuation of Saigon, numerous South Vietnamese aircraft had been flown to the huge air base. There, they and the persons they carried were interned. The Thai government wanted the aircraft either removed or destroyed, and the Knives were directed to sling-load 27 A-37 and 14 F-5 aircraft aboard the USS *Midway* for shipment back to the United States. Finally, the Knives returned to NKP on 6 May.[34]

Both squadrons brought home aircraft in dire need of maintenance, and technicians swarmed over the aircraft as the aircrews tried to enjoy a respite from their busy schedules of late. But the hiatus was short-lived, as unforeseen events began to dictate their redeployment.

SS *Mayaguez*

On 10 May, Cambodian Khmer Rouge forces seized a US-registered cargo ship, the SS *Mayaguez*, in international waters near Koh Tang Island off the southwestern coast of Cambodia. This precipitated a recovery operation that would again involve both squadrons. This mission has been well captured in many works, the best of which is *A Very Short War: The Mayaguez and the Battle of Koh Tang* by Lt Col Joe Guilmartin, USAF, retired, a participant in the operation. Only a condensed version based on the squadron histories is presented here.

At 6:30 p.m. on 13 May, the 21st SOS was alerted to prepare to deploy back to U-Tapao with Air Force security police forces on board as part of a mobility security force, along with a maintenance kit and team. The crews would fly there, drop off their Air Force personnel, and reload with US Marines who could then be used as assault troops on Koh Tang Island, where the *Mayaguez* crew was reportedly being held. The first 21st SOS CH-53s departed at 8:30 p.m. An hour later tragedy struck when CH-53 #68-10933 suffered a mechanical failure 37 miles south of NKP and crashed, killing the five-man crew and 18 security force personnel on board.[35]

After receiving its warning order on 13 May, the 40th dispatched one aircraft on SAR alert at Korat to U-Tapao and launched three others from NKP, led by Captain Walls and Lieutenant Comer. When the CH-53 crashed, the 40th also launched two more HH-53s on alert at Korat to proceed to the crash site for recovery operations. However, aircraft from NKP were already on the scene, so the two HH-53s then flew to U-Tapao. There, they joined the crews of six HH-53s and five CH-53s. Early the next morning, two HH-53s were launched to find and recover a US Navy crew of 10 persons possibly down in the Gulf of Thailand. The two rescue crews searched fruitlessly and received some hostile fire before they were notified that the loss report was a mistake.

In the early morning hours of 15 May, the Knives and Jolly Greens launched to Koh Tang with their assault forces. The reported enemy force in the immediate area of the insertion was expected to be an element of 18 Khmer Kraham soldiers from a small battalion of 250 troops on the island of Koh Tang. The Marines would be inserted on the east and west shores of a small isthmus of the island that pointed north, only 250 meters wide.

Knife 21, 22, 23, and 31 approached the island just at early nautical twilight, with Knife 32 and Jolly Green 41 a few miles behind. The first two went to the west beach and the second two to the east. Just as Knife 21 settled over the beach and began to disgorge its Marines, the aircraft was raked with heavy small arms and automatic weapons fire and grievously damaged. Its aircraft commander, Colonel Denham, also the 21st SOS squadron commander, tried to fly out of danger but was forced to ditch the aircraft three-fourths of a mile to the west. Upon hitting the water, CH-53C #68-10926 rolled over and sank. The crew scrambled to escape the sinking aircraft.

Close behind Knife 21, Knife 22, commanded by Capt Terry Ohlemeier, was just settling to unload its Marines when it suffered the same fate. With the aircraft severely damaged, the commander aborted his delivery before any Marines were able to get off, flew his aircraft back to Thailand, and put the aircraft down on a beach. On the east side of the island, Knife 23, commanded by 1st Lt John Schramm, also had to abort its insertion because of the enemy fire. As it turned to leave, ground fire destroyed the tail rotor, and the aircraft, CH-53C #70-1627, crashed about 20 feet offshore. All on board scrambled to safety, although several were wounded. They set up a perimeter and began to engage the enemy force, which was now obviously larger than 18 soldiers. Right behind them, Knife 31, commanded by Maj Howard Corson, received the same withering fire. As Corson turned his aircraft to exit the area, CH-53C #68-10925 was mortally damaged and crashed just a few yards south of Knife 23. The copilot, 2d Lt Richard Vandegeer, was killed. The rest of the crew made its way out into open water and was picked up by the US Navy. Observing the demise of three fellow Knives, the crew of Knife 32, commanded by 1st Lt Michael Lackey, aborted its run-in to the east beach. It spotted Knife 21 ditching and immediately diverted to pick up the crew. One flight mechanic on the stricken aircraft, SSgt Elwood Rumbaugh, was never found. The crew of Knife 32 then delivered its Marines to the west beach, where its aircraft was again badly damaged and two on board were wounded. Fortunately, the crew was able to make it back to U-Tapao.

After the Knives had departed U-Tapao for their first sorties, three HH-53Cs—Jolly Greens 11, 12, and 13, commanded by 1st Lt Don Backlund, Capt Paul Jacobs, and 1st Lt Charles Greer, respectively—departed with another load of Marines. The Jolly Greens' objective was to offload the Marines onto the USS *Holt*, a destroyer supporting the operation. As they did that, two more Jolly Greens—42, commanded by 1st Lt Phil Pacini, and 43, commanded by Capt Wayne Purser—joined with Jolly Green 41, commanded by 1st Lt Tom Cooper, who had not yet put in his Marines, and all three put their troops onto the west beach. Overhead, an AC-130 gunship and several flights of fighters began pummeling enemy targets to support the Marines.

The situation then turned into near chaos as ground units could not make communications linkups with their own units or even with the aircraft above. Many of the helicopters were also seriously damaged and had to fly back to U-Tapao with escorts. As they were

Two CH-53s shot down on Koh Tang Island, Cambodia, during the *Mayaguez* recovery operation

departing, the USS *Holt* deployed some Marines aboard the *Mayaguez* and took possession of the ship. Additionally, another destroyer, the USS *Henry B. Wilson*, joined the fight and took up a position off the east beach. Her gunners began engaging enemy targets, and they launched the ship's gig to pick up Airmen and Marines in the water from Knife 31. Meanwhile, Sailors aboard the *Wilson* spotted a small boat outbound from the mainland approaching the island. They were able to determine that it was carrying the crew of the *Mayaguez*.

Attention turned to extracting the Marines. But it was not that simple. All helicopters except Jolly Green 41 had departed the area. Jolly Green 41 made several attempts to insert its troops before finally succeeding. They and the supplies that they brought were badly needed. Jolly Green 41 then limped back to U-Tapao and would not fly again without extensive repairs. Tactical airpower, and especially the AC-130 gunships, provided top cover for the Marines until the helicopters could return.

At U-Tapao the crews from both squadrons mixed and compared notes. Now much wiser and true combat veterans, they prepared to deliver a second wave of Marines. Jolly Greens 11 and 12 were able to insert their loads onto the west beach at about noon, followed shortly by Knife 51, commanded by 1st Lt Richard Brims; Knife 52, commanded by 1st Lt Robert Rakitis; and Jolly Green 43 after an abortive attempt to get in on the east beach. This addition of manpower allowed the Marines to suppress enemy firepower and link up scattered Marine elements from the west to the east beach. However, Jolly Green 43 was seriously damaged in the effort. The crew had to land aboard the aircraft carrier USS *Coral Sea* for repairs to its fuel feed system. Jolly Green 11 escorted it and then refueled.

Incredibly, the quick planning for the *Mayaguez* recovery effort did not include the use of any FACs. By early afternoon though, commanders recognized that mistake and dispatched several OV-10s to U-Tapao. There, the assigned FACs refueled, received quick tactical briefings, and then launched to take over as on-scene commanders at Koh Tang. Arriving overhead, they were able to use their multiband radios to contact all participants and then coordinate what was now a rescue mission for the Marines below. As the FACs coordinated the efforts of the Marine elements, the two destroyers providing support, the gunships and fighters, and the remaining flyable H-53s supplemented by two SH-3s from the *Coral Sea* would have to bring out the Marines. Given the damage done to the fleet from NKP and the fortuitous arrival of another HH- and CH-53 from that base, four H-53s—Jolly Greens 11, 12, and 43 and Knife 51—would have to accomplish the rescue.

As the day began to ebb, the FACs pounded enemy positions with numerous air strikes and the AC-130 gunships. Sensing that the situation was right and noting the lowering sun, they cleared Jolly Green into the east beach to pick up Marines there. With a raging battle ensuing around them, the crew members of Jolly Green 11 held their hover for three minutes until the aircraft was filled with 25 Marines and helicopter crewmen. As they were pulling off the beach to head to the *Coral Sea*, a C-130 dropped a 15,000-pound bomb several miles to the south to "apply maximum psychological pressure" to the enemy. Almost immediately, Jolly Green 12 attempted to pick up survivors believed left in the wreckage of the earlier crashed Knife aircraft. There were none, but enemy gunners took advantage of the crew's efforts and seriously damaged the aircraft so that it had to make an emergency landing on the *Coral Sea*.

As the sun set and light slowly faded, Knife 51 and Jolly Green 43 were joined by Jolly Green 44, which had come down from NKP.

They cycled into the west beach and extracted the Marines as the FACs and AC-130 gunships provided the best support they could in the dwindling light. Jolly Green 11, now flown by Capt Barry Walls and 2d Lt Rich Comer, also relaunched and joined the fray. But their efforts were not needed, as the others extracted all the Marines and Airmen. Finally, at 8:10 p.m. with everybody apparently recovered or accounted for, the helicopters were released to return to U-Tapao, and the operation was terminated.[36]

It took several days for all the aircraft and crews of the two squadrons to return to NKP. Numerous aircraft were so badly damaged that they needed extensive repairs just to make the flight home. And the crews? One participant wrote later that it was "an incredibly intense experience." They were drained but extremely proud of their actions and acutely aware that they had just participated in a historically significant event.[37]

For the two units, the cost of the battle was high. Every aircraft was damaged to some extent. The 21st SOS was devastated with the destruction in combat of three aircraft. Combined with the aircraft lost in January and the second one in the initial deployment to U-Tapao, the squadron had lost one-half of its aircraft. The materiel, logistical, and personnel ramifications of that loss would be huge.

Analysts, too, were puzzled by the fact that the 21st had three aircraft shot down while the 40th, operating in the same locations, had none. Was that due to the HH-53s having more armor plating than the CH-53s and a third minigun on the back ramp to specifically protect the rear of the aircraft? Was it due to some difference in tactics? Or, perhaps, was it just the whims of happenstance and the fact that the battle plan called for the two units to have somewhat different roles to play in the overall effort? Regardless, one thing was immutably clear: HH-53s were large targets. Their survival in clear daylight in an area well defended by massed antiaircraft artillery (AAA) or even small arms was problematic. A career rescue veteran, Lt Col Joe Tyner, stated in a later overall mission analysis that "in the last stages of the Southeast Asia conflict, the enemy got more man-pads [shoulder-fired surface-to-air missiles] and better AAA. . . . The tragic helicopter losses during 'Mayaguez' seemed to mark the end of helicopters on a modern battlefield."[38]

Congratulatory messages arrived from many commands and individuals. The CJCS, Gen George Brown, said that the success of the unique operation to recover the SS *Mayaguez* and her crew by the combined efforts of the Air Force, Navy and Marine Corps represents an outstanding display of the versatility, dedication and professional competence of all participants. It is not possible to praise too highly the bravery and determination exhibited by all concerned in the assault on Koh Tang Island. The overall operation, fraught with unknowns from the outset and extremely difficult to execute under even the best conditions, was conducted by all airmen, sailors and Marines in the highest tradition of our armed forces. I want every individual who participated in this operation to receive my personal congratulations.[39]

The crews were also individually rewarded for their efforts. Jolly Green 43 aircraft commander Capt Wayne Purser, Jolly Green 11 aircraft commander 1st Lt Don Backlund, Knife 51 aircraft commander 1st Lt Richard Brims, and Knife 31 flight mechanic SSgt John Harston all received the Air Force Cross for their heroic actions. Many others were presented Silver Stars, Distinguished Flying Crosses, and Air Medals for their actions that day. One more "honor" accrued to the *Mayaguez* veterans several years later. The last names inscribed on the Vietnam Memorial in Washington, DC, were those lost in this last mission.

Perhaps more importantly, though, now the crews of both squadrons were well bloodied in the heat of combat. At the beginning of the year, most of the aircrews were inexperienced. It had been 20 months since the squadrons flew sustained combat operations, and an entire iteration of aircrews had come and gone. Fortunately, they had passed down through their training programs and unit heritage a pride and level of performance and professionalism that had now been inculcated into the psyches of a new generation of young officers and Airmen. This stunning trial by fire matured these two squadrons, one for rescue and the other for special operations, into units that could separately or in tandem now handle a wide range of missions. It gave them the confidence to do anything that their helicopters could do. Maj Joe Guilmartin of the 40th explained the power of this confidence:

Units with confidence in the will and ability of their members to perform under stress assume competence and rise above it. If they have practiced some of the options in training, the self-reinforcing mechanism is stronger still. Units in which no such confidence exists tend to assume individual incompetence, a lack of will, or both, making group incompetence a self-fulfilling prophesy.

These expectations flow from the cohesive mechanism that holds units and crews together in combat. That mechanism is a group phenomenon, not an individual one.[40]

Returning to NKP, both units resumed their training programs and reviewed the other contingencies under which they could be tasked. Operation Talon Blade was a highly probable mission as communist forces now overran all of Laos, and both units kept aircraft and aircrews on alert for that contingency.

In June, the 21st SOS was notified that its aircraft losses would not be replaced and that the squadron would inactivate in January 1976, as the government of Thailand decided that it wanted all US forces removed from the country as soon as possible. Many squadron members received orders curtailing their tours. At the end of the month, the 56th SOW was moved to MacDill AFB, Florida, and the 656th SOW was activated to essentially shut down NKP by 31 October 1975 as part of the overall American withdrawal from Thailand.

The 21st SOS inactivation was further moved up to 23 September, and it was directed to fly several of its aircraft to U-Tapao. There, they would be moved by ship to Europe where they would be assigned to a less challenging mission set with the newly forming 601st TASS at Sembach AB in Germany. That unit belonged to the 601st Tactical Control Wing (TCW). The wing controlled and operated the tactical air control system (TACS) for US and allied units in Europe. With a vast array of mobile radars and ground control teams, the CH-53s and crews would facilitate the control of US and allied airpower over Europe as part of the great North Atlantic Treaty Organization (NATO) alliance. The CH-53s had as their assigned mission the requirement to "assist redeploying units, provide logistics support to mobile TACS units, assist in the rapid movement of the air support radar teams, and render assistance in emergency rescue or medical evacuation missions."[41]

The 21st SOS remained on call to support Operation Talon Blade until early September, when all local flying was terminated, and the last aircraft were then moved to U-Tapao for transfer. The remaining unit personnel remained at NKP and dismantled the squadron as their reassignment orders trickled in. Most aircrews were reassigned to the 601st TASS in Germany, with a few going to Hurlburt Field, Florida, and other scattered locations. There is no record that any consideration was given to reassigning the 21st SOS with its aircraft and highly experienced crews to the 1st SOW at Hurlburt Field, as the 16th SOS with its AC-130 gunships was being so assigned. Instead, the proud 21st SOS—a repository of eight and a half years of accumulated special operations combat experience—would be moved to the inactive list and its personnel and aircraft dispersed to other units for other jobs.[42]

Upon returning to NKP from the Mayaguez operation, the 40th ARRSq resumed its alert duties while also maintaining two aircraft on alert at Korat. Training flights resumed as personnel continued to rotate in and out. The unit also had to remain prepared to respond as part of Operation Talon Blade. The personnel section was busy processing over 150 major award recommendations for the missions just flown. The unit continued to get calls for local civic actions support and medevac missions. In July a Korat alert aircraft was launched to assist a ship in danger of sinking. The next month, an HH-53 launched to recover an American pilot who bailed out over the Gulf of Thailand. He was subsequently picked up by a Thai fishing boat and moved to a local airport where the Jolly Green crew picked him up.

In September as NKP prepared to close down, the 40th was ordered to move to Korat AB, Thailand. It did so by the end of the month and absorbed a flight of four HC-130s from the inactivating 56th ARRSq. Still with the unit and now a first lieutenant, Rich Comer was the last pilot to upgrade to aircraft commander in Thailand. In November the unit was notified that it would be inactivated on 31 January 1976, with personnel, aircraft, and equipment reassigned to other units. Several of the aircrew received orders to the 601st TASS at Sembach, Germany, its sister unit; the 701st TASS at Bergstrom AFB, Texas; other rescue units; or the 1st SOW at Hurlburt Field, Florida.

The 40th maintained aircraft on rescue alert as top cover for the remaining USAF units in Thailand until all tactical aircraft had departed. Comer flew as the recovery aircraft in the last combat rescue exercise with the A-7s before its unit, the 3d Tactical Fighter Squadron (TFS), redeployed to the CONUS. The 40th finally ended its alert commitment as the last Jolly Green flight landed at 1 p.m. on 20 December 1975. The unit then loaded its aircraft aboard C-5s. Two went to Kadena AB, Okinawa, one to Royal Air Force (RAF) Woodbridge AB in the United Kingdom, and six to McClellan AFB near Sacramento, California. The personnel themselves were some of the last to leave Thailand, taking with them a wealth of knowledge and experience based upon eight years of HH-53 combat rescue experience in that long and divisive war.[43]

☆ ☆ ☆ ☆ ☆

Observing the success of the USMC with the newly developed CH-53A, the USAF determined that variants of the H-53 could meet its needs generated by combat action in Southeast Asia for a large rescue helicopter and a cargo helicopter for special operations use. For almost eight years, the HH-53s and CH-53s served in two rescue squadrons that ultimately consolidated as the 40th ARRSq and the 21st SOS. Those units saw duty in almost every corner of the war. By the end of the conflict, 52 USAF HH-53s and 20 CH-53s had been produced. Of those, nine HH-53s and seven CH-53s had been destroyed in the war, with another two HH-53s and one CH-53 lost to accidents in the United States.

Both the squadrons performed myriad missions befitting heavy-lift helicopters, besides their primary functions of rescue and special operations. Yet, given the exigencies of that war, on many an occasion each would delve into the other's specialty as operational requirements dictated. By the end of the conflict, both were highly experienced and motivated units, well schooled in their mission areas.

Beyond that, though, each made a specific contribution. The HH-53s in the 40th became the test bed for newly evolving technology, called for initially to provide a night, all-weather capability that would allow quick recovery of downed aircrews. The concept never came to full fruition in SEA. But the seeds had been sown and were being further developed in the United States, as many believed that the technology would have applicability far beyond rescue.

The men of the 21st SOS developed a squadron capable of supporting classic special operations activities. Successive iterations of aircrews learned the heritage and traditions of the unit, added to them, and so passed them to later arrivals. Tactical lessons hard-learned by the H-3 crews were adopted and adapted by the crews of the later CH-53s as they carried on those traditions and air commando spirit. The unit's "can-do/will-do capability," which Colonel Crews cited when he commanded the unit in 1974, was its standard of performance and tradition. After the war, a noted USAF historian, Col Ray Bowers, wrote, "The distinguished work of the . . . 21st Squadron in Southeast Asia strengthened the Air Force's entitlement to future special air operations roles."[44] Both squadrons had become "units with confidence," as Major Guilmartin said, "with the will and ability of their members to perform under stress" and create "the cohesive mechanism that holds units and crews together in combat . . . a group phenomenon, not an individual one."[45]

Each squadron, the 40th and the 21st, in its own way made signal contributions to what would later become Pave Low and spawned a generation of Airmen who would initially develop and fly them. In the rush to withdraw from SEA, though, the USAF inactivated both squadrons and dispersed their aircraft and personnel to other units, locales, and missions. That was unfortunate because just about five years later, their skills would be desperately needed in another part of the world. Their nonselection, or even availability, for a variety of reasons in that operation would contribute to a failure that would precipitate significant changes in the US military.

Notes

1. Bowers, *United States Air Force in Southeast Asia: Tactical Airlift*, 456.
2. Ibid., 425.
3. History of the 56th Air Commando Wing, 1 Oct–31 Dec 1967, 1.
4. Ibid., 1 Jan–31 Mar 1968, vol. 1, 26; ibid., 1 Apr–30 June 1968, 7; History of 56th SOW, 1 July–30 Sept 1968, vol. 1, 5, 11; ibid., 1 Oct–31 Dec 1968, vol. 2, table 1, 7; and Hobson, *Vietnam Air Losses*, 169.
5. Message, 56SPOWG to 7AF/DO and MACVSOG/Saigon, subject: Prairie Fire Missions, in History of 56th SOW, 1 Jan–31 Mar 1969, vol. 2, 2.
6. History of 56th SOW, 1 July–30 Sept 1969, vol. 2, 5–7.
7. Ibid., 1 Oct–31 Dec 1969, vol. 2, n.p.
8. Ibid., 1 Jan–31 Mar 1970, vol. 1, 7; and ibid., 16.
9. "First CH-53C Goes to US Air Force," *Sikorsky News*, Apr 1970, 6.
10. History of 56th SOW, 1 July–30 Sept 1970, vol. 1, 8, 46.
11. Ibid., 1 Oct–31 Dec 1970, vol. 1, 5; and Haas, *Apollo's Warriors*, 307.
12. Haas, *Apollo's Warriors*, 312.
13. Grove, interview; and Hobson, *Vietnam Air Losses*, 213.
14. Green, interview.
15. History of 56th SOW, 1 Jan–31 Mar 1971, vol. 1, 7.
16. Ibid., 7–8.
17. Grove, interview.
18. Ibid.
19. History of 56th SOW, 1 Apr–30 June 1972, vol. 1, 6.
20. Ibid., 1 July–31 Dec 1972, vol. 1, 54; and Stiles, interview.
21. Ibid., vol. 2, supporting doc. 26.
22. Haas, *Air Commando!*, 92; and History of 56th SOW, 1 Jan–31 Mar 1973, vol. 1, 35. Note: At the time, the author was a Raven FAC assigned to Laos and provided air cover for this mission.
23. History of 56th SOW, 1 Apr–30 June 1973, vol. 1, 32; and ibid., 8.
24. Ibid., 1 July–30 Sept 1973, vol. 2, 5, doc. 13.
25. Stiles, interview.
26. History of 56th SOW, 1 Oct–31 Dec 1973, vol. 1, 3–4; ibid., 1 Jan–31 Mar 1974, vol. 1, 4; ibid., 1 Apr–30 June 1974, vol. 2, 6; and ibid., 1 July–30 Sept 1974, vol. 1, 6.
27. History of 40th ARRSq, 1 July–31 Dec 1973, 2.
28. Ibid., 7.

29. Weikel, interview.

30. Comer, interview.

31. History of 3d ARRG, 1 Jan–31 Mar 1974, 12.

32. History of 56th SOW, 1 Jan–31 Mar 1975, vol. 1, 4–5 and addendum doc.

33. Ibid., 1 Apr–30 June 1975, vol. 1, 5; History of 40th ARRSq, 1 Jan–30 June 1975, 4; and Weikel, interview.

34. History of 40th ARRSq, 1 Jan–30 June 1975, 4–5; and History of 56th SOW, 1 Apr–30 June 1975, vol. 1, 5–7.

35. History of the 656th Security Police Squadron, 1 Apr–30 June 1975, 3.

36. History of 56th SOW, 1 Apr–30 June 1975, vol. 1, 7–8, app. 1; History of 40th ARRSq, 1 Apr–30 June 1975, 5–13; and Guilmartin, *Very Short War*, 84–141. In fact, three young Marines were left behind and subsequently executed by Khmer forces; remains were repatriated in 2001. See Dunham and Quinlan, *U.S. Marines in Vietnam*, 262; and Wetterhahn, *Last Battle*.

37. Guilmartin, *Very Short War*, xix.

38. Tyner, *AF Rescue and AFSOF*, 27.

39. DCS/Plans and Operations, HQ USAF, summary report, subject: Assault on Koh Tang, 23 June 1975, in History of 56th SOW, 1 Apr–30 June 1975, vol. 3, supporting doc. no. 73, 38.

40. Guilmartin, *Very Short War*, 41–42.

41. History of the 601st Tactical Control Wing (hereafter referred to as History of 601st TCW), 1 Apr–30 June 1980, vol. 4, 33.

42. History of 56th SOW, 1 July–30 Sept 1975, vol. 1, 1–5.

43. History of 40th ARRSq, 1 July 1975–31 Jan 1976, 9–17; and Comer, interview.

44. Bowers, *United States Air Force in Southeast Asia: Tactical Airlift*, 425.

45. Guilmartin, *Very Short War*, 41–42.

PART II

From Concept to Capability

Chapter 4

Black Knights and Red Scarves

~1973–80

When they were building it, Frank [Pehr] and Leo Gambone came down here and pitched this and said, "We've got something you guys want to see. We built this for rescue, but it's really a special ops machine."

—Steve Connelly

By early 1976, all USAF H-53s had been transferred from Thailand. The HH-53s had been dispersed to rescue units across the globe. The change had been even more dramatic for the CH-53s. All of the 21st SOS aircraft had been either moved to the CONUS to the 701st TASS, which had been activated at Bergstrom AFB, Texas, in late 1974 as part of the 71st Tactical Air Support Group, or shipped to Germany for duty with the 601st TASS at Sembach. At both locations, their mission was starkly different from what they had been doing in SEA. Now, instead of team insertions, covert force movements, and major evacuations, the two units' assigned duty was to move heavy equipment, such as TACAN stations and radar sites, to support tactical air control units equipped and organized to integrate airpower on modern battlefields like the plains of central Europe. Somewhat more frivolously, the Sembach aircraft and crews were called upon to provide VIP transport and "Rhine River tours" for visiting dignitaries, much to the disdain of the flyers. As the 601st received its aircraft and crews, it suffered a terrible tragedy on 26 September 1975, when CH-53C #70-1632 crashed near Gütersloh, Germany. The crew of four Airmen and 12 passengers were en route to conduct a site survey of a training area just east of the town of Oldendorf when the aircraft experienced in-flight icing, causing both engines to flame out. The pilots attempted to autorotate to the ground but were not successful. There were no survivors. Flight operations were curtailed until an accident board determined the cause of the accident and the lost members were properly honored. Crew training then resumed, and the unit was fully integrated into training exercises with US and allied units across the theater. Six months later, the 601st lost another aircraft when CH-53C #68-10927 crashed on a training sortie near Sembach AB, killing the four crew members. The aircraft was a scarred veteran of the mission to Koh Tang Island. All four of the crew members were also hard-trained veterans of that war, both rescue and special operations. It was another tragic loss.[1]

After his tour with the 40th ARRSq at NKP, Capt Rich Comer was posted to the 601st TASS at Sembach and reported to the unit in January 1976. As a new aircraft commander, he found that the flying was not as tactically challenging as the rescue missions. However, he and all the pilots became proficient at instrument flying, facilitated by the challenging European weather. They also got to fly over much of the continent using simple VFRs. All aircraft had been stripped of armor and guns, and the mission focus was on the sling-load movement of the heavy field equipment. The pilots became adept at hovering with 5,000-pound loads and placing them precisely where needed. Except for the tragic helicopter accidents, though, Comer enjoyed his tour at Sembach. He was able to upgrade to IP and served in the 601st until December 1978, when he received orders to move to Kirtland AFB, New Mexico, to serve as an HH-53 IP.[2]

Aerospace Rescue and Recovery Service

When the 40th ARRSq and the 3d ARRG inactivated, their aircraft and personnel, for the most part, were reassigned across the larger ARRS command as it resumed its overall responsibility of providing a global rescue capability, albeit with combat rescue as its priority mission. As 1976 began, the command had its headquarters and staff at Scott AFB, Illinois, and commanded three wings and numerous separate squadrons, detachments, and operating locations. Its subordinate wings were the 39th Aerospace Rescue and Recovery Wing (ARRW), the 41st Rescue and Weather Reconnaissance Wing (RWRW), and the 1550th ATTW.

The 39th ARRW at Eglin commanded and controlled three rescue squadrons and smaller detachments in the CONUS and Europe. Its primary emphasis was on combat rescue. In particular, its assigned 55th ARRSq, also at Eglin, was charged with the responsibility to develop, test, and document combat rescue tactics. The unit was also tasked with responding to requirements for support in contingency operations and exercises such as the new Red Flag combat training program that TAC was just beginning at Nellis AFB, Nevada. Given its location, the 55th was able to work with USAF special forces units at Hurlburt Field, just nine miles to the west of Eglin, and the Tactical Air Warfare Center, also at Eglin.

Other theaters were beginning to ask for combat rescue capability. After commanding Seventh Air Force in Saigon in 1973–74, General Vogt was reassigned to Europe, where he commanded the United States Air Forces in Europe (USAFE). Using his experiences from the heavy aerial combat in SEA, he began to make changes in the command. One of the first shortfalls he noted was a lack of combat rescue capability in Europe. He also noted that the HH-53s did more special operations–type missions than rescue. He requested that the ARRS form or move an HH-53-equipped squadron to central Europe and suggested consolidating it with the CH-53-equipped 601st TASS at Sembach. Staff analysis, though, determined that the base could not properly support such a combined helicopter force without significant construction. As an interim solution, the 67th ARRSq at RAF Woodbridge, UK, was directed to modify its war plan tasking to be prepared to move significant rescue forces forward for contingency operations and also to increase its participation in USAFE exercises.[3]

Courtesy Wayne Mutza

CH-53C #70-1629 at Sembach AB, Germany, in the late 1970s

The 41st RWRW at McClellan AFB, California, commanded and controlled all rescue units in the Pacific area that provided air recovery support for air and space personnel and equipment. As a collateral mission, it also commanded and controlled several weather reconnaissance units. This was a recent change caused in part by the movement of the wing headquarters from Hickam AFB. When that move took place, the long-resident 76th ARRSq assigned under the wing was inactivated, leaving a void of rescue capability in the area. There were, however, some USAF HH-53s and HC-130s at Hickam. Six HH-53s were assigned to the 6594th Test Group, a subordinate unit of the Air Force Systems Command (AFSC). Its mission was to recover high-value air and space vehicles as part of the overall national space program, and it carried the motto Catch a Falling Star. As the 76th prepared to inactivate, the MAC commander, Gen Paul Carlton, contacted Gen Samuel Phillips, the AFSC commander, to explore the possibility of having the 6594th assume SAR tasking for long-range missions in the central Pacific region. After dual staff analysis, the commanders signed an agreement specifying that the 6594th would perform the mission on a noninterference basis. The agreement also specified that the 6594th crews were not trained or equipped for combat recovery.

The 1550th ATTW at Hill AFB was the ARRS schoolhouse and commanded the squadrons that trained all rescue crews. The wing also oversaw testing and evaluation of all rescue aircraft and equipment. It was slated to move to Kirtland AFB in early 1976. At that time, the ARRS possessed 32 HH-53B/C aircraft assigned as follows: 1550th Flying Training Squadron (FTS), Hill AFB—nine (plus one CH-53 as a trainer aircraft); 41st ARRSq, McClellan AFB—six; 55th ARRSq, Eglin AFB—six; 67th ARRSq, Woodbridge RAF, UK—five; and 33d ARRSq, Kadena AB, Japan—six.[4]

Pave Low

The two predecessor programs, Pave Star and Pave Imp, had provided only a limited night or all-weather capability, and to meet the requirements of MAC ROC 19-70, the Pave Low project was initiated in 1972. At Edwards AFB, Sikorsky engineers installed a forward-looking radar, the AN/APQ-141—initially designed for the US Army AH-56 Cheyenne gunship—on HH-53B #66-14433, an NRS-modified aircraft and veteran of combat duty in SEA. Lt Col Richard Boivin, the project engineer, directed the program. The project pilot, Maj Paul Balfe, was assigned to the helicopter section of the 6512th Test Squadron and was assisted by fellow 6512th pilot, Maj Jon Hannan. Maj Don Jensen, a test pilot from the 1550th ATTW at Hill AFB also joined the effort. Jensen needed another pilot to assist him and asked a fellow SEA combat veteran, Maj Frank Pehr, to join the project. A bevy of experienced helicopter veterans was being collected to address this challenge.

Courtesy Lt Col Frank Pehr, USAF, Retired

HH-53B #66-14433, the "Black Knight," first Pave Low prototype

Pehr was a highly experienced HH-53 pilot, currently serving as an instructor at Hill. He had entered the USAF in 1956 through the Aviation Cadet program. After pilot training and commissioning, he flew F-84s and F-100s. He was then transferred to B-52s and flew them until receiving an assignment to fly B-58s at Bunker Hill AFB, Indiana. In 1970 he was assigned to fly HH-53s. After attending helicopter transition and the HH-53 course at Hill AFB, he reported to the 37th ARRSq at Da Nang in August 1970 and served with Jensen. Things were relatively quiet then, and he mostly flew training sorties. However, he did launch on a sortie to recover a wounded Soldier in the A Shau Valley of South Vietnam in March 1971. Pehr was wounded in the leg by enemy fire as the crew hovered for the pickup. Evacuated back to the CONUS, he spent several months at Chanute AFB, Illinois, recovering from the wound. Then he reported for duty as an HH-53 IP at Hill AFB, where he eventually became the lead instructor for the NRS program. When he received Jensen's invitation to join Pave Low, he did not hesitate.

Test flights started in April 1972 and ran until December. The pilots logged a total of 73 flights that showed the efficacy of the combination of the radar with the helicopter. The crews also identified numerous technical and material deficiencies for later correction. The final flight report stated that "further development and testing is required before a production model can be achieved."[5] Pehr was generally impressed with the concept, although he felt that the Doppler navigation system was wholly inadequate for the requirement. Nevertheless, the radar did provide for terrain avoidance, and he reported, "This is great stuff. We really need it and recommend it. Yes, we should go ahead toward production."[6]

Consequently, the Air Staff directed the Pave Low II program to develop a "night/adverse weather rescue system" with the ability to avoid terrain during low-level operations—including exposure to hostile radar / sensor-directed weapon threats, to navigate precisely to the rescue area at low level, and to accurately locate and hold a hover position over a survivor. Specifically, the new system needed to harness two distinct capabilities:

1. Low-level penetration of enemy territory. A ... TF/TA radar could provide the pilots with the necessary information while maintaining a minimum altitude of 200 feet over the ground.

2. Increased navigation accuracy. Existing Doppler technology could be harnessed with improved on-board systems and a projected map display system (PMDS) and flight director instruments that would give the pilots a visual display correlated to the radar ground map display. The existing ELF [extremely low frequency] system could be integrated to allow point hover hold over the survivor's location. Enhanced low-light-level television (LLLTV) and night viewing devices would facilitate night operations.[7]

The Pave Low II effort was a three-phase research and development effort also conducted at Edwards on HH-53B #66-14433. Jensen and Pehr, augmented with other MAC/ARRS pilots, flew the operational effectiveness evaluation and found that the TF/TA radar and existing NRS capability significantly increased the capability to perform the night rescue mission. Subsequently, the AFSC Directorate of Combat Systems at Wright-Patterson submitted a development plan to spend $14.2 million to modify eight NRS HH-53s to the Pave Low II configuration. However, when all tests were completed, the cost estimate was revised to $20 million. Concerned about the cost increase and unwilling to spend that amount of money, the Air Force CSAF directed a full review of all possible alternatives to develop a Pave Low production prototype helicopter for a maximum of $3 million. The project was assigned to the Aeronautical Systems Division Specialized System Program Office (ASD/SDY) in the Prototype Directorate of the AFSC at Wright-Patterson. The division put together an in-house team of experts who developed a concept that used mostly off-the-shelf equipment already in the Air Force supply inventory and proposed a prototype for $3.2 million. Now called Pave Low III, the program was initiated in February 1974 as a Class V modification to an existing aircraft.[8]

The team consisted of several individuals who had successfully developed modifications for several cargo aircraft, such as the C-130, to be used as gunships in SEA. As that effort was winding down, team director Col Ronald Terry, USAF, was looking for another project to hold those members together and volunteered them for the Pave Low III task. When assigned the project, they reviewed MAC ROC 19-70 and began working.

Using DOD inventories, Terry and his team were able to identify and begin procuring required components for the modification. Three specific and special items had to be directly procured: a Doppler radar borrowed from the Canadian Marconi Company; a forward-looking infrared (FLIR) radar unit borrowed from Texas Instruments, Incorporated; and a symbol generator from Systems Research Laboratories, Incorporated.

Again, HH-53B #66-14433 was selected for the tests and flown to Wright-Patterson AFB, where the 4950th Test Wing would do all of the prototype fabrication and modification. Preliminary structural analysis indicated that modifications to the aircraft nose and operations console would be required and that an avionics rack would need to be built in the cargo area to hold all of the additional avionics components. Additionally, electrical modifications were necessary throughout the entire aircraft to provide for the new components. To better support the added weight being put on the aircraft, #66-14433 received upgraded T-64-GE-7A engines.

When Colonel Terry received transfer orders, he passed direction of the project to Lt Col William Craven. Reviewing the background of his team members, Craven realized that he did not have anybody with experience on helicopters and asked MAC for an operational HH-53 pilot who had an engineering degree and combat experience. Major Jensen was asked to suggest a pilot, and he immediately suggested Frank Pehr. Pehr did not have an engineering degree, but he had the other requirements in spades. The MAC staff concurred with Jensen's recommendation and agreed to assign Major Pehr to the project. He would be assigned to the MAC detachment at Wright-Patterson and act as the MAC liaison to the system program office (SPO). Since the 4950th Test Wing did not have any HH-53 aircraft or pilots assigned, he also served as the chief of the HH-53 section of the wing standardization/evaluation (stan/eval) division. His supervisor there was Lt Col Vic Genez, a test pilot on H-3s. Pehr would teach him to fly the HH-53. TSgt Rick Simmon and SSgt Andy Straughn would serve as the flight mechanics.[9]

After his return from NKP in March 1973, Simmon had served at Hill AFB as a flight mechanic instructor and worked with new crews in the flight simulator. He had also gotten to know Pehr and was excited to hear that he would be working with him on Pave Low. He and

Courtesy Lt Col Frank Pehr, USAF, Retired

Black Knight test members. *Left to right*: Capt Ron Swarz, maintenance officer; Lt Col Vic Genez and Maj Frank Pehr, project pilots; and Lt Col William Craven.

his enlisted compatriots would approach Pave Low from the practical view of the enlisted crew members so that the equipment and procedures were optimized, as much as possible, for the intense crew coordination necessary to make the system work. The overall cockpit workload was high enough that it could not be accommodated by just the two pilots; thus, the flight mechanic had to perform many more functions than in the "Slick" HH-53. This required a careful allocation of duties between pilots and flight mechanics—to the point where control panels had to be located within reach of the crew member assigned to operate the system. Sergeant Simmon's contributions to the development of crew coordination and workload allocation were invaluable in achieving a workable solution.[10]

As the team began to earnestly work the project, Craven solicited the members for a project name. When Craven received no responses, he made one himself. Drawing upon the realization that the Pave Low was being designed to do its best work on dark nights, he suggested that the team seize upon that theme by labeling it the "Black Knight." No one objected, and the team had a patch designed that showed a black chessboard knight under the classic rescue motto That Others May Live.[11]

Team members recognized early on that the TF/TA radar was perhaps the most critical component to the modification, and they scoured DOD inventories for the existing unit that could best fulfill the mission. They selected the AN/APQ-126, a radar produced by

Figure 2. The Black Knight patch designed by Lt Col Bill Craven. (Courtesy Air Force Historical Research Agency.)

Texas Instruments and used by US Navy A-7s that provided excellent terrain following/avoidance and ground mapping. After procuring one, they began adapting it to the HH-53. Specifically, Pehr had them modify it so that the aircraft could use it at 100 feet above the ground. He also emphasized to all that, as important as the TF/TA system was, the key component was a precision navigation system. More than the Doppler system was needed, and he suggested a Doppler / inertial navigation system (INS) combination. Additionally, it all had to be tied together by a central computer to accept all of the data and then synthesize it into accurate navigation information useable by the other subsystems.[12]

By early 1975, the test aircraft had been modified with the initially identified components. To signify the achievement of that milestone, Colonel Craven wanted to hold a formal rollout ceremony and scheduled a preceremony for essentially the entire test team in March. In preparation, the crew members accomplished a series of electrical power-on checks to ensure that all components were working properly. Unfortunately, when they applied full power, the aircraft began to fill with smoke. They removed the power, and an investigation determined that an electrical wire carrying a 400-volt charge was improperly connected and had allowed a short to occur.

The preceremony was rescheduled for April. However, before that could occur, the aircraft had to be flown on an FCF. Bad luck struck again. Pehr and his crew started engines normally and made ready to fly. When the crew chief pulled the arming pin from the ejection charge on the right-side external fuel tank, the charge detonated, and the fuel tank—filled with 320 gallons of JP-4—dropped from the aircraft and split open, spilling the fuel beneath the aircraft. Pehr immediately taxied the aircraft away from the volatile fuel as the base fire department responded and hosed down the fuel spill.

The project was put on hold while this potentially serious accident was investigated. Ultimately, technicians determined that a jettison toggle switch had been improperly installed when the aircraft had been manufactured, allowing the charge to fire at that moment. The problem was corrected and the project restarted. The crew flew the initial FCF on 9 June 1975, and the overall flight test program proceeded. When the FLIR and radar arrived, they were installed and included in the tests.[13]

With all now proceeding according to plan, Colonel Craven scheduled the formal ceremony for 18 September 1975. Over 200 people were invited, including the commanders of the ASD, the ARRS, and the 4950th Test Wing and the mayor of Fairborn, the city just outside of Wright-Patterson AFB. The ceremony was also open to the public. The aircraft was set up for static display, and visitors were allowed to walk through the aircraft as the test team personnel answered questions. Local media covered the event.

Once the flight test plan was completed and all components were properly evaluated, Pehr worked with representatives from MAC, the 4950th Test Wing, and the 1550th ATTW to write the flight test report, ASD-TR-75-15. Essentially, all agreed that the concept was valid and that Pave Low III could achieve its required operational capability. The pilots reported one problem with the FLIR: its line of sight needed to be biased one and a half degrees below aircraft horizontal to ensure ground clearance.[14] Evaluating the aircraft from the flight mechanic perspective, Simmon was impressed and remembers that "it was a lot of stuff, yes. Initially, I thought it was almost too much stuff, but as time went by, and learning the systems on my own or being taught by Colonel Pehr, it started to come to me. . . . I began to realize that, yes, it can be done with just three people in the cockpit and, of course, the crew members in the back. I think that the mission was able to be accomplished successfully."[15]

The results were forwarded to MAC. It had two choices: first, terminate the program and return the test aircraft to its original configuration and mission; and, second, decide on modification of a specific number of aircraft to fulfill MAC ROC 19-70. After intense staff analysis, MAC decided to have eight aircraft modified to Pave Low III standards and also receive new T-64-GE-7A engines that delivered 11 percent more power and could better provide for the added weight of the avionics. The prototype would be demodified and returned to the fleet. General Carlton was briefed on the program. He was well pleased and informally suggested that perhaps the entire ARRS HH-53 fleet could be modified to Pave Low III.[16]

The ASD then determined that the total cost for modifying the eight aircraft would be $27.5 million and that it would take 34 months to complete after the program management directive (PMD) was signed. Reviewing the entire process, Brig Gen Robert Bond, deputy director of operational requirements on the Air Staff, signed the PMD on 29 April 1977. It called for the delivery of the first modified aircraft in early 1979 and delivery of the eighth aircraft no more than one year later. The aircraft designated for modification were HH-53C numbers 69-5790, 69-5791, 73-1647, 73-1648, 73-1649, 73-1650, 73-1651, and 73-1652.[17]

MAC then focused on developing an operational employment and deployment concept. At a follow-up Pave Low III project meeting, its representatives proposed that

> the P[ave]L[ow] III system is required to operate worldwide in terrain and climatic extremes. The PL III helicopters may be employed in areas that contain the best of enemy defenses in support of the primary mission of combat rescue. Mission scenarios will be varied and designed to counter the expected hostile threat levels. Mission options may include in-flight refueling waiting for the cover of darkness or weather, the use of several support aircraft, and the use of forward staging locations. The cover of darkness will be used to the utmost for hostile area missions. . . . Peacetime humanitarian and rescue missions may be supported on a 24-hour capability.
>
> *Employment*—The eight PL II helicopters will be employed in one unit located at a main operating base with the capability of supporting contingency operations. The helicopters can be employed in secondary combat roles or peacetime search and rescue. Air crew training, developing new tactics as the threat dictates, and maintaining a state of readiness will be the foremost requirements. Humanitarian and rescue mission[s] involving the civilian population will be secondary missions.
>
> *Deployment Plans*—The first four aircraft will be delivered to Kirtland AFB, New Mexico, where initial qualification of aircraft will be accomplished. The fifth through eighth will be deployed to a non-CONUS location after completion of system acceptance checks. . . . The unit will remain at the non-CONUS location with a deployment capability of operating from a forward operating base (FOB) for thirty days independent of the main operating base (MOB) or deploying to an overseas area with a contingency plan to operate indefinitely from an FOB or MOB.[18]

With that guidance, the various commands could now begin to develop logistical and personnel support plans to ensure that the new capability would get the materiel and properly trained Airmen it required to fulfill its mission.

The ASD team, working with personnel from the Warner-Robins Air Logistics Center (WR-ALC) that provided logistical support for all USAF H-53s, then turned its attention to finding a contractor to modify the aircraft. However, when it conducted a search to determine which companies could do the modifications, it found only five companies capable of handling the project. Of those five, the ASD team had a high degree of confidence only in Sikorsky. However, Sikorsky proposed a price well beyond the available funding.

One of the personnel on the Pave Low team suggested that the team consider using the Naval Air Rework Facility (NARF) at Pensacola Naval Air Station (NAS), Florida, as the prime contractor. That facility did the major periodic maintenance on all US Navy and Marine H-53s. The facility was full of master craftsmen highly experienced in fabricating and installing aircraft parts on complicated aircraft. Colonel Craven and several assistants traveled to Pensacola to visit the facility and speak with the commander. In his trip report, Craven wrote that "all functions at NARF, Pensacola, relative to Pave Low III modification requirements have been investigated and found to be totally adequate and clearly superior in comparison to projected industrial facilities. . . . It is the Program Office's decision to solicit US Navy acceptance of the modification workload as a true joint service program."[19]

Craven began working with his counterparts at WR-ALC and the NARF to craft the contract proposal for the project. When the package was complete, Craven flew to the Pentagon to brief the responsible US Navy commanders on the project. They agreed to do the modifications, and the parties signed the Depot Maintenance Interservice Agreement, coded NAVAIR 25BFTG and dated 18 November 1976. The first aircraft modification would begin in September 1978, and the last would be completed by January 1980, within the original PMD.[20]

20th Special Operations Squadron

Following the removal of US forces from SEA, special operations forces (SOF) helicopter responsibilities were assigned to TAC. As the Pave Low III aircraft was coming to fruition in late 1975, TAC directed that the 20th SOS, the veteran unit of long service in SEA, be reactivated as part of the 1st SOW at Hurlburt Field to serve as a residual helicopter SOF and repository of experience. Initially authorized four CH-3E and six UH-1N aircraft, primarily from ARRS stocks, the 20th slowly began taking possession of the aircraft as assigned personnel arrived, some from duty with other units in SEA but most from throughout the USAF. A high percentage, though, were veterans of the war and were determined to reestablish the "Green Hornets" as a professional and highly spirited combat-ready unit. As the squadron once again came to life, its assigned missions were as follows:

Primary:

> Conduct day/night infiltration, exfiltration, reinforcement, and resupply
> into hostile or enemy controlled territory using air-land and airdrop tech-
> niques over land or water. Conduct psychological operations, to include
> aerial dispensing of leaflets.

Secondary:

1. Recovery of personnel.

   a. Escape and evasion operations.

   b. Combat search and rescue operations for unconventional warfare
      (UW) forces. Where ARRS forces are not readily available, SAR opera-
      tions include locating survivors, recovery by air-land or aerial recovery by
      rescue hoist, minimal first aid, and transportation to the nearest medi-
      cal facility.

2. Shipboard operations.

3. Medical evacuation of personnel.

4. Humanitarian and civic action operations.

5. Limited photoreconnaissance, either by handheld or modularly installed
   camera systems.

6. Other missions as directed. [21]

To accomplish its missions, the unit was authorized 32 pilots and
44 support personnel and was initially commanded by Lt Col Robert
Mayo. Capt Gary Weikel reported to the 1st SOW, having recently
returned from his tour with the Jolly Greens at NKP. Originally, he
had intended to transfer to the Air Force Reserve (AFR) and serve
as an Air Reserve technician at Luke AFB. However, he had a change
of heart when he heard that the 20th SOS was being reactivated, and
he accepted orders to Hurlburt. He had to go through the school at
Hill AFB again, this time to qualify in the UH-1N. Now a highly
experienced combat pilot, he was assigned to the wing tactics office
but flew regularly with the 20th. Another early assignee was 1st Lt
Joe Vallimont, also just returned from the 40th at NKP. He took
over as the squadron tactics officer and quickly began to develop
tactical training plans for the unit.[22] A few new pilots just out of
flight school also joined the unit. Lt Michael Collins recounted during that time, "I came to the 20th from flight school and was one of
five lieutenants assigned. Most of the squadron's first crew members

were battle-hardened pilots, flight mechanics, and gunners from Vietnam. It was a humbling feeling for a 2d Lt . . . to be placed with such a dynamic mix of characters."[23]

Throughout the year, the squadron was busy with self-help projects to develop the squadron area and facilities. Weikel and Vallimont began a review of UW doctrine and the role that the 20th SOS could play in that arena. They gave briefings to the staffs of several superior headquarters. Additionally, they began to build a tactics database for all possible missions and began looking at the use of evolving night vision goggles (NVG) to enhance their night operations. The two also established low-level training routes for crew qualification and M-60 machine gun training for the aircrews. By September the unit had received its first two CH-3s and now had four UH-1N crews fully trained and ready to be mobilized. Two more of both CH-3s and UH-1Ns had been identified for the squadron.[24]

The 20th Squadron's parent unit, the 1st SOW, was the remaining special operations force in the USAF. The 1st SOW was the lineal descendent of the air commandos formed in World War II, where it saw heavy action in the China-Burma-India theater. This force was reduced to almost nothing until it was rejuvenated for the long war in SEA. During that period, USAF special operations forces grew to over 10,000 personnel operating 550 aircraft. The postwar drawdown was severe, though, and by early 1976, the 1st SOW, with affiliated ANG and AFR units and one small squadron each in Europe and the Pacific, consisted of about 3,000 Airmen, who were assigned 28 aircraft, including CH-3Es, UH-1Ns, AC-130As and Hs, and MC-130s.[25] Almost all the aircraft were over 20 years old. The SOF units were the lowest priority for TAC funding, and Hurlburt Field was considered a "sleepy hollow, nice place to visit or retire."[26] The reactivation of the 20th breathed a bit of life back into the wing.

Aerospace Rescue and Recovery Service

As these events were occurring at Hurlburt, Major Pehr continued the developmental testing and evaluation of aircraft #66-14433 at Wright-Patterson, stressing the integration of the Doppler/INS system with the central avionics computer and the projected map display. SecDef Donald Rumsfeld visited the base and took a ride on the aircraft.

At the same time, the 1550th ATTW accomplished its move from Hill to Kirtland AFB. Aircraft #66-14433 was flown to Hill AFB for some navigational testing because the initial strip maps used by the Pave Low navigational system were made for that area. Then the aircraft was flown to Kirtland for the formal IOT&E, which was conducted in two phases at Kirtland and at Howard AFB in the Panama Canal Zone. For the tests, Pehr worked with the test group and flew with several highly qualified HH-53 IPs, such as Capt Don Backlund, Capt Phil Pacini, Capt Bill Kramer, and Maj Ken Ernest from MAC/DOV (stan/eval). These early pilots were joined by flight mechanics SMSgt R. A. Hohl and Technical Sergeants E. J. Koebernik, Rick Simmon, and Andy Straughn, who focused on flight mechanic duties and overall crew integration.[27]

The results were encouraging. However, Pehr and the team constantly made or suggested refinements to the various systems. It became obvious, too, that future pilots and flight mechanics transitioning to the aircraft would need to receive a considerable amount of training to be able to operate the evolving technology and execute advanced tactics for safe and effective mission accomplishment. Overall, though, the IOT&E was very successful, and the test report, unanimously agreed to by all who flew in the flight series, stated:

> The results showed that operational crews could fly the system down to 100 feet set clearance above the ground level (AGL) at night and navigate to the survivor's area while employing terrain masking techniques. . . .

> The flight crews determined that with sufficient training and with two flight mechanics on the crew, they could satisfactorily accomplish terrain following / terrain avoidance flight, inertial/Doppler navigation, and survivor location/recovery without the addition of a systems operator at a separate console. . . .

> Future training requirements were assessed and it was determined that individual training must be increased for pilots and flight mechanics for the Pave Low III mission. . . .

> The FLIR performance was very good in cool, dry climactic conditions but marginal in hot, humid conditions. . . .

> The recommendation of this evaluation is to proceed with procurement of the Pave Low III system. The unanimous opinion of each crew member that participated in the evaluation is that Pave Low III provided the first realistic capability to accomplish the combat rescue mission in conditions of total darkness and in marginal weather.[28]

The report also contained specific recommendations concerning the selection and training of Pave Low crew members, saying:

> The personnel assigned to a Pave Low III unit must be screened. The mission is demanding and personnel not properly motivated will have difficulty learning the system. The system does not allow strong crew members to carry weak ones. If one man cannot perform, it will degrade the entire performance. The mission does not allow for a margin of error. Basic experience and high motivation should be the driving forces when considering Pave Low III crew members.[29]

It was also becoming obvious to anyone who cared to notice that this radically modified aircraft had capabilities well beyond combat rescue. When the aircraft first went to Kirtland, Pehr and another team member, Leo Gambone, met with the HH-53 pilots and said, "We've got something you guys want to see. We built this for rescue, but it's really a special ops machine." On another occasion, Pehr and Gambone made a pitch for the aircraft to some USAF special operations personnel. Pehr and Gambone told them, "You guys ought to get on board this program. This is the kind of system you need." Their response was dismissive. "Ha, you give us a set of NVGs and a stopwatch and we can go anywhere in the world and do anything we need to do. We do not need all of this sh--," said the young tigers in the 20th SOS.[30]

The MAC commander, General Carlton, closely monitored the Pave Low program. Satisfied with the developmental results, he directed his staff to establish a requirement for 29 Pave Low III aircraft for a projected cost of $55 million. He also directed his staff to explore the possibility of requesting the transfer of the 10 remaining CH-53s from TAC and USAFE for conversion to Pave Low III.[31] One young staff officer, Capt Jerry Shipman, briefed the proposal to a senior commander at Bergstrom AFB. The officer was unimpressed with these possible expansion plans and only wanted to know when the helicopters were going to get "the hell off my ramp."[32]

As Pave Low was proceeding according to plan, the ARRS commander, Maj Gen Ralph Saunders, continued to work with USAFE concerning the movement of significant numbers of HH-53s to Europe. When the Sembach option was rejected, he proposed moving all of the NRS HH-53s from McClellan and Kirtland AFBs to RAF Woodbridge for integration into the 67th ARRSq. The currently assigned HH-53s and crews were already integrating into ongoing USAFE operational exercises with NATO partners. Saunders briefed the USAFE commander, Gen Richard Ellis, on present and developing ARRS capabilities, and Ellis supported his ongoing initiatives.[33]

Saunders also had his staff participate in an ongoing DOD study to consider some form of "interservice helicopter commonality." Subsequently, the study group recommended that if commonality appeared to be cost effective, then procedures for its implementation merited further study. Seizing upon that theme, General Saunders informally proposed that ARRS become the single manager for all USAF helicopters. This would include the current ARRS forces and missions plus Air Force Special Operations Forces (AFSOF), the Strategic Air Command (SAC) missile site support mission, rescue support at TAC ranges, support of AFSC missions, and the distinguished personnel mission in the Washington, DC, area. However, in post-SEA mission and unit planning, MAC and the ARRS had agreed that rescue forces should perform combat rescue functions but should not perform covert combat operations, as had become somewhat commonplace in later years in SEA. MAC/ARRS would focus on the "white hat" missions while leaving other forces to focus on the classic SOF, or "black hat," missions, but under one common command. However, the idea was premature. Following the removal of special operations forces from SEA, the SOF helicopter responsibilities were assigned to TAC. It was up to TAC to form and equip units such as the 20th SOS to carry out those missions, and it did not support the single manager proposal. This concept would be revisited in the future.[34]

During 1976 HH-53s were also used in contingency operations. In June, two HH-53s from the 67th ARRSq at RAF Woodbridge deployed to RAF Akrotiri on the island of Cyprus for possible use in a noncombatant evacuation operation (NEO) for American citizens in Lebanon. However, their services were not needed when all personnel were evacuated by US Navy ships. Two months later, HH-53s from the 33d ARRSq at Kadena AB responded as part of a large USAF task force to the murder of two US Army Soldiers by North Korean troops at Panmunjom, Korea. For 19 days, the helicopters maintained a combat recovery alert at Osan AB, Korea, to provide support for possible air operations against the North Koreans. However, the incident was resolved without further bloodshed, and the rescue forces returned to Kadena. ARRS forces, including the HH-53s, also became steady participants in large USAF and joint exercises such as Red Flag at Nellis and several held by overseas commands. These exercises produced many lessons learned, highlighting a continuing need for realistic training and equipment improvements. Overall, the exercises were highly successful. Lt Col Bruce Purvine, ARRS director of tactical operations, described how "Red Flag has provided outstanding realistic combat training for our participating aircrews . . . , increased our aircrews' knowledge of the enemy . . . , [and] given them the opportunity to develop an ability for combat decision making. Red Flag has unearthed numerous problem areas that must be corrected."[35]

ARRS HH-53s and other helicopters also participated with TAC fighter units to begin a long-term program to determine the best tactics for fighters to use to attack helicopters and for helicopters to use against fighters and other attacking helicopters. This program was called Joint Countering Attack Helicopter (J-CATCH) and the tests, initially done at Hill and Eglin AFBs, would eventually also involve the 20th SOS. The results, from a helicopter perspective, were significant. The recommendations were that helicopter crews emphasize low-level tactics with a corresponding adjustment in training, radar warning systems be installed on all combat rescue helicopters as soon as possible, and heat-seeking missiles be installed on all combat rescue helicopters. These results correlated with those of a supporting threat study on expected enemy defenses in the central European area. It concluded that to survive, trained aircrews would need to conduct night operations using nap-of-the-earth (NOE) navigation down as low as 50 feet AGL while utilizing radar homing and warning equipment and infrared countermeasures. Pave Low III was being designed specifically to address these requirements.[36]

20th Special Operations Squadron

By early 1977, the 20th SOS had received three of its CH-3s and five of its UH-1Ns. In January the unit generated an in-house exercise to practice new tactics based on post-SEA threat analysis and assigned mission tasks. This included NOE navigational techniques, which put a real premium on accurate map reading. Captain Weikel in wing tactics scripted ROCs for aircraft radar warning receivers, radar altimeters, infrared jammers, and upgraded engines for both aircraft. The enhanced tactical training served the squadron well when it received a TAC operational readiness inspection (ORI) in March, passing with no answerable write-ups. Nonetheless, it was still limited in mission capability because of shortages of required aircraft radios as well as armor and maintenance problems caused by the aircraft's old age.

Later in the year, the 20th had an opportunity to participate in a TAC-sponsored Blue Flag exercise at Hurlburt Field. Unit crews were able to fly several tactical sorties, including a simulated combat recovery of an aircrew shot down deep behind enemy lines. They also began to conduct mountain flying in northern Georgia and lift training for US Army Ranger exercises in that area and the swamps just north of Eglin AFB, affording excellent joint training for both service units. The 20th's tactics division also participated with Headquarters TAC to write a helicopter tactics manual for the CH-3 and UH-1N aircraft. It also sent a representative to meetings at TAC headquarters to establish an analysis and training program for helicopter air-to-air tactics against both fixed- and rotary-wing adversaries. In November the unit deployed two UH-1N aircraft with aircrews and maintenance support to participate in a Red Flag exercise at Nellis. Other unit aircrews rotated in at the midpoint of the exercise, providing valuable training for almost all UH-1N crews. While there, the Green Hornets flew almost every day as well as on several nights. Their missions were SOF-focused, allowing them to make numerous low-level flights into hostile territory to work with the threat simulators, engage in air-to-air battles with opposing force fighters, and practice basic SOF skills. The Hornets became adept at inserting small special forces teams optimized to destroy SAM sites. The results of the exercise showed that the 20th's aircraft and crews could reasonably survive in a medium- to high-threat area with proper training and support. However, several continuing limitations now became readily apparent and were noted in the unit after action report, which stated, "We found the UH-1N to have adequate power to work in the high desert, but found that the lack of radar warning receivers (RWR), infrared countermeasures (IRCM), night terrain following equipment, and precise navigation equipment made night work very difficult. Another shortcoming of the UH-1N is that it does not have sufficient range."[37] These limiting factors suggested that the 20th SOS, with its current equipage, was not able to provide significant infiltration capability for any SOF forces beyond small teams over short distances.[38]

Maj John Grove joined the unit in November. Since returning from SEA in late 1971, he had been at Shaw AFB, initially as an H-3 IP and then as director of the base altitude chamber. In that position, he had worked for the base hospital commander, an arrangement that did not benefit Grove's career. The new 1st SOW commander, Col Richard Dunwoody, had known Grove at NKP and felt that his vast experience could be of benefit to the 20th. Dunwoody called him with a job offer. Grove gladly accepted and moved to Hurlburt. The first day on base, he ran into Captains Weikel and Vallimont at the Officers' Club. Both were hip deep in building up the unit's capabilities, in large part through their strong personalities. Weikel was a bona fide hard charger who did everything at max press and seemingly never slept. He was a whirling dervish of ideas and favored seeking forgiveness vice requesting permission. Joe Vallimont matched Gary Weikel stride for stride. Weikel described him as

> one of the most colorful characters ever. Middle linebacker . . . almost an ace (married four times that I know of), semi-pro ice hockey star, carried his "ax" (guitar) with him everywhere he went. Was lead for JG [Jolly Green] rock and roll band . . . could play/sing almost any/all 50s/60s/70s rock, knew all the SEA songs/lyrics, could entertain/regale for hours, started fights everywhere, and was an endless source of scandal and humor. Fu Manchu out-of-limits walrus mustache . . . the total "up-yer-ass" package.[39]

Weikel and Vallimont briefed Grove on what the squadron was doing, and he felt right at home. His services were immediately put to good use; he initially began instructing in the H-3 and then progressively moved into other positions of authority and responsibility.[40]

Aerospace Rescue and Recovery Service

At the outset of 1977, the ARRS engaged with MAC and TAC in an extension of the interservice helicopter commonality discussions to examine an Air Staff proposal to transfer SOF helicopter support for joint special operations to the US Army. If such a mission transfer occurred, it would be without any personnel or aircraft. The TAC UH-1N and CH-3E aircraft would then be transferred to the ARRS. As this discussion was ongoing, General Saunders pointed out that if the CSAF and MAC commander decided to assign the SOF mission to the ARRS, it could certainly provide the necessary leadership and management expertise to handle the mission. However, no further action was taken on the proposal.[41]

Throughout the year, rescue units were always on call to provide civil SAR. The HH-53s would occasionally be called for recoveries.

On 14 January, an HH-53 crew from the 55th ARRSq helped rescue 32 US Army Rangers caught in a flood in the swamps north of Eglin. On the same day, another HH-53 crew from the 41st ARRSq at McClellan recovered eight campers trapped in the deep snow of the High Sierra Mountains north of Lake Tahoe.

General Saunders also reengaged USAFE concerning an increase of HH-53s at RAF Woodbridge. In a visit to that command in January 1977, he met with the new USAFE commander, Gen Richard Ellis. Based upon USAFE's continued desire for increased combat rescue capability, Saunders suggested moving all NRS HH-53s to Europe, possibly based at RAF Woodbridge. When Saunders back-briefed General Carlton, however, Carlton stated that at least two NRS aircraft and all NRS training would remain at Kirtland.

The ARRS lost another HH-35C when #68-10368, assigned to the 67th ARRSq at RAF Woodbridge, crashed near Stuttgart, Germany, on 24 June 1977. The aircraft was transporting personnel to a training site in Germany and was approaching a US Army air base when the accident occurred. All 14 on board were injured but survived.[42]

The ARRS, MAC, and USAFE staff had begun doing the necessary coordination for the movement of the aircraft when, in July, the director of plans on the Air Staff nonconcurred. Instead, he stated that the eight Pave Low III aircraft would be assigned to RAF Woodbridge as they were modified and flight-tested. However, the ARRS and MAC were directed to move five more HH-53s to the 67th to replace the crashed aircraft and to provide increased daytime combat recovery capability for USAFE. The ARRS then proposed that the NRS aircraft be split between the 41st ARRSq at McClellan AFB, California, and the 33d ARRSq at Kadena AB, Japan. This would move NRS capability into the western Pacific region and also allow continuous NRS participation in the ongoing Red Flag exercises at Nellis. However, analysis showed that this could not be done while still maintaining the NRS training capability at Kirtland, and the project was dropped.[43]

Throughout the year, aircraft #66-14433 continued its operational testing and evaluation (OT&E), conducted at both Wright-Patterson and Kirtland AFBs, and accomplished all milestones. HQ USAF formally declared that all Pave Low III aircraft would now be officially identified as HH-53H aircraft. HQ USAF also authorized MAC to program for 21 more aircraft modifications, starting with the NRS-modified aircraft. However, funding was not yet provided.

Anticipating full funding for all 29 aircraft, which now included the prototype, #66-14433, the MAC staff began planning for full implementation based upon modification of the initial eight. A revised concept of operations was published on 18 August 1977. It specified the following:

1. Initial basing of six Pave Low aircraft would be at the 67th ARRSq in the UK and mixed with three standard aircraft to provide day and night combat rescue capability.

2. Two Pave Low aircraft would be retained at Kirtland AFB for crew and maintenance training.

3. Pave Low and NRS aircraft would not be mixed.

4. Pave Low aircraft would be reserved for high-threat and/or night/bad weather conditions and not used in day/VFR conditions unless the only [ones] available. Pave Low aircraft could conduct other heavy-lift operations such as sling lifts and evacuations.

5. Pave Low aircraft could operate single ship behind enemy lines.

6. The requirement for Pave Low aircraft to have active onboard ECM was still current (MAC ROC 12-73).

7. Both organizational and intermediate level maintenance would be established in Pave Low III units to support their unique systems and ARRS general systems such as ELF, RHAW, and flare dispensers.

8. Pave Low required unique specialists for

   a. light controls, AFCS, and hover

   b. instrumentation

   c. radar, ELF, and nav aids

   d. TF/TA radar system, Doppler, and IMU

   e. FLIR sensor

9. Pave Low units must be manned for 24-hour operations.[44]

The 55th ARRSq at Eglin AFB began working on tactical procedures, and the MAC staff did preliminary studies with the training personnel at Kirtland AFB to develop a Pave Low training program for initial projected students in the summer of 1979. All first-cadre aircrews and maintenance personnel would have previous H-53 experience. Crew coordination would be essential, and each crew was to have two pilots, two flight mechanics, and two pararescue specialists.[45]

At Kirtland the 1551st FTS trained all H-53 crews and was directed to expand its program to include Pave Low III qualification for the selected crews. It had just revamped the helicopter combat recovery portion of its training to include the tactics necessary to deal with new and evolving threats. Now the 1551st began to develop its training program specifically for the Pave Low. The squadron commander, Lt Col Gary Lunt, and his senior IPs and flight mechanics started working directly with Major Pehr and Sergeant Simmon, who came TDY from Wright-Patterson AFB to script both flying and academic curricula for aircrews anticipated to begin arriving by late 1978.[46] Following the abortive planning to move the NRS aircraft to Europe and the Pacific areas, MAC finalized an ultimate 29-aircraft HH-53H beddown plan. It called for nine aircraft at the 67th, RAF Woodbridge; five at the 41st, McClellan AFB; five at the 55th, Eglin AFB; five at the 33d, Kadena AB; and five at the 1550th, Kirtland AFB.[47]

Throughout the year, HH-53 crews continued to participate in major training exercises such as Red Flag, Brave Shield, and Bold Eagle, both in the CONUS and overseas, as well as in several smaller SAR exercises. HH-53 crews from the 41st and 55th ARRSqs and the 1550th ATTW participated in the ever-expanding J-CATCH program.[48]

As 1978 began, the ARRS continued to push the concept of a consolidated helicopter force. TAC initially expressed interest in its proposal, especially when a USAF audit indicated that $2 million a year could be saved in tactical range support missions. General Saunders's proposal received increased emphasis when Maj Gen Hoyt Vandenberg Jr., director of operations and readiness at HQ USAF, voiced support for the concept and asked the various commands to state their positions. Again ARRS and MAC supported it. However, Maj Gen Billy Ellis, the TAC DCS for operations, nonconcurred. He cited the close integration of the SOF and TACS helicopters with the Army special forces and tactical units they supported, stating, "SOF and TACS helicopters should remain separate from Rescue and immediately responsive to their respective missions. The proposed single manager concept does not offer benefits in readiness for the rotary wing force." That effectively ended the discussion.[49]

Pave Low

At about the same time, HH-53B #66-14433 was moved permanently to Kirtland AFB for its follow-on operational test and evaluation (FOT&E). Now promoted to lieutenant colonel, Frank Pehr
came with the aircraft because the 1550th ATTW commander said
that he would not take the aircraft without him. Pehr became a special assistant to the commander and director for Pave Low. The wing
test section was commanded by Lt Col Sid Gurley, and Pehr worked
closely with him to do all operational testing and begin the logistic
and maintenance planning to put the aircraft into operational use.
One of the test pilots there was Capt Steve Connelly. He and Pehr
were well acquainted from their time at Hill AFB, where Pehr had
become a bit of a legend for his great flying abilities and no-nonsense
professionalism. To many of the younger men, Pehr was a mentor.[50]

Following his tour with the 40th at NKP in 1972, Connelly had
returned to HH-53 duty at Hamilton AFB, California, with the 41
ARRSq. However, that unit inactivated in the summer of 1973, and
Connelly was reassigned to instructor duties in the HH-53 school
with the 1550th ATTW at Hill. Still a first lieutenant, he threw his
meager belongings in his car and drove to Utah. He had a volunteer
statement in for another SEA tour but remained at Hill AFB for the
next two years, eventually becoming an instructor on the NRS aircraft. In 1975 he received orders to proceed to Webb AFB, Texas, to
go through fixed-wing conversion flying T-37s and T-38s, with a follow-
on return to operational flying in either fixed- or rotary-wing aircraft.
While at Webb, he received a call from a USAF assignments officer
who had another idea. The officer had been reviewing Connelly's personnel file and noticed that he had an electrical engineering degree
and a strong academic record. The USAF was looking for a young officer to send to helicopter test pilot school, and the assignments officer
wanted to know if Connelly would consider being nominated for the
slot. He needed a quick answer because the selection board started
the next day. Connelly agreed, and his selection package was the only
one with a full record but no actual application. Regardless, he was
selected, and instead of a fixed-wing assignment, he reported to the
US Navy Test Pilot School at the Patuxent NAS, Maryland, in January
1976 for the helicopter test pilot course.[51]

Completing the program in December, Connelly was ordered back
to the 1550th ATTW, now at Kirtland, for duties as an HH-53 test

pilot in the wing flight test section. Arriving there in January 1977, his first assigned task was to do a test and evaluation on problems with the NRS system identified in a recent accident. It involved erroneous radar altimeter inputs that caused problems with both the Doppler navigation system and the hover coupler. When the project was complete, he worked several other programs and also checked out as an instructor in the HH-53 qualification course. Later that summer, his boss, Lt Col Ron Olsen, told him that he would be assigned to the Pave Low III project when the aircraft and Frank Pehr were moved to Kirtland. That was just fine with Connelly because he had already heard a great deal about it and especially looked forward to working with Pehr. He made several trips to Wright-Patterson, where he flew with Pehr on #66-14433 and began to integrate into the overall program. When Pehr and the aircraft permanently arrived at Kirtland, Connelly was ready.

Capt Bob Stankovich also transferred from Hill to Kirtland as part of the unit relocation. He had flown CH-53s with the 21st SOS in Thailand in 1973 and 1974 and had returned to duties as an H-53 instructor and training officer. Pehr also asked him to join the Pave Low effort, and he eagerly grabbed the opportunity to fly and qualify on the aircraft. He then focused on developing training programs for the aircraft.[52]

Pehr and his slowly growing cadre flew together quite often. Several of their missions were flown over Cabezon Peak, a flat-faced mountain about 50 miles northwest of Kirtland AFB and in the Grand Canyon, to test the TF/TA radar and determine the best procedures for ridge crossing. In September 1978, they took the aircraft to Nellis AFB to participate in a Red Flag exercise. To prepare the aircraft for the sorties, they had to manually open the projected map display to put in a map strip for the Nellis region. They actually accomplished that tricky task at one point, with the map filmstrip stretched out along the length of the cabin. That was no small feat because the strips had to be aligned exactly right, or they would cause navigational errors.

One of the crew's assigned missions was to do a night recovery of a "downed" Airman deep in enemy territory, actually the Tonopah Test Range, an area filled with a variety of "hostile" radars and threats. The "survivor" was 1st Lt Jim Teeple, a former Army warrant officer pilot who had switched over to the Air Force and was assigned to fly HH-53s with the 41st ARRSq. While temporarily assigned to Kirtland

AFB, Teeple had met Steve Connelly and expressed an interest in getting involved in the Pave Low. The aircrew took him along to Nellis, and he volunteered to be the survivor.

The weather was windy and cold. Teeple and a survival instructor were driven to a site a few miles from the projected rescue area and directed to walk in. As Teeple was in good physical condition, he quickly separated from the instructor, who was later recovered by ground transportation. Equipped with a locating device, Teeple moved into the assigned area. At the appointed time, he set it up so that the Pave Low crew could find him.

Using the full capabilities of the Pave Low, Pehr and Connelly flew through the dark—*undetected across the middle of the range*—and came to a hover over the survivor's location. In the cabin, Rick Simmon saw Teeple and announced, "Penetrator is going down." When the cold, soaked survivor was on board, they departed the range—again, fully undetected—and allowed Teeple to get some flying time on the machine.[53] Simmon remembers that "it was a pretty interesting environment to be in with the capabilities of the aircraft. Low-level flying, in actual terrain at that point, on NVGs, what I call 'down in the dirt.' [It was] actually lower than the capability of the radar to carry us. It was some fun flying. I was a little nervous a few times, but it was pretty good flying."[54]

That feat drew a lot of attention to the project. On another day, low clouds and fog again covered the tactical areas, and all missions except a few F-111s and the Pave Low were cancelled. Pehr and Connelly flew an operations normal mission through all of the ranges and never had to abort because of the weather.[55]

When flying into and out of the Nellis ranges, the Pave Low occasionally needed in-flight refueling, and HC-130 tankers would be sent up to rendezvous with them. Connelly and Pehr set up no-communications procedures so that radio calls were not necessary, just a few light signals. Their integrated navigational system allowed them to navigate precisely to the rendezvous point exactly on time. On one occasion, just as they were finishing, the tanker crew was not sure where it was. Connelly checked his map display and was able to direct the tanker crew to make a turn before the aircraft entered one of the restricted areas.[56]

Thinking tactically, Connelly felt that such precise low-level navigational capability made the Pave Lows natural lead aircraft for formations of other helicopters, such as Army CH-47s for larger unit infiltrations or exfiltrations or for virtually any tactical purpose. He developed a test plan to validate the concept. However, the ARRS staff disapproved the plan with the pithy comment that "the Pave Low would never be used like that."[57]

Hearing about these successes, the 1550th ATTW commander decided to take a flight with Connelly and Pehr. They went out at night and flew on NVGs as low as 15 feet above ground level through the ranges. When they landed, the commander demanded to know who authorized such a mission, clearly in violation of MAC regulations. Pehr pointed out to him that they flew that way because it was called for in the test plan that the commander himself had signed! Regardless, the commander called MAC headquarters and had them restricted to 100 feet. Additionally, they were forbidden any further use of NVGs until a proper test program had been conducted. Pehr could not believe the commander's and MAC's reluctance to accept the capabilities of the aircraft. Pehr said to them, "Listen guys, this is the best thing that ever happened to you. It is making you viable as a rescue organization, and it's probably the best thing that's ever going to happen to rescue. And you people are shooting it down. What is the matter with you people?"[58]

However, orders were orders, and Connelly developed a program to determine the best initial NVG use. Given the collage of lights of various colors arrayed throughout the cockpit, Pehr and Connelly rigged an old Army wool blanket from the ceiling so that the pilot flying could turn down all lights and use his NVGs, while the copilot and flight mechanic could then use their lights without bothering the pilot flying. It worked just fine. They could not admit that their light restrictor was just an old Army blanket. Instead, they had to list it as a "light isolation device." Connelly later said that "we could have painted the windows black, and we could have done the mission."[59] Pehr later described the rationale for their expediency:

> Maybe we were being a little devious and a little untruthful, but it was almost like if we told them exactly what we were going to do or what we had to do, they wouldn't have let us do it. And in order to get through the test phase, if we didn't test it, how could we say that this is a way we could operate the aircraft? So we had to test all of this stuff beforehand so that we could put it into the training program so we could develop the capability to do that stuff. Of course, later they developed the night vision lighting package that made light compatible with both the goggles, and you could have the lights on and still be able to see outside with the goggles. But earlier in the program, you couldn't do that. The lights would shut down the goggles; you couldn't see past the windscreen.[60]

They were determined to aggressively carry out their testing of this revolutionary new technological marvel by seeking forgiveness for any discovered transgressions instead of requesting permission from a doubting and hesitant bureaucratic organization. But there were so many who just refused to believe in the system. Connelly and Pehr tried to talk some of the other HH-53 pilots into volunteering to fly with them. There was a dearth of interest. "You do not want to fly 'Grave Low,'" the pilots said. "They are all going to kill themselves."[61]

Aerospace Rescue and Recovery Service

In April, in anticipation of the initial assignment of Pave Low IIIs to the 67th ARRSq, that unit began to prepare for the arrival of the aircraft. It received manning authorization for a four-person intelligence cell to develop procedures for intelligence support for combat recovery in the theater. The squadron started coordination with various European governments for the use of air traffic routes and training areas, especially low-flying areas in Wales, Scotland, and Belgium. MAC and the ARRS plans divisions published MAC Programming Plan 78-18 designating an aircraft flow that showed all aircraft in place and operational at RAF Woodbridge by early 1981. MAC personnel began to program the necessary manpower billets to provide for an aircrew manning of 1.5 full crews per aircraft and enough maintenance and support personnel based upon 26 man-hours of support for each flying hour.

As the designated conversion aircraft began to flow through the NARF at Pensacola, the ARRS did an overall reevaluation of the seven NRS aircraft. Given the increasing sophistication of enemy antiaircraft weaponry, it was now blatantly obvious that the NRS aircraft did not belong in high-threat arenas, day or night, especially with an increasingly obsolete navigational system. Accordingly, a special Rescue Study Group was convened to review the issue and offer recommendations. Realizing quickly that the aircraft was still operated as it was designed—for duty in SEA and viable only in low-threat environs—the study leader, Col Don Gibson, recommended that the NRS aircraft be relieved of its "special mission" requirements and restricted to night SAR missions only. General Saunders concurred, and the NRS capability was no longer maintained, nor were crews now trained to perform it.[62]

Other modifications were also programmed or considered for the HH-53 fleet in general. The ARRS took part in developmental work to design IRCMs that could defend the aircraft against SA-7-type heat-seeking missiles, now becoming a favorite weapon of enemy forces of all sorts. The ARRS also assigned one HH-53, #67-14994, to take part in the Army and Navy's program "Compass Cool" to determine the feasibility of developing an infrared warning receiver. Additionally, 24 HH-53s were modified with hover couplers. These systems had been added to the NRS aircraft and allowed pilots to hold hover directly over a survivor. Lastly, the more powerful T-64-GE-7A engines were programmed for all of the non–Pave Low aircraft and would be installed over the next year.[63]

In November 1978, the 39th ARRW received a tasking to support recovery operations in Guyana, South America, when a US congressman was killed in a mass murder at a religious cult settlement near Jonestown. The 55th ARRSq was directed to deploy three HH-53s with a maintenance package to stage out of the Roosevelt Roads NAS in Puerto Rico in support of the operation. The crews deployed with aircraft numbers 73-1649, 73-1651, and 73-1652. They arrived at the site on 22 November and shuttled in and out of the compound for the next two days, flying 30 sorties to recover 603 bodies from the disaster site. It was a sad and macabre mission for the men of rescue, but they did not get to pick their missions.[64]

20th Special Operations Squadron

By the beginning of 1978, the 20th SOS now had all of its authorized UH-1Ns and all but one of its authorized CH-3s. The unit also welcomed a new commander, Lt Col John Roberts. Unit assigned missions remained the same as unit personnel participated in several more large exercises. Weikel and Vallimont attended a conference at TAC headquarters concerning 20th SOS participation in the J-CATCH program, also attended by several representatives from MAC/ARRS and the other services. Weikel made a strong pitch that his unit had the equipment and expertise to replicate a Soviet helicopter force. That got the unit included in the program.

Captain Vallimont also attended training on the use of NVGs. Based upon the findings from recent Red Flag exercises, the 20th was given 12 sets of AN/PVS-5 NVGs. Vallimont felt that once the already well-trained crews of the 20th were further trained and certified to use the NVGs, they could be just as mission effective at night, thus adding to their mission capability and threat survival. Initially, though, TAC authorized only limited training with the NVGs. Consequently, he and Weikel sent their crews out at night with NVGs, jeeps, and tactical maps and had them navigate all over the tactical ranges to develop basic NVG proficiency.

Additionally, Vallimont worked on a proposal to install a LORAN C/D navigational set on the unit helicopters. He flew with one on a UH-1N on a 50-kilometer flight, arriving within 80 meters of the target designated by the universal transverse mercator (UTM) and missing his time on target by 10 seconds. LORAN units were subsequently installed on two unit CH-3s. On one mission in the north Georgia mountains, the crew led a formation of 22 US Army helicopters on a 73-mile course and arrived within 10 seconds of the planned time. It also used the LORAN-equipped CH-3 to perform a combat recovery of a "survivor" in the mountains.

The unit participated in two exercises with Army special forces units in the Fort Bragg, North Carolina, area. In Solid Shield 78, the unit supported the Joint Unconventional Warfare Task Force, Atlantic, with two CH-3s and three crews who flew 116 hours, again using the LORAN with favorable results. Several missions included moving personnel and equipment on and off of ships, both day and night—valuable training for joint operations. In Operation Diamond Jim, unit crews inserted and extracted several small special forces teams at night using NVGs on the small islands along the Carolina coast.

As part of the J-CATCH project, the 20th deployed all of its helicopters, crews, and maintenance and support personnel to Fort Rucker, Alabama, to participate in air-to-air engagements with an opposing force of US Army helicopters. Serving as the red force, the 20th aircraft were "equipped" with various captive missiles and gun systems to replicate anticipated enemy threats and with video recording systems to record the engagements and flight parameters for data and kill analysis. Over a period of six weeks, unit crews flew in 54 events, logging 418 individual sorties and 432 flight hours. The data collected was voluminous and was forwarded to TAC for analysis and dissemination. Needless to say, all crew members enjoyed the experience and received a great deal of excellent and timely training.

All of these developments were encouraging and provided the crews with a heightened confidence that they could perform their increasingly joint missions as effectively as possible with the maximum chance of survival. At a commander's call, the crews were also briefed on a new USAF tactical air force (TAF) statement of operational need (SON), 313-79, for a new special-operations-capable aircraft as a viable replacement for both the CH-3 and UH-1N. One possible candidate could be the new H-60 that Sikorsky was developing primarily for rescue but that was certainly adaptable for other missions. The crews were also allowed to make suggestions as to the capabilities that such an aircraft should possess.[65]

As 1979 commenced, the 20th continued its participation in J-CATCH, flying air-to-air operations against fixed-wing opponents and then combinations of both fixed- and rotary-wing formations. The squadron eventually logged 700 flight hours on 547 sorties in all phases of the operational test. The tests generated a trove of information then used to develop classified TTP changes to both fixed- and rotary-wing crews to use against potential modern adversary aircraft. Major Grove participated in many of the J-CATCH missions and felt that they were particularly good training for the helicopter crews. He could also not help but notice the pointed cockiness that developed in his pilots as they quickly learned to use the natural advantages of their helicopters against the fighter aircraft. He recalls that

> our tactics were pretty much restricted to what we thought the Russians would do, except when it came to our fighters. The more arrogant they thought they were, the harder we fought with them. But it's easy to do in a helicopter because you just fly in a crab—you point the nose to one side or the other and go in the opposite direction. . . . Fighter guys couldn't figure out why we were pointing that way. . . . All you have to do is break lock once and you are home free. So we did that to them, . . . and that really pissed them off.[66]

Needless to say, the fighter guys did not like getting beaten by the helicopters. At a J-CATCH operations review conference, the TAC commander, Gen Wilbur "Bill" Creech, became irate when he was briefed on the exercise results. At one point, the Ninth Air Force commander, Lt Gen Arnold Braswell, visited the 20th and flew a mission in one of the CH-3s as it was engaged by F-15s. He was favorably impressed with the flight and unit and so told the assembled members. The 20th was gaining quite a reputation within the fighter community. It now was continuously getting invitations to various flag exercises, testimony to the realistic training the unit was conducting.[67]

On another occasion, the 20th guys were celebrating at the Officers' Club with some fighter guys, when one of the fighter "pukes" teased them about not wearing any distinctive colored scarves that were the staple of any well-dressed fighter pilot. Never one to miss the moment, Gary Weikel grabbed a red tablecloth, sliced it into sections with his boot knife, and handed the sections to his mates. They then wrapped them around their necks and tucked them down into their flight suits just above the zipper—totally nonregulation but in keeping with their independent and cocky ways. From that point on, the scarves were part of their attire. Picking up on the theme, the 20th SOS maintenance crews also draped a red tablecloth from their maintenance vehicle out on the flight line.[68]

Capt Joe Vallimont continued to expand the NVG training, and the 20th became the only USAF unit fully qualified to use NVGs. He and the tactics division were then directed to begin working with other special operations units to help them develop NVG capabilities. Additionally, the unit received authorization to equip all of its helicopters with RWRs optimized for helicopter use.

Throughout the year, the unit received ever more opportunities to jointly exercise with special forces elements from other services. These took place primarily at Fort Bragg or in the tactical ranges just north of Eglin AFB. By the end of 1979, the 20th had developed into a fiercely spirited and highly trained unit. Its pilots were capable of performing their disparate and demanding unit missions to the limits that their assigned aircraft would allow. Addressing the limitations of the assigned aircraft, the 1st SOW commander, Colonel Dunwoody, forwarded to Ninth Air Force a detailed list of requested improvements to the 20th SOS aircraft in early 1980. Citing the need for an overall new aircraft presented in TAF SON 313-79, he pointed out that the current 20th SOS aircraft needed the following upgrades to maintain mission viability:

1. New SOF helicopter to replace the general purpose CH-3 and UH-1N based on 1950s technology, per the validated but unfunded TAF SON 313-79.

2. Precision, self-contained navigation system to permit accurate night terrain flight at very low altitudes using NVGs.

3. CH-3 aerial refueling for worldwide deployment capability without dedicated strategic airlift and extensive teardown and buildup requirements.

4. Adequate number of NVG sets to meet mission needs.

5. Longer-range defensive systems, such as .50-caliber machine guns, and possibly Stinger or Hellfire missiles, as dictated by the threat environment.

6. Infrared countermeasures equipment for helicopters to jam, suppress, or provide shielding against heat-seeking missiles.

7. CH-3 engine upgrades to provide better performance at higher elevations.

8. UH-1N engine and/or rotor blade improvements to be able to carry full fuel loads and weaponry on longer-range tactical missions.[69]

Since its reactivation in January 1976, the 20th SOS—as the only special operations helicopter squadron in the active Air Force—had embraced its mission and developed a cadre of hard-charging men who aggressively pursued every avenue available to them to optimize their capability to accomplish that mission. They leveraged evolving navigational and NVG technology and seized upon available joint and air-to-air training opportunities to hone their skills. Acting almost as a human Petri dish, they formed, molded, and gestated a squadron that proved in inspections and exercises that they had rekindled the air commando spirit and were now limited only by their antiquated equipment.[70]

Aerospace Rescue and Recovery Service

The new year of 1979 started off badly for the ARRS when, in February, HH-53C #69-5787, assigned to the 33d ARRSq, crashed into the Pacific Ocean 53 miles northeast of Kadena AB. While refueling, the crew moved too far forward and hit the refueling hose with the main rotor blades. Collateral damage to the blades stimulated severe lateral vibrations and caused the tail rotor to separate. The aircraft crashed inverted near a coral reef, killing three crew members. The fourth man was rescued by a local fisherman.

Shortly thereafter, PACAF asked MAC/ARRS for another aircraft to make up for the loss. No new aircraft were being built. MAC subsequently coordinated with TAC and HQ USAF to move CH-53C #68-10923 from the 701st TASS at Bergstrom to Kirtland for training purposes, thus freeing up an HH-53 to be sent to the 33d ARRSq at Kadena. The 701st TASS was also ordered to inactivate on 1 January 1980.[71]

On 13 March 1979, the first production Pave Low III, HH-53H #69-5791, was rolled out of the hangar at Pensacola. Newly elected congressman Earl Hutto from the Pensacola area attended, as did the city's mayor and the commanders of the ASD and ARRS. Hutto's attendance was prescient. His congressional district also included Eglin AFB and Hurlburt Field, and in a few years, he would become a staunch champion of special operations forces in general and the Pave Low in particular. Addressing the crowd, William Craven, now a colonel, talked about the great challenges overcome to get to this point. He expressed that if the Black Knights had been available in SEA, perhaps the number of POWs would have been cut in half—a bittersweet commentary to the citizens of that Navy city, which had suffered more than its share of POWs during that long war. Colonel Pehr and crew then flew the aircraft to Robins AFB, Georgia; Andrews AFB, DC; and Wright-Patterson for static displays and orientation flights.[72]

Arriving at Kirtland AFB, the aircraft was used for more FOT&E designed to validate reliability standards, verify training programs, and evaluate technical data and evolving tactics. Immediately, weaknesses appeared in three key areas: the TFR gave low crossing altitudes when set to 100-foot clearance altitude, the inertial measuring unit (IMU) gave intermittent and erratic navigation performance, and the hover coupler caused vertical oscillations with the altitude hold feature engaged. Steadily, Frank Pehr, Steve Connelly, Rick Simmon, and the other 1550th personnel worked to resolve all discrepancies. Additionally, classes began for several new maintenance technicians needed for the new subsystems. The necessary manuals had not yet been published, and the Airmen had to work with various publications provided by the companies that had produced the individual components. Said SMSgt John Doyle, the senior Pave Low noncommissioned officer (NCO), "They [specialists] accept the challenge and don't gripe about the lack of information. . . . They are going to keep it working. They've had to go ahead and take it upon themselves, relying on their past experience. With this system, they have to be well versed in their avionics specialty." Quickly, too, they discovered that the integration of the various systems meant that many times, the fix to any particular problem required analysis and adjustments to several individual components. Maintenance on this aircraft required a "holistic" approach, and the maintenance technicians soon realized that they needed to know much more than just their individual specified specialties. Working with the pilots, they learned how to keep the aircraft operational. Said one of the technicians, TSgt Michael Mayhew, with a definite air of pride, "The plane wasn't just handed to us. We—the Air Force—built it, and we're taking out the bugs ourselves, . . . the pilots, we mechanics and the ASD people at Wright-Patterson."[73]

Capt Rus Stiles was now one of the test pilots working on the Pave Low FOT&E. After his duty in Southeast Asia with the 21st SOS, he had been transferred to Hawaii, where he flew for three years with the 6594th Test Group. The HH-53s assigned there, code-named Crested Rooster, were highly modified for the satellite recovery mission. They had INSs, an internal auxiliary fuel tank, and a winch/carriage system to recover the capsules. Many of the recoveries were hundreds of miles out in open ocean. Stiles had great respect for the PJs, who would, when necessary, jump out into open water to facilitate the recoveries. He also participated in a collateral recovery mission for a Japanese sailor who needed immediate medical care for a ruptured appendix. That was a 14.7-hour mission, one of the longest on record. Finishing that assignment in May 1977, he then proceeded to Webb AFB for fixed-wing conversion training and was subsequently posted to the US Navy Test Pilot School at Patuxent NAS, where he completed the rotary-wing test pilot course and qualified as a helicopter test pilot. From there, Stiles was posted to the 1550th ATTW, where he joined the test division in January 1979. Well aware of the Pave Low III project and intensely interested in new technology development and adaptation, he asked Colonel Pehr and Captain Connelly to allow him to work on Pave Low as one of his projects. He was assigned to do the maintenance and reliability analysis tracking and follow-on studies. Subsequently, Captain Stiles flew many sorties working with the TFR and initial use of NVGs with various iterations of cockpit lights. He was also able to use the experience he gained in Hawaii with the INS to work through issues with overall flight navigation system integration.[74]

Through the year, four more HH-53s, #73-1650, #73-1651, #73-1652, and #73-1649, went through the modification line, passed acceptance, and were also sent to Kirtland AFB for follow-on testing and validation. By year's end, they would be followed by #73-1647, #73-1648, #67-5790, and the prototype, #66-14433, which would also be formally modified to the HH-53H configuration but not completed until 1980.

Courtesy Lt Col Frank Pehr, USAF, Retired

Cabezon Peak, New Mexico, a well-known landmark used to calibrate and validate the TFR on the Pave Low

However, the modification schedule did not run that smoothly. The technicians at the NARF encountered numerous technical challenges that slowed the process for the last six aircraft, and the entire production line was slipped two and one-half months. This caused a cascading scheduling problem for the various crew and maintenance qualification classes at Kirtland AFB. The first two pilots for H-53 training and then Pave Low qualification had arrived in May and were slated to begin Pave Low training in September. However, their Pave Low training had to be slipped to January 1980, when they would join with four other pilots and six flight mechanics currently serving on HH-53s to attend the first Pave Low qualification course.

Maj Mark Schibler was in that first group. When his tour with the 40th at NKP ended in early 1973, he reported to Hill AFB to serve as an instructor on the HH-53 and the NRS system. While there, he also taught academics and worked with Frank Pehr, Steve Connelly, and Bob Stankovich to produce new HH-53 crews. Captains Backlund and Pacini also joined him there when they returned from SEA and flew with him several times on Red Flag exercises at Nellis as they worked to integrate NRS rescue operations into the large aerial war games being conducted there.

In early 1976, Schibler was reassigned to Nellis to join the Red Flag staff as a rescue liaison officer for the purposes of institutionalizing ARRS participation in the ongoing exercises. For the next three years, he worked closely with the exercise planners to coordinate rescue assets that would provide real-world rescue capability on-site, as well as to insure that the various commanders and staffs trained there learned how to integrate rescue forces into their overall theater warfare air campaign planning. Major Schibler also worked with A-7 and A-10 pilots to teach them rescue escort tactics so that they could provide direct support to the rescue helicopters, as the A-1s had so ably done in SEA. In the summer of 1979, he was ordered to Kirtland to requalify on the HH-53 and then to be one of the first line pilots to upgrade into the Pave Low in the first class. He also had follow-on orders to the 67th ARRSq in England.[75]

The delays in the aircraft modification schedule also affected the IP cadre at Kirtland being formed by Maj Lou Grant in the 1551st FTS, now commanded by Lt Col Jerry Shipman. Captain Comer arrived at Kirtland in January from his tour at Sembach to serve as a Pave Low IP. But there was a problem. Since he had not received his IP training from MAC, that command did not consider him qualified to teach at the school without first completing its IP course. Fortunately for Comer, the training squadron scheduling officer was Maj Barry Walls. Comer went to Walls, who was able to work Comer into the schedule to get the necessary qualifications he needed to be an HH-53 IP. Those were six long and frustrating months, and he spent a lot of time serving as a classroom and simulator instructor. Once he was qualified though, he was certified as a flight examiner and began to fly quite a bit in the non–Pave Low aircraft. However, he still had to wait his turn to get the Pave Low qualification.

Then fate intervened. Comer had been the top graduate in English studies in his class at the Air Force Academy, and he was invited to apply to be an English instructor there. Such an assignment would mean a break from operational flying. Comer weighed the plusses and minuses and decided to apply. He was subsequently interviewed and selected. His orders specified that he would depart Kirtland in March 1980 to report to the University of North Carolina to study for a master's degree in English, preparatory to his faculty assignment at the Air Force Academy.[76]

As Pehr, Connelly, Stankovich, and Simmon conducted the FOT&E testing at Kirtland, they determined that the aircraft was much more demanding on the aircrews than initially anticipated, and as a minimum, each aircrew member would need to fly at least 26 full Pave Low sorties every six months to maintain full aircraft currency. Such a schedule necessitated proper training areas, ideally close to the base. However, the first unit slated to get the aircraft, the 67th ARRSq at RAF Woodbridge, did not have adequate local areas for training of this intensity. This was a potentially huge issue that would need to be addressed if the Pave Lows were to be assigned there.[77]

Throughout the year, ARRS HH-53 crews were constantly engaged in operational exercises around the globe as well as in numerous civil SARs. The HH-53s from the 6594th Test Group at Hickam AFB also participated in the recovery of 19 sailors off of a sinking Japanese cargo ship 120 miles south of Hilo.

Rescue forces including HH-53s were also deployed on two occasions in response to international crises. The first deployment was ordered when fundamentalist Islamic elements rose up against Shah Mohammed Reza Pahlavi in Iran. Events began to spin out of control in late 1978 when riots broke out in several cities. In early 1979, as the violence escalated, the Joint Chiefs of Staff (JCS) directed MAC to deploy C-5s and C-141s to assist in evacuating American civilians. When the Shah subsequently abdicated his throne and left the country, he left behind a weak central government with little support from the people. An exiled Islamic leader, Ayatollah Ruhollah Khomeini, returned from France and called for the formation of an Islamic republic. Fighting broke out between his followers and the military and supporters of the standing government. Anti-American acts became more frequent, and a group of Iranians temporarily seized the US Embassy. Americans and selected foreigners rallied to the major airports, and MAC airlifters evacuated 5,732 passengers to sites in Europe. The JCS then directed the ARRS to provide six HH-53s from the 67th ARRSq at RAF Woodbridge to deploy with aerial refueling HC-130s and maintenance and support personnel to Incirlik, Turkey, and to be prepared to evacuate additional personnel as directed. Colonel Purvine, vice-commander of the 39th ARRW, led the deployment.

One of Purvine's HH-53 aircraft commanders was Capt Mike Russell. Russell had been commissioned into the USAF in 1972. After pilot training, he initially served as a T-37 IP at Craig AFB, Alabama. When that base closed down, he served for a short time in a non-rated job before receiving his HH-53 assignment to the 55th at Eglin. He enjoyed flying the H-53 and usually volunteered for the TDYs, including the Jonestown, Guyana, debacle. Russell had heard about Pave Low, especially all of the bad rumors. Assignment to the 67th in England intrigued him somewhat. However, he decided to stay right where he was at Eglin. When augmentees were needed to support the Turkey deployment, Russell raised his hand and was shortly on his way.[78]

The HH-53 aircraft, crews, and support troops departed Woodbridge on 12 February. However, weather problems delayed the arrival of all aircraft and personnel until 18 February. The appearance of the aircraft at Incirlik was reported by the world press. Sensitive to the changes sweeping Iran, the Turkish government forbade the carrying of any weapons on board the helicopters and directed that the crews not launch until cleared by the Iranian government. During the next several days, the political situation in Iran stabilized somewhat, and almost all Americans except for a skeleton crew in the embassy were able to depart the country. At the end of February, the rescue task force was directed to redeploy to their home stations, and the force of 225 ARRS personnel was completely home by 11 March. The crews on the HH-53s logged 226.6 flight hours on the operation.[79]

Three months later, the ARRS was called to provide another evacuation force, this time to Central America. When the forces of the Sandinista National Liberation Front overthrew the government of Pres. Anastasio Samoza Debayle of Nicaragua, the JCS directed the ARRS to establish a rescue task force to deploy in support of the US Southern Command (USSOUTHCOM) to evacuate Americans and selected foreigners from that nation. Accordingly, a task force of four HH-53s and crews, commanded by Col Barry Kamhoot, was collected from three different bases. The aircraft deployed with five supporting HC-130s for Howard AFB in the Panama Canal Zone, with most arriving by 21 June. Again, one of the pilots was Captain Russell from the 55th ARRSq at Eglin.[80]

As the situation continued to deteriorate in Nicaragua, US-SOUTHCOM stepped up efforts to evacuate as many Americans as possible by civilian and military transport aircraft. As the remaining Americans were again consolidated in the US Embassy, USSOUTH-COM directed the HH-53s to move forward to the Llano Grande Airport in Liberia, Costa Rica. However, their arrival generated strong opposition from the civilian populace in Costa Rica, who especially objected to the fact that the Americans were armed. Colonel Kamhoot then ordered the helicopters back to Howard AFB, and the US Navy positioned the USS *Saipan*, an amphibious assault ship off of the east coast of Nicaragua, and A-7s and AC-130s were readied at Albrook AFB, Panama, to provide fire support if necessary.

The four HH-53s then deployed aboard the *Saipan* and assumed alert posture there. On 18 July, as the government fell to the Sandinistas, all crews assumed immediate alert in their aircraft. However, all American personnel still in the country were able to depart in C-130s, and the HH-53s never launched. As the Sandinistas then consolidated their control of the nation, the situation quieted down, and the rescue task force was released to return home. The four HH-53s and crews stayed aboard the *Saipan* as it proceeded to Guantanamo Bay, Cuba. From there, they flew back to their home bases. The HH-53s and their crews logged 251 flight hours in the operation.[81]

Another one of the HH-53 pilots was Capt Ed Reed. He had graduated from the Citadel in 1975 with a USAF commission and had gone directly to helicopter pilot training at Fort Rucker. He did well in the course, especially enjoying the low-level navigation, and selected an assignment to HH-53s. Reed was in the last group of HH-53 crew members to report to Hill AFB before the entire training program was moved to Kirtland AFB. In fact, his group did its simulator training there and proceeded to Kirtland for flight training. He then reported to the 41st ARRSq at McClellan, where he was one of a few lieutenants among several SEA veteran lieutenant colonels and majors. The older Airmen mentored the younger troops and instilled in them a real passion for the rescue mission, along with a few nonregulation tricks and endless war stories. Reed got the opportunity to upgrade to aircraft commander and qualify on the (now antiquated) NRS aircraft. He also flew long-distance sorties on both the Jonestown and Nicaragua missions. Reed had watched the scenes of the last Americans fleeing Saigon in 1975 while still at the Citadel, and the pictures now coming out of Nicaragua looked very similar. He waited on the

Saipan with the others for the order to launch, which never came. Returning to McClellan AFB, he began preparations to move to RAF Woodbridge to join the 67th ARRSq as that unit converted to the Pave Low III aircraft due to arrive there in the not-too-distant future. He had seen the aircraft when Pehr and Connelly brought it up to McClellan for a visit and decided that he wanted to fly that machine. He was going to get his wish.[82]

Pave Low

For all the testing, studies, and training, though, Pave Low was still just a concept. While the dramatic test missions proved that the system would perform as expected, it took an unforeseen event to conclusively prove that Pave Low III would actually do what it was designed to do. That event occurred just a few miles northwest of Kirtland AFB on a low overcast Friday night in January 1980.

After a day of primarily maintenance checks and engine runs on HH-53H #73-1652, just recently received from the NARF at Pensacola, the crew chief put the aircraft in the hanger and started accomplishing the last postflight items. Captain Connelly happened to walk through the small flight operations center when one of the operations controllers said, "Hey, there has been a crash out on the Albuquerque mesa."

A quick check with the control tower confirmed that, indeed, a small private aircraft had gone down. A light commercial helicopter had tried to fly into the area but could not get in because of low clouds and fog. The weather was worsening, and Kirtland AFB itself was about to close for traffic. Connelly was asked if he could take off in the Pave Low to find the wreckage and possibly recover any survivors. He said that he would and then told the crew chief to get the aircraft ready to fly. Next, he called the bowling alley to get Sergeant Simmon and MSgt John Adrian as his flight mechanics. When he "confirmed" that they had not yet had any alcohol, he directed them to get their flight gear and meet him at the aircraft. They dutifully excused themselves from their wives and proceeded. Connelly also asked for two PJs to accompany them and checked with the new wing commander, Colonel Purvine, who granted permission for the flight. Connelly was impressed that Purvine had such confidence in the aircraft and the crew that would be flying it. Connelly then called the 1551st FTS and procured Maj Barry Walls to fly as his copilot.

When the crew members arrived at the aircraft, they discovered that it was still warm from earlier engine runs and that the crew chief and Connelly had already aligned the INS and started up the systems. By the time they were aboard and had the engines running, the weather had completely moved in, and the airfield was closed. Connelly gave Walls a basic brief on the Pave Low system and loaded the survivor's reported position into the navigation computer. Then they taxied out and took off into a very dark night at 7:00 p.m. Barry Walls said, "When we took off, I immediately had vertigo for the rest of the flight."

The pilots checked in with departure control for potential traffic and terrain separation, then turned northwest toward the crash site, descended to 100 feet AGL, and began using the TF/TA radar and FLIR. Connelly was well familiar with the area and was comfortable flying there at such low altitudes. The pilots turned on their spotlight and could barely see the ground. Connelly made several passes over the reported location before finally seeing some lights. As they flew over, Simmon stored the position in the central navigation computer. Connelly then set up an approach to the position and came to a hover 100 feet above it. Nobody on board could see the ground, so he descended in the hover until the crew was able to see the crash site, and Connelly maneuvered the aircraft 100 feet away and landed. The PJs immediately deplaned, rushed to the crash, and began treating the injured pilot, a Catholic priest. Fortunately, the crash site was near Interstate 40, and police and news crews were already on site. The pararescue specialists had their pictures taken as they treated the pilot.

Connelly did not shut down the engines. He noticed, though, that he was slowly losing oil pressure in the transmission and told the specialists to hurry, or they would have to spend the night right where they were. They immediately moved the injured pilot to the helicopter, and Connelly took off. The airfield was still closed, and he used his TF radar to climb above the terrain and obstacles and then guided on the instrument landing system to align with the runway and land about 1,000 feet past the threshold and on the centerline. The elapsed time from takeoff to landing was 55 minutes, and a valid save was logged. The after action report said it best: "This successful employment of Pave Low III under actual night adverse weather conditions brings us in ARRS a long way from the dreams we had for NRS in the late 1960s."

Technologically, Pave Low had come to fruition, and all of the skeptics had been proven wrong. Pehr was ecstatic over the mission and expected MAC to fund the modification of more HH-53s. However, that was another battle for another time. Reflecting on the accomplishment, though, from a longer perspective, Lt Col Ken Ernest, a bloodied veteran of the heroic rescues of 1972 and now the assistant project manager, said, "In Vietnam, what you had was one little war for the rescue mission. . . . Now we can sneak in at night, comfortably and solo. . . . I'll tell you, it's hard to describe the feeling when you had a guy down on 'Thud Ridge' with a beeper and darkness set in and you had to go home without him. With Pave Low's new capability—thank God!—we won't be in that position anymore."[83]

Returning from the long war in SEA, the helicopters and crews of the combined H-53 fleet were dispersed to other locations around the globe. The CH-53s were reassigned to direct duty to provide mobility support for USAF TACS units in Germany and Texas. The HH-53s were dispatched to rescue units in the CONUS, Europe, and the Pacific.

The ARRS and MAC continued and expanded the Pave Low III development project, and as the 1970s were ending, that project, initially stimulated by SEAOR 114 in 1967 and transformed into MAC ROC 19-70, was finally coming to fruition. Nine aircraft were either modified to the HH-53H configuration or were in line to do so. Training courses were being readied and initial crews being selected. Based upon operational needs, an initial beddown base had been identified and was being prepared. Finally, the rescue forces of the USAF would have a day/night, all-weather rescue capability—a fact dramatically demonstrated on a cold wintry night at Kirtland AFB in January 1980. The rescue forces had finally achieved their long-sought capability, but it was perhaps constrained by uneven enthusiasm on the part of some ARRS commanders.

During the same period, TAC reactivated one special operations helicopter unit, but it was equipped with older UH-1 and CH-3 helicopters. The organization was of limited value other than as a repository of vast tactical and practical helicopter experience that resided in the cocky attitude of just a few hard-charging young captains and majors. Although suffused with enthusiasm, the unit was greatly constrained by equipment capability.

Regardless, troubling events were occurring in other parts of the world. The rescue deployments in 1979 to Central America and the Middle East portended perhaps turbulent times ahead in those particular regions, further reinforced when the Sandinista forces consolidated their hold on Nicaragua. On 4 November 1979, American diplomats, military personnel, and private citizens were taken hostage at the US Embassy in Tehran, Iran.

As the decade ended, nobody could foresee that within barely six months MAC's entire Pave Low plan would be in tatters and that those Pave Low III aircraft and crews would be presented with a much different demand for their services, leading to a fortuitous combination of capabilities and enthusiasm that would bring Pave Low to its full potential.

Notes

1. History of 601st TCW, 1 Apr–30 Sept 1975, vol. 1, 8; ibid., 1 Jan–31 Mar 1975, vol. 1, xx, app. A; The Pave Cave, MH-53H/J/M Pave Low community website, http://www.thepavecave.com; and Whitcomb, *Combat Search and Rescue in Desert Storm*, 28.

2. Comer, interview.

3. History of ARRS, 1 July 1974–31 Dec 1975, vol. 1, 31; and Gen John Vogt, USAF oral history interview, transcript, 197, AFHRA.

4. History of ARRS, 1 July 1974–31 Dec 1975, vol. 1, 6, 16–19, 31, 62, CD–12.

5. Boivin, Schmidt, and Balfe, *Pave Low—Evaluation of a Terrain Following Radar System for the HH–53 Helicopter*, Technical Report no. 73–11, 48.

6. Pehr, interview.

7. Gambone, *Pave Low III: That Others May Live*, 15–18.

8. Ibid., 4, 18.

9. Pehr, interview.

10. Simmon, interview; and Stiles to the author, e-mail, review comments.

11. Gambone, *Pave Low III: That Others May Live*, 70.

12. Ibid., 73; Pehr, interview; and Stiles to the author, e-mail.

13. Gambone, *Pave Low III: That Others May Live*, 95–96.

14. Ibid., 103–5; and Connelly to the author, e-mail, review comments.

15. Simmon, interview.

16. History of ARRS, 1 July 1974–31 Dec 1975, vol. 1, 66.

17. Gambone, *Pave Low III: That Others May Live*, exhibit 22, 121–23; and "Pave Low III Qualification/Acceptance Tests," July 1981, in ibid., vol. 2, supplemental doc. 6, v.

18. Gambone, *Pave Low III: That Others May Live*, 133–34.

19. Ibid., exhibit 27.

20. Ibid., 149.

21. History of the 1st Special Operations Wing (hereafter referred to as History of 1st SOW), 1 Jan–31 Mar 1976, vol. 1, 1–9.

22. Ibid.; and Weikel, interview.

23. Mutza, *Green Hornets*, 56.

24. History of 1st SOW, 1 July–30 Sept 1976, vol. 1, 1–9.

25. Whitcomb, *Combat Search and Rescue in Desert Storm*, 18; and Tyner, *AF Rescue and AFSOF*, 9–10.

26. Weikel, interview.

27. "Operational Test and Evaluation: Pave Low III," HQ MAC report, B–1; and Simmon, interview.

28. "Operational Test and Evaluation: Pave Low III," HQ MAC report, iv, 28–29.

29. Ibid.

30. History of ARRS, 1 Jan–31 Dec 1976, vol. 1, 63; and Connelly and Pehr, interviews.

31. History of ARRS, 1 Jan–31 Dec 1976, vol. 1, 64.

32. Whitcomb, *Combat Search and Rescue in Desert Storm*, 17.

33. History of ARRS, 1 Jan–31 Dec 1976, vol. 1, 37.

34. Ibid., 22, 34–35. See also Koskinas, *Black Hats and White Hats*, for an eloquent discussion of this issue.

35. History of ARRS, 1 Jan–31 Dec 1976, vol. 1, 75–77, 80–84.

36. Ibid., 92.

37. History of 1st SOW, 1 Oct–31 Dec 1977, vol. 1, 1–13.

38. Ibid.; ibid., 1 Jan–31 Mar 1977, vol. 1, 1–12; and ibid., 1 July–30 Sept 1977, vol. 1, 1–10.

39. Weikel to the author, e-mail, 25 Mar 2009.

40. Ibid.; and Grove, interview.

41. History of ARRS, 1 Jan–31 Dec 1977, vol. 1, 4–5.

42. Ibid., 58.

43. Ibid., 20.

44. Ibid., vol. 2, supplemental doc. no. 103.

45. Ibid.

46. History of the 1550th Aircrew Training and Test Wing (hereafter referred to as History of 1550th ATTW), 1 July–31 Dec 1977, vol. 2, doc. 8.

47. History of ARRS, 1 Jan–31 Dec 1977, vol. 1, 65–68.

48. Ibid., 79–80.

49. Ibid., 1 Jan–31 Dec 1978, vol. 1, 23–24; and ibid., vol. 2, supplemental doc. I–74.

50. Connelly, interview.

51. Ibid.

52. Stankovich, interview.

53. Teeple, interview.

54. Simmon, interview.

55. Connelly and Pehr, interviews; and History of 1550th ATTW, 1 July–31 Dec 1978, vol. 1, 5.

56. Connelly, interview.

57. Ibid.

58. Connelly and Pehr, interviews.

59. Ibid.

60. Pehr, interview.

61. Connelly, interview.

62. History of ARRS, 1 Jan–31 Dec 1978, vol. 1, 60–63.

63. Ibid., 62–64.

64. Ibid., 76–81.

65. History of 1st SOW, 1 Jan–31 Mar 1978, vol. 1, 1–20; ibid., 1 Apr–30 June 1978, 1–13; and ibid., 1 Oct–31 Dec 1978, vol. 1, 24–26.

66. Grove, interview.

67. Ibid.

68. Weikel, interview; and 1st SOW/History Office (HO), file 120.00. However, there are many variations to this story.

69. 1st SOW/CC to 9AF/CC, letter, subject: Special Operations Capability Requirements, 7 Mar 1980, in History of 1st SOW, 1 Jan–31 Mar 1980, vol. 2.

70. History of 1st SOW, 1 Jan–30 June 1979, vol. 1, 1–6.

71. History of ARRS, 1 Jan–31 Dec 1979, vol. 1, 100–102.

72. Gambone, *Pave Low III: That Others May Live*, 207; History of ARRS, 1 Jan–31 Dec 1979, vol. 1, 107; and Hutto, *Captain Supreme Goes to Washington*, 238.

73. Pugh, "New Eyes for the Giant," 31–33.

74. Stiles, interview; and History of 1550th ATTW, 1 July–31 Dec 1979, vol. 1, 10.

75. Schibler, interview.

76. Commander's assessment, 23 May 1979, in History of 1550th ATTW, 1 Jan–30 June 1979; ibid., 1 July–31 Dec 1979, 5; and Comer, interview.

77. History of ARRS, 1 Jan–31 Dec 1979, vol. 1, 108–10.

78. Russell, interview.

79. History of ARRS, 1 Jan–31 Dec 1979, vol. 1, 116–20.

80. Russell, interview.

81. History of ARRS, 1 Jan–31 Dec 1979, vol. 1, 121–25.

82. Reed, interview.

83. Gambone, *Pave Low III: That Others May Live*, 223; Connelly and Simmons, interviews; and Pugh, "New Eyes for the Giant," 33.

Chapter 5

Necessity to Nadir

~1980–84

The jewels in the crown of our helo fleet were the . . . Pave Low H-53s.

—Maj Gen Richard Secord, USAF

Kirtland AFB, New Mexico

Just a few weeks after his rescue mission up on the Albuquerque flats, Capt Steve Connelly was assigned another engineering project of sorts. Delays incurred in the recent deployments of rescue aircraft and support teams indicated that the tactical procedures for mobilizing and shipping the helicopters needed to be analyzed and streamlined. While self-deployment of the aircraft was the preferred option, for longer-range movements, time/distance tradeoffs had to be considered. Connelly was directed to conduct a mobilization drill to generate the data for safe and quick loading of HH-3s, HH-53s, and, specifically, the HH-53Hs for deployment aboard C-5 aircraft.

Connelly received a nine-man team led by a senior maintenance NCO for each aircraft. The team had to determine the minimum teardown requirements for each machine, capture the amount of time required, catalog the necessary procedures and possible tech order changes needed for tactical load procedures, and determine the necessary team skill requirements needed. Over a two-day period, team members disassembled the aircraft as necessary to fit them into the C-5. This required them to remove the main rotor blades, one tail rotor blade, the main rotor head and gearbox, tip tanks, and sponson pylons. The crews saved cargo space by storing many of the components inside the helicopter or by building special cradles for the outsize items such as the blades. After each aircraft was loaded, it had to then be unloaded and test flown.

The test clearly showed that two aircraft of either model could be successfully loaded aboard a C-5 and that the nine-man team was optimum for the procedure. Suggested changes to tech order data were drafted for both helicopters and the C-5s. The computed total time of the entire operation from teardown through arrival test flight was 24.5 hours for the HH-53s and 20.5 hours for the H-3s. The test also confirmed that the C-5 was the optimum option for deployments beyond 2,500 miles from current H-3 or H-53 locations. Connelly was pleased with the results. He had to wonder, though, at the timing of the test. Rumors were running rampant about some kind of operation in the Middle East, possibly involving the American hostages in Iran. Of late, officers from Headquarters MAC had been on the base soliciting helicopter crew volunteers for something, but—whatever it was—it was close-hold information. Several weeks later, Colonel Pehr was read into the mission, one of very few on the base who were so briefed. However, he was not invited to join the effort.[1]

Aerospace Rescue and Recovery Service

As the new decade began, the Pave Low program was rapidly approaching fruition. Five aircraft had been modified and were back at Kirtland, where follow-on testing was being conducted and the initial flight and maintenance crews were being trained. As per MAC Programming Plan 78-18, the first two HH-53Hs would be deployed to RAF Woodbridge, UK, in March 1980. There they would be assigned to the 67th ARRSq, slated to become operational with the aircraft in April 1981, thereby fulfilling a long-standing requirement for day/night, all-weather combat capability for USAFE.

Unfortunately, though, worrisome problems began to appear. British authorities balked when they discovered the amount of night and low-level flying the Pave Lows would need to do. In fact, at the beginning of the year, they had just established restrictions against any night flying below 1,000 feet between the hours of 2300 and 0700. USAFE and MAC representatives met with British Ministry of Defense representatives at RAF Mildenhall in January. The British made it clear that no immediate resolution of the problem was possible.

The MAC staff scrambled to develop alternative options. When briefed, the MAC vice-commander, Gen Thomas Ryan, directed that the Pave Lows be reassigned to the 41st ARRSq at McClellan AFB, near Sacramento, California, and ordered that all aircraft and personnel transfers to Woodbridge be stopped. HQ USAF initially concurred with the action but, citing war-fighting needs, directed MAC and USAFE to either work out the UK basing issues or establish a war plan to rapidly move the HH-53Hs to forward European bases for contingencies. Subsequent in-depth analysis by the MAC staff indicated that McClellan had all of the facilities and flying areas necessary for full Pave Low beddown and training. Additionally, the recent mobility testing at Kirtland provided the necessary planning data to rapidly deploy the unit to Europe if necessary. After considering and favorably reviewing all factors, the Office of the Secretary of the Air Force announced on 27 March 1980 that all nine of the Pave Lows would now be assigned to the 41st ARRSq at McClellan. MAC then published Programming Plan 80-6 directing the move and also ordering the 41st to send its currently assigned HH-53Cs to the 55th ARRSq at Eglin to make room for the Pave Lows.[2]

On 16 April 1980, the NARF at Pensacola completed modification of the last of the HH-53s, #66-14433, and returned it to the Air Force for ferry to Kirtland. All of the alterations had been completed on time and almost $2 million under budget. MAC finally had a tried and proven fleet of Pave Low helicopters capable of performing all-weather, day/night rescues.[3]

Crisis in Iran

On 22 April, the 1550th ATTW received a short-notice order to deploy two Pave Low aircraft with crews and a maintenance team to a classified location to support Exercise Flintlock '80. Steve Connelly and Frank Pehr were given the mission and were able to put into practice the lessons learned in the mobility project in which Connelly had participated two months prior.

Maj Mark Schibler would also go along as one of the mission pilots. He had just completed his initial upgrade in the Pave Low and was about to start IP qualification. Schibler enjoyed flying the HH-53 again and quickly felt comfortable handling the aircraft. However, he found the Pave Low avionics, integrated systems, and computers intimidating. He was also impressed with the amount of crew coordination necessary to properly fly the Pave Low, especially the critical role that the flight engineers now played in flying the aircraft. Until recently, they had been designated as flight mechanics. However, the Air Force changed their title to correspond to the enlisted flight positions on fixed-wing aircraft and to reflect their status as an integral part of the flight crew vice maintenance personnel. Schibler remembers that "the [flight] engineer became a backup to the pilots . . . and ran the equipment that the pilot flying could no longer access. . . . He was a big part of the cross-check."[4]

MSgt Rick Simmon was one of the flight engineers assigned to the mission, and the crews and aircraft departed the next day aboard C-5s en route to Dover AFB, Delaware, and then on to Bahrain. There they would assume SAR alert for a mission being conducted to recover the American hostages held in the American Embassy in Tehran. While crossing the Mississippi River, though, they were notified that the rescue force had suffered a terrible crash and that the mission had been aborted. They proceeded on to Dover, where they remained for a day, and then were ordered to return to Kirtland, where they learned the horrible details of what had happened at a remote site in the Iranian desert called Desert One.[5]

The debacle at Desert One began the previous November, when radical supporters of Imam Ayatollah Khomeini seized the American Embassy in Tehran as his minions overthrew the Iranian government. In the seizure, they captured 53 Americans, who were now being held hostage in the embassy compound. Pres. Jimmy Carter ordered the US military to prepare a recovery operation. Defense secretary Harold Brown and JCS chairman Gen David Jones directed Maj Gen James Vaught, USA, to form JTF 1-79 to carry out the mission. Assigned to assist him were Maj Gen Philip Gast, USAF, as a special advisor and Col Jim Kyle, USAF, as his air deputy. The assigned mission was direct: "Prepare a plan and train a force to rescue American citizens illegally held in Iran, and be prepared to execute it 'ON ORDER.' "[6]

Vaught named the project Operation Rice Bowl. Over the next five months, JTF 1-89 was assigned US Army Soldiers from the Special Forces Operational Detachment–Delta (SFOD-Delta), activated two years prior and commanded by Col Charlie Beckwith. A USAF element, it consisted of MC-, EC-, and AC-130s and combat controllers from the 1st SOW; a US Navy squadron of RH-53D helicopters capable of operating from aircraft carriers; as well as a large support force from the various services.

The mission would involve moving the force with the MC- and EC-130s to Desert One. The AC-130s would provide direct, on-call fire support. As the tasking came down to Hurlburt, the wing units shifted into high gear to train for the mission. Still working in the wing tactics office, Capt Gary Weikel was read into the program. While he tried to define a need for the 20th SOS in the mission, he clearly saw no role for the unit's aircraft. Weikel's suggestion that many pilots like himself at Hurlburt and throughout the USAF, experienced in flying such missions in HH- and CH-53s, could enthusiastically contribute to the mission was for naught. US Navy pilots from Helicopter Mine Countermeasures Squadron 16 (HM-16) would fly the helicopters. They would launch off of aircraft carriers and join the force at Desert One. The Soldiers would transfer to the helicopters for the flight to a hide site 50 miles from Tehran. The Army assault force would then move to the embassy by truck. A smaller unit would also move to retrieve three hostages being held at another location. After recovering the hostages, the force would move to a soccer field in the city. The helicopters would then pick them up and move them to the air base at Manzariyeh, 40 miles southeast of Tehran, where C-141s would be waiting to fly them all to safety.[7]

It was an ambitious plan and required many of the elements to do things they had never trained to do. Regardless, the various teams began working together to develop the synergy and cohesion necessary to enter the hostile city and bring home the hostages. As the training proceeded, though, it became clear that the US Navy pilots assigned to the mission were not up to the task, as determined by their poor performance on early rehearsals. After a mission review, USMC pilots from tactical units largely replaced them. A USAF captain, Russell "Rotor" Rakip, a CH-53 standardization and evaluation pilot assigned to the 701st TASS at Bergstrom, also joined the task force.

USAF Helicopter Reorganization

Observing the difficulties that the Rice Bowl task force was having in developing the necessary helicopter component, Lt Gen Charles Gabriel, the USAF DCS for operations, plans, and readiness, decided to reinitiate the on-again-off-again intra-USAF discussion of consolidating all USAF helicopters under a single manager. He believed that dispersing the existing 244 helicopters among commands with units assigned to specific missions (e.g., combat rescue; special operations; or tactical air control system, tactical range, or missile site support) would allow them not only to better accomplish their assigned functions but also to improve their support of special taskings such as Rice Bowl.

Gabriel sent a message to General Gast, now serving as the vice-commander of TAC, with copies to his contemporaries at MAC, SAC, PACAF, and USAFE, suggesting that to address both issues, such a force could be formed under a reinvigorated AFSOF headquarters or hub that could then function as a counterpart to the Army's John F. Kennedy Center at Fort Bragg. He further recommended using the 1st SOW at Hurlburt Field as the basis for such an organization. The responses were generally supportive. MAC responded that it was anxious to be part of any new SOF structure. USAFE stated that the current fragmentation of SOF forces among several commands was counter-productive and suggested a possible consolidation of combat rescue forces into any new AFSOF structure. PACAF endorsed the idea and the consolidation of combat rescue forces into the new structure. However, the discussion was tabled as the events in Iran unfolded.[8]

Desert One

The eight RH-53Ds of HM-16 would launch from the aircraft carrier USS *Nimitz* and fly to Desert One. From that point, the operation needed a minimum of six to continue. On 24 April, all forces were in place; President Carter gave the order to execute Rice Bowl. As the sun set over Iran, the disparate elements of the task force began to move. The RH-53s lifted off of the carrier at 7:05 p.m. and entered Iranian airspace at low level. Almost two hours later, as the formation was about 145 miles inside Iran, the commander of aircraft number six landed his machine when a warning light indicating a serious problem with his main rotor blades illuminated. Helicopter number eight landed with him, recovered the crew and all classified material, and then relaunched to rejoin the flight.

In the clear night air, the helicopter crews could see the M/EC-130s proceeding to Desert One. The good visibility ended a few minutes later when the helicopters entered a dust storm. The pilots had to tuck in tight to hold formation. This increased their workload, made even more uncomfortable by the fine sand grit leaking into the cockpit and an air temperature that had risen to about 100 degrees Fahrenheit. When the flight leader in aircraft one could no longer see the ground, he made a left 180-degree turn. The pilots in number two saw him and

Courtesy AFSOC History Office

US Navy RH-53Ds aboard the USS *Nimitz*

followed. The other five aircraft did not see the maneuver and proceeded on course. The group of seven helicopters was now scattered and badly disorganized. More importantly, the pilots were becoming unnerved as they guzzled water and tried to keep the sweat and grit from getting in their eyes. They increasingly began to suffer disorientation and vertigo, and all realized that they had never trained for a mission like this.

The formation experienced further misfortune when the number five aircraft suffered a series of failures to the primary flight and navigation systems. Its aircraft commander decided to turn back. He made a right 180-degree turn and set course for the *Nimitz*, with the full realization that the aircraft barely had enough fuel to do so.

The other six helicopters pressed on and, after five tense hours of flying, arrived at Desert One. They parked behind the waiting C-130s and began refueling. All aircraft still had their engines running as the Army troops began to marshal onto their assigned helicopters. Unfortunately, the number two helicopter arrived with a serious hydraulic malfunction. USAF colonel Jim Kyle was the air commander and discussed this with the crew and senior Marine officer on site. They agreed that the aircraft could not be flown, leaving five aircraft available. However, all planning and analysis had determined that six aircraft were needed to continue to the next stage of the operation. Kyle then discussed the situation with Beckwith, the Army commander, and recommended that the mission be aborted. Colonel Beckwith reported this to General Vaught, who forwarded the recommendation to Washington. President Carter was then briefed and concurred with the recommendation.

At Desert One, the Army troops returned to the C-130s while the flyable helicopters were ordered to return to the *Nimitz* as soon as they refueled. Helicopter number two would be destroyed in place. To expedite the refueling of the helicopters, numbers three and four had to be air taxied to new positions. As number three lifted off, though, its pilot became disoriented by the billowing dust and collided with one of the MC-130s. The resulting explosion and fire engulfed the area as men scrambled away from the burning wreckage. Working through the chaos, Colonel Kyle, subordinate commanders, and NCOs worked feverishly to bring some semblance of order to organize the departure. The collision, fire, and secondary explosions caused collateral damage to three of the helicopters. The senior Marine ordered his crews to abandon all the helicopters and get on the C-130s. Kyle began releasing the C-130s to take off and got on the last one when he was sure nobody had been left behind. Sitting in the

Courtesy AFSOC History Office

Debacle at Desert One

back of the aircraft surrounded by demoralized and wounded Soldiers, Airmen, and Marines, Kyle tried to reckon the losses and understand what had gone wrong. Eight Airmen and Marines were killed in the crash, and five more were seriously wounded. It was a somber flight back to their staging base at Masiriah.[9]

The postmortems began immediately. All key leaders were swiftly flown back to Washington for debrief. Within two weeks the JCS had commissioned a special operations review group to conduct a "broad examination of the planning, organization, coordination, direction, and control of the Iranian hostage rescue mission, as a basis for recommending improvement in these areas for the future." Quickly dubbed the Holloway Commission after its leader, Adm James Holloway, USN, retired, the group dug intensely through the entire operation before releasing its findings in late August. It would identify a plethora of issues, from command and control to weather support. However, the group quickly sensed significant issues with the helicopter portion of the effort, citing questions on the number of helicopters assigned—which could easily have been increased—and especially on pilot selection. While USN and USMC pilots had been selected because of expediency and their skill in the aircraft, they lacked familiarity with the mission. At the time, the USAF had 114 pilots qualified on HH/CH-53s and another 86 with relatively recent experience on them. Given these pilots' background, the commission members believed that some of the pilots could easily have converted to the RH-53Ds and accomplished the mission.[10] The report stated,

> The real question to be addressed is: is transition to a new and highly complex mission in the same aircraft more or less difficult for an experienced pilot to master than transition to an aircraft variant in the same mission? Mastering a new, difficult, and more complex mission requires a pilot to acquire and hone new skills and more importantly, a new mind-set. Transitioning from an HH- or CH-53 to an RH-53 requires only learning a few new flight parameters and slightly altering already established procedures, something every experienced pilot has done several times. This point is not new. Experience gained in Project "Jungle Jim" (circa 1961) illustrated that learning new and vastly different complex mission skills is far more difficult than transitioning to an aircraft of similar design and performance characteristics.[11]

The specific reference to Project Jungle Jim is instructive, particularly since one of the commission members, Maj Gen John Piotrowski, USAF, served with the Jungle Jim team in South Vietnam in 1961 as a young pilot.

Colonel Kyle, the air component commander, felt that the Navy/Marine pilots showed poor judgment at several points and should have been leavened with experienced USAF H-53 pilots. His Army counterpart, Colonel Beckwith, the Delta Force commander, had an even more pungent view of the pilots. He thought that they simply did not have the necessary skills or attitude for the mission: "We were looking for aces, daredevils, barnstormers, guys who flew by the seat of their pants, hot rodders, pilots who could pick it up, turn it around on a dime and put it back down with flair. These Navy pilots didn't believe in taking the risks we knew were required of the pilots flying into an enemy-held city."[12] Perhaps Beckwith's words should be tempered somewhat—to many he seemed to have a bias against anyone on the task force who was not Delta. Mark Bowden in his book *Guests of the Ayatollah* noted that "it had not been lost on the other commanders working with him, most of whom outranked Beckwith, that the pugnacious colonel regarded them all as inferiors, as supporting players. The pilots, navigators, the aircrews, the fuel equipment operators, the rangers, the combat controllers . . . were all ordinary mortals, squires, spear-carriers, water boys. Their job was to serve Delta, to get his magnificent men in place for their rendezvous with destiny."[13]

As Beckworth had built up the SFOD-Delta organization over a long process of several years and had trained his pilots to such an edge, his frustrations were certainly understandable. At one point at Desert One, as he realized that only five helicopters were capable of continuing, he believed that the USMC pilots wanted to scuttle the mission. Not familiar with the complexity of the helicopters, he felt that the problem was not one of failed equipment but of faltering courage.[14] Regardless, it is somewhat disheartening to recall that just five years earlier, the USAF had two squadrons—the 40th ARRSq and the 21st SOS at NKP, Thailand—that performed challenging long-range missions similar to Rice Bowl at Phnom Penh, Saigon, and Koh Tang Island. Notably, during the initial response planning that followed the taking of the hostages, the Air Force considered using its special operations helicopters. Lt Gen William Boykin, then a young captain assigned to SFOD-Delta and quickly detailed to the Pentagon planning team, later recalled that "a Spec Ops colonel said: 'We're looking at going in on Air Force helos. Spec Ops has CH-53s, so we're looking at those and Army Chinooks to see if they can play a role.' "[15]

The results suggest that perhaps the 40th and 21st individually, or in some combination or derivation, were the missing piece at Desert

One. They were considered, at least initially, but were not available. Regrettably, their absence was the result of USAF leadership taking a particular course of action. Instead of bringing the squadrons back from Thailand as formed and cohesive units, like the AC-130-equipped 16th SOS when it returned to Hurlburt Field, the two units were inactivated and their equipment and personnel disbursed around the world. Perhaps more disappointing was the decision to take the CH-53s from the 21st SOS and assign them to logistical support vice SOF duties. Colonel Kyle certainly thought so, writing later that "Special Ops had recently taken another blow . . . when some myopic planner gave all of our heavy-lift [CH-53] choppers to a tactical communications unit. This left us without the means to deliver assault forces deep into enemy territory—short-sightedness that would come back to haunt us."[16]

Why wasn't an extant ARRS squadron used for the mission as at Son Tay? USMC colonel Charles Pittman was the senior Marine aviation planner and officer in charge of the Marine pilots assigned to Rice Bowl. A few years later, while he was visiting the Army Command and General Staff College at Fort Leavenworth, Kansas, one of the USAF students there asked why the military had not used ARRS helicopters and avoided refueling in the desert. Pittman replied that "when we called the Air Force special operations folks, they answered that the Air Force could not do the mission. All they had were some Huey gunships and some old CH-3Es. At that point, we [hung] up the phone and looked at the Marines."

That was certainly true enough. But when the student persisted with a follow-up question, Pittman recalled that the Marines did not call the ARRS after that because they went to the AFSOF as the experts for special operations. Once the corporate Air Force said it could not do the mission, the planners looked elsewhere. They concluded that this response reflected the USAF corporate attitude because General Gast, the TAC vice-commander, would have been part of making such a decision, perhaps reinforced by the "white hat" bias of General Saunders, the ARRS commander. Notably, one year prior, 67th ARRSq HH-53s had been dispatched to Incirlik, Turkey, for the initial evacuations from Iran, a classic "white hat" mission.[17]

Would the use of a squadron such as the 40th ARRSq or the 21st SOS have made a difference? The Holloway Commission looked at the selection of the RH-53D unit to do the mission as issue 13. The members agreed that it was the right choice since that unit's aircraft was selected for the mission. However, the report stated, "It is believed the preservation of an established squadron's inherent unit cohesion could have facilitated the training, enhanced the information flow, and increased aircrew knowledge, all of which could lead to more integrated unit operation. It cannot be demonstrated nor is it suggested that these factors would have altered the outcome. However, they would have enhanced training and more likely increased the chance of success."[18]

Perhaps the best summation of the failure at Desert One from an Air Force perspective was offered by another member of the Holloway Group, Lt Gen Leroy Manor, USAF, retired. He led the Son Tay raid and later observed that "in the decade of the seventies, we allowed our capability to dissipate to zero. When this happened in Teheran, we didn't have the capability. We could have taken B-52s and bombed the hell out of Iran, but that would not have solved the problem. . . . The only capability that had been developed and maintained was Delta. It had a tremendous capability, but there wasn't the means to get it where it was needed. The Air Force is largely at fault for not having maintained that capability."[19]

Other findings dealt with numerous issues of organization, command and control, operational security, training, equipping, and so forth. The report concluded with two recommendations:

1. Establish a counterterrorist joint task force (CTJTF) as a field agency of the JCS with a permanent staff and permanent small, limited forces with unique capabilities in special operations.

2. Create a special operations advisory panel of senior defense personnel (active and retired) to provide the most objective and independent assessment possible of considered operations. Members should have backgrounds in special operations or at the commander-in-chief or JCS levels and have maintained an interest in special operations or defense policy matters.[20]

A Second Effort—Operation Honey Badger

The postmortem process, though, would take several months. President Carter was not prepared to wait that long. On 28 April, he ordered Secretary Brown to prepare another effort. As Col Jim Kyle arrived back at the Pentagon for his mission debrief, he noticed another group of officers and Airmen sequestered in a nondescript room and had to assume they were the beginning of that effort.

General Vaught was kept on to lead the second mission. General Secord was directed to serve with him as his vice-commander and air component commander. Several other key staff members, especially in the intelligence division, were also kept on board, and within two weeks were again working long shifts. Defense Secretary Brown made it clear that this time all needed resources would be available. The planning operation was given the unclassified title of Honey Badger and would be done by the Joint Test Directorate assigned to the Office of the Joint Chiefs.

Secord did a quick read of all available after action reports and then began to analyze the overall air operation. He decided that the helicopters were key and wanted the HH-53H Pave Low III aircraft for the operation. Eight were currently available at Kirtland, where they were being made ready for transfer to the 41st ARRSq at McClellan AFB. The ninth was still at the NARF at Pensacola. Subsequently, General Secord requested that MAC deploy the aircraft with crews and support personnel to the 20th SOS at Hurlburt Field to support Honey Badger. The MAC commander, Gen Dutch Heyser, objected but was overruled. On 14 May, Gen Robert Mathis, the USAF vice-chief of staff, sent a message to MAC, TAC, and other support commands directing the move of the nine Pave Low III aircraft from Kirtland to Hurlburt Field. On 15 May, the secretary of the Air Force, Dr. Hans Mark, visited Kirtland AFB. While there, he was given a full briefing on the Pave Low III aircraft.[21]

The FOT&E for Pave Low III was suspended. All Pave Low III training was immediately curtailed as the wing rushed to comply with the order. Within four days, the eight aircraft at Kirtland were flown to Hurlburt, accompanied by 21 aircrew and operations support personnel and a 41-man maintenance team. The ninth aircraft would arrive directly from Pensacola two weeks later when it finished its modification. Colonel Pehr, as the de facto team leader, and Captain Connelly led the aircraft and Airmen down, along with several of the instructors—Majors Mark Schibler, Ken Ernest, Lou Grant, and Joe Barnes and Captains Jim Blewitt and Don Thompson—and crews flying the other machines. Additionally, the 20th would be reinforced with six more Slick HH-53B/Cs and eight HC-130 tanker aircraft for the operation. At the 41st ARRSq at McClellan, Captain Reed heard about the request for supplemental Slick HH-53s and crews and

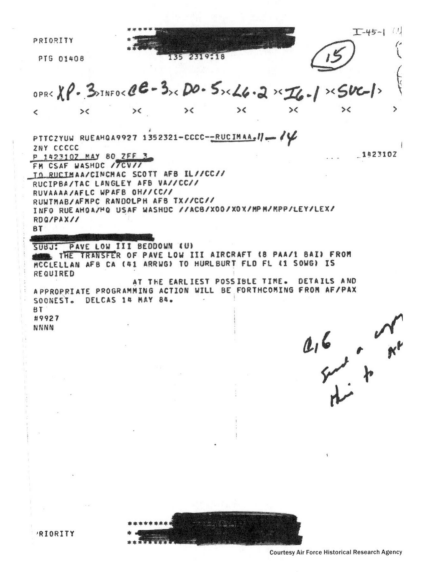

PRIORITY

PTG 01408   135 2319:18   (15)

OPR< XP-3 >INFO< CE-3 >< DO-5 >< L6-2 >< I6-1 >< SVC-1 >

<   ><   ><   ><   ><   ><   ><   >

PTTCZYUW RUEAHQA9927 1352321-CCCC--RUCIMAA. 11—14
ZNY CCCCC
P 142310Z MAY 80 ZFF 3   142310Z
FM CSAF WASHDC //CV//
TO RUCIMAA/CINCMAC SCOTT AFB IL//CC//
RUCIPBA/TAC LANGLEY AFB VA//CC//
RUVAAAA/AFLC WPAFB OH//CC//
RUWTMAB/AFMPC RANDOLPH AFB TX//CC//
INFO RUEAHQA/HQ USAF WASHDC //ACB/XOO/XOX/MPM/MPP/LEY/LEX/
RDQ/PAX//
BT

SUBJ: PAVE LOW III BEDDOWN (U)
      THE TRANSFER OF PAVE LOW III AIRCRAFT (8 PAA/1 BAI) FROM
MCCLELLAN AFB CA (41 ARRWG) TO HURLBURT FLD FL (1 SOWG) IS
REQUIRED
                AT THE EARLIEST POSSIBLE TIME. DETAILS AND
APPROPRIATE PROGRAMMING ACTION WILL BE FORTHCOMING FROM AF/PAX
SOONEST. DELCAS 14 MAY 84.
BT
#9927
NNNN

PRIORITY

The transfer message directing the initial movement of the Pave Lows to Hurlburt Field

immediately volunteered. Within days, he was given one of the 41st's NRS aircraft and dispatched to Hurlburt. As the helicopters arrived there, they were immediately fitted with mounts for .50-caliber machine guns.[22]

At Hurlburt the men and machines would be attached initially in TDY status to the 20th SOS, commanded by recently appointed Lt Col George Borinski, a CH-3 pilot. That was somewhat problematic because the 20th would keep its assigned UH-1Ns but lose its CH-3s and crew members to make room for the Pave Lows, which would eventually be assigned permanently to the unit. Plans called for 200 additional personnel and $2.4 million for military construction for the 20th SOS. Captain Weikel and others were out on the ramp to greet the Kirtland crews as they arrived, handing them cold beers and red scarves. However, the welcome was not universally congenial. The men of rescue proudly wore the ARRS patch on their flight suits. Connelly was shocked to notice when he went to the men's room that someone had placed decals of the rescue patch in each of the urinals.[23]

General Secord also paid a visit to Hurlburt. He had served there during the Vietnam War and was stunned to see how it had changed. Gone were the A-26s, A-1s, AT-28s, and A-37s used to train a generation of the air commandos who served in that conflict. The only helicopter unit, the 20th SOS, was equipped with antiquated machines. The conventional USAF had cut spending to special operations, and it showed. The morale was low, and the base seemed to be in a stupor. He resolved that many changes had to be made and began working to have key wing leaders replaced.

As in Rice Bowl, a multitude of 1st SOW men and equipment would play a key role in Honey Badger. Once again, the MC- and AC-130s would be involved. This time they would be joined by the HH-53s now assigned to the 20th SOS. Although Secord could see that the rescue pilots needed a lot of training, he believed that the merger of the Pave Low III aircraft with the 20th SOS was a good move. It was, indeed, a critical one because he envisioned using the Pave Lows as pathfinder aircraft for the rest of his rescue force.

That force was growing in size. In addition to the Delta Force and other special operations elements, the Army would also provide two Ranger battalions and an aviation unit designated Task Force (TF) 158. It consisted of new UH-60s from the C and D Companies of the 158th Aviation Battalion and CH-47s from the A Company of the 159th Assault Support Helicopter Battalion, both from the 101st Airborne

Division (Air Assault). Capt Bryan D. Brown commanded C Company and worked tirelessly to build the task force into a strong and capable unit. The task force also included OH-6s, procured from a Mississippi Army National Guard unit and flown by 101st pilots from the 229th Attack Helicopter Battalion. In toto the aviation package would consist of almost 100 aircraft directly assigned, with countless support aircraft performing a myriad of functions.[24]

At its height the task force included almost 4,000 troops. The basic plan was to insert the Delta Force with the HH-53s led by the Pave Lows to secure the hostages. The helicopters would use in-flight refueling to proceed directly to the hostage locations. A larger force would seize the Mehrabad Airport, located on the western edge of Tehran, with a Ranger-led assault. C-130s, C-141s, and C-5s would immediately land and disgorge the Army helicopters, which would then fly to support the hostage rescue force and bring them to Mehrabad. However, intelligence sources indicated that the captives were now being moved between possibly five different locations. Consequently, the plan had to develop 12 different iterations depending upon the actions of the Iranians.[25]

As the plan was evolving, the 20th SOS was training hard to perform its role. However, the squadron was nowhere near combat ready with the Pave Low III and had much individual training to do to certify its crews. Several students from the initial course at Kirtland also accompanied the aircraft. Mark Schibler, now a qualified IP, would do much of the training. Upon meeting the pilots from the 20th SOS, he was shocked to realize that they had no idea of how challenging it was going to be for the aircrews to qualify on the aircraft. He was further chagrined when a 1st SOW senior officer told the pilots at a crew meeting that they weren't going to use the Pave Low equipment those airplanes had but were going to learn to fly by map reading, compass, and clock.[26]

Fortunately, that line of thinking did not prevail, and the Kirtland crew members were quickly assimilated into the squadron, developing a shared sense of purpose and synergistic combination of the best of what both groups brought to the mix. Pilots and flight engineers previously qualified on any version of the H-53 were offered transition to the Pave Low III. Major Grove and Captains Weikel and Vallimont enthusiastically volunteered, as did Captain Reed from the 41st. Connelly, Blewitt, and Grant quickly designed a training program. Maj Bob Stankovich also joined them. The previous year, he had departed Kirtland for a staff job at ARRS headquarters. To help support the rapid conversion of the 20th, he was sent TDY to Hurlburt to help train the needed new crews and also serve as an aircraft commander for Honey Badger. He was crewed with Capt Mike Damron. Capt Mike Homan also joined the unit. Formerly an HH-1H pilot with a missile support unit, he was at Kirtland going through the H-53 and Pave Low transition, with an assignment to RAF Bentwaters, when he was diverted to the 20th at Hurlburt.[27]

Given their backgrounds flying H-53 aircraft, Grove, Vallimont, and Weikel were immediately inserted into training and qualified with just a few sorties, Weikel eventually becoming an instructor and then evaluator in the Pave Low. Two pilots came over from the 55th ARRSq at Eglin. One was not comfortable with the program and withdrew. The other, Capt Mike Russell, was good friends with Maj Joe Barnes and expressed an interest in the program. Barnes put in a good word for him, and he was ordered to report to the 20th SOS.

The disparate young officers took to the new challenge and embraced it. Russell recounts that

> the hardest part was learning the systems and learning how to use an analog computer that they had in there with maximum 18 waypoints. . . . As far as running the crew and stuff like that, I didn't have a lot of trouble with that. . . . Learning to do the coupled approaches—that was something that was new and always a challenge because the parameters that you had to fly to were pretty exacting, and the system just wasn't all that great. If you were outside the parameters, it would do really weird things. There you are at 100 feet, in a zero-illume night with no NVGs, trying to figure out what the system is doing so you could compensate for it. That was kind of a challenge. But the 53 is a 53; they flew well. I love the helicopter; it's an absolutely amazing machine.[28]

As the pilots qualified, they were placed on FCF orders and used their additional time on the aircraft to fully learn the new systems. Reed and Maj Ken Ernst, from the 1550th ATTW, also volunteered for FCF duty and began working part-time at the NARF as the aircraft rotated in and out of that facility for various modifications. When not testing or training on the Pave Low, Reed was "hard crewed" with Capt John Folkerts to fly an NRS HH-53 for the actual mission.[29]

It was a stressful time for the Airmen of the 20th as they transitioned the unit to the new aircraft and scrambled to fulfill their designated role in Honey Badger. But it was not just the process of converting a squadron to a new aircraft. Certainly, that was happening, but the men of the 20th were also essentially validating the aircraft under the most demanding of conditions. They had to show not only that the new technology would work but also that the aircraft *and aircrews* could handle the pressure of such a demanding task. Everybody knew that another failure would be a huge shock to the nation, and the decision makers wanted to make doubly sure that the helicopter force would not fail.[30]

At one point, Captain Connelly was sent to the Pentagon to brief Secord and the JTF 1-79 planners on Pave Low III capabilities and employment options. He was straightforward with them, pointing out that the aircraft was still not fully developed because much of the field testing was still in progress and logistical support was in development. Once he returned to Hurlburt, leaders in the 1st SOW who took great exception to what he had briefed in the Pentagon accosted him. Incensed, they directed him and a few others to return to Kirtland. Colonel Pehr was offered command of the 20th SOS. When he declined the offer, he was also told that his services were not needed. He went back to Kirtland and resumed his duties there.[31]

By June 181 ARRS personnel were TDY at Hurlburt Field. In an attempt to reduce costs and insert some stability into the program, HQ USAF on 17 June 1980 directed the permanent change of station (PCS) assignment of the Pave Low III aircraft and personnel to the 1st SOW. On that date, all of the ARRS transferees removed the MAC patches from their uniforms and replaced them with TAC patches. Additionally, MAC had to adjust manning and aircraft assignments at several rescue squadrons to support the continued temporary duty of the additional HH-53s and HC-130s. Almost 300 ARRS personnel would ultimately support Honey Badger in a TDY status. This caused many hardships, personnel stress, and family problems.[32]

Lt Col George Borinski had taken command of the 20th in January and spent long hours struggling with the transition. However, he had no experience in H-53s and did not train into the Pave Low III. Senior leaders in TAC and MAC decided that the 20th needed an experienced H-53 pilot to take his place. When Pehr declined, Lt Col Bill Takacs replaced Borinski in August.[33]

Takacs was a career USAF helicopter pilot with thousands of hours of flight time as an aircraft commander, IP, and evaluation pilot on several different helicopters, including the HH/CH-53, and a tour as an advisor in SEA. Described by one of his pilots as "a no-nonsense, straight-talking, out-front leader who was totally intolerant of excuses, bureaucratic impediments, and personal agendas," he was con-

Lt Col Bill Takacs (shown as a colonel in a later assignment) commanded the 20th SOS as it converted to the Pave Lows.

sidered one of the finest helicopter pilots in the entire Air Force. Takacs was the right guy at the right place and time to bring together the evolving technology of Pave Low III and the highly spirited young men of the 20th SOS and the rescue units. Transferring from Bergstrom, where he had commanded the 701st TASS and then served as the 602d Tactical Air Control Wing assistant deputy commander for operations, he seized control of the unit and steadily forged it into a unit capable of meeting its tasking for Operation Honey Badger.[34]

Takacs set a challenging pace for the unit because the mission demanded it. However, he always took care of his troops. He told his Airmen, "Do what I say, and if it is wrong, I will take the heat." Mark

Schibler accepted Takacs as a hard-nosed commander who had a keen sense of mission and "could get the crews motivated to do whatever it took." At one point, his flyers were having trouble getting travel vouchers filed because they worked and flew mostly at night and had to rest during the day. When the wing finance officer complained about tardy vouchers from the 20th, Takacs turned tables on him and demanded that he have clerks available all night so his troops could submit their vouchers without having to break their crew rest. The finance office went on 24-hour service.[35] Capt Ed Reed was also mightily impressed with Takacs, remembering that "he just knew how to get things done. You would do anything for him. It was obvious that he had his act together. . . . He immediately got great respect, and there was no doubt that somebody in charge had picked the right guy to run the operation.[36]

Reed subsequently decided to stay with the 20th, and Takacs gave him two weeks to go back to McClellan AFB to sell his house and move his wife and child to Hurlburt. Reed got it all done. However, he, like many others on the mission, discovered that the intense program at Hurlburt was tough on families. The men had to deploy frequently and often on short notice. They could not tell their families what they were doing; nevertheless, the families watched the nightly news and were able to surmise what was going on and why their men were training so hard. Some families were deeply tested by the strain.[37]

Sergeant Simmon also made the initial move to Hurlburt and developed excellent relationships with Colonel Takacs, whom he deeply respected, and most of the unit pilots and crew members as they earnestly trained for their mission. He also decided to stay with the 20th and became intimately involved in training the Pave Low flight engineers. The dramatic change in mission forced him to alter his mode of operation. He explains that "being in a rescue unit . . . , everything needs to be done by the book. The book has been written, and there are no changes to it. . . . With the 20th . . . it became evident that the book wasn't written and it needed to be written and rewritten again. That's what we did. My mind finally changed [to] figuring out ways to do things to make things simpler and to just get that 'can do' attitude and do it."[38]

So adapt he did to fit into the mission, eventually developing a fondness for it and a deep pride in being able to wear the "red scarf." He trained young flight engineers like SSgt Dean Larsen, who had been crewed on the CH-3s with the 20th but came over to the Pave

Low fleet. Larsen found the academic and tactical training load challenging and even intimidating. Regardless, under the leadership of "old guys" like Simmon, he was able to adapt to the special operations world, even coming to enjoy the challenges of the criticality of their immediate tasking and the new skill sets necessary to accomplish the larger mission.[39]

As the units assigned to Honey Badger completed their individual training needs, they began to work together with other task force elements. Crews were merciless in using what came to be called their "cowboy priority" to bump other aircraft off of the ranges around Eglin so that they could train. They deployed to many Army bases to work with the "customers" that they would be hauling into Iran. Focusing on conducting night operations and airfield seizures and living in austere field conditions, they also went through intense training in Texas, Nevada, the White Sands Missile Range in New Mexico, the Dugway Proving Grounds in Utah, Fairchild AFB in Washington, and Fort Huachuca in Arizona. All units trained to use NVGs, a new and challenging skill for many. Nightly, the Paves practiced leading ever larger formations of TF-158 helicopters on ever longer missions as all the crews developed the skills and edge necessary for such a challenging mission. Before going back to Kirtland, Connelly flew several of these missions.

> We would use the Pave Lows as lead with the TF system and navigation system and do the packages of support helicopters. During a typical night, we would launch four Pave Low assault ships, which would have four or five assault Blackhawks in trail with a ton of gas. We would send out four Pave Lows with two Chinooks and a Slick-53 as Chalk 4 as support guys filled with gas. . . . The assault packages would come in. The -53s would hit the [HC-130] tankers . . . the Blackhawks . . . would suck fuel out of the . . . H-47s . . . and then we would be off to our strike.[40]

Overall, though, Captain Russell was not impressed with the Army crews. He found the joint training to be challenging and recalls how

> the Army guys didn't join us until we went to Michael Army Airfield. There was a lot of tension at first. . . . We tried to work together with those guys. . . . The company commander—a captain, [was] charismatic, fast-charging, knew what he wanted and [went] after it. . . . We did a big graduation exercise out there, and I'll never forget this. We were in the theater. . . . It really went bad. . . . We scattered 53s all over the countryside; the 60s didn't join up with the Pave Lows like they were supposed to at the rendezvous point. Everybody made his way back in bits and pieces instead of in a big formation and accountability and all of this other stuff.

I'll never forget in the hotwash, in the theater, typical Air Force . . . we bare our souls so we could fix things and make things better the next time. When it came time for the Army portion of it, I still remember [the Army captain] walking down the aisle of the base theater going, "You guys f---ed this up; we did everything right." That was my first eye-opener, first exposure to the way the Army . . . operated.[41]

Michael Army Airfield, Utah, one of the sites used by the joint force as it trained for Honey Badger

Gary Weikel was also not impressed with the Army pilots, noting that the majority did not have instrument ratings. But they did become adept at flying formation off the Pave Lows. As the 20th pilots began to adapt to their role, they began to repeat the mantra "Pave Low leads." It just seemed to be the natural occurrence.[42]

On 18 July, one of the support HH-53Cs, #69-5786, crashed at the San Juan County Airport, Utah, while supporting an exercise. Of the seven men on board, one was killed and five were injured. The crew experienced a flight control malfunction caused by a lateral fuel transfer failure. When it tried to make an emergency landing, the aircraft hit hard, rolled over, and burned.[43]

In late summer, a major portion of the task force staged a practice assault on Reese AFB, a USAF pilot training base near Lubbock, Texas. This was done on a Saturday night under "blacked out" conditions to cause minimum disruption to the units there and to draw minimum local attention. Unfortunately, the noise generated by the aircraft and weapons charges did alarm many of the locals near the base, who reported it to the police. A cover story had been developed for such an event and blamed the whole episode on overly aggressive training by a Texas Army National Guard unit.[44]

At the 20th SOS, Colonel Takacs used his career knowledge of the tactical helicopter community to try to recruit "sharp young guys" to join the unit. He approached Captain Connelly, but Connelly had had enough of Hurlburt and TAC. When he returned from the initial deployment to Hurlburt, he had intended to resign from the Air Force and had all of his papers ready. However, his commander at Kirtland talked him out of it. He subsequently took another job in flight test, working on the new rescue variant of the H-60 now being considered by MAC.[45]

Takacs also tried to recruit Major Stankovich, who had helped qualify several of the initial pilots and was now flying practice missions for the Honey Badger effort. Stankovich knew that Pave Low was an exciting and sorely needed capability and also had some personal history with Takacs, whom he had met when assigned to the 21st SOS in Thailand. Takacs was on the PACAF Standardization and Evaluation Team and came out to NKP to give CH-53 check rides. Although Stankovich found Takacs's invitation appealing, he passed on the offer for personal and professional reasons and returned to his duties at Scott AFB.[46]

Still trying to build up his unit, Takacs called Capt Rus Stiles, who was still active with the test program at Kirtland AFB. "Rus, you have to come with us on this," Takacs pleaded. Stiles was torn because he had a long and enduring relationship with Takacs based on his visits to Thailand and later to the 6594th Test Group in Hawaii, where Stiles was stationed. Consequently, such an offer from Takacs was compelling. However, Stiles had two colonels who did not want him to leave Kirtland. He chose not to make the move to Hurlburt, remaining instead in the test community at Kirtland for another two years. As his responsibilities slowly transformed, though, from flying to desk duties, he decided to leave active USAF duty to join the Sikorsky Aircraft Corporation as a helicopter test pilot.[47]

Coincidentally, other officers were also looking for sharp pilots for Pave Low. Maj Fred Manke was serving as the helicopter assignments officer at the USAF Personnel Center in early 1980. While earlier attending a helicopter instructor course at Fort Rucker, he met Army chief warrant officer (CW-3) Jim Walters. Walters had been an Army pilot since 1969 and had served in Vietnam. He had over 3,500 hours of helicopter time and was now a highly experienced helicopter instructor and specialist in NVG operations. He had recently received a college degree and was interested in transferring to the USAF as a commissioned officer and pilot. In early 1980, Manke helped Walters do all the paperwork for the transfer and get a slot in the Officer Training School at Maxwell AFB. While there, Walters also met a USAF flight evaluation board and received a rating as an Air Force pilot. Manke then secured him an HH-53 assignment to the 33d ARRSq at Kadena, and Walters reported directly to Kirtland for qualification in the aircraft. Out on the ramp one day, he met a Pave Low crew passing through on a Honey Badger training mission and became interested in the 20th and its mission. He also heard about the squadron commander, Bill Takacs, who the Pave Low guys all said was an outstanding leader. When Major Manke subsequently called to tell Walters that he was going to get a change of orders sending him to the 601st TASS at Sembach, Walters expressed an interest in joining the Pave Low program. The next day, Manke called back to inform him that he was now going to the 20th.[48]

Jack Kelly followed a similar path. He had also been an Army chief warrant officer with combat experience in Vietnam. After procuring a USAF commission in November 1979, he went through H-53 qualification at Kirtland. He stood on the ramp there and watched Pehr and Simmon as they departed with two Pave Low aircraft for Saudi Arabia. Arriving at the 55th ARRSq at Eglin AFB three months later, he found out what was happening at the 20th and immediately volunteered, becoming another of the squadron's highly qualified senior-pilot-winged second lieutenants waiting to work their way through Pave Low qualification. In later years, many more Army warrant officers would follow this path to Pave Low and, again, add a great deal to the force.[49]

By August JTF 1-79 had conducted 10 major rehearsals, and both General Vaught and General Secord believed that the men were ready. They so reported to General Jones and Secretary Brown. Stated Secord, "The JTF was on razor's edge: morale was high, the equipment was ready, and we were raring to go." However, intelligence sources were having difficulty ascertaining the precise locations of the hostages, and without that critical information, nobody was willing to commit the task force.[50]

Regardless, the training continued as the commanders waited for favorable intelligence data. In October, under Operation Potent Charge, the Pave Lows led TF-158 elements as they inserted several teams of Delta Force troops and Rangers onto eight widely dispersed targets. Over five days and nights, the Paves and CH-47s inserted and then exfiltrated the teams, concluding the operation with a continuous 16-hour burst of activity. Three weeks later, they repeated the exercise on an even larger scale in Operation Storm Cloud as the JTF maintained its edge.[51]

Second Lieutenant Jim Walters arrived at the 20th in October. With the heavy operations and training tempo, he could not immediately enter Pave Low training. Instead, he flew the attached HH-53s to initially build up his time in type and, eventually, train the other pilots and crew members in NVG operations. Most NVG training took place at night. However, he and the other instructors became adept at using a combination of blue Plexiglas on the windscreens and yellow helmet visors on the student pilots to replicate night flying during the day. The pilot flying could use the yellow visor to restrict his vision while the safety pilot, flight engineers, and gunners wore clear visors for terrain and traffic avoidance. Walters hated this expedient, but it was necessary to get the troops trained. He later recalled that "from sitting on the ground, you had to take off, fly TF/TA en route, and land completely IMC [instrument meteorological conditions] so to speak. Although it was in daylight conditions, you were in the clouds from takeoff to landing. That was a true test of training. And that was the standard that people had to meet."[52]

The training was hard. Some pilots could not make the transition and left the program. A few months later, Walters finally was able to qualify in the Pave Low. He found the shift to a larger crew a bit of a challenge and quite different from what he had experienced in the Army. He remembered that

> in the Army, in the Huey, you just had a pilot and a copilot. . . . I went from that concept, from two people, to six people. So my learning curve was deep . . . pilot, copilot, two flight engineers—one acting as a scanner—two gunners. . . . And [I had] that plus the amount of checklists that I was introduced to in the Air Force. . . . But I just sat back, took a breath, and you just learned the teamwork that it takes to fly safely with six guys instead of two guys. Once you develop that, you got it down to such a rote, precise system that it just turned out okay.[53]

However, the continual training and operations demands levied on the 20th remained such that it would take almost a year for Lieutenant Walters to fully work his way through the myriad requirements to qualify first as an HH-53B/C and then as a full HH-53H Pave Low III aircraft commander. He would eventually upgrade to IP and then flight examiner and become a solid pillar of knowledge, experience, and strength in the squadron.[54]

With the election of Pres. Ronald Reagan in November 1980, the relationship between the United States and Iran began to shift. The Iranian leadership believed that the new president might be inclined to order an even larger military operation against their country. Diplomatic representatives of the Carter administration wanted a hostage release before the new president took over and worked earnestly behind the scenes to arrange such an outcome. JTF 1-79 was ready to go but was still constrained by a lack of definitive locations for the hostages.

However, other fundamental changes were occurring that would dramatically affect Honey Badger. At a hearing before the Senate Armed Services Committee in late summer, Senator Sam Nunn asked Colonel Beckwith what he had learned from the Rice Bowl mission and what could be done to preclude such an outcome from happening again. Beckwith waxed elegantly about the importance of teams training together vice ad hoc operations, using a Bear Bryant analogy to make his point. As far as preparing for the future, he stated that "my recommendation is to put together an organization which contains everything it will ever need, an organization which could include Delta, the Rangers, Navy SEALs, Air Force pilots, its own staff, its own support people, [and] its own aircraft and helicopters. Make this organization a permanent military unit. Give it a place to call home. Allocate sufficient funds to run it, and give it sufficient time to recruit, assess, and train its people. Otherwise, we are not serious about combating terrorism."[55]

Based upon the recommendations of the Holloway Commission for a CTJTF and testimony like Beckwith's, Defense Secretary Brown, within a month of the publication of the Holloway report, directed the creation of the Joint Special Operations Command (JSOC) at Fort Bragg. It activated on 15 December 1980. Initially, its unclassified mission was to study special operations tactics. Its real mission, not declassified until 1992, was to "provide the joint service expertise for a standing Joint Special Operations Task Force [JSOTF]." One week later, it assumed responsibility for hostage rescue in general and Operation Honey Badger, relieving JTF 1-79 of the mission. However, the JTF stayed ready to deploy until the hostages were back under US control before finally standing down. Many of its personnel subsequently joined the new organization.[56]

To provide direct support to the JSOC, the vice CSAF, General Mathis, established the Air Force Element Operations Evaluation Group at Pope AFB, North Carolina, to work directly with the new organization. Its mission was to "conduct research and testing on special procedures and projects assigned by the CSAF." Additionally, the 1st SOW was tasked to make available to the JSOC commander two MC-130s, two AC-130s, and two HH-53Hs on a daily basis.[57]

Shortly thereafter, the Carter administration was able to reach an agreement with the Iranian government for the return of all hostages as quid pro quo for the release of certain Iranian funds and assets frozen by the US government in the last year. The actual release would take place on 20 January 1981, literally moments after President Reagan took the oath of office.[58]

Although Operation Honey Badger was never executed, its benefits were incalculable. Born from failure, it became an instrument to forge a truly joint force capable of dealing with the ever-growing threat of international terrorism. JSOC was now a reality, and the Army decided to formalize the ad hoc TF-158 into TF-160 as a battalion-sized special operations aviation element within the 101st Division. Within just a year, it would be redesignated as the 160th Aviation Battalion, given the moniker of the "Night Stalkers," and eventually upgraded to the 160th Special Operations Aviation Regiment (SOAR).[59]

Honey Badger also served as the catalyst to move the Pave Low III aircraft from the ARRS to the 20th SOS, where a group of earnest and dedicated young air warriors led by the best possible mentor would bring Pave Low III to full fruition. Later, Captain Reed noted that "we were developing tactics and doing things with equipment that nobody had ever planned to do. Essentially, I think it jump-started special ops—at least the helicopter part of it. . . . Despite everyone thinking that rescue and SOF would not come together, the mission forced everybody together. The guys who wanted to leave at the end, left. And the guys who wanted to stay, stayed."[60]

A later 1st SOW award nomination for this period stated:

> Integrating the HH-53H Pave Low helicopter into special operations in the short time between May and September 1980 was a major accomplishment. The highly sophisticated helicopter possessing terrain following/terrain avoidance radar and forward-looking infrared sensor capability arrived on very short notice at Hurlburt where there were no personnel in operations or maintenance trained in the system. . . . The Pave Low provided the Wing with a heavy lift capability previously lacking and a helicopter which could, by using its terrain systems and on-board computers, operate at extremely low altitudes in areas previously denied by enemy defenses.[61]

The young Airmen of the 20th SOS turned their squadron into an asset ready to take our best Soldiers, Airmen, and Sailors to meet the enemy any time, any place. As Orr Kelly wrote in a later history of air commandos, "By the time the Honey Badger exercises were completed, the Air Force had this new weapon in its arsenal along with crews highly trained to get the most out of the new machine. It was the beginning of . . . the modern era in Air Force special operations."[62]

The dramatic changes that had swept the 20th SOS required modification of its mission statement. The unit's new designed operational capability statement specified two assigned missions: unconventional warfare and psychological operations. Its mission description now called for low-level penetration of hostile territory for infiltration, exfiltration, and resupply of unconventional warfare forces. Also, the required special equipment list included items unique to the Pave Low IIIs. All other missions—including personnel recovery, medevac, and humanitarian missions—were now listed as corollary.

In November the 1st SOW established the Special Operations Mission Planning Division under the deputy commander for operations and manned it with 11 Airmen, headed by a lieutenant colonel. It would be the coordinating facility for special 1st SOW taskings and commitments and would serve as the wing focal point and communications channel for interface with the JSOC and for coordination with other Air Force and service units and agencies tasked by the JSOC.[63]

These combined factors would have, for the Pave Low Airmen at least, a significant unforeseen consequence. Within the Air Force,

NECESSITY TO NADIR | 167

aircrews generally identified themselves with their aircraft or at least class of aircraft (fighters, attack, bombers, cargo, etc.), and each had its own "tribe," an identity and support group that created community loyalties. For the Pave Low crews, though, working as closely as they were now with the special forces from the other services, they would soon come to identify more strongly with the special forces than they did with their Air Force brethren. One air commando later wrote of this phenomenon, "It has a lot to do with association with the customer . . . generally a SEAL or SF [special forces]. We do somewhat consider ourselves the same as those guys. . . . We feel a very close camaraderie with them."[64]

Aerospace Rescue and Recovery Service

The abrupt transfer of the Pave Low III aircraft, crews, and support capability to TAC was quite an unexpected blow to MAC/ARRS. For almost 10 years, that organization had nurtured the program through all of the conceptualizing, funding, programming, testing, production, training, and now organizing necessary to convert a clear operational need into a force in being. At the very moment of its realization, it had been forced to give up the entire force to TAC for a wholly different, but critical, mission. Sensing the bitter frustration of the MAC/ARRS Airmen, on 12 June 1980, Gen Lew Allen, the CSAF, sent Gen Robert Huyser a personal note that said the following:

1. My staff has restudied problems associated with the transfer of the Pave Low III helicopters. We are in the unfortunate position of having to allocate a scarce resource between two competing demands, combat rescue and the counterterrorist (CT) mission, and we cannot satisfy full, the requirements of both.

2. . . . Senior OSD [Office of the Secretary of Defense] officials are actively working the establishment of a permanent, integrated force capable of achieving an effective response to future terrorist incidents. . . . The Joint Chiefs are developing an organization consisting of personnel and equipment from all services. Deemed essential to this structure are the unique capabilities of Pave Low.

3. . . . I have looked at alternatives to the Pave Low assignment but have concluded these assets and personnel must be organizationally integrated into TAC. . . .

4. The personnel sensitivities of this transfer are well understood.

5. It is recognized the transfer of Pave Low assets to TAC will leave an obvious hole in ARRS capability. Therefore, in event of contingency, arrangements and procedures will be worked out to pull and use Pave Low to support your needs. . . . I've directed the staff to work in conjunction with MAC to prepare options for rebuilding an enhanced combat rescue capability. The basis may be to develop some of the Pave Low capability in the forthcoming H-60 or an alternate candidate.[65]

Facing squarely the reality of this dramatic change, General Huyser on 23 July responded to General Allen, stating, "If the Air Force wants a rescue capability for both peacetime and wartime, we better get with the program on restoring some lost capability." He acknowledged that the loss of the nine HH-53Hs had devastated his command. The further assignment of the additional HH-53B/Cs from the 41st and 55th had also eliminated his capability to respond to current war plans. Huyser proposed that MAC/ARRS brief Allen on a projected "way ahead." Allen acceded, and in August the ARRS commander, Maj Gen Cornelius Nugteren, presented it. He covered several short-term intracommand steps being taken to address the combat recovery shortfall caused by the Pave Low transfer. He also suggested that, long term, the answer was the acquisition of a new rescue helicopter, labeled H-X—possibly a variant of the new H-60 being developed by Sikorsky. Missing was any request for money to modify more HH-53s to the Pave Low III configuration.[66]

In support, General Huyser also continued to push for some form of consolidation of all USAF helicopters under one command, most preferably the ARRS. It had lost the Pave Lows to TAC, but he hoped to make a case for consolidation and control of the larger collective fleet. As discussions continued between the MAC/ARRS staffs and the Air Staff, he openly declared in a letter on 12 November 1980 to Generals Allen and Mathis that the USAF's basic problem was that there were "more mission airframe requirements than existing airframes," and, again, he called for procurement of a new helicopter and more efficient management of existing resources. He further stated:

MAC owns the preponderance of USAF helicopter . . . expertise, experience, command structure, and resources. Also, MAC has extensive experience with special operations in SEA such as the Son Tay Raid, the *Mayaguez* incident, and subsequent long-range deployments like [the] Jonestown, Guyana, incident in South America. MAC has never failed to rapidly respond. I strongly believe that if all helicopters and SOF C-130s are consolidated under MAC, a stronger, more viable force could be projected in response to international contingencies without the intercommand difficulties and personnel disruptions which have occurred in the recent past.[67]

For the next few months, the various USAF commands responded to Huyser's proposal, generally in support but with numerous alternative suggestions and expansions/restrictions. As 1980 ended, though, the immutable fact was that the ARRS HH-53 fleet and commensurate combat rescue capability had been dramatically reduced. Only 21 aircraft were assigned, and they were still located at Kirtland, McClellan, Kadena, Eglin, and Woodbridge. Additionally, the five Honey Badger HH-53B/Cs were still at Hurlburt. Two weeks into the new year, General Mathis responded to General Huyser, noting that the Air Staff was considering several alternatives and that the Joint Staff was also looking at some form of DOD joint command with SOF assets from all of the services.[68]

20th Special Operations Squadron

It is doubtful, though, that any of these discussions about the overall organization of the USAF helicopter fleet were of any concern to the Green Hornets. They had been training intensely since the delivery of the Pave Lows and were more than relieved when notified that Honey Badger was cancelled. By mid-February, the five augmentee HH-53B/Cs, crews, and support personnel were released and returned to their units. NVG training continued, and the 20th began a rotation of Pave Lows to Dobbins AFB, Georgia, so that crews could accomplish training in the Appalachian Mountains. The 20th also began semipermanent rotations to Pope AFB to work with Army special forces units at nearby Fort Bragg and Camp Mackall, at one point putting on a demonstration for SecDef Harold Brown and an interdepartmental group on terrorism. A few days later, six Pave Lows and an AC-130 flew separate long, overwater navigation routes with refueling and precisely rendezvoused at a location near Dahlonega, Georgia, to exfiltrate a special forces team and fly it to Hurlburt.

In January 1981, SSgt John Sprouse reported to the 20th SOS for assignment as a gunner. Initially, the Pave Lows were manned with PJs. However, with the clear focus on special operations, they were taken off and replaced with gunners. Throughout 1980 the USAF had advertised for volunteers, and slowly individuals came forward. Sprouse enlisted in the USAF in 1975, training as a weapons load specialist and serving tours working on A-7s and B-52s before submitting his paperwork for assignment to the Pave Lows. Joining the Green Hornets, he found a small cadre of gunners consisting primarily of former SEA-era Airmen. The gunners did not undergo a formal training program. Sergeant Simmon oversaw the training and used another flight engineer, MSgt John Selfridge, and the initial gunners to conduct it.

Initially, Sprouse was trained to serve just as a crew member. Once he completed that training, he began a series of range and tactical rides to become mission ready. However, the frantic pace of squadron operations did not allow such singular focus. At the same time, he was going on mission exercises and working to develop tactics for specific tasks like fast-rope insertions of small teams and NVG operations. He also worked directly with MSgt Robert Hall as they acquired all of the accoutrements necessary to utilize both miniguns and .50-caliber machine guns on the Pave Lows. As one of the 13 original gunners on the Pave Lows, Sprouse enjoyed it all and quickly became a loyal member of the 20th. He also began to feel the uniqueness of his job and position, remembering that "we were too young to be afraid of anything. We thought we were king of the hill—which we were. We were an elite group of guys. . . . We original 13 gunners were probably some of the best helicopter gunners that have ever been. . . . We could put rounds on targets—now!"[69]

Sprouse flew several of his missions with Capt Gary Weikel, who was flying more than ever, in some months logging 70 hours as an instructor and flight evaluator. They and the other pilots continued to push the aircraft and crews hard as they literally evolved the best tactics for their missions. Weikel, John Grove, Mike Russell, and Joe Vallimont informally made up the tactical essence of the unit. Aggressive, hard-charging, always irreverent and totally unimpressed by things like rank and titular position, they were assigned the moniker of the "Four Horsemen" of the 20th SOS, as if replicating in behavior and appearance the four scourges of the Bible. The nickname arose, Weikel recalls, "after a particularly long and difficult stretch of constant TDYs, routine in-flight emergencies, tough missions, with interspersed training of new guys and the notorious amount of outrageously bad behavior and hard partying interwoven. The prevailing view [was] that we were never going to live through this, so we were going to go out with our spurs on and tall in the saddle . . . like cowboys."[70]

In March the 20th received a real-world mission. Because of instability in Nicaragua, JSOC was directed to deploy a helicopter force to Howard AFB, Panama Canal Zone, as part of Operation Nimble Warrior. By the end of the month, the 20th deployed eight Pave Lows. As in Honey Badger, they were joined by six more HH-53B/Cs from the 41st and 55th ARRSqs and the 1550th ATTW. All of the helicopters flew directly to the Canal Zone from Hurlburt, facilitated by in-flight refueling from six HC-130s.

Courtesy Col Gary Weikel, USAF, Retired

The "Four Horsemen" of the 20th SOS. *Left to right*: Gary Weikel, Mike Russell, John Grove, and Joe Vallimont.

Lt Col Bill Takacs was the commander of the helicopter task force. Based upon the requirements of the missions, he directed that his Pave Low aircraft commanders (including Lieutenants Walters and Kelly) would lead the missions regardless of their military rank. This upset many of the rescue pilots, who felt that their more senior pilots had the edge on flight experience. Takacs did not care about the ran-cor; he told them to get on with their assigned duties. In early April, several of the helicopters were used in a classified mission, and then the task force was released to return home. The Pave Lows were flown back to Hurlburt, and the HH-53B/Cs were flown by C-5 directly back to their bases. Col Owen "Al" Heeter, the 1550th ATTW vice-commander, served as the ARRS mission commander and wrote an after action report. He specifically stated that the 1550th ATTW was not organized or equipped for such deployments. While the aircraft were deployed, wing H-53 crew training was reduced by 50 percent. The wing had not been issued mobility gear for its personnel or war readiness spares kits (WRSK) for its aircraft. Additionally, to be fully capable of such combat operations, the wing HH-53s needed to be modified with updated Doppler and INSs, secure communications radios, the more powerful -7A engines, armor plating, cockpits modi-fied for NVG use, flare dispenser systems, and radar warning receivers. In subsequent correspondence, General Ryan, MAC vice-commander, and General Gabriel, on the Air Staff, agreed that the training mis-sion of the 1550th was critical for supporting overall USAF needs. The unit was subsequently relieved of such tasking responsibility un-less it was needed for a national emergency and correspondingly pro-vided necessary support and funding.[71]

In April, the 20th deployed two Pave Lows and a support team to Pisa, Italy, to participate in Operation Muflone 81. The aircraft were flown over and back in C-5s. While there, the crews gained valuable experience working with US and European special forces units. The movement by MAC assets also provided the maintenance crews an opportunity to better define their aircraft deployment procedures and needs. Later in the month, the 20th's Airmen participated in an-other major exercise, Operation Solid Shield 81, with special forces from all services. In this exercise, they flew two HH-53s and four UH-1Ns and operated out of an austere airfield in central Florida. They practiced and perfected the aircraft-to-aircraft ground refueling procedure that had been so problematic at Desert One. The training with US Navy SEALs was particularly valuable, and the Airmen learned many lessons about working with those forces. The unit also supported its share of static displays, firepower demonstrations, and mission demonstrations for VIPs.

These exercises set the pattern for the rest of the year as 20th crews and support personnel participated in several more exercises, including Gallant Knight, Marvel Exodus, Bold Eagle, Certain Tribute, and Bright Star, in the United States and overseas. Additionally, they trained for all of their mission areas and even another airfield seizure with other elements of JSOC. The 20th showed that it was capable of performing its missions either separately or as part of a joint UW task or coalition force. Pave Lows were also used in several domestic SARs. However, the pace was relentless, putting a real strain on the aircraft and maintenance. In the last three months of the year, the 20th logged 356 sorties in 92 calendar days. An influx of new aircrew members, including Capt Jeff Walls and Capt Walt Heidmous, also created a high demand for training, which suffered under the operational load. The 1st SOW history for that period notes that "the heavy operational tasking on the 20 SOS interrupted upgrade flying training and caused inconsistent and extended training."[72]

The long duty days—up to 14 hours—were also hard on the aircrews, as they again led sometimes large formations of other helicopters, day and night. Major Grove had to give up flying when he developed severe arterial blockage of the heart, which ended his flying career. He would remain with the 20th, though, as a plans officer for several more years.[73]

Colonel Takacs himself had a close call that summer. He flew on an HH-53B commanded by Maj Barry Walls in support of a JSOC exercise at Fort Stewart, Georgia. They were doing a night airfield seizure. However, when Walls came in to land, his tailskid did not extend, and the tail rotor hit the pavement. The tail rotor shattered and threw shrapnel into the aircraft. Takacs was slightly wounded by flying debris that hit his right calf muscle. An Army Ranger was also wounded, and Weikel flew him out for medical care. The medics tried to evacuate the bleeding Takacs. He would have none of it. Instead, he just taped up his leg wound and stayed out with his troops until all other flying was completed for the night before he allowed them to care for him. It just added to his stature with his Airmen.[74]

Aerospace Rescue and Recovery Service

As a result of tactical lessons learned in Nimble Warrior, the ARRS established a program to develop rescue special operations low-level (R-SOLL) techniques to facilitate combat rescue operations and contingency mission requirements. Starting 1 July 1981, the program primarily focused on HC-130 crews, but the ARRS also directed the 41st ARRSq at McClellan to begin a one-year test program to qualify all HH-53 crews to utilize NVGs to fly low-level night recovery missions. This was intended to reestablish an ARRS combat recovery capability after the loss of the Pave Lows. However, this intense training program conflicted with normal alert responsibilities. These were correspondingly relaxed, as were normal daytime training accomplishments. Within three months, the 41st had trained several crews to accomplish the mission.[75]

Reflecting the reality of current events and the growing interest in some form of helicopter consolidation, MAC and ARRS planners throughout 1981 continued to take steps to position the ARRS to be the command of choice for such a merger. After an examination of all ARRS-assigned missions, they drafted a revision of Air Force Regulation (AFR) 23-19, the ARRS mission statement. While still listing combat rescue as the primary mission of the ARRS, the AFR acknowledged its long history of involvement in special operations at places like Son Tay and Koh Tang Island—as well as the most recent operation, Nimble Warrior—and added support for special operations/UW and "other DOD/USAF requirements as directed" to its myriad list of missions. Revised missions for its subordinate wings were also published.[76]

Throughout the year, the MAC commander, General Huyser, continued to advocate for the ARRS as the single manager for USAF helicopters. However, he encountered unexpected resistance from the TAC commander, General Creech, who, responding also for USAFE and PACAF, wrote that he saw only a "marginal relationship" between most aspects of the SOF mission and the airlift mission and that TAC, USAFE, and PACAF should retain SOF resources to execute the counterterrorist and UW missions. He concluded, "In short, the SOF mission is where it belongs and we believe no case exists to move it."[77]

Realizing that he had no service consensus on the issue, General Huyser wrote a letter directly to the SecDef, Casper Weinberger, in which he stated, "I recommend the Air Force consolidate all helicopter and certain C-130 assets under MAC as a single manager. . . . I urge you to take the initiative in this area as it appears to be in the 'too hard' category below your level." Not having received a response from Weinberger, Huyser retired in June and was replaced by General Allen. Two months later, the ARRS commander, General Nugteren, was reassigned and replaced by Brig Gen William Mall. Nothing more was done on the consolidation issue for the rest of the year as the two new commanders settled into their jobs. Considering the losses that the ARRS had taken within the last year, though, one piece of good news did surface when the USAF announced that the 6594th Test Group in Hawaii would be closing in 1986 and that the ARRS would receive its six HH-53Cs.[78]

20th Special Operations Squadron

As 1982 began, most 20th Airmen were unaware of the large issues roiling above them as the various major commands bickered about the best way to organize their helicopter fleet. The squadron was the only Pave Low III–equipped unit in the USAF, and the new year was essentially a replay of the previous year except that the sophistication of the exercises increased as the proficiency of the various forces aligned with JSOC matured and became comfortable with one another. The squadron training load dropped off a bit as only two new pilots, Capt Tom Hull and Capt Clay Spriet, entered the unit. Static displays and VIP visits were constant as word of the existence of the Pave Low spread. One visitor of note was Mr. Lynn Rylander, assistant for policy planning, OSD, who wanted to see firsthand the capabilities of the Pave Low. The unit was also tasked under several war plans to support both JSOC and the new Rapid Deployment Joint Task Force (RDJTF), designed and organized after the failure of Rice Bowl. However, mission analysis showed that the unit needed at least 14 aircraft to meet any tasking beyond more than one contingency but that the preferred force would be 21 Pave Lows.

In late January, the unit provided six aircraft and crews to support Gallant Knight, a large RDJTF exercise held in Florida and focused on helping to defend a friendly nation in Southwest Asia. Performing all classic SOF missions and SAR, the crews flew 22 sorties. This exercise provided the unit with a good knowledge of that part of the world. At almost the same time, the JSOC initiated a no-notice exercise called Vagabond Warrior, and a contingent of 49 Airmen from the 1st SOW, including crews and support personnel for two Pave Lows, deployed to Barking Sands, Hawaii. Arriving there by C-5, the Pave Low crews flew 11 sorties over the next three days as the JSOC task force achieved all of its training objectives. The two deployments, while successful, completely disrupted the 20th SOS training plan. For the quarter, the 20th was able to fly only 70 percent of its allotted sorties, even though unit manning was at 105 percent.

Fully aware of the travails of the 20th SOS, the 1st SOW commander, Col Hugh Cox, addressed the problem with his superior command, TAC's Ninth Air Force. He was aware that the 6594th Test Group in Hawaii was going to inactivate in 1986 and asked if its HH-53Cs could be assigned to the 20th with additional manning and WRSK support to address its shortfalls. No swift answer was forthcoming.

In April, two Pave Lows, crews, and support personnel deployed for a return visit to Pisa, Italy, for Operation Muflone 82. The exercise lasted almost six weeks, and a second team of personnel replaced the original deployers at the halfway point to spread the training to as many Airmen as possible. While there, the 20th flew 47 missions, both operational and administrative, and the crews worked both day and night with various US and allied special forces teams. However, restrictions that the Italian authorities placed on the operation limited the effectiveness of the night missions, causing the deployed commander, Lt Col Joe Barnes, to greatly constrain his aircrews.

The next month, the unit participated in another major exercise, Ocean Venture 82. Two HH-53Hs were committed to the program, but the unit would fly out of Hurlburt Field. This was a JCS-directed exercise, working mostly with forces from the United States Atlantic Command (USLANTCOM), and ran from 26 April to 17 May. During that period, the 20th crews flew 13 sorties, primarily inserting and extracting small teams of SEALs, USAF combat controllers, and US Army special forces.[79]

Aerospace Rescue and Recovery Service

The H-53 community suffered another loss on 27 July 1982 when HH-53C #69-5792 crashed while on a training sortie at Kirtland. The crew had conducted night refueling training and was descending for a low-level navigation leg when the aircraft impacted the ground and was destroyed. The crew—Maj Barry Walls, Capt Pat Behnke, 1st Lt Hardy Delay, and SSgt Aylwyn Fortner—were all killed. Walls was a veteran of the *Mayaguez* mission and had flown with Captain Connelly on the fateful Pave Low III rescue in Albuquerque two and a half years prior. It was a terrible loss to the H-53 community.[80]

There is no record that Defense Secretary Weinberger ever responded to General Huyser's somewhat plaintive retirement letter. However, Huyser's arguments did receive promising support from two unexpected events. In late 1981, two independent studies that tangentially looked at the consolidation issue were launched. The first was an Air Force 2000 study that DOD staff conducted. Its purpose was to divine, in broad terms, USAF needs and resources in the year 2000. It considered technological developments and economic, demographic, and environmental issues. The study assumed that current trends in international relationships would not change appreciably, that terrorist activities would increase, and that the United States could expect conflicts ranging from political unrest to small-scale regional confrontations, requiring a tailored rapid response. It also stated that the Air Force's future mission would need to include augmenting counterterrorist and counterinsurgency crisis operations with airpower and special operations capabilities. The capability requirements section states that "to provide the organizational support necessary to enhance special operations, the Air Force should consider placing it under HQ USAF as a Special Operating Agency, or within a Major Command as a numbered air force."[81]

The second project was a functional management inspection that the USAF inspector general's (IG) office conducted to look specifically at the USAF's special operations capability. It examined current requirements delineated in existing directives, plans, and programs and assessed the USAF's capability to meet those requirements. The results were telling and supported the conclusion that "the Air Force is not currently capable of fully supporting JCS/unified command special operations." With shortfalls found in doctrine, command and control, and current and programmed force structure, the report recommended combining "all ARRS and USAF SO [special operations] assets under an organization or numbered air force within a MAJCOM with overseas units under operational command of AF component commanders." This report was briefed to the MAC commander, Gen James Allen, on 16 July 1982.[82]

A series of meetings took place at the Air Staff in the Pentagon to digest the results of the two reports. As colonels and then generals at the Air Force Council reviewed the issue, they came to a consensus that special operations and combat rescue functions should be consolidated under a single command. On 7 September, the CSAF, Gen Charles Gabriel, directed the TAC and MAC commanders to develop proposals to combine their two affected components. A staff team from MAC and another from TAC, led by Col Gary Lunt and Col Ron Fogleman, respectively, met separately to prepare recommendations for unit location, command and control structures, logistical and personnel support systems, fiscal issues, and a transition schedule. As the two teams were working, Generals Allen and Creech had a series of discussions concerning which major command would own the consolidated new unit. When Maj Gen Duane Cassidy, the MAC DCS, made the point to General Creech that helicopter and M/HC-130 crew members and support personnel would have a better chance at promotion in MAC vice TAC, Creech stated, "I agree with the position. I take away my objections. I will give you the special ops forces." He and General Allen then agreed that MAC and TAC teams would combine as a joint organizational working group (JOWG) and submit a single briefing to the Air Staff. However, General Creech outlined some of his core philosophies that he believed were pivotal to the transition:

1. Theater commanders would retain operational command of forces deployed in the theater.

2. They would determine rational beddown locations for SOFs.

3. Rescue and special operations forces would retain their separate identities.

4. This was not an inter–Air Force battle for real estate but a resource consolidation for the good of the USAF.

5. Residual TAC assets at Hurlburt would be treated fairly.

6. Both parties needed to recognize that the JSOC mission was only part of the special operations function.

The MAC staff had no problems with any of these issues, and the detailed planning commenced.[83]

The JOWG worked through the fall with all impacted staff elements from both commands to hammer out the details of the consolidation. The overarching new command would be the newly established Twenty-Third Air Force, located at Scott AFB and reporting directly to MAC. Subordinate to it, the ARRS would still command all rescue units. The 2d Air Division (AD)—a unit that had served in World War II, the Cold War, and SEA—would be reactivated and would command the special operations units. It would be collocated with the 1st SOW at Hurlburt Field. It would also have administrative control of the 1st SOS in the Pacific, the 7th SOS in Germany, and a special operations detachment in the Panama Canal Zone. Commanders felt that SOF personnel would have better career progression opportunities within MAC since it had the predominance of USAF helicopters and C-130 type aircraft, as opposed to TAC, which was almost exclusively a fighter command. In addition, MAC would assume programming management responsibilities for all special operations forces and equipment. The entire plan was briefed to and approved by the Air Force Council in late November and then finally approved by General Gabriel on 7 December 1982. Subsequently, the orders were published activating the Twenty-Third Air Force and 2d AD on 1 March 1983.[84]

20th Special Operations Squadron

Commanders at Hurlburt were certainly aware of the efforts being made to realign both the combat rescue and special operations forces and provided numerous background papers for the staff teams. The wing commander, Colonel Cox, favored the creation of an air division to command all of the special operations units. At that point, though, the wing and 20th SOS had more immediate matters to deal with. As the 20th was written into more theater contingency plans, the nine aircraft and personnel were stretched further and further. However, USAF programming documents did not show any increase in Pave Lows. Marginal improvements were made to the engines—allowing a slight increase in maximum gross weight—and to the TF/TA radars. The aircraft were also programmed to receive the AAQ-4 active infrared jamming system.[85]

On 1 August, Lt Col Wayne Corder replaced Colonel Takacs as the 20th SOS commander. Takacs had commanded the unit through its time of great turbulence and was deeply respected by his Airmen. He would move up to be the assistant director of operations (DO) for the wing. One of the squadron members, then a young pilot, remembers three simple truths that he learned from Takacs: "(1) Get the mission done and do it safely; (2) Develop and use your own sense of judgment; and (3) Show me you have got it, and you will do just fine."[86]

They were enduring lessons, absorbed and practiced by subsequent generations of Pave Low Airmen. In his time as the 20th SOS commander, Takacs played a crucial role in the development of the Pave Low. He proved to be the critical catalyst necessary to merge the technological advancements of Pave Low with the best and correct young crew members so necessary to utilize the aircraft to its full capacities—and beyond. It was he who infused them with the critical values of independence and unconventional thinking so that "Pave Low Leads" became a mantra for their community and the generations of Airmen that followed.

At the 20th SOS, life went on as the unit adapted to its new commander. Throughout the remainder of the year, the Green Hornets were constantly busy participating in primarily JSOC-directed training exercises. They worked with the US Army's TF-160, leading long-range infiltration missions and practicing aircraft-to-aircraft ground fuel transfer procedures. They deployed aircraft and crews to Army posts, Navy and Air Force bases, and remote training areas all over the United States, the Panama Canal Zone, and the Caribbean. Hornet crews honed their skills as they routinely flew with NVGs and perfected the techniques for small team infiltration and extraction.

The training regimen was hard on the aircrews, support personnel, and families. Lt Jim Walters (now called "Pappy" by his squadron mates) recalls that

> we had hundreds and hundreds of joint ops through JSOC in the early days. . . . When we did deploy . . . I would go home, get my bag out, start packing. My wife would say, "Where are you going?" I said, "I don't know." "When are you coming home?" I said, "I don't know." And that was the norm. It went like that for years. We trained to that level. We were not able to call home. We were not able to discuss anything with the family. So the wives would get together and joke when we were gone for weeks and weeks at a time. They would get together and play "Spin the Globe." And they would watch CNN . . . and try to determine where in the world we were. And, of course, when we came home, we couldn't tell them where we had been or what we had done.[87]

The Green Hornets worked with Army Rangers, the SFOD-Delta, US Navy SEALs from several different SEAL teams, and some special forces units from allied nations. They also trained occasionally with ARRS R-SOLL helicopter crews from the 41st ARRSq at McClellan and continued to routinely deploy aircraft and crews to northern Georgia for mountain training. In August the 20th deployed six HH-53Hs and personnel to Mountain Home AFB, Idaho, to participate in Exercise

Roughen Wood. There they received a no-notice tasking to insert a force of SFOD-Delta Soldiers to rescue POWs being held at a mock compound. Using NVGs, the crews rendezvoused with HC-130 tankers and then delivered the troops as AC-130s orbited overhead. The Pave Lows also orbited to provide fire support and then extracted the SFOD-Delta troops with their "recovered" POWs and departed the area. The troops were on the ground for only 24 minutes.[88]

Courtesy Wayne Mutza

Pave Lows training with US Army Rangers

This training pattern continued into the winter months with deployments to Fort Bragg, Fort Stewart, and Exercise Foal Eagle in Korea, where a 20th SOS crew performed a real-world SAR to recover an F-16 pilot. The unit also expanded aircrew training in joint service shipboard operations with US Navy ships and special forces units.

In December the wing was notified that General Gabriel had signed the orders to consolidate rescue and special operations. A wing transition team, headed by Col Ray Turczynski, a veteran of Operation Rice Bowl, was formed to work all of the issues that would arise with the change. The team put together a "red book," named for the color of the binder, detailing the operations and training tempo of the unit since the beginning of preparations for Rice Bowl. It laid out, in great detail, the various exercises in which wing assets participated and explained their missions, capabilities, and limitations. The book subsequently saw great use as an increasing number of high-level personnel from Washington and the other services came to Hurlburt for briefings on USAF special operations.

Because of limited space on the base, the 2d AD would move into the same building with the 1st SOW wing headquarters. The 1st SOW would lose 73 personnel billets in the realignment, with most, like the wing intelligence section, moving to the 2d AD. Many believed that the move to MAC would generate more career opportunities for personnel associated with the helicopters and C-130 aircraft than were available in TAC, almost exclusively focused on fighter operations. In January 1983, General Creech visited Hurlburt. He presented the wing two awards: an Air Force Outstanding Unit Award for the period 15 May 1980–30 April 1982 and his personal Achievement Award for the period 1 January 1979–28 February 1982. While both recognized the hard work of the wing's Airmen through an exceptionally difficult period, the second award was particularly special. When the general personally presented it, he said that

> the 1st Special Operations Wing increased the combat capability, readiness, and stature of the Tactical Air Forces by developing and testing new special operations techniques and procedures and by courageous participation in worldwide operations of great national and international significance. These achievements attest to the superior ability and dedication to duty displayed by personnel of the 1st Special Operations Wing and earn them the special recognition symbolized by this personal award from the Commander, Tactical Air Command.[89]

Twenty-Third Air Force

Throughout the winter months, the MAC and TAC staffs pounded out the myriad programming, logistical, and personnel actions necessary for such a significant reorganization involving so many units. On 28 February 1983, Lt Gen Robert Coverdale, the vice-commander of MAC, officiated at the activation of Twenty-Third Air Force at Scott AFB. Its first commander was General Mall; he was succeeded at the ARRS by Brig Gen Philip Prince, the first career helicopter pilot to be promoted to general officer. The Twenty-Third and ARRS would share a headquarters building located across the street from the MAC headquarters. Initially intended to be a command designed to consolidate all USAF helicopter units and missions, the Twenty-Third extant was much more robust and diverse.

The next day, the 2d AD was reactivated at Hurlburt Field. The MAC commander, Gen James Allen, officiated at this ceremony. In attendance were Lt Gen Robert Russ, TAC vice-commander; Lt Gen John Piotrowski, Ninth Air Force commander; Colonel Cox, the 2d AD's first commander; and Col Hugh Hunter, the 1st SOW's new commander. Colonel Takacs was the troop commander for the ceremony. After the ceremony, all of the assembled Airmen changed their command patch from TAC to MAC, although many were not happy with the move, believing that they were being reassigned to what they saw as a "support" command as opposed to the "combat" command they were leaving. To more properly "celebrate" the moment, though, SSgt John Sprouse remembered that a bunch of the 20th guys got together at the Hurlburt Officers' Club down on the Gulf Waterway. There, they took their TAC patches and put them on a small boat which—à la a Viking funeral—was then lit on fire and cast out into the waters.[90]

As General Mall began working with his staff to divide their efforts from those of the residual ARRS staff, challenges and issues rose to the fore. Twenty-Third Air Force would now lead the fight for the new HH-60 helicopter for use as a rescue platform and also now as a possible SOF asset. Additionally, Mall wanted to grow Twenty-Third Air Force to parity with the long-serving Twenty-First and Twenty-Second Air Forces in MAC and began lobbying for the transfer of the 375th Aeromedical Airlift Wing (AAW) at Scott and the 1606th Air Base Wing (ABW) at Kirtland to the Twenty-Third.[91]

Congressional Interest

In April 1983, Congress began to show interest in the changes taking place in the rescue community. The Readiness Subcommittee of the House Armed Services Committee, chaired by Cong. Dan Daniel from Virginia, held hearings on rescue forces, specifically to begin considering the possible need to create some form of overarching DOD rescue organization. General Mall testified at the hearing. He provided a short history of USAF rescue, discussed the intent of the new Twenty-Third Air Force—specifically explaining its dual tasking of combat rescue and SOF support—and detailed current equipment shortfalls and limitations. He highlighted the transfer of the nine HH-53Hs to SOF and suggested that the modification of more H-53s to the HH-53H configuration would not be cost effective. General Mall also pointed out that MAC had already received 12 UH-60A Black Hawks, but future plans rested on procuring the much more technologically advanced HH-60D Night Hawk for all-weather, day/night combat rescue. He also mentioned the developmental work being done with the joint vertical-lift aircraft (JVX), a new tilt-rotor concept, as a longer-range asset for rescue. The subcommittee members took his testimony and asked few follow-up questions; no substantial action resulted from the hearing. However, the budding congressional interest was a harbinger for future actions, and the MAC staff was already aware of political discussion concerning the reorganization of SOF assets into some sort of larger DOD-wide special operating agency for special forces or even a new US unified command for special operations.[92]

Six months later, General Mall reviewed with his staff the efficacy of the structure of Twenty-Third Air Force. Realizing that the staffs at the Twenty-Third, ARRS, and 2d AD did not have enough authorized billets to properly support all required duties, he considered several options for realignment or consolidation before finally deciding to reassign the 39th ARRW, the 41st RWRW, and the 1550th ATTW, currently reporting to the ARRS, to now report directly to Twenty-Third Air Force. MAC approved his plans and also authorized the reassignment of the 375th AAW and the 1606th ABW to the Twenty-Third Air Force.

The movement of the 39th, 41st, and 1550th Wings to the Twenty-Third effectively changed the ARRS from a functioning headquarters into a coordinating agency for all rescue activity in the contiguous United States, ending its 35-year service as "the" rescue command during which its units had saved over 20,000 lives worldwide. The ARRS commander, General Prince, was offered the position of vice-commander of Twenty-Third Air Force, but he declined and retired. It was a somewhat ignominious end for the first helicopter general officer, a fact not lost on the young helicopter pilots of the Twenty-Third who had been told they would have more promotion potential in MAC.[93]

Concurrent with all of the realignments, MAC established the Special Missions Operational Test and Evaluation Center (SMOTEC) at Hurlburt Field. This center would combine OT&E functions of the

1550th ATTW at Kirtland and the 1st SOW into one organization for both combat rescue and special operations functions. The 2d AD commander would also serve as the SMOTEC commander and report directly to the MAC commander on all SMOTEC matters. During the year, the SMOTEC would conduct testing on NVG use by rescue and special operations crews, aircraft compatibility tests for new survival radios, and the use of several types of machine guns aboard various helicopters.[94]

As the units were reorganized, Twenty-Third Air Force finalized its mission statement:

> The mission of the Twenty-third Air Force is to exercise command over assigned forces worldwide, consisting of the following:
>
> a. Two operational wings responsible for combat rescue, locating and re-covering downed Airmen on a global basis, . . .
>
> b. One training wing responsible for training USAF helicopter [crews] . . .
>
> c. One air base wing . . .
>
> d. The Aerospace Rescue and Recovery Service . . .
>
> e. The Second Air Division responsible for providing a focal point for all Air Force special operations matters. In this role, the Second Air Division develops, plans, and maintains the capability for deployment of combat ready special operations forces for use in unconventional warfare, counterterrorist operations, collective security, and other operations in any area of the world.[95]

On 30 June 1983, General Ryan succeeded General Allen as the MAC commander. Well-versed in all of the current issues, he directed his staff to maintain its sharp focus on the current MAC special operations forces and plans for enhancement to satisfy projected requirements.

Mr. Noel Koch, the principal deputy assistant SecDef for international security affairs (PDASD-ISA), was another tireless advocate for building up special operations forces. Through magazine articles, he continuously advocated for more money, personnel, and hardware for special operations forces. He also played a role in setting up another outgrowth of the Holloway report, a committee of senior retired military leaders called the Special Operations Policy Advisory Group (SOPAG). Its charter members were Admiral Holloway; Lt Gen Sam Wilson, USA; Brig Gen Donald Blackburn, USA; General Manor; Lt Gen James Ahmann, USAF; and General Secord. All were highly respected in their fields and strongly supportive of revitalized SOF forces. Koch was able to set up the SOPAG so that it could report directly to the SecDef.[96]

On 3 October, the SecDef reiterated high-level interest in this issue through a letter written by the Honorable Paul Thayer, deputy SecDef, which directed several actions to insure the revitalization of special operations forces "as a matter of national urgency." He sent his letter to the top management of the OSD, the JCS, and the secretaries of the military departments and outlined a four-point program for special operations forces:

1. Necessary force structure expansion and enhancements in command and control, personnel policy, training, and equipment will be implemented as rapidly as possible and will be *fully* implemented not later than the end of Fiscal Year 1990 (emphasis in original).

2. Collateral activities will be enhanced as necessary to provide fully effective support to the planning and execution of special operations.

3. Each service will assign SOF and related activities sufficient resource allocation priority and will establish appropriate intensive management mechanisms to ensure that these objectives are met.

4. Resource decisions for current and programmed SOF, once made at the Secretary of Defense level, will not be changed or reduced by OSD or Service staffs unless coordinated by the Principal Deputy Assistant Secretary of Defense (International Security Affairs) and the Assistant Secretary of Defense (Comptroller) and approved by the Secretary of Defense.[97]

In response to the tasking, now known as the Thayer memorandum, HQ USAF directed MAC to codevelop with the Air Staff a draft special operations master plan for submission to the PDASD-ISA by 1 March 1984. It would include information on force structure, associated command and control, personnel, training, equipment, maintenance, and logistics requirements through the year 2000. Both staffs got to work on this critical project.[98]

At the end of 1983, MAC possessed 30 C/HH-53s of several variations, as follows: 1550th ATTW (Kirtland)—two CHs and five Hs; 20th SOS (Hurlburt Field)—nine HH-53Hs; 67th ARRSq (Woodbridge)—five HHs; and 41st ARRSq (McClellan AFB)—nine HHs. The USAF had 16 additional C/HH-53s: 6594th Test Group (Hawaii)— six HHs; 6514th Test Squadron (Utah)—two HHs; and 601st Tactical Air Support Group (Germany)—eight CHs.[99]

2d Air Division

With the reactivation of the 2d AD, the USAF finally had its special operations forces under one major command. MAC was a truly diversified command with a global outlook and mission. The movement was also quite timely. While the Soviet bloc represented the most dangerous global threat, active conflict with it was unlikely. Conversely, low-level conflict or terrorism appeared to be the norm for the foreseeable future, and special operations forces could be more effective than conventional forces in such scenarios. Noted one early 2d AD study, "The overriding concerns of special operations are operational security, detailed intelligence, extensive planning, and precise execution." To properly execute their missions, special forces ground teams needed to be moved into possible hostile territory in all weather conditions, day and night, to accomplish their missions.[100]

The 2d AD and 1st SOW commanders worked through the challenges of the new command arrangement, facilitated greatly by the fact that both headquarters were in the same building. The Wing Special Planning Division, which worked closely with the JSOC, was reassigned to the 2d AD as their Special Plans Division, with the same responsibilities. The 20th SOS continued to train. First-generation Pave Low crew members were now being rotated to other assignments, and new Airmen, such as Capt Dave Harris (a USMC transfer) and Maj Horace "Bo" Johnson, were arriving. While all were H-53 qualified, they had to get their Pave Low qualification at Hurlburt, initially in the Central Training Flight and then in the 20th. Squadron detachments were constantly being dispatched to participate in joint training with JSOC and various special forces elements in CONUS exercises such as Solid Shield, Casino Dancer, and Robin Sage. On 7 June, squadron personnel again provided a comprehensive briefing and aerial demonstration to Koch, who had developed a keen interest in the Pave Low and what the 20th crews could do with it. On many occasions, MAC R-SOLL HH-53s would also participate and be led by the Pave Lows. Two Pave Lows, crews, and support personnel deployed to Europe for the 1983 version of the Flintlock series of exercises in Europe. The 20th was now integrated into European, Pacific, and RDJTF war plans, and evolving taskings indicated that eight, 12, and eight Pave Lows, respectively, were needed to fulfill anticipated needs.

Such a demand dictated a constant high ops tempo for the 20th as the sole Pave Low unit. Throughout this period, too, the 20th was directed to support counterdrug operations with its UH-1N aircraft and crews as part of Operation BAT (Bahamas, Antilles, and Turks). No Pave Lows were involved; however, for a period expected to be only a few months, the squadron leadership had to direct and supervise the unit efforts, which involved working with US Coast Guard and local police units in the BAT region of the Caribbean to interdict the flow of drugs. This "temporary" program would continue for several years, adding to the overall unit workload.[101]

Joint Special Operations Agency

In an effort to better organize and coordinate the actions of various special operations components in the disparate commands, the JCS Operations Directorate (J-3) Special Operations Division (SOD) suggested in October 1983 that each unified command have a designated special operations command (SOC). Within a few months, the various commands had redesignated their special operations and unconventional task forces as Special Operations Component, US European Command (SOCEUR), Special Operations Component, US Pacific Command (SOCPAC), and Special Operations Component, US Central Command (SOCCENT), for example, thus eliminating a seeming maze of acronyms, such as JUWTFEUR, JUWTFPAC, and SOTFE. At the same time, in an effort to finally answer the Holloway recommendation to form a high-level agency to provide oversight of special operations activities and a standing planning cell, and with the Thayer memorandum now working its way through the Pentagon, the JCS created the Joint Special Operations Agency (JSOA). Effective 1 January 1984, it would absorb the SOD and add additional personnel. Its mission was to advise the JCS on "all matters pertaining to special operations and the military activities related thereto, including national strategy, planning, programming, budgeting, resource development and allocation, joint doctrinal guidance, exercise and readiness evaluation, and employment of forces."[102]

The SOPAG recommended to the SecDef that the director be a three-star officer. Secretary Weinberger decided that the director would be rated at only two stars. The JSOA would have a field grade officer representative in each unified command. That representative would be knowledgeable of all plans under which special forces were tasked in that command. The first JSOA director was Maj Gen Douglas Rice, USMC. This organization would prove to be weak and ineffectual because it had no significant support from the individual services. However, it was the first general officer position on the JCS since the Vietnam War that was designed to provide advocacy for special operations to that body.[103]

20th Special Operations Squadron

Regardless of the changes taking place at higher levels, the 20th continued to train and participate in an endless series of exercises, static displays, and briefings for visitors and dignitaries interested in its aircraft and capabilities. In September, one Pave Low and crew were dispatched to Eglin AFB to participate in Operation Granite Star II. This was a test program designed to validate the use of new equipment on several SOF aircraft to provide countermeasures for infrared-guided antiaircraft missiles. The results were classified but were very positive for the aircrews, since these types of missiles were a serious threat to aircraft such as the Pave Low. During this period, too, the squadron deployed several crews to Georgia to work with US Army special forces teams and to conduct mountain training. For the period July–December 1983, the 20th SOS logged 527 HH-53 sorties for 1,278.3 flight hours.[104]

Operation Urgent Fury

From 20 October until early November, the 2d AD and 1st SOW were heavily involved in Operation Urgent Fury, an effort designed to protect and evacuate Americans, mostly students at a medical school, on the island of Grenada in the southeast Caribbean and to prevent a communist takeover of its government. The 1st SOW provided AC-130s, MC-130s, and CCTs to the effort as part of JTF 120, which invaded the island in the early morning hours of 25 October. The 20th SOS was initially alerted to supply eight HH-53s for the operation to insert a Ranger force to seize the large airfield at Point Salines, but it was subsequently removed from the plan when an airborne assault was judged to be the quicker option. The assault took place but was extremely dangerous and chaotic. Subsequent helicopter special operations missions were conducted by an aviation element from US Army special operations aviation, now organized as the 160th Aviation Battalion but referred to as TF-160. Combat operations lasted for only three days until all objectives were achieved. Most 1st SOW aircraft and crews had returned to Hurlburt by early November, with two AC-130s remaining over the island until late November. Ultimately, more than 600 American students and 82 endangered foreign citizens were evacuated from the island, and the communist putsch was prevented. However, the US military noted many lessons learned, primarily focusing on the challenges of joint and combined operations; the difficulty of integrating special forces operations with conventional operations; problems with intelligence planning, communications, and command and control; and the critical need for tactical mobility capable of night and all-weather operations.[105]

Action on Many Fronts

As 1983 was drawing to a close, more and more political leaders were paying attention to the travails of the special forces, especially Congressman Daniel, a firm believer in the need for SOF revitalization. Working in his office was a key aide named Ted Lunger, who had served in the US Army special forces and shared his passion. The two were a relentless force. Daniel had recently led a successful effort to create the US Central Command (USCENTCOM) as a unified command to watch over key national interests in the Middle East region. He was now ready to engage on the SOF issue. Lunger had developed extensive contacts throughout the SOF community and Pentagon, such as Noel Koch and his assistant, Lynn Rylander. He had also developed connections with a cabal of young military officers furtively called the "SOF Mafia" and mostly from the 1st SOW: Lt Col Lee Hess, Lt Col T. J. Doherty, Maj Gary Weikel, Maj Greg Colvin, and Maj Gary Heckman. All were crew members on the various 1st SOW aircraft. Several had left Hurlburt in the fall of 1983 to attend the Armed Forces Staff College in Norfolk, Virginia, and had then reported for duty in various divisions of the Air Staff in the Pentagon.

At about the same time, Capt Ed Reed left the 20th and proceeded to Headquarters MAC to serve as a systems program manager for SOFs and, in particular, to work modification issues for the HH-53s. He was the first Pave Low pilot assigned to the headquarters and was ensconced in a small office with Maj Donny Wurster. Commissioned out of the Air Force Academy in 1973, Wurster was an experienced H-3 rescue pilot with operational tours in Korea and Alaska and in-structor/evaluator duty at Kirtland AFB. He was now on the MAC staff as the weapons systems program manager for the HH-60 pro-gram. The two forged a strong friendship, working partnership, and common vision for future USAF helicopters for both SOF and com-bat rescue. Over the next several years, this relationship would have a direct and positive impact upon the fortunes of the Pave Low force in many different ways.[106]

To replace the departing Pave Low flyers, the 20th SOS received four new pilots: Captains Bob Maldonado, Corby Martin, Lyle Koe-nig, and Randy O'Boyle. Martin was arriving from duty with the 67th ARRSq at RAF Bentwaters. He had graduated from the Air Force Academy in 1980 and had gone directly to helicopter flight school. Subsequently, he went through the H-53 transition at Kirtland before going to England. There, he found it challenging to work his way into a squadron full of highly qualified SEA veterans. However, he was able to slowly build up his flying time and qualify as an aircraft com-mander before departing for Hurlburt at the end of 1983.

Arriving at the 20th in early 1984, Martin liked what he found. The unit was training hard, and the first guys he met—Jack Kelly and Tom Aldrich—were tactically oriented and focused on supporting the JSOC. This was much different than the attitude at Bentwaters. Here at Hurlburt, the tone was, "We are going to war tomorrow. We need to be ready. We need to train the way we fight." Martin believed that his squadron was more ready to go to war than any he had ever seen. He started out on night sorties, where he learned to use NVGs. How-ever, it was several months before Martin could start his Pave Low qualifications. Subsequently, he went on TDYs to Asheville, North Carolina, initially for mountain training, and then to the Philippines for jungle training.[107]

Martin was already fully experienced on the H-53, and he found the tactical mission to be interesting and challenging. However, mas-tering the new technology—the computers, INS, moving map dis-play, FLIR, and new secure radios—took some work. Martin also im-mediately saw that the flight engineer was absolutely integral to flying the aircraft; he was constantly updating the navigational gear while the pilots focused on aircraft control. Martin recalled that "you could load only eight waypoints. You'd load eight more in store points. If you had a 35-point waypoint list, you were continually updating and moving. The guy who did that was the guy sitting in the center seat because the pilots were trying to keep the 'shiny side down,' so to speak. So he did a lot of work, a lot of manual inputs."[108] He was also keenly aware that it took all six aboard to properly handle the machine and that the human dynamics of crew integration were critical to safe operations. Martin pointed out that in learning to fly the aircraft, "we took great pains to make sure that everybody was in the decision process. It wasn't always democratic, but at least everyone had a shot, and you knew what was going to happen."[109] Finally completing his training in August, Martin then joined the line as a fully qualified Pave Low aircraft commander.

As Captain Martin was mastering the intricacies of the HH-53H, Weikel was settling in at the Pentagon and was ready to apply his special operations–derived "assault mentality." Almost immediately he found common ground with others so committed. Collectively, the civilian staffers and the young officers from Hurlburt believed that the United States needed to build an effective special operations capability to deal with the evolving world where lower-intensity conflict was much more probable than high-intensity theater war. They sensed that acquisition, especially of aircraft, was essential and that there was some interest in Congress to recommend funding more Pave Lows, which various war game analyses had shown were needed. However, funding for special operations forces had always been cyclical, and the great challenge was to find a way to make it steady and predictable. The larger problem was to raise the priority of SOFs in the resource decisions that the services and OSD were making. SOF advocates emphasized the "jointness" issues demonstrated in Rice Bowl and, more recently, Urgent Fury.

SOF proponents had also closely watched the USAF's recent moves to consolidate its special operations units under 2d AD. The 2d AD appeared to be getting lost in the larger Twenty-Third Air Force, which, although initially justified as an effort to reprioritize and focus special operations, now seemed more of an effort to form another globally focused multifunctional command.[110] This observation was reinforced when, on 1 January 1984, the 375th AAW was assigned to the Twenty-Third Air Force. Subsequently, the missions of aeromedical evacuation and operational support airlift were added to the other responsibilities of the command, further diluting the importance of the SOFs and their use.

Two months later, the MAC, Twenty-Third Air Force, and 2d AD finished their version of the Special Operations Forces Master Plan as required by the Thayer memorandum. It was a milestone in the history of USAF SOF force structure development because it was the first time that the USAF held a concise document that attempted to consolidate all requirements with a plan for their accomplishment. Several hundred pages in length, the plan laid out the role of special forces in current USAF doctrine. It defined how they could support national policy and strategic and tactical objectives in the FY 1986–2000 time frame across the spectrum of conflict, within existing acquisition programs and realistic fiscal constraints. Its special operations forces would provide JSOTFs with rapid response and quick employment of long-range, low-level penetration of hostile airspace to conduct and support offensive operations. Based upon analysis of the projected scenarios and evolving technology, the plan presented suggestions for command and control, communications improvements, intelligence needs and dissemination, significant aircraft increases, and the procurement of third-generation NVGs for SOF crews. In reference to Pave Low, unclassified portions of the plan projected that the new HH-60D helicopter would be procured to serve the night, all-weather requirements and that the new JVX would be the eventual replacement for the HH-53H.[111]

In the interim, 36 HH-53s were required to meet contingency taskings for the combatant theaters. HH-53B/C aircraft equipped for the R-SOLL missions could be used to meet this requirement, as could the new HH-60Ds. However, the HH-60s could not replace on a one-per-one basis. Additionally, the HH-53s in the 6594th Test Group and the CH-53Cs in the 601st TASS in Germany could be modified to the R-SOLL configuration for the mission, as well as the HH-53s at the 41st ARRSq at McClellan. Under the plan, the R-SOLL and R-SOLL-capable H-53s were now considered SOF augmenting or collateral air assets. All H-53s should also go through a service life extension program (SLEP) and receive numerous upgrades. However, there were no recommendations that any more aircraft be modified to the Pave Low standard.[112]

MAC submitted the master plan to the Air Staff Board, which approved it on 24 February 1984, with one office stating that "the Air Force, for the first time, has a long-range plan to improve and then maintain combat capability to conduct and support joint special operations." General Gabriel signed it, as did the secretary of the Air

Force, the Honorable Verne Orr, on 4 April, although both noted that funding limitations and research and development lead times would prevent the USAF from achieving the FY 90 objectives laid out in the Thayer memorandum.[113]

Programming documents emanating from MAC and Twenty-Third Air Force indicated that, based upon the master plan, 18 more H-53s could be modified so that they were R-SOLL capable and able to perform most missions, except those that absolutely required the TF/TA capabilities of the Pave Lows. The six HH-53s from the 6594th Test Group would be used to form a special operations squadron in the Pacific. Additionally, the Pave Lows and augmentation aircraft were programmed to receive ALR-69 radar warning receivers, flare/chaff dispenser systems, secure voice / jam-resistant radios, satellite communications (SATCOM) capabilities, and improved cockpit lighting compatible with the new third-generation NVGs. The SLEP program would also be funded to allow the helicopters to operate until the year 2000.

Unfortunately, though, as the master plan was being approved, the Air Force Council reduced the HH-60D project buy from 155 to 99 aircraft. These were the only near-term aircraft acquisitions for rescue and possibly special operations use.[114]

Initiative 17

Two months later, another action took place that also seemed to indicate a lack of interest on the part of USAF leadership concerning its rotary-wing SOF forces. It originated from an effort to resolve or at least clarify a wide range of joint issues that had beguiled both the US Army and Air Force since the latter's separation from the senior service in 1947 and that had been examined in previous joint working groups and initiatives. The two current Army and Air Force chiefs, Gen John Wickham and Gen Charles Gabriel, respectively, initiated another attempt to increase cooperation for battlefield synchronization and integration by fabricating a new method of mutual force development, including cross-service budgeting and programming procedures. Increasing cohesion between the two services was also receiving renewed emphasis because the US Army, moving forward from its post-Vietnam malaise, had recently rewritten its warfighting doctrine and adopted the concept of "AirLand Battle" to meet and defeat the forces of the Warsaw Pact, should they ever attempt to invade and conquer Western Europe.

The two chiefs were old friends from their time together at West Point and, working through their respective deputies for plans and operations, in April 1983 had formed ad hoc groups within their service staffs. Bypassing formal staff processes, these groups shaped 31 initiatives to address some of the most contentious issues. The USAF team was drawn primarily from the Checkmate office of the Air Staff, led by Col Joseph Redden. It had no SOF members and did not coordinate its findings pertaining to special operations forces with the 2d AD, Twenty-Third Air Force, or even MAC. The formal memorandum of agreement between the two chiefs was signed on 22 May 1984, culminating what was really a decade-long effort to wrestle with these contentious issues about doctrine, employment of forces, and a wide range of challenges concerning the joint employment of combat power. Initiative 17 addressed SOF rotary-wing assets, stating that "the Air Force will transfer the responsibility for providing rotary-wing lift support for SOF to the Army. A detailed implementation plan will be jointly developed."[115]

The intent of the initiative was somewhat unclear. What did "responsibility" mean? Did it mean that the USAF would transfer the nine HH-53Hs, and possibly nine UH-1Ns and six CH-3s in a USAF Reserve unit, to the Army? To some US Army and even USAF officers, it seemed to make sense to give them to the Army, which operated thousands of helicopters and had just formed an aviation branch to manage its officers as a recognized career combat specialty. In fact, though, Initiative 17 represented a mortal threat to the USAF Pave Low community and had to be stopped.

Initially, the MAC staff assumed that this initiative merely involved the transfer of the mission and would not require the reassignment of aircraft, equipment, or personnel to the Army and that all planned helicopter enhancements and crew training would continue. It also estimated that the SOF master plan would require only minimal changes and that the Pave Lows, UH-1Ns, and CH-3s could be moved over to combat rescue duties under the Twenty-Third Air Force. However, strong doctrinal issues were at stake in the mission transfer. The long-range movement of forces had traditionally been a USAF function, and any mission transfer would allow the Army to argue that it would then need the aircraft and force structure to do it. The Army could argue that it should receive the Pave Low aircraft and possibly even the JVX when it entered the fleet. MAC's position was that in the mission transfer, no collateral transfer of assets, people, force structure, or funding would occur.[116]

Congressman Daniel was briefed on Initiative 17 and did not like what was happening. He called for a hearing before his Readiness Subcommittee of the House Armed Services Committee, which also included Florida congressman Earl Hutto, Democrat and chairman of the subordinate and newly formed Special Operations Panel. This assignment was quite a plum opportunity for the three-term congressman. Several Army and Navy special operations facilities were in his congressional district, as was Hurlburt Field. However, Hutto was already well familiar with the Pave Low aircraft because he was involved with the initial modification of the aircraft at NAS Pensacola in the late 1970s. He had every incentive to strongly support and protect the aircraft and the 20th SOS, in particular.[117]

Ted Lunger was still working in Daniel's office and through routine staff processes had gotten to know Maj Gary Weikel, who started feeding him back-channel data showing that Army aviation did not have the expertise to take over, maintain, and operate Pave Low. Weikel recalled his days of flying with the Army special operations crews. He felt that they did not have the necessary equipment and training to do the tasks assigned. He was aware that in the previous year, they had suffered four serious accidents that killed 22 Soldiers. He also knew that in reviewing this entire program, the Army leadership had come very close to canceling the whole endeavor outright. Weikel shared that information with the congressional staffers.[118]

On 6 September 1984, Noel Koch, the PDASD-ISA, testified about the progress being made in special operations readiness. He was generally optimistic about recent developments but also expressed strong concern about the transfer of the helicopter mission to the Army. Koch also said, "The memorandum of understanding basically says the Army is going to take over the mission. [But] if the Air Force divested itself of the [SOF aviation] mission, the Army had no ability to pick up the mission." Koch and several other "SOF Mafia" cohorts argued to all who would listen that the Army just did not have the doctrine, training base, and logistical support necessary to do the type of flying that the Pave Low crews routinely did and that it would take a very long time to develop it. In a subsequent committee meeting, General Secord, a sitting member of the SOPAG, testified that if the Army were to attempt to create such a long-range capability from scratch, it would cost "well over $1 billion" for the Army to separately match the Air Force current long-range helicopter capability. The Army requested that it be given the Pave Low aircraft and support equipment as well as the services of an Air Force training program to instruct its initial cadre of crews and maintenance personnel—an estimated 50 and 370 personnel, respectively. General Gabriel agreed to the request, stating that he wanted the transfer of the mission and the nine HH-53H Pave Low III aircraft and support equipment, but not squadron personnel, to be complete by July 1986, 22 months hence.[119]

At Headquarters MAC, staffers were shocked and upset about the possible transfer of the Pave Lows to the Army. Still new to MAC and staff duties, Captain Reed decided that he would take some action. He did some deep research and determined that the Air Staff had offered the ARRS funding for 28 more Pave Lows in 1979. However, the ARRS commander, General Saunders, wanted instead to use the money to further enhance the selection and production of the H-X, which eventually became the HH-60. Reed realized that offers of funding were opportunities best met by preparation. He determined to use his staff position to influence the Pave Low and drafted MAC Statement of Operational Need (MAC SON) 11-84, defining a need for a fleet of upgraded Pave Low aircraft.

The document called for a SLEP for all USAF H-53s to extend their service life to FY 2000, an upgrade of additional HH-53B/Cs to an improved Pave Low configuration—Pave Low III (Enhanced), modifications to enable shipboard capability, increased gross weight capability, enhanced defensive and weapons systems, improved secure communications and Global Positioning System (GPS) navigation systems, and better reliability and maintainability for all aircraft systems. The SON was coordinated through the staff and forwarded to the Air Staff for approval and action. However, the Air Staff never approved it, citing limited funding for modifications in the current fiscal year, conflicts with Initiative 17, and potential impacts on the projected acquisition of the new HH-60s. Regardless, Reed had created a document that was widely distributed and could easily be used to precipitate the modification of more H-53s if, by any chance, some funding source should avail itself.[120]

Other voices spoke out against the transfer of the aircraft to the Army. All of the SOPAG members were aware of the recent Army special operations helicopter accidents and, in unison, addressed a strongly worded letter to the SecDef that read, "We do not believe the country's best interests are served by this agreement [Initiative 17] and recommend that it be reconsidered. . . . The Air Force had been considering converting a large number of existing HH-53s to fully capable Pave Lows at a cost of about $200M. We believe it would be far more costly to start from scratch in the Army rather than build on the existing capability in this manner." One SOPAG member, Lt Gen Sam Wilson, US Army, dissented from the group opinion and submitted his own. It was more strident and said, "The Army is not capable of supporting long-range Special Operations missions with the H-60 BLACKHAWK while the Air Force has amply demonstrated in numerous joint exercises that it can do the job effectively with the HH-53 Pave Low. End of argument."[121]

At the conclusion of the hearings before his committee, Congressman Daniel, on 4 October, wrote to Deputy Secretary William Taft, expressing serious concerns about the transfer and suggesting a short-range/long-range split between the Air Force and Army. Taft responded 13 days later, saying that he approved in concept the proposal to transfer both the responsibility for the mission and the Pave Low helicopters from the Air Force to the Army. Daniel replied to him on 30 October, with copies to Generals Gabriel and Wickham, saying he still felt that the transfer was not sensible and considered neither the input from the unified commands nor the impact on combat rescue, critical contingency response, and direct support of Navy SOFs. It was evident that a huge fight was brewing between Air Force leadership and Congress, which represented a particularly difficult situation for both the MAC and Twenty-Third Air Force commanders since they had to satisfy both to do their jobs.[122]

First and Second Losses

On 17 October 1984, the Pave Low community suffered a terrible loss when HH-53H #73-1647 crashed while on a mission as part of Exercise Cope Thunder in the Philippines. It was the second aircraft of a flight of two Pave Lows led by Maj Mark Schibler. He was flying with Capt John Spier as his copilot, SMSgt John Selfridge and SSgt Greg Vanhyning as his engineers, and SSgt John Sprouse and MSgt Ron Dorazio as his gunners. On a night mission, the two aircraft encountered a thunderstorm while flying through mountains. Schibler was able to climb above the terrain. In the confusion, the second aircraft crew became spatially disoriented and flew into a mountain, completely destroying the aircraft and killing the crew of six Airmen. John Sprouse was the left scanner and watched the second aircraft hit the mountain. The squadron commander, Lt Col Lou Grant, met Schibler and his crew when they landed. Sprouse gave Grant his eyewitness report, which he had to repeat later for the accident investigation board. The loss devastated the unit.[123]

Also in October, MAC commander Gen Thomas Ryan visited Hurlburt Field to talk to the troops and personally tell them of the pending reassignment of the Pave Lows to the Army. Coming as it did just a few days after the loss of the crew in the Philippines, it was a second blow to the morale of the Airmen of the 20th. The 450 troops affected by such a move began to wonder what this meant to them and their careers. Ryan had several staff specialists to begin working the myriad personnel, logistical, and operational details. Many Pave Low personnel discovered that they would be frozen at Hurlburt for an indeterminate period as the base soon began to train the Army crews and support personnel. The maintenance specialists were flabbergasted that the Army could believe that it could maintain the Pave Low. It was full of complex systems for which the Army did not have trained specialists or even designated military operational specialties.[124] As one 2d AD staff officer lamented, "The transfer of the Pave Low helicopters to the Army would be like giving the space shuttle to Chad."[125] One unit member, MSgt Bill Halcomb, had just bought a house in Fort Walton Beach. In a fit of pique, he took the leftover "for sale" sign from his front yard and placed it in front of the squadron building. The troops loved it; however, a "senior wing officer" directed that it be removed.[126]

Returning to Scott AFB, General Ryan directed his staff to develop a plan to make the transfer move as smoothly as possible so that there was no loss of national capability during the process. All recognized that this would generate a huge training requirement for both Kirtland AFB and Hurlburt Field because the Army had no capability to train its own personnel on the Pave Low system.

Congressman Hutto was briefed on the visit and had a different opinion. He stated, "I don't feel that moving the rotary lift mission from the Air Force to the Army would be in the best interests of either service. We, in the Armed Services committee, are expressing in the strongest terms possible, our disagreement. The services have considerable latitude in what they do, but Congress funds the military and

Congress turns to our Committee for guidance. It is incumbent on us to see that the right thing's done, and the Defense Department hasn't satisfied us that this is right."[127]

Hutto was also hearing from his constituents on the proposed transfer. Gwen Grant, Colonel Grant's wife, wrote to the congressman. Citing the tragic loss of the crew in the Philippines and the parallel bad news of the Pave Low fleet, she penned on 30 October:

> The official announcement [of the crash] was difficult to deal with and split our concerns at a time when our only priority should have been honoring our dead and taking care of their families as best we could. They deserved better. . . .

> This squadron has the most professional, dedicated, and highly trained men in the helicopter world. These men and their families have sacrificed for a mission we all believe in. . . . The 20th family endures because we are *all* dedicated to the mission. . . .

> I hope in some way this letter will encourage you to continue your fight not only for this squadron, but for what I believe is for the best interest of this country.

In responding, Hutto wrote, "Your comments are very helpful—extremely supportive of my arguments for requesting the Army and the Air Force to reconsider their proposal. Let me assure you that I will do all I can to reverse this decision."[128]

On 14 November 1984, the 20th SOS experienced a second loss of an HH-53H when aircraft 73-1650 crashed on a JSOC day-training mission at Fort Bragg. The aircraft, commanded by Capt Jack Kelly, was conducting an in-flight refueling when the tail rotor gearbox separated from the aircraft. The copilot, Capt Dave Harris, was flying the aircraft when the failure happened. The aircraft reacted violently as the tail gunner, TSgt Jerry Price, said on the intercom, "Our tail rotor just fell off!" Kelly took the controls and autorotated the aircraft toward a remote clear area. While the tradeoff of rotor revolutions per minute for energy to glide to the clearing insured that the aircraft would not come down on trees, it would, however, land extremely hard. In fact, although the touchdown destroyed the aircraft, it probably saved lives.

All seven crew members and eight Army Rangers on board were wounded, three seriously, including Lt Col Bo Johnson, who was also aboard. All would fly again, except for Kelly. His grievous wounds, including a broken back, would keep the flight surgeons from ever recertifying him for flying duties. Instead, he would face a series of operations and long rehabilitation. He would be highly rewarded and decorated for his quick actions that saved the lives of the crew and passengers. These included a Distinguished Flying Cross and the Kolligian Award for 1984. However, they were dismal consolation for a flying career too soon ended.[129]

The next night General Gabriel, Congressman Daniel, and several staff members, including Ted Lunger, arrived at Fort Bragg for Pave Low rides and briefings. That evening, Daniel called all the 20th Airmen together in the hangar and gave them a pep talk. Essentially he said, "Your problem is that you have never had a daddy rabbit. Now, I am your daddy rabbit." He left, resolved to lend the full weight of his key legislative position to Pave Low. His support was timely and critical because Pave Low was at its absolute nadir. His words were exactly what the men standing before him needed to hear. Those officers and Airmen had become the initial cadre that brought Pave Low to its tactical fruition. They were supporters—zealots—who devoutly believed in it and were not about to give up the fight.[130]

Notes

1. Reiter, "Packing Rescue for Special Delivery," 18–23; and Connelly, interview.
2. History of ARRS, 1 Jan–31 Dec 1980, vol. 1, 71–77.
3. Assistant Secretary of Defense/Public Affairs (ASD/PA), Wright-Patterson AFB, OH, news release, Public Affairs Memorandum (PAM) 80-126, n.d.
4. Schibler, interview.
5. History of 1550th ATTW, 1 Jan–30 June 1980, vol. 1, xi; "Commander's Assessment, 23 May 1980," ibid., vol. 2, doc. 6; Connelly, interview; and Kyle, *Guts to Try*, 154.
6. Lenahan, *Crippled Eagle*, 39. Gast had recently served for two years as chief, Military Assistance Advisory Group, Iran, and was currently on the TAC staff. He was slated for promotion to lieutenant general and assignment to the position of vice-commander of TAC effective 1 March 1980. For this operation, he provided his knowledge of Iran and also supervised the training program for the helicopter crews. Koskinas, *Black Hats and White Hats*, 185.
7. Marquis, *Unconventional Warfare*, 1–2; and Greeley, "Desert One," 1–9. The Iranian rescue attempt has been well documented. Perhaps the best reading is *The Guts to Try* by Col James Kyle, USAF, retired.
8. History of ARRS, 1 Jan–31 Dec 1980, vol. 1, 17–18.
9. Kyle, *Guts to Try*, 268–345.
10. Holloway, *Holloway Report*, "Issue 11: Helicopter Force Size"; and "Issue 12: Alternate Helicopter Pilots," 33–36.
11. Ibid., Issue 12, 35.
12. Beckwith and Knox, *Delta Force*, 224.
13. Bowden, *Guests of the Ayatollah*, 453.
14. Ibid.

15. Boykin, *Never Surrender*, 110.

16. Kyle, *Guts to Try*, 27.

17. Lenahan, *Crippled Eagle*, 52. Beckwith later said of Gast, "He knew all there was to know about navigational systems, but he didn't know how to fly a helicopter. He'd been a jet jockey." Beckwith, *Delta Force*, 229.

18. Holloway, *Holloway Report*, "Issue 13: Helicopter Unit," 37.

19. Kelly, *From a Dark Sky*, 254.

20. Holloway, *Holloway Report*, chap. 5, "Recommendations," 61.

21. Message, 142310Z MAY 80, CSAF/CV [vice-commander] to MAC and TAC commanders et al., subject: Pave Low III Beddown, in History of ARRS, 1 Jan–31 Dec 1980, vol. 2, supplemental doc. I-45; and History of 1550th ATTW, 1 Jan–30 June 1980, vol. 1, xii.

22. Koskinas, *Black Hats and White Hats*, 110; History of 1st SOW, 1 Apr–30 June 1980, vol. 2, 52; and Connelly and Reed, interviews.

23. Connelly and Schibler, interviews.

24. Pushies, *Night Stalkers*, 15.

25. Secord, *Honored and Betrayed*, 153–59; and Lenahan, *Crippled Eagle*, 160–64.

26. Schibler, interview.

27. Stankovich and Homan, interviews.

28. Russell, interview.

29. Grove, Reed, Stankovich, and Russell, interviews.

30. Weikel, interview.

31. Connelly and Pehr, interviews. Lt Col Frank Pehr retired from the USAF in 1985. Subsequently, he was hired by the Systems Research Laboratory and helped design and engineer the highly upgraded MH-53J. He remained with that firm, overseeing Pave Low and other programs as a technical representative until 1999, when he retired again. He then went to work for Lockheed Martin at Kirtland AFB as an academic and simulator instructor for the Pave Lows, until finally retiring in 2002. He claims 30 years of service—1972 to 2002—on the Pave Low (Pehr, interviews).

32. History of ARRS, 1 Jan–31 Dec 1980, vol. 1, 78–79, 101–2.

33. Pehr, interviews.

34. Nomination package for Col Bill Takacs for the Air Commando Hall of Fame, n.d., provided by Col Gary Weikel, USAF, retired.

35. Grove and Schibler, interviews.

36. Reed, interview.

37. Ibid.

38. Simmon, interview.

39. Larsen to the author, e-mail.

40. Connelly, interview.

41. Russell, interview.

42. Grove and Weikel, interviews; and Pushies, *Night Stalkers*, 15.

43. History of ARRS, 1 Jan–31 Dec 1980, vol. 1, 79.

44. Secord, *Honored and Betrayed*, 159–60; and Kelly, *From a Dark Sky*, 255–6.

45. Connelly, interview.

46. Stankovich, interview.

47. Stiles, interview.

48. Walters, interview.

49. Kelly, interview.

50. Secord, *Honored and Betrayed*, 162–3.

51. Lenahan, *Crippled Eagle*, 179–83.

52. Walters, interview.

53. Ibid.

54. Ibid.

55. Beckwith and Knox, *Delta Force*, 295.

56. Ibid., 299; and Lenahan, *Crippled Eagle*, 170–71, 184.

57. History of ARRS, 1 Jan–31 Dec 1980, vol. 1, 24–25.

58. Lenahan, *Crippled Eagle*, 185.

59. Pushies, *Night Stalkers*, 16.

60. Reed, interview.

61. History of 1st SOW, 1 Oct 1982–28 Feb 1983, vol. 1, I-10.

62. Kelly, *From a Dark Sky*, 264.

63. History of 1st SOW, 1 Oct–31 Dec 1980, vol. 1, II-28–29; and designed operational capability statement, in ibid., vol. 2.

64. Koskinas, *Black Hats and White Hats*, 112; and Marquis, *Unconventional Warfare*, 56.

65. History of ARRS, 1 Jan–31 Dec 1980, vol. 1, 20–21.

66. Ibid., 22.

67. Ibid., 25–27.

68. Ibid., 29, 63.

69. Sprouse, interview.

70. Weikel to the author, e-mail, 20 Aug 2010.

71. History of ARRS, 1 Jan–31 Dec 1981, vol. 1, 78–81; History of 1st SOW, 1 Jan–31 Mar 1981, vol. 1, II-66–67; and ibid., vol. 2, 3.

72. History of 1st SOW, 1 Oct–31 Dec 1981, vol. 1, II-72.

73. Ibid., 1 Apr–30 June 1981, vol. 1, II-44, II-47–48; ibid., vol. 2, 3; ibid., 1 Oct–31 Dec 1981, vol. 2, 4; and Grove, interview.

74. Weikel, interview.

75. History of ARRS, 1 Jan–31 Dec 1981, vol. 1, 96–97.

76. Ibid., 3–4.

77. Ibid., 15–16.

78. Ibid., 16–17.

79. History of 1st SOW, 1 Jan–31 Mar 1982, vol. 1, I-11, II-45, II-62, II-66; and ibid., 1 Apr–30 June 1982, I-12, II-40–46, II-52–53.

80. History of ARRS, 1 Jan–31 Dec 1982, vol. 1, 30.

81. Cross, *Birth of the Twenty-Third Air Force*, 6–7.

82. Ibid., 7–8; and History of ARRS, 1 Jan–31 Dec 1982, vol. 1, 10–12.

83. Cross, *Birth of the Twenty-Third Air Force*, 8–10; and History of ARRS, 1 Jan–31 Dec 1982, vol. 1, 13–16.

84. Cross, *Birth of the Twenty-Third Air Force*, 11–15.

85. History of 1st SOW, 1 July–30 Sept 1982, vol. 1, I-6, I-32.

86. Stiles, interview.

87. Walters, interview.

88. History of 1st SOW, 1 July–30 Sept 1982, vol. 1, II-78, II-89; and Reed, interview.

89. SSgt Phil Rhodes, "From TAC to MAC Transition Tuesday," *Commando*, 25 Feb 1983, 1; and History of 1st SOW, 1 Oct 1982–28 Feb 1983, vol. 1, I-14.

90. History of the Twenty-Third Air Force and Aerospace Rescue and Recovery Service (hereafter referred to as History of 23d AF and ARRS), 1 Jan–31 Dec 1983, vol. 1, 14–16; Koskinas, *Black Hats and White Hats*, 120; and Sprouse, interview.

91. History of 23d AF and ARRS, 1 Jan–31 Dec 1983, vol. 1, 18–19.

92. Ibid., 19–20; and Maj Gen William Mall, "Presentation to the Committee on Armed Services, Readiness Subcommittee," 5 Apr 1983, in ibid., vol. 5, supplemental doc. I-40.

93. History of 23d AF and ARRS, 1 Jan–31 Dec 1983, vol. 1, 21–28.

94. Ibid., 26.

95. Ibid., CD-3.

96. Marquis, *Unconventional Warfare*, 82.

97. History of 23d AF and ARRS, 1 Jan–31 Dec 1983, vol. 1, 139–41.

98. Ibid.

99. Ibid., 44, 54.

100. History of the 2d Air Division (hereafter referred to as History of 2d AD), 1 Mar–30 June 1983, vol. 1, I–28–I–30.

101. Ibid., chap. 3; ibid., vol. 6, 248–50; and "Background Paper on Special Operations Force Structure Requirements," ibid., vol. 2, 468. The background paper also suggests procuring and modifying the six HH-53s of the 6594th Test Group in Hawaii, slated to inactivate in FY 86.

102. History of 2d AD, 1 July–31 Dec 1983, vol. 1, I-6–I-8.

103. Ibid.; and Marquis, *Unconventional Warfare*, 85–86.

104. History of 2d AD, 1 July–31 Dec 1983, vol. 1, II-55, II-69, II-88.

105. Ibid., IV-123–IV-171; and Marquis, *Unconventional Warfare*, 105–6.

106. Weikel and Reed, interviews; and Reed to the author, e-mail, review comments, 3 Jan 2011.

107. Martin, interview.

108. Ibid.

109. Ibid.

110. Marquis, *Unconventional Warfare*, 86–87.

111. The FY 1985 USAF budget request included money for 24 HH-60Ds and start-up money for 54 JVXs. History of the Twenty-Third Air Force (hereafter referred to as History of 23d AF), 1 Jan 1984–31 Dec 1985, vol. 1, 25.

112. "Special Operations Forces Master Plan," 4 Apr 1984, History of 23d AF, 1 Jan 1984–31 Dec 1985, vol. 2, B-1-7, B-1-14–15.

113. History of 2d AD, 1 Jan–31 Dec 1985, vol. 1, I-32, I-64.

114. "Chronology of the 23d Air Force," AFSOC/HO, permanent file, box 5.

115. Davis, *31 Initiatives*, v, 111.

116. History of ARRS, 1 Jan 1984–31 Dec 1985, vol. 1, 28; and point paper, subject: Implications of the MAC Position on Transfer of SOF Rotary-Wing Responsibility to Army, 19 Sept 1984, in ibid., vol. 2, II-289–90.

117. Cong. Earl Hutto, "Report from Washington," newsletter, July 1984, box 1989–1994, file: Newsletters, Congressman Earl Hutto Special Collection (hereafter cited as Hutto Collection), John C. Pace Library, University of West Florida, Pensacola, FL.

118. Stewart, Sandler, and Fischer, *Command History of the United States Army Special Operations Command: 1987–1992*, 225–27; and Weikel, interview.

119. Marquis, *Unconventional Warfare*, 88; History of ARRS, 1 Jan 1984–31 Dec 1985, vol. 1, 30; History of 2d AD, 1 Jan–31 Dec 1984, vol. 1, I-90; and Weikel, interview.

120. Reed, interview; USAF MH-53J Helicopter Requirements, point paper, n.d.; and PMD 5249 (2), 10 Jan 1986.

121. To secretary of defense, memorandum, subject: Rotary-Wing Support for Special Operations, 10 July 1984.

122. History of ARRS, 1 Jan 1984–31 Dec 1985, vol. 1, 30.

123. Ibid., 67; Schibler, interview; Schibler to the author, e-mail, 17 Sept 2010, follow-up comments; and Sprouse, interview.

124. Hester, interview.

125. Koskinas, *Black Hats and White Hats*, 137.

126. Halcomb to the author, e-mail.

127. Brian Doyle, "Fight Brewing over 20th SOS's Future," *Okaloosa Daily News*, 24 Oct 1984, 1.

128. Mrs. Gwen Grant to Cong. Earl Hutto, letter, 30 Oct 1984, and Hutto to Grant, letter, 14 Nov 1984, box 329-87-142, file 12 of 20, Hutto Collection.

129. Kelly, interview.

130. History of 2d AD, 1 Jan–31 Dec 1984, vol. 1, II-21; ibid., vol. 2, 134–38; and Weikel, Kelly, and Harris, interviews.

Chapter 6

Congress Acts

~1984–86

We could no longer wait around for something to be done . . . .
So . . . Congress acted.

—Cong. Earl Hutto

Washington, DC

Congressman Daniel's words were certainly heartening to the Pave Low troops. However, they served as a preamble to the difficult work that lay ahead. On 29 November 1984, Deputy Secretary Taft responded to Daniel's 30 October letter, stating, "I understand that you will be holding hearings on this matter. I have suggested to Generals Wickham and Gabriel that they meet with you personally to explain their rationale and discuss your concerns. We will of course reconsider the transfer proposal if further deliberations produce a convincing set of arguments for doing so." Taft added a handwritten note at the bottom of the letter that said, "Mr. Chairman: If you are not satisfied after meeting with Generals Wickham and Gabriel, please let me know. I think that they have made a good case. If you disagree after having heard them, however, we will not pursue this over your objection."[1]

Congressmen Daniel and Hutto met with the generals on 3 December. There are no notes of what they discussed. However, Hutto followed up with a strong letter to General Gabriel expressing his concern that the transfer might be phase one of a plan by the Air Force to divest itself of the entire special operations mission. He wrote, "These realignments . . . signal a willful abrogation of a combat mission, eventually leaving a truncated Air Force totally unable to operate in the lower end of the spectrum of warfare."[2]

On 11 December, Daniel also sent a memo to General Gabriel relaying that he could see no way to implement Initiative 17 without unacceptably degrading this critical national capability. He communicated that he favored the Army supporting the short-range mission and the Air Force retaining the long-range mission. In a follow-up memo to Deputy Secretary Taft, he explained that his study of the issue indicated that the 1st SOW should receive a force activity designator (FAD) rating of FAD-1 (highest supply priority, something that young Maj Gary Weikel had been pushing both overtly and covertly). Daniel's memo also said that nine HH-53s should be sent to Hurlburt from the 41st ARRSq at McClellan and that unit backfilled with UH-60s from the 55th ARRSq at Eglin. It added that during the programmed H-53 SLEP, 27 more H-53s should be modified to the Pave Low configuration.

In response, on 20 December the USAF chief of plans and operations sent a message to all commands stating that the Army and Air Force should continue to work to implement the intent of Initiative 17. However, the transfer of Pave Low assets would be deferred. Accordingly, all personnel, programming, and logistical actions initiated in conjunction with the transfer of the Pave Lows would be rescinded, and MAC should move quickly to meet the deferred operational needs of the 20th SOS. Within just a few days, MAC stopped all transfer actions, cancelled all Army training classes, returned the 20th SOS to full SOF combat-ready status, and transferred an HH-53C from McClellan AFB to Hurlburt to partially make up for the two aircraft recently lost. Additionally, MAC drafted plans to transfer the four UH-1Ns still in the 20th SOS to a rescue squadron within the next year.[3]

It was a stunning reversal of fortune for the Pave Lows. In a period of just seven months, the community went from the specter of complete transfer to another service to the development of political top cover that aborted the reassignment. Now just seven helicopters, the struggling fleet seemed to face a much brighter future that included possible growth. The *Air Force Times* announced this victory in a 7 January 1985 article, "Plans Scrubbed to Transfer Helicopter Mission to Army," disclosing that the Air Force intended to keep the Pave Lows for the "immediate future." However, Initiative 17 had not yet been totally cancelled.

In April 1985, Mr. Thomas Cooper, the USAF assistant secretary for research, development, and acquisition, stated that Initiative 17 was dead. The PDASD-ISA, Noel Koch, seemed to signal as much when he proposed in an *Armed Forces Journal* article, "I'd leave the mission with the Air Force. Those guys have done brilliant work, and they've committed their careers to a tough and thankless job. There's a body of experience there that it will take the Army years to duplicate. . . . I can argue about hardware: The Air Force has it; the Army doesn't; and the costs for the Army to get it [are] backbreaking if not prohibitive."[4]

The actions at the DOD and congressional levels had sent a signal to senior USAF officers that special operations needed their attention and support.[5] It seemed, though, that the reports of the death of Initiative 17 were a bit premature. The two chiefs still favored the idea and continued to discuss it. The Army intended to build another aviation battalion equipped with either new MH-60s or MH-47s to service the mission. By May they both agreed on the split-mission idea roughly based upon range, with the Army taking the short-range requirement and the Air Force remaining with the long-range mission requiring in-flight refueling, at which the USAF pilots were very proficient. At some point, it was also expected that the Army would develop a longer-range capability. However, to do that, it would have to develop the ability to refuel in-flight.

At a program review with Taft in May, the Army was asked to explain how its pilots would do the refueling. The Army briefer explained how the pilot would fly the helicopter up behind a refueling aircraft, usually a USAF MC- or HC-130. That aircraft would be trailing a refueling drogue, or basket, that was 27 inches in diameter and on the end of an 81-foot-long hose. The helicopter pilot would then have to insert the end of his 33-foot refueling probe into that basket, regardless of the weather or turbulence, day or night. When pressed for the details of how that was actually accomplished, the briefer rather smugly stated that it was far too technically complicated to explain to a bunch of civilians and they should just trust the Army on the soundness of the plan. Koch was at the briefing. Sensing an opportunity to make a point, he had brought along his key assistant, Lynn Rylander. When the Army brief was finished, Koch had Rylander lay out a 33-foot section of rope that stretched into the hallway. Standing at the end of the rope, Koch then held out a 27-inch piece of paper replicating the refueling drogue and said for all to hear, "Ladies and gentlemen, this is 33 feet." He also reminded them that the drogue would most probably be moving around a bit in the wind stream and would most likely be a bit difficult for the pilots to see in the weather or at night while wearing NVGs. Koch's dramatic act shattered the audience's confidence in the briefer's flippant suggestion that Army pilots could easily master this challenging procedure.[6]

In May and June 1985, Deputy Secretary Taft sent memos to the two chiefs directing that the Army develop cost estimates for a long-range helicopter program and show that the Army could do the in-flight refueling through a valid test. Additionally, the USAF was to continue restoring the capability of the 20th SOS and add additional Pave Low III or enhanced aircraft while supporting controlled transfer of SOF rotary-wing aircraft to the Army as it built capability. Three months later, after the Defense Review Board assessed the initiative and noted the Army's estimate that it would cost $1.3 billion to fully absorb the SOF rotary-wing mission, Taft, in a Solomonic decision, specified that the Army would accelerate MH-60 development and acquisition and develop the MH-47 at a reduced rate. Furthermore, the USAF would retain the mission of long-range rotary-wing support for special operations and modify more HH-53Hs to the Pave Low III (Enhanced) configuration by reprogramming funds. The program decision memorandum that accompanied this decision, signed by Assistant Secretary of Defense David Chu, required that the Army improve its short-range capabilities and plan for the procurement of the MH-47E by 1991. The USAF was to procure 10 Pave Low III (Enhanced) aircraft and retrofit two existing helicopters to make up for the two Pave Lows recently lost.[7]

The next month, the House Committee on Appropriations directed no transfer of the mission to the Army without full and comprehensive congressional budget review. It inserted into the FY 1986 Defense Appropriations Bill $76 million to facilitate the H-53 SLEP, modify two H-53s to replace the two lost in 1984, and modify 10 more to the Pave Low configuration. Capt Ed Reed felt vindicated. When it became apparent that the money would be available, his MAC SON 11-84 magically resurfaced and became the basis for the program management directive that was then published to facilitate the initial modification of the first two aircraft to the HH-53H configuration. This reactivated the Pave Low modification line at the NARF at NAS Pensacola, reenergizing the subcontractor production lines necessary for the acquisition of all the components necessary for the conversion. Once that support system was remobilized, the only thing lacking was more funding to modify as many aircraft as the USAF or Congress desired. Congressman Hutto was happy, too. More funds would flow to the NARF and to Hurlburt, both—just coincidentally—in his congressional district.[8]

Courtesy Hutto family

Cong. Earl Hutto (D-FL), a key supporter of Pave Low

20th Special Operations Squadron

During 1985 the 20th maintained its busy schedule of training, static displays, VIP visits, deployments to mountain training in Georgia and New Mexico, and exercises—both CONUS and overseas. The heavy emphasis was still on working with "customers" from the other services' special operations communities. The transfer of the Slick HH-53C from the 41st ARRSq at McClellan AFB helped with proficiency training and currency, but actual Pave Low operations were reduced because of the loss of the two aircraft in 1984. In October 1985, the unit transferred its UH-1Ns and some personnel to the newly activated 48th ARRSq at Homestead AFB, Florida, where they continued Operation BAT. Several UH-1N pilots—Captains Grant Harden, Jack Hester, Don Hoover, Dennis Jones, and Jim Shaffer—were selected to stay with the squadron and transition to Pave Lows. Now the 20th was a pure H-53 unit with one HH-53C and the seven remaining HH-53H Pave Low III aircraft. They continued to be modified with improvements as they were developed and approved; however, the larger H-53 fleet SLEP program encountered funding difficulties and was slipped almost two years.

In another unfortunate accident, the 6594th Test Group lost HH-53C #68-10355 on 15 January 1985. The aircraft was launched as the lead of a two-ship formation to recover a seriously ill seaman aboard a merchant vessel 540 miles northwest of Hawaii. As the aircraft came to a hover over the ship, it suffered a main blade structural failure and crashed on the ship's deck. All seven crew members were killed, and the resulting fire damaged the ship's main deck and superstructure. With the loss of a third aircraft in less than six months, the USAF H-53 fleet continued to shrink.[9]

While all of these changes were taking place, MAC was undergoing a budget shortfall that was affecting numerous programs. In August 1985, the Air Force Council cancelled the entire HH-60 program and delayed the follow-on JVX. However, to replace the two Pave Lows lost in 1984, HQ USAF did approve the modification of two CH-53s, #68-10923 and #70-1629, to be converted to the Pave Low III configuration. As before, the NARF in Pensacola would do the work, to be completed in 1986. In conjunction with this action, MAC requested the conversion of 25 more H-53s to either the Pave Low III standard or a new "enhanced" version redesignated the MH-53J, in keeping with the "M" aircraft prefix identifier generally used for special operations–specific aircraft.

The enhancements, to be done in conjunction with the SLEP program, included a detailed listing of upgrades to the single central avionics computer—the Doppler/INS navigation system—such as a new ring-laser gyro system. Also specified were the possible installment of the new GPS navigation kits on the aircraft, IRCM jamming pods, flare/chaff dispensers for those aircraft not currently equipped, upgraded ECM jamming pods, improvements to the FLIR system, better

NVG-compatible cockpit lighting and computer display units, crash-worthy crew and passenger seats, an improved suite of secure radios, crashworthy 650-gallon external fuel tanks, and improved mounts for the machine guns. Titanium composite main rotor blades that provided almost 2,000 pounds more lift capability were also pre-scribed, along with hydraulic system upgrades, an external reskin-ning, and several structural refinements enabling an increase in gross weight lift capability. All of this was good news to the Airmen of the 20th as they did the best they could with their seven Pave Lows and one Slick HH-53. Additionally, such an expansion of aircraft sug-gested more Pave Low–equipped squadrons, possibly even overseas.[10]

However, the current paucity of Pave Low aircraft was highlighted in another way when the MAC IG team arrived at Hurlburt on 2 De-cember 1985 to conduct an ORI and management effectiveness in-spection (MEI) for the 1st SOW. While the results were classified, the ORI had to be terminated on 11 December. Overall, the wing was graded satisfactory, but problems were cited on the operational mis-sions dealing with "HH-53H operational restrictions." Press reports indicate that at one point in the inspection, the wing was not able to generate any operational aircraft to meet a mission tasking. Obvi-ously, many challenges still needed to be addressed.[11]

Twenty-Third Air Force

In September 1985, General Mall completed his tour as the Twenty-Third Air Force commander and was replaced by Maj Gen Robert Patterson. Given the now high-level military and political in-terest in special operations and cancellation of critical aircraft pro-curement programs, Patterson immediately directed his staff mem-bers to conduct a study to see if his forces were optimally organized to accomplish their assigned missions and, if not, to recommend changes. For the next two months they dutifully conducted the study titled Forward Look. Their central idea was, first, to emphasize the capabilities of the units' resources rather than allocating resources to each of the various missions of the command and, second, to develop a plan for basing new MC-130s and the projected increase in Pave Lows while still focusing on the two primary missions of combat re-covery and special operations.

The staff concluded that the command should retain the 375th AAW, the recently renamed 1550th Combat Crew Training Wing (CCTW), and the 1606th ABW at Kirtland AFB as currently configured. However, it recommended the reorganization of the 2d AD and its three operational wings—the 1st SOW, 39th ARRW, and 41st RWRW—into four multipurpose "special air warfare" wings, one in the Pacific, one in Europe, and an eastern and a western wing in the CONUS. All of this could be done without any appreciable manpower increases except those authorized for the additional MC-130s and Pave Lows. Under Forward Look the 2d AD would be inactivated, and the 1st SOW would report directly to Twenty-Third Air Force—as had been done with the ARRS and its operational wings in 1983. When completed, the plan was briefed to the new MAC commander, Gen Duane Cassidy, in November. He endorsed it and directed the MAC staff to begin detailed planning to carry it out.[12]

In early December, General Patterson briefed Forward Look to the Special Forces Panel of the Readiness Subcommittee of the House Armed Services Committee, chaired by Congressman Hutto. Fully aware of the criticisms voiced by the chairman, Congressman Daniel, and a growing number of others, Patterson explained his command plan for reorganization and detailed how the forward wings could be much more responsive to theater needs. He updated the panel on the status of the SOF master plan and detailed the modifications that were scheduled for SOF aircraft, especially the Pave Lows.[13]

The plan was an honest look at the command, with the recognition that smaller, low-intensity conflicts were more likely than a large regional conflict to occur in the near future. Forward Look concluded that special operations forces were more likely to be used than larger conventional forces. The current structure of Twenty-Third Air Force was not optimized to integrate forces and enhance special operations. Moving to the projected four wings would help better position forces and command structure to provide "maximum integration and flexibility of the forces available to the theater and specialized users—a true melding of core and augmenting forces.[14]

Under the plan, the four special air warfare wings (later changed to special operations wings) would provide streamlined command, control, and coordination for AFSOF in the CONUS, Europe, and the Pacific, providing theater focus and responsiveness across the spectrum of conflict. The Twenty-Third Air Force would remain as the lowest level of worldwide AFSOF management. It would still provide planning, logistics, intelligence, training, and standardization of all subordinate units and, in addition to the four wings, would place small detachments with various other commands to facilitate the swift movement and integration of AFSOF forces when needed in any theater. It would expand its staff to better accomplish these functions by inactivating the 2d AD. The plan also presented initial guidance for each of the projected wings.

In the Pacific, the wing (initially projected to be the 353d SOW) would be built around the 1st SOS, an MC-130 unit, currently located at Clark AB, Philippines. There the 31st ARRSq would be reassigned from the 41st RWRW and equipped with MH-53 Pave Lows as they were available and become the 31st SOS. It would provide the long-range capability for special operations and combat rescue. Other rescue squadrons in the region would be reassigned from the 41st RWRW to the new wing. Additional special operations squadrons could be added as new aircraft became available.[15]

In Europe the 39th ARRW would move from Eglin to Rhein-Main AB, Germany, to provide the nucleus for its wing. The 7th SOS with its MC-130s would transfer, as would the 67th ARRSq with its HH-53B/Cs. They would eventually be replaced by MH-53s as they became available to provide the long-range special operations and combat rescue capability needed in that theater. The 67th ARRSq would inactivate and be redesignated as the 21st SOS, recapturing the rich heritage of that unit from its eventful days in Southeast Asia. Again, new squadrons could be added as aircraft became available. Congressional approval was required to exceed authorized theater manpower ceilings.[16]

In the CONUS, the West Coast wing would be formed around the 41st RWRW. It would maintain its focus on weather reconnaissance but still command several rescue squadrons with older H-3s and HC-130s.[17] The East Coast wing would form around the 1st SOW with the 8th, 16th, and 20th SOSs. It would also be assigned the 55th ARRSq, equipped with U/HH-60s, and possibly the 48th ARRSqs, equipped with UH-1Ns and HC-130s. All rescue squadrons would be redesignated as special operations squadrons. This wing would be the primary deployment force for short-notice contingency tasking and for forces tasked to SOUTHCOM and USLANTCOM. The 20th SOS would gain up to 14 MH-53s as they became available. The inactivated 2d AD would provide some necessary manpower positions to the wing.[18]

Such dramatic reorganizations would generate large personnel movements. MAC staff was working that issue, with the understanding that personnel authorizations would not increase. Training for aircrews had to be addressed, particularly for the Pave Low crews. Given the small number of modified aircraft, all specific mission qualification training had to take place at Hurlburt. Crew training had been consolidated there in the Central Training Flight. However, that unit worked closely with the 20th SOS, and the impact of training sortie needs was a constant drain on the unit as it struggled to answer its real-world commitments, especially after the loss of the two aircraft in 1984. However, the modification of more H-53s to the Pave Low configuration created the possibility of perhaps assigning some to the 1550th CCTW so that initial Pave Low qualification could take place at Kirtland as part of the aircraft qualification courses.

Logistical planning continued with the assumption that the H-53 SLEP and similar programs for the other aircraft would proceed apace. The designation of FAD-1 status for AFSOF forces was key to the success of Forward Look. Most necessary unit movements and equipment changes would start in FY 86 and be completed by FY 88, except for those involving anticipated use of the new JVX tilt-rotor aircraft, which was now projected to be available in FY 95 at the earliest. General Patterson also considered moving the Twenty-Third Air Force from Scott AFB to Hurlburt Field because he believed that the command needed an increased focus on special operations. In late December, General Cassidy approved the plan, including the Twenty-Third Air Force relocation to Hurlburt.[19]

As 1986 began, Twenty-Third Air Force was now well immersed in the details of Forward Look. On 28 May, the Air Force Council approved the plan. However, the plan was modified significantly to include several unit inactivations or consolidations as Congress initiated significant budget cuts for the DOD. Larger changes, too, were on the horizon as Congress also finally determined to make significant organizational changes to the US military in general and its special operations forces in particular.

Pave Low IV

In March 1986 at Scott AFB, Captain Reed finished his tour with the MAC staff and was transferred to Washington, DC, to work for

Brig Gen Tom Eggers in the acquisition office under the secretary of the Air Force. He would handle special operations programs, the perfect billet from which to quietly implement the still unapproved MAC SON 11-84 and a similar program for the MH-60Gs and MC-130P/Ns. Reed also made a special effort to get to know the senior OSD secretaries and staffers working in key offices in the Pentagon. Many had served in the building for long periods and were a sort of collective corporate knowledge, especially when it came to funding sources and management. They were able to show him many tricks that allowed him to tap into funding sources and draw off what eventually amounted to a large amount of money through small but widespread "donations" from numerous Air Force programs for Pave Low projects as part of the MH-53 SLEP and safety modification process. He also began to develop "hidden in plain sight" pots of money for future use.[20]

Reed also worked directly with several "competing" Army aviation staff officers who were working their service programs, and in congressional staff meetings, he never passed up an opportunity to extol the virtues of the Pave Low aircraft and crews. He developed some close relationships with key congressional staffers and was able to brief them frequently on Pave Low advancements. He was also keenly aware of the dangers inherent in Initiative 17 and understood that while Congress had slowed its funding for Army special operations aviation, the still agreed upon intent of the Army and Air Force was that the senior service would assume the long-range delivery mission if/when the MH-53s went away.

Resolved to delay or forestall that action as much as possible, Reed, with help from Weikel, resorted to subterfuge. They knew that the Army was behind the Air Force in the technological advancement of its SOF helicopters and sensed that the Army could use a little "help." Consequently, Reed developed a concept for a new iteration of Pave Lows called Pave Low IV. He created a briefing and technical specifications to convince the Army staffers that this new Pave Low would be fully state of the art. The presentation included made-up slides with highly detailed cockpit and airframe illustrations, complete with a full glass cockpit and a new TF/TA radar initially designed for the now cancelled HH-60D. Weikel then conveniently arranged for the Army staff officers to "steal" a copy, which they then used to redesign their proposal for the new and expensive MH-60K and MH-47E helicopters to replace the MH-53s. This caused significant and costly delay in the Army's program, such that when the funding was forth-coming, the MH-53J Pave Low III Enhanced modification line was ready to go, while the Army was at least two years away from even prototype production. Said Reed later, "It was amazing what you learn at the Hurlburt Special Operations School—you can actually use those things in the Pentagon." Pave Low IV never existed (in this iteration), but it successfully accomplished its mission, costing the Army substantial development and testing delays and embarrassment with the Government Accountability Office (GAO) and Congress.[21]

A New Command

After six years of trying to prod the military services to place in-creased emphasis on their special forces components, key leaders in both the House of Representatives and Senate now felt that their ef-forts were for naught and that they would have to take strong legisla-tive measures to make those changes. Joining Congressmen Hutto and Daniel in this effort were Senators Sam Nunn (D-GA) and William Cohen (R-ME). Each of these gentlemen served on their respective Armed Services Committees. All were convinced that the nation had to establish clearer organizational focus and chains of command for its special operations forces and that those forces should also be pro-vided with their own funding authority, which could not be siphoned off by the individual services for other programs. In the spring of 1986, after a series of hearings, Senator Cohen introduced a bill in the Senate that called for a joint military organization for special forces and the establishment of an assistant secretary position in the De-fense Department to insure adequate funding for and policy emphasis on low-intensity conflict and special operations.[22]

In the House, Congressman Daniel took a different tack. He and writer Ben Schemmer (with lots of back-channel factual and ghost-writing support from Ted Lunger, Major Weikel, and Maj Greg Colvin) had been openly speaking out for over a year in a series of articles in the *Armed Forces Journal,* calling for a "sixth service" and arguing that "SOF has never been [a] truly institutional part of [the other] services" or their core imperatives, and because of that, SOF needed its own "unifying, intellectual core of philosophy; a professional home; a budget that does not compete directly with [conventional forces]; an acquisition system; a high level advocate; [and] a direct link to the National Command Authorities."[23] Daniel knew, though, that there was no general support for his position and dropped the sixth service idea, proposing, instead, a national special operations agency headed by a civilian who would bypass the JCS and report directly to the secretary of defense. This structure would keep the services out of the SOF budget process, a key concern for Daniel.[24]

Throughout the summer, the two Armed Services Committees held hearings on the two proposals. The JCS and DOD opposed both bills. The chairman of the JCS, Adm William Crowe, proposed an alternative Special Operations Forces Command (SOFC) led by a three-star general. In support of SOFC, Richard Armitage, the assistant secretary of defense for international security affairs (ASD-ISA), testified before the Senate Armed Services Committee. Noting in detail how spending on SOF programs had expanded almost fourfold since 1980, Armitage specifically pointed to force expansions in the Army, with its 1st Special Forces Command, and the Air Force, with its creation of Twenty-Third Air Force. He also cited the criticality of the SOF rotary-wing force by referring to it as "the long-range infiltration/exfiltration capacity without which such operations cannot be conducted." Moreover, he pointed out that authorization was now in place to fund 12 newly modified MH-53 helicopters and 33 Army special operations helicopters. In addition, he suggested that such a new command should have access to a new funding line for special operations that would be controlled by the individual services.[25] However, the committees were not happy with his suggestions. They wanted a four-star commander and were supported in this by numerous retired officers, including several of the SOPAG members.

Both committees passed their versions of the SOF reform bills. They then went to a conference committee for reconciliation; they reached a compromise that satisfied most concerns voiced by both committees. The resulting bill directed the president to establish a unified combatant command (COCOM), led by a four-star general for special operations forces. The SecDef would be authorized a position for an assistant secretary of defense for special operations and low-intensity conflict (ASD/SOLIC). Additionally, a new major force program (MFP-11) would be created specifically for this new command to have control over its own resources, better enabling it to modernize its forces. Subsequently titled the Nunn-Cohen Amendment, the bill was attached to the FY 1987 Defense Appropriations

Act and signed by the president on 14 November 1986 as Public Law 99-661.

The act amended the recently passed Goldwater-Nichols Act, Public Law 99-433, passed into law in October 1986, which had been a larger effort to enact numerous changes to the organization of the United States military forces. Goldwater-Nichols strengthened the role of the unified COCOMs, streamlined the command and control of operational forces, and, overall, placed a long-needed increased emphasis on joint force operational procedures. The changes now mandated by the Nunn-Cohen Amendment fit very well into the structure created by the Goldwater-Nichols Act. The amendment also specified that the secretary of defense, after consulting with the CJCS and the commander of the new command, could designate those forces from each of the services to be assigned to the new command. The new command was assigned 10 activities as they related to special operations: direct action, strategic reconnaissance, UW, foreign internal defense, civil affairs, psychological operations, counterterrorism, humanitarian assistance, theater SAR, and other activities as specified by the president or SecDef.[26]

Later that summer, at a conference sponsored by his Special Operations Panel, Congressman Hutto offered five findings, or truths, especially for fellow congressional leaders that seemed to define the essence of what special forces were:

1. Humans are more important than hardware.

2. Their quality is more important than quantities.

3. Special operations forces cannot be mass-produced.

4. Competent SOF [units] cannot be created after emergencies occur.

5. Most special operations require non-SOF assistance.[27]

Over the next several months the JCS dealt with the details of creating the new command. It asked the JSOA for recommendations on how to proceed. That group reported back with a recommendation that they name it the United States Special Operations Command (USSOCOM) and have it take the place of the US Readiness Command (USREDCOM) at MacDill AFB, which could be inactivated. The SecDef accepted the plan. In January 1987 USREDCOM was inactivated, and its facilities, billets, and many of its personnel were assigned to USSOCOM. President Reagan subsequently approved the establishment of the new command, and the DOD activated US-SOCOM on 16 April 1987, with Army general James Lindsay as its first commander. Congressman Hutto was most pleased to see the fruits of his and Congressman Daniel's labor, ably assisted throughout by their various staff members and the "SOF Mafia," or "a bit of a fifth column," as General Cassidy labeled them. Hutto later wrote, "We could no longer wait around for something to be done. The Defense Department and the military services would not do it, so . . . Congress acted."[28]

Those young Air Force officers, out of a genuine belief that their service could not forsake its SOF units, also took great delight in the role they played in this accomplishment. Said Maj Ed Reed later,

> Imagine being in an organization which was trying to get rid of the mission, get rid of an aircraft, and, at the same time, your task was to make sure that didn't happen and that new aircraft were built. Thank goodness we had some understanding and tolerant generals at the time on the Air Staff who understood that the chief of staff of the Army and the chief of staff of the Air Force cut a bad deal. General Gabriel sooner or later would leave the Air Force, and the guy coming behind him might not be so willing to get rid of the mission of the aircraft. Congress stepped in and made sure it didn't happen.[29]

Notes

1. History of ARRS, 1 Jan 1984–31 Dec 1985, vol. 1, 31.
2. History of 2d AD, 1 Jan–31 Dec 1984, vol. 1, I-94.
3. History of ARRS, 1 Jan 1984–31 Dec 1985, vol. 1, 32–34; and message, USAF chief of plans and operations to all commands, subject: Update of SOF Rotary-Wing Issue, 20 Dec 1985, in ibid., vol. 2, II-384–5.
4. History of 2d AD, 1 Jan–31 Dec 1984, vol. 1, I-98.
5. History of ARRS, 1 Jan 1984–31 Dec 1985, vol. 1, 33; and History of 2d AD, 1 Jan–31 Dec 1984, vol. 1, I-95, I-98.
6. Marquis, *Unconventional Warfare*, 114.
7. Ibid., 114, 128; and Meyer, "Taft Makes 'Solomonic' Decision," 85, 28.
8. General Patterson's testimony to House Armed Services Committee panel on SOF forces, point papers, 4 Dec 1985, Heritage File, box 51, AFSOC/HO; PMD 5223 (2) 13262, 26 June 1985, author's personal collection; Gambone, *Pave Low III: That Others May Live*, 258; and Reed, interview.
9. History of 23d AF, 1 Jan 1984–31 Dec 1985, vol. 1, 88.
10. Ibid., 51–52, 90; and ibid., vol. 2, supp. docs. 124–26.
11. History of 1st SOW, 1 Jan–31 Dec 1985, vol. 1, I-24; and Schemmer, "December Was Not a Good Month for USAF Special Operations," 26.
12. History of 23d AF, 1 Jan 1984–31 Dec 1985, vol. 1, 18–21.

13. General Patterson's testimony to House Armed Services Committee panel on SOF forces, point papers, 4 Dec 1985, Heritage File, box 51, AFSOC/HO.

14. Forward Look, Twenty-Third Air Force staff study directed by General Patterson, 1985, 2–4, in ibid.

15. Ibid., 11–12.

16. Ibid., 18–19.

17. Ibid., 13–14.

18. Ibid., 15–17.

19. Ibid., 22–27.

20. Wurster, interview.

21. Reed, interview; and Reed to the author, e-mails, review comments, 18 Oct 2009 and 5 Sept 2011.

22. USSOCOM, *United States Special Operations Command 10th Anniversary History*, 2.

23. Marquis, *Unconventional Warfare*, 122.

24. Ibid., 139.

25. "Statement by Mr. Richard Armitage, Asst. Secretary of Defense (International Security Affairs) before the Subcommittee on Seapower and Force Projection, Committee on Armed Services, US Senate Second Session, 99th Congress, Special Operations Forces Reorganization," 5 Aug 1986, AFSOC/HO.

26. The National Defense Authorization Act for Fiscal Year 1987, Public Law 99-661, 99th Cong., 2d sess., 14 Nov 1986; Establishment File, Assignment of Forces to SOCOM, United States Special Operations Command (USSOCOM)/HO; and Marquis, *Unconventional Warfare*, 145–46.

27. Collins, *Green Berets, Seals and Spetsnaz*, xiii.

28. USSOCOM, *United States Special Operations Command 10th Anniversary History*, 14; Gen Duane Cassidy, USAF oral history interviews, transcript, 4 Aug and 17 Aug 1989, 19, AFHRA; and Hutto, *Captain Supreme Goes to Washington*, 239.

29. Reed, interview.

Chapter 7

The Buildup

~1986–89

We relied on that cadre of Pave Low guys to train all the rest
of us and make us one whole unit. It was really, really good.

—Brig Gen Mike Kingsley

Hurlburt Field, Florida

As the definitive changes mandated by Congress and the Twenty-
Third Air Force were being orchestrated, the Green Hornets of the
20th SOS continued to train to meet their multiple mission taskings
as still the sole Pave Low–equipped squadron in the Air Force. In
January 1986, they were called upon to perform a capabilities demonstration for Gen John Piotrowski, now serving as the vice chief of
staff of the Air Force. He was the highest ranking SOF officer in the
service and held a proprietary interest in the success of the SOF
forces. Later that month, the squadron sent another team to Dobbins
AFB, Georgia, for mountain training and then a series of deployments to work with Army troops at Fort Bragg. It also dispatched
aircraft and crews to Kirtland AFB for radar update testing for the
SMOTEC and to NAS Norfolk for several ship-boarding exercises
with naval forces. In April the squadron received another aircraft
when HH-53H #68-10923 (the first converted CH-53) arrived from
its modification at the NARF at Pensacola. In May five aircraft and
crews deployed to austere sites in the western United States to participate in Exercise Elated Cyclone. On 21 May, one of the unit aircraft, HH-53H #73-1651, crashed north of Nellis AFB and was completely destroyed. The aircraft was on a classified low-level mission
with a team of 16 personnel and was leading two HH-53s from the
41st ARRSq when it went down. One of the Pave Low pilots, Maj
Richard Brims, a recipient of the Air Force Cross for his actions on
the mission to Koh Tang Island and just a few months into his tour
with the 20th SOS, was killed. The accident report was highly classified

but did state that the Pave Low crews needed to develop better formation procedures when working with the HH-53B/Cs. Briefed on the tragic accident, Congressman Hutto, ever watchful over the Airmen at Hurlburt, wrote a letter to Brims's wife expressing his deepest sympathy at the loss of her husband, offering any help he could provide her, and further stating, "I have always considered our crew members of the PAVE LOWs as unique resources—highly trained and extremely motivated and skilled individuals."[1]

On 2 July, Lt Col Horace "Bo" Johnson replaced Lt Col Lou Grant as the squadron commander. One of the first things he was assigned to do was to dispatch several of his aircraft and crews to Kirtland AFB and fly with several R-SOLL-qualified crews from the 41st ARRSq to refine flight procedures but, more importantly, to resolve the level of distrust that had built up between the two units. The Pave Low guys labeled the program "Forced Friendship." One of the 20th copilots, Capt Dennis Jones, recollects that "there was a lot of bad blood there between the two units after that accident. They basically said, 'You guys will go out to Albuquerque; you will train together'—which is why we called it Forced Friendship—'so that you can learn to trust each other and be an effective team.'"[2]

Bo Johnson also attended the training. At one point, he called all of the crews together and announced that he wanted to build the 20th into the best helicopter squadron in the USAF. He invited the 41st guys to transfer down to Hurlburt. Maj Rich Comer had just recently returned to flight duty after his assignment to the Air Force Academy and was now an HH-53 pilot with the 41st. Comer called Maj Gary Weikel—who had just left the Pentagon and joined Johnson as his operations officer—and expressed his interest in joining the 20th. Weikel then talked to Johnson, who subsequently invited Comer to join the 20th.[3]

Also with Johnson at Kirtland at that time was Capt Corby Martin. However, he was not there for the exercise. Instead, he was to go through the formal IP upgrade so that he could return to Hurlburt and work with Lt Col Mark Schibler and Maj Walt Heidmous in the Central Training Flight to train and requalify the new crews necessary to fly the expanded Pave Low fleet.[4]

Weikel was glad to be out of the Pentagon, especially to be sent back to Hurlburt to train and lead those new Pave Low crews. As Johnson gave Weikel the job, he said, "[Training] is your job. You are going to have to fly every night and be an IP and flight examiner and check these guys out and help screen them." Weikel eagerly seized his duties. Feeling good about his successes in the Pentagon, he looked forward to infusing another generation of Pave Low warriors with the assault mentality of special operations and his pet proclivity to "seek forgiveness vice permission."[5]

Indeed, new personnel were inbound. When MAC announced that the 41st ARRSq at McClellan AFB would inactivate in September 1987 as part of Forward Look, its aircraft were dispatched for Pave Low conversion, and HH-53 crew members from the unit began receiving orders to the 20th. Major Comer was one of them and joined the unit in May 1987. Fully qualified and experienced in H-53 aircraft, he flew mostly with Capt Tommy Hull and Capt Corby Martin and found the Pave Low checkout to be challenging—especially the heavy emphasis on night tactical training and the integrated use of the various Pave systems. As a senior major, Comer was then directed to run the scheduling and training programs.[6]

Another 41st pilot, Capt Joe Becker, was right behind Comer. Joe had been commissioned in 1982 through ROTC at San Diego State University. He reported directly to Fort Rucker for undergraduate helicopter pilot training. After receiving his wings, Becker got an HH-53 assignment to the 41st. While there, he upgraded to aircraft commander and qualified with NVGs. He also became deeply involved in the R-SOLL program and operational plans, giving him exposure to the 20th SOS. After three years in the 41st, he was available for reassignment and possibly even fixed-wing conversion. However, he wanted to go into special operations and the Pave Low and made his interest in the 20th known to Johnson and Weikel.

His timing was just right. As the squadron was expanding, Weikel and Johnson had started an informal recruitment program and began "inviting" USAF helicopter pilots and flight engineers to apply for Pave Low. They accepted Becker. Like Lt Col Bill Takacs seven years earlier, they also expanded their efforts surreptitiously to the USMC and Army in an attempt to entice their rotary aviators, officers, and warrant officers to do interservice transfers for Pave Low duty. Their efforts were successful, and soon Weikel and his other IPs had a lot of training to do.[7]

Becker reported to the 20th SOS in April 1987. Walking into the squadron building for the first time, he literally ran into Bo Johnson and Steve Connelly, who welcomed him to the unit. They told him that he would soon be starting his Pave Low upgrade and work in the plans section with Capt Dave Harris and Capt Randy O'Boyle. However, first they needed to send him TDY to Fort Bragg to support some customers. Within days, he was at Bragg and in the midst of what special operators do. He was impressed because in the rescue community he would never have been given such responsibility so soon.[8]

Also arriving from the 41st ARRSq was SMSgt Tom Green. After he left SEA, he served with several rescue units and on the ARRS staff before joining the 41st as the senior flight engineer. With the demise of that unit, he decided to transfer to Hurlburt. Arriving there, though, he had to make a choice. Recently selected for promotion to chief master sergeant, he was offered the position of senior enlisted advisor to the 1st SOW wing commander, Col Dale Stovall, with whom he had flown combat in the 40th ARRSq at NKP, Thailand, in 1972. However, Green was very proud of the young flight engineers whom he had trained in the 41st and wanted to insure that they were properly accepted into the rapidly building 20th SOS. He decided to pass on the advisor job and go into the 20th. It was a fateful choice. He found a hard core of established flight engineers who had developed a strong sense of brotherhood and were slow to accept outsiders, especially guys from rescue units. Green worked diligently to help the unit expand and train the large number of flight engineers needed to fly the rapidly growing fleet and projected new operational squadrons. Challenges abounded as the new troops of varying backgrounds worked through the numerous qualifications and types of training necessary to become fully combat qualified on both the HH-53H and MH-53J variants of the Pave Low. Although Green had some difficulties with other NCOs in the 20th, they were able to work through the issues as the unit trained hard on the endless exercises that had the troops continually on the road.[9]

Joining Pave Low at about the same time as Tom Green was Sgt Jim Kradel. He had enlisted in the USAF in 1983 and initially trained as a weapons specialist. While serving a remote tour in Korea, he heard that enlisted gunners were needed at Hurlburt Field, and he volunteered, not knowing that he would be going to helicopters. Arriving at the 20th, he was overwhelmed by what he found, realizing that he did not even know how to put on a flight suit. The 20th SOS superintendent, SMSgt John Selfridge, took him under his wing and pointed him in the right direction. He was able to fly a few training sorties at Hurlburt to begin learning his crew duties before going TDY to Kirtland for his initial qualification. While at Kirtland, he learned the Pave Low aircraft and weapons systems, the basics of crew coordination, and scanning duties. However, because of aircraft scheduling problems and lack of weapons range availability, he was not able to fire any of the Pave Low weapons. Returning from the school after a month, he received the rest of his crew and combat qualification training at Hurlburt and was fully qualified for tactical missions by February 1988. Now the proud wearer of a red scarf to go with his flight suit, he was assigned to a crew and began to deploy for the endless exercises to work with all of the "customers" now requesting Pave Low support.[10]

Another individual who heard about the Pave Low program through the grapevine was Maj Gene Correll. Commissioned out of the Air Force Academy in 1973, he initially flew as a T-37 IP before receiving an assignment to HH-53s in 1978. After rotary wing conversion and then H-53 school, he reported to the 6594th Test Group of AFSC in Hawaii to fly in the Crested Rooster program. He flew with the group until 1982, upgrading to flight examiner and participating in numerous satellite recovery missions and some shipboard medical extractions. With over 1,000 hours in the H-53, he then transferred to Kirtland AFB to serve as a MAC H-53 instructor. Unfortunately, MAC did not recognize his flight examiner status in AFSC, and he had to go through its qualification program before he could teach. However, he could instruct in the H-53 simulator and went right to work doing that. Between the two jobs, he became quite familiar with numerous Pave Low guys, including Gary Weikel. In 1987 he talked to Weikel, who asked that Correll be assigned to the 20th. Correll received orders soon after.[11]

Another of the new arrivals was Capt Mike Kingsley, a native of Sacramento, California. He had watched the HH-53s fly around McClellan before being commissioned in 1984. After attending helicopter pilot training, he served a tour in Korea flying H-3s with the 38th ARRSq and upgraded to aircraft commander. At the completion of that tour, he received orders to RAF Bentwaters, UK, to fly the HH-53 with the 67th ARRSq. He completed his HH-53 upgrade at Kirtland during 1987 and also attended the Squadron Officer School at Maxwell AFB. While at Maxwell, his orders were changed, and he was diverted to Hurlburt to join the 20th. Kingsley had to scramble to reroute his hold baggage and autos before they were shipped to the UK.

Arriving at Hurlburt, Kingsley met his immediate supervisor, Capt Steve Otto. The training pipeline was a bit backed up, and Otto arranged for Kingsley to take a TDY to work directly with a team of Soldiers from the 3d Special Forces Group (SFG) on a long exercise in northwest Florida. When that was completed, he started upgrade training on the HH-53H. His initial impressions of the unit were strongly positive. He remembers that

> we had a cadre of people who were diehard Pave Low: Tommy Aldrich, Pappy Walters, Corby Martin. They had flown Pave Lows, so they were the cadre who were instructing other people who were coming from different organizations. We had people from the 41st—like Joe Becker and J. D. Clem. We also had people coming from Europe—Jim Eustace came from Germany. . . . We had a menagerie of people who were coming from lots of different experiences. We relied on that cadre of Pave Low guys to train all the rest of us and make us one whole unit. It was really, really good. I thought the morale was very high. We had quite a bit of flying that we were doing, and there were lots of exercises.

For the next 18 months, Captain Kingsley would be in constant upgrade mode as he initially qualified on the HH-53H. Like all the other Pave Low crew members, Kingsley trained at Hurlburt and at Asheville, North Carolina, for mountain training. He finally became a fully qualified Pave Low aircraft commander in 1989.[12]

Maj Steve Connelly also joined the unit that summer. After he returned to Kirtland from Hurlburt in 1980, he continued in flight test and was then reassigned to Edwards AFB for the HH-60D program. In the spring of 1987, he contacted Weikel and talked himself into a job. Arriving as a lieutenant colonel select, he became an assistant operations officer and focused on the myriad issues involved with routing aircraft to and from the NARF at Pensacola, as the Pave Low modification line was again open.

A few days after Weikel started his new job, he and Johnson were subsequently called to attend a "close-hold" briefing by MAC for selected commanders and personnel on the Forward Look Twenty-Third Air Force reorganization, especially the inactivation of 2d AD and the impact on Hurlburt and its units and personnel. The next week, the squadron received another aircraft when HH-53H #70-1629 arrived from its modification at the NARF. Through the rest of the year, the crews participated in major exercises Display Determination and Gallant Eagle, although MAC put limitations on the number of major exercises they could be tasked to support so they could focus their training on their "customer" base within JSOC. Consequently, the crews continued to deploy to Army and Navy bases around the country for continuous training, focusing on NVG long-range operations, infiltrations/exfiltrations, and shipboard operations. In November the 20th hosted a rotary-wing Special Operations Aircrew Interchange Program for crews from 14 different units. For four days the crews of HH-53s, HH-3s, and UH-60s flew with each other, exchanging tips and experiences as they practiced air refueling, hot ground refueling at austere locations, NVG operations, and formation procedures.[13]

Throughout the year, the aircraft began to receive the various navigation, avionics, communications, and countermeasures modifications previously approved, and available flying time for the aircrews was reduced as the aircraft were being modified. Additionally, Deputy Secretary of Defense Taft directed the USAF to upgrade the 10 previously designated H-53s to the Pave Low III Enhanced or MH-53J configuration by the beginning of 1988. This number was increased to 11 after the crash in May, as $59.6 million was made available for the project that the NARF would accomplish. The enhancement would include the installation of the INS/GPS combined navigational systems as well as improvements to the radar and FLIR, the NVG-compatible head-up display (HUD), the NVG-compatible instrument lights, internal fuel bladders for increased range, and further improvements to countermeasures systems and secure communications. In anticipation of the aircraft increases, the unit was authorized more personnel, and they began to slowly join the unit.

That same summer, Congress directed that 41 H-53s of any variant in existence be converted to the Pave Low III Enhanced configuration and become MH-53Js. MAC published Program Management Directive 5249(4)/3279 to direct the Pave Low III Enhanced modification funded at $451 million. In Washington, Maj Ed Reed kept visiting myriad offices using the FAD-1 designation for Pave Low to get priority for equipment modifications. He was aggressive in insisting that the Pave Low aircraft should be some of the very first USAF aircraft to receive GPS navigational systems. Reed relays that

> we had a FAD-1 designator for the H-53 aircraft. So I went to the first GPS meeting. I was a junior major there and everybody listed all of the aircraft that were going to get GPS and . . . every fighter was covered, every bomber was covered. And then some line in the nineties, the H-53 was going to get it. Wrong answer! I said, "Sorry, I've got a FAD-1 so I move to the front of the line." They said, "You can't do that. We've got this list!" I said, "You'd better call this office and find out if that's going to be your list at the end of the day. So later I got a nice

phone call. They said, "You can have the first boxes off the line." I said, "That would work just fine."[14]

To support this growing and ever more complex fleet of aircraft, MAC began to assign more maintenance specialists to Hurlburt to learn and maintain these sophisticated and integrated systems.[15]

In related developments, on 30 September 1986, the 6594th Test Group at Hickam AFB, Hawaii, inactivated. Its five HH-53s were loaded aboard MAC C-5s and flown to Kirtland. There they were assigned to the 1550th CCTW, with the understanding that they would soon be in the queue for MH-53J modification.[16]

Exactly one month later, HH-53C #68-10354, assigned to the 6514th Test Squadron at Hill AFB, Utah, crashed while carrying a survey team to a designated remote landing site on Swasey Peak, 120 miles southwest of the base. The crew made a hard landing at the site, which was at 9,500 feet elevation, and a subsequent fire destroyed the aircraft. Fortunately, the crew and all passengers successfully egressed the aircraft without any significant injuries; however, it was a tragic loss of an aircraft slated for Pave Low III Enhanced modification.[17]

Twenty-Third Air Force

As 1987 began, the USAF announced that Twenty-Third Air Force would move to Hurlburt Field by 1 September. The announcement stated that the move "would allow the Twenty-Third Air Force to perform its special operations functions more efficiently and . . . eliminate the need for 2d Air Division." Consequently, on 1 February the 2d AD quietly inactivated, and the 1st SOW reverted to direct control of the Twenty-Third Air Force with minimal impact on the subordinate squadrons. Units in the Pacific and Europe also started to realign as directed under Forward Look, and Twenty-Third Air Force activated an FOL at Hurlburt to begin the preliminary planning and coordination of the move.[18]

United States Special Operations Command

When USSOCOM was activated in April, it was not initially assigned any forces or components. However, the enabling legislation stated that "unless directed by the Secretary of Defense, all active and reserve special operations forces of all armed forces stationed in the United States shall be assigned to the Special Operations Command." Accordingly, Secretary of Defense Weinberger assigned the Twenty-Third Air Force to USSOCOM as the Air Force component (AFSOC), along with the 1st SOCOM from the Army (ARSOC), and the Naval Special Warfare Command (NAVSPECWARCOM). A few months later, he would also assign the Joint Special Operations Command when USSOCOM was fully operational.[19]

However, Twenty-Third Air Force was still a numbered air force in MAC, and the commander, General Patterson, now had to answer to two commanders as well as move his command to Hurlburt. The command, now being informally referred to as AFSOC, was in place by 1 August, and in early September, General Lindsay and his operations officer, USAF major general Hugh Cox (former commander of the 1st SOW and 2d AD), visited the base. While there, General Lindsay made it very clear that he did not consider rescue a special operations mission and also that he wanted to "purify" the command of any missions except special operations. As General Lindsay and General Cassidy conferred on Lindsay's concerns, the Twenty-Third Air Force staff began to draft a plan to divest the non-SOF-type units over the next few years. In parallel, based upon guidance from Headquarters USAF, MAC published a special order in September reassigning the 375th Aeromedical Airlift Wing, the 1606th ABW, and several other smaller units from Twenty-Third Air Force to other MAC commands. The Twenty-Third commander, General Patterson, was in a tough position as he tried to placate and serve two very different commanders.[20]

Initiative 17

As General Lindsay worked to bring his command up to full speed, he also directed a reevaluation of Initiative 17. Dutifully, his J3 and J5 reviewed the initiative to date and reported back to him that it was alive and well. However, current funding provided for both MH-53s and MH-47Es. The Air Force remained committed to retaining its SOF helicopter mission until the Army produced and fielded sufficient MH-47Es to meet SOF requirements. The Air Force MH-53s would support SOF until at least the mid 1990s. However, the MH-53s were projected to be serviceable until at least 2000, making them available for other missions. USSOCOM would definitely have its rotary-wing support from both the Air Force and Army, with their portions being dictated by funding, and with the underlying "understanding" that at some nondefined point in the future, the Army would take over the entire mission.[21]

20th Special Operations Squadron

Given the missions assigned to the new command, the 20th SOS was considered a key element of the AFSOC. Its aircraft and crews represented the command's ability to vertically insert and extract the special operations teams. The 20th crews and support personnel realized that many more aircraft and Airmen were coming to the unit. Additionally, they would be the forming cadre for more Pave Low squadrons. The training load was staggering. Consequently, the 20th cut back on its participation in exercises and dramatically stepped up its training program. In April the squadron deployed four aircraft and crews to Knoxville, Tennessee, to conduct mountain training. This was considered a better site than Dobbins AFB because around Knoxville the crews could get almost twice as much actual mountain flying per sortie than in Georgia. During the seven-week period, the crews logged 210 student sorties and completed mountain training for 19 pilots, engineers, and gunners.

The mountain training was critical for both qualifying the crews and developing unit identity and cohesion. The focused training away from home station also afforded the new troops an opportunity to show that they could achieve those standards and establish themselves as members of the 20th.

The aircrews were now entering the squadron from diverse backgrounds—rescue, tactical lift, and test squadrons; former 20th SOS UH-1N guys; and the general USAF helicopter fleet. Major Correll felt that the unit devolved, somewhat, into individual cliques and noted, too, that there was a bit of resentment on the part of some of the "original" Pave Low crew members, who believed that such a large and rapid expansion was degrading unit standards. They also seemed to feel that they had a proprietary right to first consideration on the flight schedule and should be able to amend and modify it to fit their personal desires. To Maj Rich Comer, it seemed that the squadron had informally developed an "A" team / "B" team mentality. He remembered the problems that existed like this back when he was in the 40th ARRSq at NKP, Thailand, and moved aggressively to staunch such cronyism, believing that the squadron needed to train to one standard and prepare all of its personnel to be able to handle any one mission or a long-duration air campaign.[22]

Additionally, several of the new pilots were nonvolunteer assignees from the 601st at Sembach. They were not happy with the assignment and also held hard feelings toward the 20th because of the death of one of their heroes, Dick Brims, in the Nellis crash. Johnson and Weikel were certainly aware of these buzzings but felt that these issues would fade as more aircraft arrived, flying hours for all increased, and the troops got their training, refocusing them on the missions.

The squadron kept a four-ship of Pave Lows up at Knoxville, initially using the H models until the new J models (even with missing FLIR and radar units) could replace them. Much of the conversion training took place there too, as the pilots and flight engineers developed and then practiced new procedures to fully capitalize on the capabilities in the new enhanced INS/GPS system. In a larger sense, though, the deployed mountain training program contributed greatly to unit bonding. Several more deployments were made to Knoxville throughout the year. However, the training load was almost stifling to a unit that had to be ready to respond to a real-world tasking on short notice, and the 1st SOW, Twenty-Third Air Force, and MAC training officers held discussions about possibly moving some of the mission training to the 1550th CCTW at Kirtland AFB.[23]

The 20th SOS also supported several classified equipment tests conducted by the SMOTEC and deployed an aircraft and crew to Robin AFB, Georgia, to test new titanium main rotor blades for the aircraft. As much as possible, the 20th also responded to requests from JSOC to provide lift support for other service elements. On 17 July, the squadron took possession of the first Pave Low III Enhanced MH-53J, #67-14994, when the aircraft was flown to Hurlburt from the NARF at NAS Pensacola. Coordinating the movement of the aircraft from the NARF to Hurlburt, Lt Col Steve Connelly was also heavily involved with the testing and validation of the aircraft. He, Capt Joe Barnes, and Capt Tom Hull spent a great deal of time at Pensacola performing flight tests and equipment verifications. Those tasks and the heavy training and deployment regimen continued throughout the year. By the end of December 1987, the aircraft and crews of the 20th had logged 1,912 sorties and 4,192.8 flight hours, a record for any USAF H-53 squadron ever. All indicators seemed to suggest that 1988 would be even busier.[24]

Maj Ed Reed visits the Pensacola NARF for the delivery of the first MH-53J, #67-14994.

The new year of 1988 started on a sad note when a long-time staunch supporter of SOF, Cong. Dan Daniel of Virginia, died on 23 January. He had courageously led the fight for SOF renewal and revitalization, and his steady hand and great concern for the servicemen and women of the nation would be sorely missed. A few months later, Lt Col Mark Schibler nearly suffered the same fate when he experienced a severe heart attack one Sunday afternoon. After Honey Badger, he had stayed at Hurlburt, upgrading to Pave Low flight examiner and helping to train the second generation of Pave Low crews. He eventually moved up to the standardization and evaluation office at the 1st SOW, and then Twenty-Third Air Force, until his affliction caused his permanent removal from flight status. Instead of taking a medical retirement, though, he continued to serve until he reached his mandatory retirement date in November 1990.[25]

Twenty-Third Air Force

At the headquarters, General Patterson had a full plate of issues to deal with as he addressed the challenges of his two roles. In February he formed a special commander's staff group to focus on the AFSOC-unique issues as they arose and to insure that they were tracked and resolved as expeditiously as possible. He also directed his vice-commander, Brig Gen Hanson Scott, to form a special operations program integration team to oversee all of the phenomenal changes that AFSOC's existing and newly acquired aircraft were undergoing. *Eight* programs were now going on simultaneously involving the MH-53s, MC-130s, AC-130s, U/H-60s, and several other classified projects. Additionally, the team also monitored the development of new training devices and flight simulators at Kirtland AFB, where the equipment was used in the integrated flight training program.

Patterson was also becoming increasingly more involved with US-SOCOM as that command settled in and began to function. General Lindsay made it clear that he wanted his command to begin utilizing the acquisition authority it now had under MFP-11. He commissioned a study group to define the process so that USSOCOM could work through the Planning, Programming, and Budgeting System (PPBS) process and submit a program objective memorandum (POM) for 1992–96. He was also aware that with the creation of US-SOCOM, the services had dramatically cut their budgets for special operations forces, and he had to lobby heavily with key members of Congress to realign that authority under MFP-11. He also had his staff build a classified joint special operations forces baseline master plan to determine what capabilities his command currently possessed and what needed to be developed through the POM cycle. Under its enabling legislation, USSOCOM could function as a supported or supporting command and had to develop the ability to do both deliberate and crisis action planning.[26]

Since Twenty-Third Air Force was still a numbered MAC air force, it got funding from both commands, which drew their monies from different MFPs. This was a real challenge for the Twenty-Third staff to keep straight. However, General Patterson did take advantage of his dual status in one particular instance. When the Twenty-Third Air Force received its dual tasking, the command was not authorized any more manpower. Patterson had the staff develop a concise plan for needed staff augmentation with 137 new billets, which he then presented to both MAC and USSOCOM for validation and funding. By the summer, 121 of the billets were validated, and they received funding within the next six months.[27]

Pave Low Training

Another specific issue which had to be resolved was that of aircrew training, a responsibility that both MAC and USSOCOM felt was theirs. A special working group with representatives from both and the DOD studied all aspects of the problem, including the heavy training load managed by the Central Training Flight at Hurlburt. It was still conducting all mission qualification training for all of the aircrews in AFSOC, now running at about 200 students per year and expected to grow with the expansion of AFSOC aircraft and forces. The working group recommended that all MH-53 and MC-130 training be moved to Kirtland AFB. Congressman Hutto learned about this proposal and moved as he could, with the backing of Cong. John Kasich from Ohio, to block it. He wanted the training to be kept at Hurlburt and wrote a letter to Secretary of Defense Frank Carlucci requesting his support. The issue would take more effort to resolve.[28]

In March 1988, the two commands conducted another study and once again recommended that the training be moved to Kirtland AFB. Additionally, USSOCOM wanted to designate the training location as the United States Special Air Warfare Center to serve on a par with collateral centers established by the Army and Navy at Fort Bragg, North Carolina, and Coronado Naval Base, California, respectively. In June the deputy secretary of defense, William Taft IV, reviewed the study and directed another, much broader, study that would develop a series of recommendations. This Air Force Special Operations Forces Aircrew Training Working Group reviewed all the studies to date and then in coordination with the acting ASD/SOLIC, the Honorable John Marsh, also the serving secretary of the Army, developed a series of options varying by time phasing of aircraft and locations of units. Col Charles Holland, the 1550th CCTW commander, and his staff developed an entire program to modify the wing and base for the expanded training mission and were able to brief that plan to the MAC staff, the Twenty-Third Air Force staff, and Marsh. Marsh then reviewed the options and determined that Kirtland AFB was the best choice for MH-53J and MC-130E/H training. USSOCOM acquiesced but did not lose its desire to turn the 1550th into some form of special operations organization.[29]

As these various actions were taking place, the 1551st FTS was still conducting H-53 training, although its fleet of aircraft had been added to the Pave Low modification schedule. Regardless, it still had a cadre of IPs and engineers who could act as a logical nucleus for a Pave Low school, as well as specialized tactical and NVG training. Anticipating that the Pave Low training would be transferred to Kirtland AFB, the 1551st FTS sent two flight engineer instructors, MSgt Sam Moore and MSgt Peter Zilink, to the Central Training Flight at Hurlburt Field to develop and write courseware for the MH-53J flight engineer's course. Additionally, both were certified as academic instructors on the aircraft while there. Both then returned to Kirtland AFB, where they established the course under the direction of Capt Mark Perkins.

Captain Perkins and Capt Brandon Thompson also traveled to Hurlburt to become certified as MH-53J academic instructors so that they could begin building the qualification course for the MH-53J pilot and copilots. Their initial plan was to begin Pave Low qualifications by the beginning of 1989. However, that was predicated upon a final basing decision and the assignment of MH-53J aircraft to the 1550th CCTW.[30]

More MH-53s and Aircrews

At Hurlburt Field, the operations tempo remained high as the 20th SOS maintained its capability to answer national taskings and prepared for the influx of the added Pave Lows and crews. Occasionally, though, more mundane missions occurred that put the crews to good use. On 26 April 1988, Colonel Weikel with Maj Mike Letica and crew were conducting a night training mission with NVGs when they heard a distress call from the Eglin AFB tower controller asking for assistance to locate a US Army helicopter with a patient that had landed somewhere in the area because of a mechanical problem. The patient was a young woman who had suffered a severed arm in an aircraft accident, and the Army helicopter was transporting her to a hospital in Mobile, Alabama, but had to land in a field near Crestview, Florida. Weikel had a flight surgeon, Capt Kory Cornum, on board and diverted to Crestview, where he landed next to the Army helicopter. There his engineers and gunners transferred the patient to the Pave Low. Cornum immediately comforted her and made sure that the severed arm was properly cared for as Weikel and Letica used the sophisticated navigational gear on the aircraft to chart a course from Crestview directly to the hospital in Mobile. Fortunately, several intervening limited-use areas were inactive, and traffic controllers helped with the necessary air traffic clearances. Arriving at the hospital, Weikel and his crew discovered that it had a very small landing area. Regardless, the crew members put their special training to good use and were able to land on the pad. The young woman was quickly taken into surgery where the doctors worked to stabilize her condition and reattach her arm. For the Pave Low crews, their training mission turned into a good night's work.[31]

The transformation of the USAF H-53 fleet was going well. Throughout the year, the aircraft cycled through the NARF at Pensacola for the SLEP and their MH-53J modifications. Five CH-53Cs were transferred from the 601st TCW at Sembach AB to RAF Woodbridge to be flown by the forming 21st SOS before being returned to the CONUS for MH-53J conversion. Another two CH-53Cs were returned to the CONUS for conversion and assignment to Kirtland and Hurlburt. Additionally, the USAF and USMC concluded an agreement that allowed for the assignment of six CH-53As, numbers 66-14468, -14469, -14470, -14471, -14472, and -14473, to the 1550th CCTW at Kirtland AFB for use as TH-53A trainer aircraft. In April the SMOTEC at Hurlburt Field conducted a qualification OT&E using the recently modified MH-53J #67-14994 to validate that the aircraft in this configuration could accomplish its stated capabilities. The classified test was successful. However, the community suffered a setback on 20 October when two aircraft, HH-53H #70-1629 and MH-53J #68-08286, were damaged while conducting a training mission at Fort Picket, Virginia. The first aircraft suffered a hard landing when the crew members encountered brownout conditions as they approached the landing zone to extract 28 Army troops. The pilots of the second aircraft abandoned their approach and attempted another from a different angle. As the aircraft came to a hover, the crew once again encountered brownout conditions. The right scanner also informed the pilot that there were people below them, and he arrested the aircraft's rate of descent. Unfortunately, while in the dust cloud, the aircraft drifted to the left, hitting a power pole, power line, and some large trees. The aircraft came to a rest 75 feet from the landing zone. Fortunately, only one crewman was injured. But the repairs to the two aircraft cost $6.7 million, money somehow acquired by the magical Maj Ed Reed.[32]

The 20th was also steadily receiving more Airmen. A few more arrived from the 601st TASS at Sembach as that unit also inactivated. In

March 1988, 1st Lt Tom Trask reported for duty as a Pave Low pilot. He had been commissioned almost four years earlier out of the ROTC program at Embry-Riddle University, Daytona Beach, Florida. Trask had originally intended to be an aeronautical engineer. However, one of his professors had been an Army helicopter pilot in Vietnam. He told Trask that the Air Force was about to buy a bunch of HH-60Ds and suggested that he go to pilot training and fly helicopters. That sounded reasonable, so Trask took the tests and got a training slot to Fort Rucker. His class of 90 students also included future Pave Low pilots 2d Lt Al Bridges and 2d Lt Matt Shazda.

Trask enjoyed the training, especially the NVG work and tactical navigation. Graduating in June 1985, he received an assignment to fly UH-1Ns with the rescue detachment at Edwards AFB. While there, he upgraded to aircraft commander and IP. His unit still trained for combat recovery, and he was able to participate in several training exercises with the new A-10s at England AFB, Louisiana, to sharpen his skills.

In the summer of 1987, MAC had determined that the UH-1N was no longer viable as a combat recovery aircraft, and the various detachments were inactivated. Trask wanted an assignment to the Pave Lows at the 20th SOS. Before he could get the assignment, though, he had to conduct a telephone interview with the 20th commander, Lt Col "Bo" Johnson. Surviving that 30-minute forthright conversation, Trask reported to Kirtland AFB in October for his transition training.

There he joined with 1st Lt Larry Munz and 1st Lt Brad Webb, also former UH-1N pilots from sister detachments, who had also received assignments to the 20th. The qualification course was six months long and was conducted on C/H-53Bs and Cs. Trask was also able to stay at Kirtland for six more weeks to receive formal NVG training, which was a separate course. While there, he also received training of another sort. He found out that the red scarf worn by the men of the 20th was something really special and not lightly earned. As part of his move to the 20th, he had contacted the squadron and had been assigned Capt Kevin Ewing as his host officer to help him get established in the unit. Ewing had himself just arrived from the 41st ARRSq and—not aware of the squadron traditions—sent Trask patches for his flight suit and a red scarf. When Lieutenant Trask received them, he was impressed and decided to put the patches on his flight suit and to wear the scarf. A few days later, he heard that a 20th Pave Low had just flown in. He found out that the crew was at the

Officers' Club and decided to go over and meet them. He walked in and found Maj Jeff Walls and Capt Pappy Walters. As Trask approached, Walters spotted him *and* his red scarf. Trask remembered,

> I didn't know what it meant. It was just like any other squadron; you get the patches and you put them on. . . . Pappy Walters . . . saw me wearing the red scarf, and he came across that bar just about as fast as I have ever seen him move before or since. He started thumping me in the chest. "Who the hell are you, and why the hell are you wearing my scarf? What gives you the right? Who told you that you could wear it? If I don't know who you are, you definitely never earned it!". . . The other guys had to drag him off of me. We were about to go to blows right there. We hadn't even been drinking yet; . . . it was only about 5 o'clock in the afternoon. I learned that I was not to wear my scarf until I got qualified in the Pave Low.[33]

Lieutenant Webb also met Walters at Kirtland, although the encounter was much more benign. He recalled Walters saying that "you had better be prepared to play hardball when you come to the 20th. It's going to happen, and it's going to happen big." That was fine with Webb. The son of an Air Force officer and SEA combat veteran, he graduated from the Air Force Academy in 1984 and selected helicopter pilot training. He then picked a UH-1N assignment in hopes of doing a lot of flying. Assigned for two years at Hill AFB, Utah, he learned a great deal about the nuances of helicopter and mountain flying from the "old heads" and participated in some civilian rescues while also learning to fly with NVGs. He was ready and eager to fly the Pave Low.[34]

When Lieutenant Trask finally arrived at the 20th, Walters saw him and profusely apologized for his actions. Trask then found Colonel Johnson and formally reported in. Johnson had a million things on his mind at that moment, but he still took the lieutenant into his office for a quick brief. He made it clear that Trask was a lucky guy to get the assignment and that if he did not measure up, Johnson would have no problems with showing him the door. He also explained that Trask was arriving just ahead of a large influx of personnel and might be able to get right into his Pave Low conversion. With that, he gave the lieutenant a handshake and sent him down to the orderly room to begin his in-processing.

Walking through the squadron, Trask was rather put off by the arrogance which radiated from the Pave Low crewmen. Several tried to grab him to work various projects that needed a goodly amount of "grunt" work, and the squadron flight scheduler explained to him how low he really was on the training list. By the end of the week, Trask was a bit dispirited and beginning to wonder just what he had gotten himself into. Fortunately, he met Steve Connelly. Seeing Trask's despondent mood, Connelly told him that they were going over to the Officers' Club. There, he assured Trask that the week just completed would be his worst in the squadron and told him how neat it was going to be flying the Pave Lows with such a great group of Airmen. Trask was further heartened on Monday when he again saw Colonel Johnson, who told him that he would be put to work in the plans office working for a sharp young captain named Randy O'Boyle. A few days later, he was also told that he would be able to start his academics with the Central Training Flight, thus beginning his Pave Low qualification.[35]

Six weeks later, Colonel Weikel replaced Lt Col Bo Johnson as the commander of the 20th SOS. He chose Lt Col Mike Russell to serve as the operations officer. One of the initial 20th SOS Pave Low pilots, Russell left the unit in 1984 for a one-year tour in Korea. That was followed by duty in the classified programs division on the Twenty-Third Air Force staff at Scott AFB and then at Hurlburt when the Twenty-Third Air Force headquarters was moved down there. Settling into the 20th, Russell had to receive a requalification on the HH-53H. He took several local rides in the aircraft, and then Capt Randy O'Boyle gave him his check ride, writing on his evaluation form, "Once a Pave Low God, always a Pave Low God."[36]

With Weikel's concurrence, Russell reorganized the flight system in the squadron to better prepare for the large influx of crew members coming to the unit. He also had to deal with a number of personnel issues. Several transferees from the Sembach unit were not volunteers for Pave Low and openly resented being there. Additionally, some of the transplants from the 41st ARRSq believed that the 20th SOS was a clear step down from their old unit and said so openly. Of more concern to Russell, though, was what appeared to be a lack of professionalism across all areas of performance. Some higher-ranking Twenty-Third Air Force officers, including the commander, General Patterson, believed that the three Pave Low crashes were, in part, a manifestation of an atmosphere of sloppiness. Russell later related,

> What I found when I got to the 20th was for the most part [that] General Patterson's concerns were not as bad as he had made them to be but that they were founded. The guys—some of the old guys—were, in fact, running on the extremes. They were good pilots; they flew the aircraft really well; but there

was a lack of discipline. That was my big challenge as the DO: to bring discipline and what I call "professionalism" in all aspects of the mission and to give us a little bit better credibility with the customer. . . . Working on our image and professionalism was my big challenge as the DO.[37]

Lt Col Rich Comer was elevated to assistant operations officer and given responsibility for the war readiness section, which included mobility, plans, and tactics. Unfortunately, he and Russell had different personalities and found it challenging, at times, to find common approaches to issues. Their differences did cause some friction in the unit.[38]

MSgt Rick Simmon was still involved in training Pave Low flight engineers. He had left the squadron in 1986 for a tour on H-3s with the 31st ARRSq at Clark AB in the Philippines. Returning in late 1987, he was now working with the 1st SOW Standardization and Evaluation Office with Capt Pappy Walters. Both were using their extensive aircraft and mission knowledge to insure that the new flight engineers and pilots were fully trained and mission capable.[39]

The squadron was also filling up with enlisted troops to serve as the flight engineers and gunners. One of them was SSgt Ed Hux. He had grown up in California and, after high school graduation in 1978, had enlisted in the USAF. He initially trained as an aircraft mechanic and served as a crew chief on F-4s before switching over to helicopters and then qualifying as a flight engineer on UH-1Ns. He did tours with UH-1N units in Nevada and then Panama, where he entered special operations and began to train for the uniqueness of the missions. When the Panama unit was inactivated, he transferred to the 20th SOS in late 1987. For the next 18 months, he attended initial H-53 qualification training at Kirtland and then worked his way through the myriad of NVG and tactical qualifications at Hurlburt and mountain training at Dobbins. He trained on both the HH-53H and the MH-53J, discovering that his initial special operations training acquired on the UH-1N actually gave him an advantage in getting through the program. However, like all of the other crew members, he found it challenging to rise to the level of performance needed to serve as one of six men on board the Pave Low. He was intimidated by all that he had to learn about aircraft systems and performance, the new enhanced navigation system, the self-protective equipment, and all of the sophisticated radio gear. Hux remembered that "it was actually pretty awe-inspiring at the time. It was quite a step up. What helped me was having that prior [special operations] experience."[40]

Most important, though, Hux realized that the safe and efficient operation of the Pave Low, in any variation, required full and complete crew integration regardless of the relative rank among the crew members. He said,

> If they [were] not working as one team, you couldn't do the mission. The FE [flight engineer] is running stuff up front; he obviously can't fly the aircraft. The guys up front . . . we take a huge load off so they can concentrate on actually flying and executing the mission. It's almost a voice-activated cockpit; they can ask for information or ask for something to be done, and the FE in the seat is hopefully doing it already or getting it done for him.
>
> As they go to make their approaches or landings, . . . the pilots lose sight of the LZ [landing zone]; they are relying on those three guys in the back to get them in. The Pave Low is 88 or 90 feet long; they have no idea what is going on behind them that last 75 to 80 feet. It's got to work as a well-orchestrated team, or the mission just never gets done. Sometimes the [flight engineer] in the seat [has the] job to keep everybody focused and on track. What was neat was sometimes if he got overtasked or maybe he wasn't on his game, there were five other people to pull him back. You had another FE in the door. "Hey, have you run such-and-such a checklist yet?" "Oh!"
>
> The Pave Low is clearly and truly a crew airplane. We trained it; we harped on it.[41]

The entire mission qualification process for new pilots like Trask and Webb took, on average, nine full months after their Kirtland training. It culminated with a long TDY to Dobbins or Knoxville to get mountain training so necessary to qualify with the TF/TA radar. Trask began his training on the HH-53H. While he was working through the course, though, the squadron began to receive the MH-53Js. As they became available for flight, some were immediately used for training duties. However, as Trask noted, the two aircraft models were hugely different. They were a full generation apart in their level of technology. Given the vagaries of aircraft availability on the flying schedule, Trask had to learn to fly both. This vastly increased his training load but qualified him to fly both aircraft models. Finally, though, in early 1989, he was fully qualified as a copilot on both aircraft, giving him a real advantage.[42]

Then he earnestly threw himself into learning the planning process. He became a Pave Low liaison officer to the US Army Rangers and spent a great deal of time with the 2d Battalion of the 75th Ranger Regiment. This required him to travel quite a bit with the battalion, including two rotations to Panama in 1989 for focused training there. On the second exercise, called Pave Jungle, he, Maj Rich Comer, Capt

Brad Webb, and several other pilots got to fly missions in the Canal Zone and became quite familiar with the area and specific landing zones. USSOCOM contingency planners noted this fact and filed it away for future use. Ultimately, all three Ranger battalions rotated through the training and also gained a goodly bit of familiarity with the geography of Panama. One specific Pave Low flight, though, had unintended consequences. Comer and Webb inadvertently flew over a Panamanian restricted area where a key Panamanian unit, Battalion 2000, was located. This caused quite a reaction from the Panamanian government, which protested the "aggressive behavior" of the US forces.[43]

In the summer of 1989, Trask qualified as a Pave Low aircraft commander. Just a few days behind him was Webb. However, Webb received only a minimal qualification on the HH-53H before being switched over to the MH-53Js, where he then progressed through the full local and mountain training and deployments and qualified as a new aircraft commander on the Pave Low IIIE. Completing the long and intense process, he remembered thinking then, "I love this machine, really love it." He and Trask were the youngest aircraft commanders in the unit.[44]

39th Special Operations Wing and
21st Special Operations Squadron

On 1 March 1988, per the Forward Look plan, the 39th ARRW at Eglin AFB was redesignated the 39th SOW, commanded by Col James Hobson. The wing's subordinate 55th ARRSq was also redesignated as the 55th SOS. It had been equipped with the initial nine H-60s purchased by the USAF. After completing his tour on the MAC staff, Maj Donny Wurster transferred to the unit. He brought a wealth of rescue and staff experience to the 55th to help develop it into a top-notch special operations unit capable of performing both SOF and combat search and rescue (CSAR) taskings and showing that the H-60 could serve as a viable replacement for the now aged H-3s as a CSAR aircraft. Like the growing Pave Low fleet, the aircraft and crews of the 55th also became direct competitors with the US Army 160th SOAR.

Additionally, the 9th SOS was activated at Eglin and assigned HC-130s. The 39th also received command of the MC-130-equipped 7th SOS, still based at Rhein-Main, and several other smaller detachments stationed in the Atlantic region. Two months later, the 21st

SOS was reactivated at RAF Woodbridge after a 12-and-a-half-year hiatus from its great service in Southeast Asia. The 21st would receive its MH-53Js starting that summer as they completed their modifications at the NARF.[45]

Lt Col Steve Connelly was assigned to take command of the 21st, and he transferred over from Hurlburt Field. The unit was authorized 63 personnel and picked up several pilots and flight engineers from the 67th ARRSq, which was converting to an HC-130 unit and redesignating as the 67th SOS. As the aircraft were being modified, the 21st crews would fly the HH-53s from the 67th and CH-53s passed from the 601st TCW at Sembach, Germany.

The 21st also needed 16 gunners, and they were slow to arrive. One of the first to come over was TSgt John Sprouse. Connelly recruited him to serve as his initial weapons and tactics gunner and basically build the program for the 21st SOS. He and others not only did the paperwork necessary to establish the supply accounts for all of the weapons and ammunition but also built an armory for the unit. They also worked with the UK authorities to procure access to weapons ranges so that the gunners could accomplish live-fire training. After six months, Connelly moved Sprouse over to serve in the squadron standardization and evaluation office as his gunner evaluator. However, Sprouse had a wild side to him—having earlier received several Article 15s—and occasionally needed a bit of guidance. At one point, Connelly had to admonish him by saying, "Either I'm going to walk your ass into a mud puddle, or you're going to straighten up and fly right." Sprouse held great respect for Connelly and took that advice. He was later selected to attend the USAFE NCO Academy.[46]

The two flying units and the collocated 667th Consolidated Aircraft Maintenance Squadron formed a cohesive team. All were under the OPCON of the SOCEUR, the European component of USSO-COM. Their mission was to conduct special operations as directed by SOCEUR.

Almost immediately the 21st dispatched aircrews to Hurlburt for Pave Low qualification. In July it dispatched three CH-53s to participate in a joint and combined classified mission and two more for NATO exercise Display Determination in Italy. Through the rest of the year, more crews went to Hurlburt for their qualifications, and the unit dispatched the CH-53s to many locations to begin intensive training with various special operations forces, both US and NATO. They practiced all of the classic SOF missions and focused on shipboard training and NVG operations. In October, the first two MH-53Js arrived aboard a C-5 direct from NAS Pensacola. The next month, two more MH-53Js arrived, and the last CH-53s were all loaded aboard C-5s and flown to the CONUS. With four Pave Lows now on station, the direct operational training was almost continuous as the squadron received increasing calls for support.

However, not all of the aircraft arrived with their full complement of Pave Low modifications completed. Some of the suppliers had trouble meeting the delivery dates for specialized components like the TFR and FLIR kits, and the aircraft were shipped to Bentwaters with only partial modifications. Flight training had to be modified accordingly, and the crews did the best they could until the modifications were complete. As word of their arrival spread, though, helicopter units from other NATO countries began sending their crews to Woodbridge to work with the Airmen of the 21st on NVG techniques and special operations flight procedures. Between July and December, the squadron flew 378 sorties for 672.5 flight hours.[47]

Yarrawonga

The new year of 1989 started off dramatically for the Pave Low community, when the 21st SOS at RAF Woodbridge was called upon on 14 January to launch its MH-53Js in support of a rescue operation for the bulk carrier *Yarrawonga*. An 827-foot-long Cypriot freighter ship with 32 persons aboard, it was floundering in heavy seas and in danger of possibly sinking 360 nautical miles northwest of Shannon, Ireland. Conditions were terrible, with 500-foot ceilings, visibility at 1,500 feet, winds gusting from 50 to 80 knots, and seas cresting at 30 to 40 feet. Two Pave Lows—#66-14431 (a veteran of the *SS Mayaguez* crew rescue) and #69-5796—were prepared, along with two HC-130s from the 67th SOS, to attempt a recovery. The SOCEUR commander approved the rescue plan.

A support team was immediately dispatched to the Shannon Airport, and the crews prepared for what would be a grueling mission. After delays caused by maintenance problems and worsening weather over most of Great Britain, the two helicopter crews—led by Capt Dennis Jones and Capt Dave Freeman, along with extra copilots, PJs, and fight surgeons—launched for the effort. However, because of continued severe weather, the helicopters had to land at the Shannon Airport to await better conditions.

Weather conditions were markedly better the next morning. The two MH-53 crews launched and immediately rendezvoused with an HC-130 to refuel before heading for the ship, which was now rapidly taking on water and listing 30 degrees to port. Arriving at the ship, they discovered that the cloud ceiling was now at 2,000 feet and that winds were still gusting from 50 to 60 knots. Captain Jones took his helicopter in first and hovered over the ship. He lowered one of his PJs so that he could organize the ship's crew for rescue. As the helicopter buffeted and rocked in the ferocious winds, 17 survivors were hoisted up from the dying ship. Jones then moved away, and Captain Freeman repeated the procedure, rescuing the remaining persons on board. Once all crew members were safe, the two helicopters then refueled from the HC-130s and proceeded to Shannon Airport, where the survivors were provided medical care for their extended exposure to the harsh elements. The rescue crews then had to deal with the crush of media teams awaiting them. Adm William Crowe, the chairman of the JCS, and General Lindsay both sent their congratulations, as did a long list of other individuals and organizations for a tough job expertly done by the outstanding crews of the 21st and 67th and all of the support personnel who made the missions possible.[48]

Courtesy Air Force Historical Research Agency

Pave Lows from the 21st SOS flew rescue operations for the *Yarrawonga* bulk carrier when it floundered in heavy seas west of Ireland.

On 5 May 1989, the 39th SOW lowered its flag at Eglin AFB, Florida. Its subordinate 9th SOS and 55th SOS transferred to the 1st SOW at Hurlburt Field. Three days later, the 39th flag was raised at Rhein-Main AB, Germany, as the unit, with its assigned 21st and 67th SOSs and support units, became the European wing of the Twenty-Third Air Force.[49]

Pave Low Training

Reluctantly, Cong. Earl Hutto concurred with the operational decision to move to Kirtland as earlier recommended by the series of studies and, ultimately, the ASD/SOLIC, Secretary John Marsh. However, the USSOCOM commander, General Lindsay, still wanted the establishment of the Special Air Warfare Center. Hutto insisted that it be activated at Hurlburt. In further conversations, though, General Lindsay and the MAC commander, General Cassidy, decided that the center would be duplicative of other existing headquarters, and the issue was dropped.[50]

With the resolution of the basing issue, the 1551st FTS of the 1550th CCTW prepared to begin MH-53J qualification training in May 1989. The qualification course would last seven and one-half months, divided into three phases: day tactical, night tactical, and Pave Low. Four MH-53Js had returned from the Pave Low modification but lacked some key components that would require alternations to the training schedule. Additionally, the course could start with four of the six CH-53A aircraft from the USMC. However, to bring them up to USAF standards for use as trainer aircraft, they needed 20 significant modifications and upgrades. Consequently, they were also being sent to the NARF at Pensacola NAS for extensive rework and refurbishment. Regardless, the first class started on time with two student pilots and two student flight engineers. In June the squadron received two fully qualified Pave Low IPs and a fully qualified flight engineer from the 20th SOS. Now it was capable of gradually relieving Hurlburt of its training load so that the Green Hornets could focus on operational training. However, the 1551st training load also included qualifying other residual H-53 pilots and flight engineers remaining at Kirtland on the Pave Low. It was a very busy time.[51]

Additionally, the 1551st FTS did not have any training aids for the radar, FLIR, or enhanced navigation systems and had to use the aircraft themselves as they arrived or until training components were manufactured and delivered. However, the equipment and aircraft steadily arrived, and by the end of 1989, the 1551st squadron operations officer, Maj John Folkerts, noted that the unit now had 16 qualified H-53 IPs with two—Maj Jim Eustace and Maj Hugh "Paco" Burrell—fully Pave Low qualified. Additionally, the unit also had four other pilots in instructor upgrade, plus five more inbound to the unit. Very soon, the unit would be prepared for a significant increase in training, as it would train the pilots, flight engineers, and gunners necessary to crew a fleet of 41 Pave Lows.[52]

A New Air Rescue Service

As the Twenty-Third Air Force steadily matured and focused ever more of its attention on special operations, the rescue portion of the command atrophied. The ARRS had been divested of its operational wings and basically converted into a headquarters to monitor rescue operations. In 1985 there were 18 squadron-level rescue units; only four were projected by 1990. When the PACAF commander, Gen Merrill McPeak, questioned this dramatic reduction, the USAF chief of staff, Gen Larry Welch, raised this issue with General Cassidy. After a staff review, Cassidy directed that MAC redesignate the ARRS by its original title, the Air Rescue Service, by 1 August 1989 and that the ARS fall under MAC and be assigned all of the rescue squadrons.

The MAC staff began the detailed planning needed to make the transformation. Consequently, as the ARS reactivated as scheduled, it commanded the 37th ARRSq at F. E. Warren AFB, Wyoming; the 41st ARRSq at Patrick AFB; the 56th ARRSq at Keflavik Naval Installation, Iceland; and the 71st ARRSq at Elmendorf AFB, Alaska. The two rescue squadrons in the Pacific region—the 33d ARRSq at Kadena and the 38th ARRSq at Osan—would be assigned to the ARS as opposed to the newly forming 353d SOW at Clark AB, as projected under Forward Look. Additionally, five rescue units would be reactivated and assigned to Misawa AB, Japan; Nellis AFB, Nevada; Holloman AFB, New Mexico; Hill AFB, Utah; and Incirlik AB, Turkey. Concurrently, the 41st RWRW would be inactivated and the ARS headquarters moved to the vacated 41st RWRW facilities at McClellan AFB.[53]

The mission statement of the ARS was straightforward, declaring that "Air Rescue Service is the focal point for USAF rescue. . . . The

primary mission of the ARS is combat rescue which traditionally involves the helicopter recovery of downed aircrew members from a
hostile environment, usually supported by HC-130 tankers and dedicated fighter aircraft."[54]

Because of the conversion, though, of all the HH-53s to Pave Low,
the rescue squadrons were or would be equipped with the older and
much less capable H-3s. In a practical sense, the ARS was now back
to where it was in 1967 before it became the ARRS, received HH-53s,
or even conceptualized what would become Pave Low. It was as if the
command had gone through a 22-year time warp. Perhaps adding to
the insult was the realization that the one squadron of U/HH-60s that
belonged to the Twenty-Third Air Force was the 55th ARRSq, which
was converted to the 55th SOS with the 39th SOW. As it reactivated,
the ARS effectively did not have the aircraft needed to perform its
mission of combat recovery in anything other than a low- or perhaps
medium-threat environment. To address this need, General Cassidy
had to replace his aged H-3s. He directed his staff to program for the
acquisition of new HH-60s at the rate of 10 per year for FY 90–98,
with the first arriving in February 1990.[55]

353d Special Operations Wing and 31st Special Operations Squadron

The unit changes dictated by Forward Look continued to take
place. On 6 April 1989, the 353d SOW was activated at Clark AB as
the Pacific component of AFSOF. Its heritage derived from the 3d Air
Commando Group, which operated in the Philippines in World War
II. The MC-130-equipped and collocated 1st SOS was assigned to the
unit, as was the 31st ARRSq, which was redesignated as the 31st SOS.
The squadron had been stationed at Clark AB almost continuously
since 1952. The commander was Lt Col Dale Cook, a career helicopter
pilot. The 31st was equipped with C/HH-3s but was slated to receive
MH-53J aircraft as they were available, possibly in 1990. A few
months later, the 17th SOS was activated with HC-130 tankers and
also assigned to the wing.

In the interim, the 31st SOS performed its mission with its assigned
HH-3s. It still responded to SAR taskings and calls for medevac but
began to shift its training emphasis to the development of special
operations skills, especially the infiltration and exfiltration of small

teams into sensitive or denied areas. The crews began to work with special operations forces from other services and countries in the region. They also flew some operational missions in December 1989, when they supported Thirteenth Air Force involvement in the coup attempt against the Philippine government administration of Pres. Corazon Aquino. Several of the missions involved working with USMC CH-53s as well as with their US Army and Navy counterparts. This pattern continued into the first half of 1990 as the squadron increased its crew training with NVGs, deck landing qualifications, and deployments to work with US and allied special operations forces in major exercises like Cobra Gold in Thailand. The squadron was also notified that it could expect to receive its first MH-53J aircraft by the second half of the year.[56]

United States Special Operations Command

As Twenty-Third Air Force restructured and prepared to lose its rescue units as per General Cassidy's decisions, its relationship with USSOCOM continued to evolve. In November 1988, General Lindsey approved a statement on his views about USSOCOM and CSAR.[57] While allowing that the recovery of personnel from "hostile, denied, or politically sensitive Territory" could be a special operation, he emphatically stated that "Combat Search and Rescue is not a mission for which Special Operations Forces . . . are trained, organized, and equipped. . . . Accordingly, it is the view of this headquarters that . . . it is inappropriate to assign overall theater CSAR responsibilities to the theater SOC, assign SOF units the dual mission of both SO and CSAR, or to place SOF air assets on standing alert to meet short notice SAR/CSAR requirements."[58]

There is no indication that this declaration was coordinated with the newly reforming ARS. That command, as it reconstituted, lacked the ability to perform combat recovery or—as USSOCOM was now calling it—CSAR. In reality, a disconnect of sorts had been created. ARS now had the CSAR mission but would not, for at least 18 months, have the aircraft or trained crews to perform it. Conversely, USSOCOM was now eschewing the mission, preferring its classic assignments, while owning both the aircraft and crews best equipped and trained to perform the mission in dangerous areas.[59]

Courtesy Sikorsky historical archives

A Pave Low crew practicing rope insertions with a special forces team

In January 1989, Assistant Secretary of Defense Taft signed a memorandum giving the USSOCOM commander budget authority over MFP-11, effective in FY 1990, marking the first time that a combatant commander was given such financial authority and responsibility. General Lindsay intended to use it. He continued to press for a closer alignment between his command and the Twenty-Third and suggested that the Twenty-Third be declared a USAF major command and a component command of USSOCOM. In July Headquarters MAC held a summit. Generals Lindsay and Cassidy were there, as were the USAF chief, Gen Larry Welch, and several other senior commanders. General Welch was aware of the changes being made within the Twenty-Third Air Force and agreed to the divestiture of non-SOF elements from the command. However, the sticking point was the validation and prioritization of SOF requirements and the development and acquisition of SOF-peculiar equipment. The generals could not come to agreement on those issues, and they were deferred for later action. The next week, General Lindsay signed out the USSOCOM Operational Concept that clearly defined the command mission, principles, organization, mission activities, and joint mission analysis program, which emphasized the closely integrated nature of USSOCOM operations. General Patterson attended many of the meetings. However, his time was drawing short, and he gave up command of the Twenty-Third Air Force to Maj Gen Thomas Eggers on 7 September 1989.[60]

At about the same time that Taft sent his letter, the 20th SOS, as part of the 1st SOW, deployed to Pope AFB and received a four-week ORI. The inspection was conducted as the 1st SOW participated in the JCS-directed USSOCOM exercise Jaguar Bite. The wing received an overall rating of excellent, but the mission and unit specifics were classified. While there, the crews flew long day and night missions to Florida, the Upper Peninsula of Michigan, and Fort Campbell, Kentucky, to insert and extract various teams as the inspectors watched. The troops lived in open-bay barracks and worked extended days and nights. It was a tremendous bonding experience for the unit and showed how far it had progressed. Colonel Weikel was most pleased. It validated his belief that with more aircraft and more flying hours, unit pride and morale would rise accordingly.[61]

21st Special Operations Squadron

After the excitement of the *Yarrawonga* rescue, the 21st Squadron settled into the steady regimen necessary to become combat ready with the MH-53J. Training continued as the crews returned from their mission qualifications at Hurlburt Field. However, tactical training was hampered somewhat by equipment limitations because not all of the aircraft arrived with their full complement of Pave Low equipment—primarily the FLIR and TF/TA radars. The crews just had to work around the shortages as they became ever more deeply engaged in training exercises across Europe with US and other NATO special forces units. Additionally, as their presence in Europe became known, they received a steadily increasing number of requests for training support.

The 21st finally received 12 gunners and by June had its full complement of 65 authorized personnel. In the fall, it received visits from Brig Gen Richard Potter, the SOCEUR commander, and Maj Gen Thomas Eggers, the new Twenty-Third Air Force commander. For 1989, its first full calendar year in operation, the unit flew 913 sorties for 1,759.8 flight hours—with just four MH-53Js.[62]

20th Special Operations Squadron

In its own way, the 20th was helping the 21st stand up so quickly because it mission-qualified all of the 21st's crew members. That continued at an ever-higher pace during 1989, as the unit steadily received the MH-53Js as they came from the modification line at Pensacola. Indeed, many of its aircrews logged extra flight time supporting the NARF with FCFs and operations checks on components as they were installed. With the aircraft also came more troops, and the squadron swelled to 210 assigned personnel against 147 authorized positions, with another 35 Airmen attached for various lengths of time for training or exercises.

One of the early 1989 arrivals was Capt Charles "Mike" Beard. A 1981 graduate of the Air Force Academy, he had initially served as a T-37 IP before receiving an assignment to HH-53s with the 67th ARRSq at RAF Bentwaters. He arrived there just as that unit began its transition to the 21st SOS. He received his Pave Low qualification at Hurlburt and, after a small amount of training at Bentwaters, conducted FCFs on the MH-53Js as they came off of the modification line. He was given an opportunity to cut short his tour with the 21st and transfer to the 20th, and he did not hesitate.[63]

By June all but three of the 20th's HH-53H aircraft had been dispatched for conversion, and the flight line was jammed with 15 MH-53J aircraft with a projected growth to 24 Pave Lows. With so many machines and personnel now, some element of the unit was on the road at almost any time—participating in capability exercises at Fort Bragg, deploying to Dobbins AFB for mountain training, doing deck landing qualifications with the Navy, or working with special forces teams somewhere in the CONUS or overseas in exercises like Flintlock or Solid Shield.[64]

In July the 20th deployed four aircraft, crews, and support personnel to Soto Cano AB, Honduras, for four weeks to support joint/combined exercise Cabanas 89. There they worked primarily with JTF-Bravo ground and aviation elements to develop operational procedures and experience operating in that region of the world. Using their new GPS navigation systems, they determined that the tactical maps for the area were inaccurate and needed to be resurveyed before they could be used for operational missions. Unit personnel also participated in several civic action missions, delivering goodwill items and medical teams to several local villages. Two months later, the

20th dispatched another team of two aircraft, crews, and support troops to Mountain Home AFB to support Exercise Knife Blade 90. In this exercise, the crews did a fair amount of mountain flying and led flights of Army aircraft, especially at night. Operations were classified, but the 20th crews logged 46 flight hours in the exercise.

That summer the 20th lost one of its best and most highly qualified pilots when Capt Pappy Walters decided to retire. Not comfortable with the rapid expansion of the Pave Low community, he believed that he had contributed what he could as an Air Force officer. With 21 years of flying, he had seen almost everything and accomplished about all that he could. Even though he had kept up his professional development as an officer, he was clearly much older than others in his referential group, meaning that his chances for promotion were problematic at best. Weikel tried to talk him out of leaving, pointing out that he could still contribute in staff duties. However, Walters was able to gain a position with Aeronautical Radio, Incorporated (ARINC), which had established a maintenance subsidiary at the NARF at Pensacola NAS to manage the Pave Low modification and SLEP line. There he would be able to put his extensive experience to further use overseeing the modification flow and eventually being able to again fly the Pave Lows on maintenance and acceptance flights.

As he left active duty though, he said of the men he flew with:

> I thanked all the guys in the back first—the flight engineers and the scanners because they saved our lives more times than we could count because they would see things that I couldn't see or didn't see. At that time we had only had [three] crashes, but our counterparts in the Army had had dozens and dozens of crashes that most people do not know about to this day. So that crew concept was critical in saving our lives on many, many occasions.
>
> I think everyone just sensed that we were the tip of the spear. You've heard that term before, but we truly believed that we were trained to be the tip. If there was something that the national command authority needed to be done, anywhere in the world, under any conditions, we felt like we were trained to a level to go out, right out of the chute, complete the mission—sight unseen, no rehearsal. . . . It was "you either do it, or you fail."
>
> [We had] an incredible sense of pride. . . . People worked so hard 24/7 [and had] such a strong work ethic together. We were all . . . like true brothers. It didn't matter if you were the pilot, the flight engineer, the gunner—we were all one crew. . . . Everybody knew what his job was, and you weren't about to screw up and let the other guys down.[65]

Of such men, great units are made.

Operation Pokeweed

During this period, the 20th also received a classified real-world mission in the Caribbean region designated Operation Pokeweed. Weikel was ordered to generate four aircraft to fly to the USS *Forrestal* at a location in the Caribbean, south of Jamaica. There they would pick up a team of SEALs and fly them to Panama for an attempt to capture Pablo Escobar Gaviria, the Colombian drug lord from the Medellin cartel. Intelligence sources indicated that he would be traveling to the island of Bocas del Toro off the northern Caribbean coast.

The 20th had most of its aircraft and crews deployed to several locations, and Weikel had to work closely with his maintenance troops to get the required number of aircraft airborne. The plan called for a long overwater outbound leg to the *Forrestal*, with in-flight refueling by MC-130s at low altitude in bad weather; a landing aboard the ship to pick up the SEALs; a delivery leg; and a long flight home. Capt Joe Becker planned the mission, and Colonel Weikel led it. The 1st SOW commander, Col George Gray, was aboard one of the aircraft to witness his men in action. Capt Tom Trask was aboard as the copilot on the second aircraft with Corby Martin and Becker as a spare pilot.[66]

The mission went well for the first three refuelings, but then the aircraft ran into a heavy line of thunderstorms that could not be avoided. The helicopters needed one more refueling to make the aircraft carrier, and no safe alternate airfields were in range. The remaining MC-130 had only the right refueling hose working. To best avoid the weather, the pilot dropped down to 300 feet above the water. As the crews fought to hook up and receive their vital fuel, Trask remembers, "Lightening was going off everywhere; everyone's got vertigo. It's just black as . . . . You couldn't see anything, even with goggles . . . except when the lightning bolts illuminated the sky."[67]

During this refueling, Trask was in the right seat, with Martin in the left. The weather was so rough that they fell off the boom several times. Martin and Trask swapped the controls about every 90 seconds because fighting the turbulence was so fatiguing. Joe Becker came up and offered, several times, to swap seats with either pilot. Both refused because they did not want to have even a few seconds where two pilots were not in position to control the aircraft. All pilots also experienced severe vertigo and had to strictly discipline themselves to maintain full and thorough instrument cross-checks to control it. All they really knew was that they were flying to a set of coordinates in the midst of a large body of water where they were supposed to find the *Forrestal*, which was proceeding to the designated position at over 35 knots.[68]

There was a palpable sense of relief when they began to see the ship on their radars. Then they saw it through their goggles. The entire mission was taking place with the barest communications so that the possibility of detection was minimized. They could see that the deck was clear, and the four helicopters landed on it, with Weikel putting his aircraft out on the angle deck. As they settled, no Navy personnel were visible. One of the Pave Low gunners jumped off of his helicopter and literally went over and banged on the deck door to the carrier island. Navy personnel then came out to secure the aircraft and instruct them to shut down their engines and come inside. The crews did so, logging 12.8 hours on the flight. The Sailors were horrified to discover that one aircraft had landed on the angle deck, explaining that "nobody ever goes out there in the dark." The admiral wanted to know who landed there. "Of course, it was Weikel," recalled Trask, "once again, seeking forgiveness, I'm sure. That was his way."

Weikel and his somewhat shaken Airmen then joined the ship crew inside, only to be notified that the mission had been scrubbed when the intelligence sources reported that Escobar had not traveled as planned. Regardless, the *Forrestal* crew warmly welcomed the Pave Low guys aboard. In fact, Colonel Gray was personal friends with the ship's captain because they had previously served together on the staff at US Atlantic Command. The captain told the assembled Pave Low crews that he thought the plan was absolutely crazy and expected that at least one Pave Low and possibly crew would be lost in the operation. The commander of the air group then debriefed the Pave Low crews on the complete operational aspects of the mission. When he had finished, the captain allowed Weikel to conduct a crew-only debrief. It was an astounding event. Deeply shaken by the experience, Trask felt that he could not do this job for a living, that it was much too scary, and that he was on the very edge of his capabilities. He just could not believe that Corby Martin could be sitting there so calm and cool throughout the mission, while he was at his wits end. Trask assumed, too, that he was the only one who was so rattled. The crew debrief was an epiphany. Trask recounts,

> We get into the debrief, when everyone left, and we were in the ward room. They left us to do a crew debrief, and even Weikel, after everyone else had left, nothing but Pave Low pilots in the room, said, "Damn, that was the most scared I

have ever been in my whole f---ing life!!" Everyone kind of exploded with emotion about how rough that flight had been. Then I felt much better that at least I was not the only one who had been scared to death through that night.[69]

The 1st SOW commander, Colonel Gray, also sat in on the debrief. However, he had a very different opinion. Sure, the flight had been rough, but they had made it, and he was ecstatic at their performance. Several years of hard training by the right crews matched with the right equipment had recreated the piece of the puzzle that was missing at Desert One. It was a seminal event for Pave Low, and Gray sensed the signal importance of their accomplishment. Approaching Puerto Rico, the Pave Lows lifted and flew to Roosevelt Roads NAS. There Gray put the crew members up in a nice hotel for a few days so they could unwind before returning to Hurlburt.[70]

Clear and Present Danger

Almost coincidentally the Pave Low fleet received some surprising advertisement when the preeminent military action writer Tom Clancy published his latest techno-thriller, *Clear and Present Danger*. Clancy was already famous for several great novels that used recent developments in global events and the modernization of US military forces as the basis for the story line. This one focused on the growing danger of narcotics trafficking from South to North America and a mythical covert US military response. An MH-53J and crew were featured in the story as they infiltrated American Soldiers deep into Colombia to conduct intelligence collection and interdiction raids. Clancy's presentation of the aircraft and crew was uncanny, highlighting the criticality of crew coordination and the "uniqueness" of the Pave Low crew members. He even included a flight through a hurricane and shipboard operations as he weaved his tale.

However, Clancy had received firsthand information on the Pave Low. While writing the novel, he had sent a request to USAF public affairs asking to be allowed to speak with a Pave Low pilot. That tasking went to Maj Ed Reed, who met the author at the Officers' Club at Fort Myer, Virginia, for drinks and helped him to understand the intricacies of the Pave Low, even suggesting some modifications to the story line. Reed was just finishing his Pentagon tour and departing to be a Pave Low instructor at Kirtland AFB when the book came out. He took great delight when his Army special operations competitors in the Pentagon "went absolutely nuts" upon discovering that Clancy had used the Pave Low instead of one of their aircraft in the story. The popularity and timeliness of the book immediately spawned discussion of a movie adaptation and speculation that a Pave Low would be used in the filming.[71]

Mountain Training

Not every mission was as exciting as Pokeweed. During the entire year, the 20th supported 28 exercises and had Airmen deployed to Dobbins for 275 calendar days. Weikel again used the mountain training TDY as a bonding experience for the Airmen who were joining Pave Low from many different backgrounds and, collaterally, as an opportunity to give his sharp lieutenant colonels, majors, and even captains some leadership opportunities. In the last six months of the year, the squadron trained 46 pilots and 47 flight engineers while constantly supporting the NARF and also provided aircraft and manning for 89 static displays. The 20th logged 6,597 flight hours and 3,185 sorties for the year and qualified 28 pilots on the Pave Low, bringing the total number of pilots qualified on the Pave Low since Frank Pehr first flew it to 99.

The performance of the 20th SOS in 1988 had been phenomenal. Its continued efforts in 1989 built upon that solid foundation and produced an enlarged cadre of Pave Low Airmen able to provide the essential tactical mobility necessary for USSOCOM to place its forces wherever and whenever they were needed—a capability demonstrated through many tactical deployments and operations such as Pokeweed. In the very near future, the men of the 20th would be able to display that capability for all to see.[72]

Notes

1. History of 2d AD, 1 Jan–31 Dec 1986, vol. 5, 791–800; History of 23d AF, 1 Jan 1986–31 Dec 1987, vol. 1, 93; and Cong. Earl Hutto to Mrs. Richard Brims, letter, 17 June 1986, box 329-91-169, file 15 of 27, Hutto Collection, John C. Pace Library.
2. Jones, interview.
3. Comer, interview.
4. Martin, interview.
5. Weikel, interview.
6. Comer, interview.

7. Joe Becker and Weikel, interviews.

8. Joe Becker, interview.

9. Green, interview.

10. Kradel, interview.

11. Correll, interview.

12. Kingsley, interview.

13. History of 23d AF, 1 Jan 1986–31 Dec 1987, vol. 1, 164.

14. Reed, interview.

15. History of 2d AD, 1 Jan–31 Dec 1986, vol. 1, I-35–36; and Reed, interview.

16. History of 23d AF, 1 Jan 1986–31 Dec 1987, vol. 1, 92.

17. Ibid., 93.

18. Ibid., 42.

19. USSOCOM, *United States Special Operations Command 10th Anniversary History*, 7.

20. History of 23d AF, 1 Jan 1986–31 Dec 1987, vol. 1, 47.

21. Staff Summary Sheet, Doctrinal Employment Concept of MH-53 and HC-130 Aircraft, 7 Dec 1987, and supporting docs., file: SOJ3 MC-130/MH 53 Basing Proposals, USSOCOM/HO.

22. Comer and Correll, interviews.

23. Comer, interview.

24. History of 1st SOW, 1 Jan–31 Dec 1987, vol. 1, II-112, II-180; ibid., vol. 3, 689–98; and Connelly, interview.

25. Schibler, interview.

26. History of 23d AF, 1 Jan–31 Dec 1988, vol. 1, 7–16.

27. Ibid., 45–46.

28. Ibid., 19–25; and Congressman Hutto to Adm William Crowe, letter, 8 Dec 1987, 1988, box 2: Directorates and Components, file: Rotary Aircraft, Hutto Collection, John C. Pace Library.

29. Marquis, *Unconventional Warfare*, 180; and History of 23d AF, 1 Jan–31 Dec 1988, vol. 1, 3–4, 19–28.

30. History of 1550th CCTW, 1 Jan–31 Dec 1988, vol. 1, 23–27.

31. Victoria Hanson, "MH-53 Crew Flies Rescue Mission," *Commando*, 6 May 1988, 1.

32. History of 23d AF, 1 Jan–31 Dec 1988, vol. 1, 53–55, 104; and History of 1st SOW, 1 Jan–31 Dec 1988, vol. 1, II-112.

33. Trask, interview.

34. Webb, interview.

35. Trask, interview.

36. Russell, interview.

37. Ibid.

38. Ibid.; and Comer, interview.

39. Simmon and Walters, interviews.

40. Hux, interview.

41. Ibid.

42. Trask, interview.

43. Joe Becker, interview.

44. Trask and Webb, interviews.

45. Reed to the author, e-mail, review comments, 3 Jan 2011; History of 23d AF, 1 Jan–31 Dec 1988, vol. 1, 3; and Wurster, interview.

46. Sprouse, interview.

47. History of the 39th Special Operations Wing (hereafter referred to as History of 39th SOW), 1 Jan–30 June 1988, vol. 1, vii, 1–2; and ibid., 1 July–31 Dec 1988, vol. 1, n.p.

48. Ibid., 1 Jan–30 June 1989, vol. 1, n.p.

49. History of 23d AF, 1 Jan–31 Dec 1989, vol. 1, 9–11.

50. History of 1550th CCTW, 1 Jan–30 June 1989, 17–18.

51. Ibid., 7–10, 25–29; and History of 23d AF, 1 Jan–31 Dec 1989, vol. 1, 87–90.

52. History of 1550th CCTW, 1 July–31 Dec 1989, supporting doc. 60.

53. History of 23d AF, 1 Jan–31 Dec 1989, vol. 1, 4–8.

54. History of the Air Rescue Service (hereafter referred to as History of ARS), 1 Jan 1989–31 Dec 1990, xxx.

55. Whitcomb, *Combat Search and Rescue in Desert Storm*, 35.

56. History of the 353d Special Operations Wing (hereafter referred to as History of 353d SOW), 1 July–31 Dec 1989, vol. 2, 9; and ibid., 1 Jan–30 June 1990, vol. 1, 3, 7, 13.

57. When created, USSOCOM was assigned theater search and rescue (TSAR) as a mission. To divorce the recovery mission from the more classic SOF missions, SOCOM planners began using the term *CSAR* instead.

58. "USCINCSOC Position Statement on Combat Search and Rescue," 3 Nov 1988, in History of 23d AF, 1 Jan–31 Dec 1989, vol. 6, supporting doc. 1-12.

59. Whitcomb, *Combat Search and Rescue in Desert Storm*, 46–47.

60. USSOCOM, *United States Special Operations Command 10th Anniversary History*, 10; and History of 23d AF, 1 Jan–31 Dec 1989, vol. 1, 25–34.

61. History of 1st SOW, 1 Jan–30 June 1989, vol. 1, ix; and Weikel, interview.

62. History of 39th SOW, 1 Jan–30 June 1989, vol. 3, n.p.; and ibid., 1 July–31 Dec 1989, vol. 3, n.p.

63. Beard to the author, e-mail.

64. History of 1st SOW, 1 Jan–30 June 1989, vol. 1, II-67; and ibid., vol. 3, n.p.

65. Walters, interview.

66. Waller, *Commandos*, 210; and Weikel, Trask, and Gray, interviews.

67. Trask, interview.

68. Trask and Gray, interviews.

69. Trask, interview.

70. Joe Becker and Gray, interviews.

71. Clancy, *Clear and Present Danger*, numerous references; and Reed to the author, e-mail, 18 Sept 2009. Several individuals claim to have been the background source.

72. History of 1st SOW, 1 July–31 Dec 1989, vol. 1, II-35, II-63, II-77; ibid., vol. 3, n.p.; and Comer, interview.

Chapter 8

First Combat

1989

None of us were the same. It wasn't just training anymore.

—SSgt Dave Duffy

Just Cause

As 1989 was ending, events in Panama, 1,600 miles to the south, drew the attention of the American leaders. For decades that small country had been a bit of a backwater as the United States focused on other threats overseas. However, contingency plans still existed to defend it and the vital Panama Canal. Increasingly, the US bases still there were used as staging sites for possible contingency operations against the communist intrusions into the area. US forces, particularly special operations forces, trained in the area with steady frequency.

After a military coup in 1968 overthrew the last elected government, a series of military dictators had ruled the country. The latest was Gen Manuel Noriega, an intelligence officer. He ingratiated himself with other officers through bribes, intimidation, and corruption, eventually seizing power.

Noriega also assisted the United States through the Central Intelligence Agency (CIA) when it was conducting covert operations against Nicaraguan and El Salvadoran leftists. However, Noriega's operations eventually became so extreme that he was indicted in a Florida court for involvement in the drug trade, the smuggling of weapons to antigovernment rebels in Colombia, and collusion with Cuba to evade US economic sanctions. Within Panama he also conducted a bloody and brutal campaign against all opposition. He used his power to nullify national elections conducted in May 1989 and survived a coup attempt, declaring himself "maximum leader for life."[1]

As Noriega consolidated his power, relations between the Panamanians and US personnel soured. Missions to other nations in the region stopped as the US military shifted focus to the political situation within Panama. Life slowly deteriorated as businesses closed down and public services fell into disrepair. When American leaders questioned Noriega's harsh tactics, he ordered his heavily armed Panama Defense Forces (PDF) and paramilitary forces to harass US troops. When several Americans were detained and killed and one man literally had to fight his way out of a possible hostage situation, Pres. George H. W. Bush decided to take action in mid-December 1989.

Panama was within the area of responsibility of USSOUTHCOM. Its commander, Gen Maxwell Thurman, had watched these developments with growing unease and had directed increasingly more detailed planning for military intervention. He slowly but steadily moved more military combat units into the country. When directed by President Bush to act, he initiated Operation Just Cause to secure the Panama Canal, protect US personnel, restore the Panamanian government to its elected officials, and take Noriega into custody to stand trial on drug-trafficking charges.

As part of a JTF, the XVIII Airborne Corps deployed 13,000 Soldiers from the 82d Airborne and 7th Infantry Divisions (ID), a USMC battalion task force, and a JSOTF consisting of the 75th Ranger Regiment and other special operations units. The JSOTF's mission was to specifically attack the PDF leadership, command and control facilities, and airfields. Special ops forces would also rescue hostages, conduct reconnaissance, and locate and seize Noriega. The conventional and special forces were airlifted into Panama to join locally assigned forces, 13,000 more Soldiers from other units, and Marines who had been quietly moved there in the preceding months.[2]

USSOCOM planners designated the 1st SOW to support both the JSOTF and conventional forces in the operation and its commander, Col George Gray, to lead his force of over 500 Airmen with nine AC-130A/Hs, three MC-130Es, two HC-130s, four MH-60s, and five MH-53Js. On 18 December, Lt Col Gary Weikel was aboard one of the MC-130s with the command element. Lt Col Mike Russell led the Pave Lows and three US Army MH-47s as they flew nonstop from Hurlburt with HC-130 tankers to the Canal Zone. Capt Corby Martin and Lt Col Rich Comer did not deploy because they had both signed out on long-planned vacations. Martin was on board an Amtrak train heading for the West Coast, and Comer was on a skiing trip to Colorado and out of immediate contact. Capt Tom Trask was aboard Russell's aircraft as a relief pilot and additional pilot for the operation. All of the Paves had extra crews, ammunition, and maintenance equipment in their cargo compartments because Weikel anticipated 24/7 operations and hard flying. Many of his crews had already flown in Panama because of the frequent deployments there, and Weikel felt an added confidence in his aircraft because he knew that they had been partly optimized for Central American operations since the Pave Low's earliest operational testing.[3]

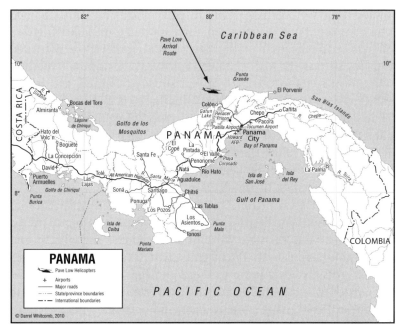

Figure 3. Panama—Operation Just Cause. (Copyright Darrel Whitcomb, 2010. *Adapted from* map provided by Brig Gen Thomas Trask.)

Capt Jack Hester and Capt Joe Becker were flying the number three aircraft in the Pave Low flight. The formation flew through quite a bit of weather to get to Panama. During one of the refuelings, they climbed up to 10,000 feet to conduct it in the clear. The CH-47s did not need to refuel and stayed down at low level, below the weather. When the Pave Lows all had their fuel, the flight descended back into the weather to rejoin the CH-47s below. As Hester and Becker were descending, Hester experienced severe vertigo, and Becker took control of the aircraft. Unfortunately, their windscreen fogged up as they descended, and they lost sight of the other aircraft. Of necessity,

Becker then turned the aircraft away from the flight as per the "lost wingman" procedures and announced his predicament on the radio. They then climbed back up above the clouds and watched as the rest of the flight also popped up into the clear air. Once they were reestablished as a formation, they were able to descend back down to rejoin the CH-47s. The entire process took about 100 miles but was just one part of the 14-hour flight.[4]

Capt Steve Otto and Capt Bob Leonik were flying another Pave Low. As they were getting ready to go at Hurlburt, their assigned extra pilot could not be contacted. They spotted Capt Mike Kingsley, who was out on the ramp preflighting spare aircraft. He was not slated to deploy because he had scheduled some leave for a family reunion in California. His wife and child had already departed, and he intended to leave the next day. However, as directed, he had reported to the squadron with all of his required mobility equipment. He was ordered to board Otto's aircraft and flew as their relief pilot on the flight to Panama. Above the flight of Pave Lows and CH-47s heading south, a gaggle of over 250 USAF aircraft of all varieties was moving the massive force into the small country.[5]

Arriving at Howard AFB, Panama, the Pave Low teams went into crew rest at a house on base for anticipated operation within 24 hours. For the last several months, the 20th had been training with several special ground units to conduct a grand raid to capture Noriega at his big villa, possibly obviating any other significant operations. The unit participated in several full rehearsals, even from home station, flying all night to an old Army maneuver area in Louisiana, where a replica of one of Noriega's hacienda locations was constructed. The members of the 20th arrived in Panama ready to do the mission. In fact, the conduct of a big, fully orchestrated grand mission—the "Big Mish" as some called it—had been in a way the stock in trade for the 20th since Honey Badger. Trask had flown in the rehearsals but would be preempted on the mission by Colonel Russell. The five designated crews were ready to go.[6]

In the early morning hours of 20 December, US forces attacked the PDF and "dignity battalions" of street thugs at locations and facilities across the country. US Army Rangers and a brigade from the 82d Airborne Division parachuted onto the Torrijos-Tocumen Airport and several other sites. In conjunction with several other conventional force task forces and the special operations elements, they overwhelmed the Panamanian forces. In one especially vicious engagement, US ground and air forces, including AC-130s, attacked a strong Panamanian force in La Comandancia, the PDF headquarters, and literally destroyed the facility. Several of the Pave Low crew members climbed up on the roof of their quarters and watched the gunships work. It was not hard to see since it was only two miles away.[7]

However, when the attacks were launched, intelligence sources indicated that Noriega had gone into hiding, and the big raid on Noriega's villa was cancelled. The Pave Low crews were told to stand by for tasking. Needless to say, the disappointment within the Pave Low ranks was palpable. Russell recalled the impact on the crews: "That mission was cancelled. [Headquarters] went into an ad hoc mission [mode]; they put us into crew rest, and the planning group came up with a mission. You put crews against it; you planned, worked with the customer, and flew the mission. We spent the next week doing that."[8]

US forces were organized into task forces of varied sizes. From the initiation of combat operations, the Pave Low crews were told to be ready to support Task Force Red (75th Ranger Regiment), Task Forces Green and Black (other Army special operations forces), and Task Forces Blue and White (Navy SEAL Team 4 and special boat units). With no idea how long the operation would last, Russell then split his force into night and day crews. They were ordered back into crew rest so that they would be ready to go in 12 hours. Capt Mike Kingsley was paired as a copilot with Capt Tim Minish as a day crew.[9]

At the initiation of hostilities, the Pave Lows began to receive taskings. Captain Hester and crew were first to fly. He joined with two MH-60s led by Capt Gene Haase from the 55th SOS. Hester's aircraft had been configured as the medevac aircraft for the raid on Noriega's villa, and he launched to carry several Soldiers to support Navy SEAL Team 4, badly shot up at the Paitilla Airfield, until it could be extracted. He could also provide gun support for the SEALs with his .50-caliber machine guns, which were more powerful than the miniguns the MH-60 carried. Flying with Hester was SSgt Dave Duffy as the left gunner. He saw more than his share of enemy gunfire that night. However, he did not return fire because all of the incoming was inaccurate. Instead, the crew trusted the cover of the darkness. This was the first-ever actual combat mission for a Pave Low.[10]

Captain Trask and crew launched to track a helicopter thought to possibly be carrying Noriega. After completing that assignment, he and the crew began to respond to continuous taskings until they were out of fuel and had to return to base. Pave Low crews were then directed to insert small teams and snipers at locations in Panama City. Capt Tom Aldrich and Major Correll and crew were next to go. They launched with a load of reinforcements for raiding forces that secured the key Pacora River Bridge northeast of the city, attacked several prisons, and released American and Panamanian hostages. Furthermore, they provided overhead direct fire support for SEAL teams at Paitilla Airfield so that Noriega could not use a private aircraft based there to escape.

Courtesy Col Gene Correll, USAF, Retired

Combat crew during Operation Just Cause with MH-53J #68-10363. *Left to right*: Lt Col Gene Correll, MSgt Vic Morrow, Capt Tom Aldrich, SSgt Bob Brumble, SMSgt Phil Mitchell, and TSgt Mike Weber.

Captain Trask and his crew also conducted several fire support missions. At one point, Trask's gunners asked him what rules of engagement (ROE) to use for determining when or when not to fire their guns. No one had given Trask any ROEs. He thought for a moment and then concocted what he thought sounded reasonable based upon previous training and experiences. He so instructed his gunners, and they followed his rules explicitly. He could not have been prouder of them.[11]

On the second day of the operation, Pave Lows supported Army Ranger operations at the Tocumen Airport and exfiltrated Soldiers from a sharp fight at the Pacora River Bridge. Captain Trask and his crew flew another support mission for Navy SEALs at Paitilla, as did Aldrich and Correll. Both crews flew top cover for the SEALs to prevent snipers from firing at them as other SEALs in rubber boats resupplied their unit. That night, Capt Randy O'Boyle led two Pave Lows carrying a force of 174 heavily armed Army Rangers and other special forces units to the American Embassy when it was threatened by Panamanian forces. Trask and his crew flew as part of a larger formation of helicopters carrying 140 troops sent to secure a bunker where Noriega was reported to be located. However, the mission was aborted when, again, intelligence reported that Noriega had moved.[12]

Capt Lou Caporicci and Captain Becker supported another SEAL operation but in a different way. The SEALs wanted to use an MH-6 to quietly insert a small team into a beach house. However, the MH-6 did not have any precision navigation capability. Consequently, Caporicci and crew used their GPS and the TF/TA radar to vector the "little bird" crew to the target and then break off so as not to alert the defenders. The Pave Lows and crews could be utilized to do many things, giving new meaning to the motto "Pave Low leads."[13]

Pave Lows were used in another mission when they combined with a mixed fleet of helicopters to move 150 Rangers to attack the Caldera Airfield so that Noriega and his senior leaders could not use it to flee. They orbited over the Ranger force to provide direct fire support and engaged and destroyed some Panamanian antiaircraft guns that tried to challenge them. Capt Rob Schmaltz and Capt Mike Kingsley flew one of these missions. They picked up their Rangers in the enclosed quadrangle of square-shaped barracks. As they attempted to take off, though, they realized that they were too heavy to get up and over the building. Kingsley was flying and followed the guidance of his scanners as they talked him down onto the helipad. His seat flight engineer then calculated how many Rangers had to dismount to allow a safe takeoff. He told the pilots, "If we estimate that each Ranger weighs 300 pounds with their ruck [sic] and everything, we'll be able to reduce our weight by 1,500 pounds, and we should be able to get over the barracks." They immediately unloaded five Rangers, and the heavily laden aircraft then cleared the high walls. Kingsley was deeply impressed with his crew, remembering, "The coordination was amazing with the gunners and flight engineers . . . being able to safely guide our helicopter. Throughout my career . . . my life has been saved many times by these brave men in the back of the helicopter."[14]

However, Weikel was upset with this operation. It was conducted during the day, when his aircraft and crews were much more vulnerable. He felt that they should have had escorting fighters or gunships, a lesson hard learned in SEA. He was also appalled at the poor communications procedures between the various units. Operation Urgent Fury had highlighted the necessity of joint communication capability, and the USAF and USSOCOM had purchased outstanding radios for their units. However, radio discipline among the units was almost nonexistent, with callers interrupting one another constantly and not using proper, complete call signs. The sloppiness caused a great deal of confusion in far too many instances.[15]

Monitoring the action closely, Weikel called back to the 20th and had it prepare six more Pave Lows, crews, and support personnel for deployment to Panama. Weikel wanted to bring them down because he was especially concerned about the wear and tear on his Airmen, as he and Russell adjusted the squadron operations schedule to allow for 24/7 operations for an undetermined length of time. Despite his efforts, JSOC headquarters refused the request, and the extra helicopters and personnel were not deployed.[16]

Lt Col Rich Comer heard about the invasion on the television news and tried to return to Hurlburt. However, a heavy snowfall enveloped the Colorado mountains, and the passes were not open. It took a day before he could drive back to Denver to catch a flight. Returning to Hurlburt, he encountered the 1st SOW vice-commander, Col Gary Vycital, who told him to join his unit in Panama. Very soon, he was on a C-141 heading south, arriving on the afternoon of 23 December.[17]

When Colonel Comer arrived, he found the 20th and reported in. Colonel Russell was not happy that he had come down, believing that he should have stayed at Hurlburt to watch over the squadron personnel and aircraft still there. Regardless, Comer was there and subsequently set up a schedule with Russell so that either was in the squadron operations area around the clock. This was critical because after two days of heavy fighting, helicopter support was becoming scarce. The 160th Special Operations Aviation Group had also deployed significant assets to Just Cause: 22 A/MH-6s, seven CH-47s, and 19 MH-60s. However, each aircraft brought only one crew vice the two per aircraft that the 20th SOS brought. Consequently, after about 36 hours of continuous operations, the 160th commander, Col William Miller, had to ground his crews for necessary crew rest. Regardless, the Pave Lows continued to fly.[18]

As the fighting tapered off, the Paves began to receive taskings to fly logistical missions and sat alert to fly medevac. Pave Lows used their precision navigation system to lead forces dispatched to other cities and locations throughout the country as the search for Noriega and his key commanders widened. Working closely with AC-130s and Army attack helicopters, they covered special forces ground units as they convinced Panamanian units to surrender. Two Pave Lows also supported special forces units that attacked and defeated Panamanian elements at a major military compound near the small city of La Coronado, 20 miles west of Panama City, and other classified missions.

Within four days all operational objectives were met, and the governmental leaders elected in May 1989 were rightfully installed in office. At that point, General Thurman's focus shifted to rounding up the scattered and disparate remnants of the PDF and capturing Noriega, who had sought refuge in the Papal Nuncio in Panama City.

On 23 December, Pave Lows carried Army forces as they conducted a raid on PDF facilities at Playa Coronado. That same day, two Pave Lows inserted a force into Panama City to recover several Panamanian hostages and supported a task force pursuing dispirited enemy elements at Nueva Guerra. Throughout, too, the Pave Lows received constant requests to fly general support missions for the various task forces.[19]

On 24 December, Captains Trask and Becker flew a mission with CMSgt Tom Green as flight engineer and SSgt Jim Kradel as one of the gunners to carry a special forces element to capture a "Major Hernandez," reportedly a high-level intelligence officer in the Noriega regime. Colonel Comer flew on board as a mission commander. The crew flew two sorties in support of the operation, which netted Hernandez and three other enemy soldiers. On most missions the Pave Lows would be leading the task force, taking advantage of their precision navigation capability. However, after the first day, there was little actual combat. Like Kradel, most gunners never fired their weapons.[20]

As the Panamanian forces dispersed, General Thurman was concerned that a residual force would move into the high mountains in the western sections of the country and develop a guerilla force to be led by Noriega. He initiated Operation Surrender, designed to talk enemy forces into peacefully laying down their weapons.

On Christmas Day, Colonel Weikel, Captain Otto, and crew were directed to fly a reconnaissance mission to look for evidence of enemy activity. They took off with several Army special forces troops on

Operation Just Cause combat crew. *Left to right*: (*standing*) Capt Tom Trask; SrA Bill Smith; TSgt Mike Barton; Capt Joe Becker; and crew chief, SSgt Marty Moore; (*kneeling*) SSgt Jim Kradel; CMSgt Tom Green; and SrA Jim Sergeant.

board and proceeded along the Pacific coast before turning inland west of the city of David. The crew then had to maneuver to avoid rain showers and thunderstorms as they climbed above the rising terrain. As they entered the clouds, they used the TF/TA radar and skimmed 100 feet above the terrain. Flying over the objective area, the crew realized that nobody with conventional helicopters could have gotten there. Checking in with their command headquarters, they were directed to proceed to David and help facilitate the surrender of a PDF force at a military facility in the city, commanded by Col Del Cid.

Approaching the city, Weikel could see a small baseball stadium near the facility. In the darkness, he landed the aircraft right on the pitcher's mound. Some of the Army special forces troops then got off and went to talk to the Panamanian forces commander while Weikel and his crew stayed alert. They had a full complement of ammunition on board for their mini and machine guns, as well as their personal weapons.

After speaking with the local forces, the Army troops reported that the area was safe and decided to remain there. They asked that an additional security force be flown in the next day. Weikel had shut his engines down to save fuel. Suddenly, the stadium lights came on, shocking the crew. Local civilians began to swarm into the stadium, even climbing over the fences. The crew was alarmed as the mass approached the aircraft. Weikel ordered everybody to stand by his station and arm the guns. He had no idea of the intentions of the crowd and had to consider that it was possibly going to attack the aircraft and crew. He ordered his crew not to let anybody board the aircraft and began the start sequence for the number two engine. However, it rapidly became evident that the people were excited to have the Americans in their midst with their "Star Wars" machine. Some of the Army troops on board then disembarked and spoke with the people. Several reached up to Weikel, and he shook their hands. "*Vayan ustedes con Dios,*" they shouted, as they pushed their children forward to shake hands. It was a love-in, thought Weikel.

When his Army team commander told him that all was secure in David and that he and his team intended to stay, Weikel started the other engine. He had the people back away from the aircraft and turn off the stadium lights so that the crew could adjust their eyes for night vision, and then they lifted off into the now clear night sky for the flight back to Howard AFB. As they reached altitude, one of the flight engineers called on the intercom and wished the rest of the crew a Merry Christmas. Weikel recalled that "on that night, coming back on Christmas night, just leaving the town of David, we left some deliriously happy people who were delighted to have a chance to sort out their lives and families once again." It was, he later remembered, a "sweet but intense feeling of accomplishment and personal satisfaction."[21]

While Weikel was in David, the other four Pave Lows joined several Army aircraft to airlift a company-plus-sized force into the David airfield just to make sure that the PDF actually did what they had agreed to do. Instead of opposition, though, they received the same type of friendly greeting.[22]

On 27 December, two crews led by Lt Col Mike Russell flew a medevac mission to the San Blas Islands off the east coast of Panama to rescue an eclectic group of 19 sick international students at a resort. The crews had to work their way through heavy rain and thunderstorms for six hours before depositing the students at the Howard AFB hospital.[23]

With the sequestering of Noriega in the Papal Nuncio, calm was rapidly restored to Panama. Pres. Guillermo Endara had been sworn into office as American forces began their attacks and subsequently ordered the Panamanian military to stand down. Except for a few die-hard elements, it did so. US Army civil affairs units then began to arrive, and Operation Promote Liberty was initiated to restore public safety, health, and population control measures. On 3 January 1990, Noriega surrendered to US forces and was extradited to the United States for trial. Operation Just Cause was winding down, and the Airmen of the 1st SOW, along with their USSOCOM and conventional forces compatriots, were sent home.

During the operation, the crews of the 20th flew 193 sorties and logged 406.1 hours of flying time.[24] But their accomplishments are told in more than statistics. As Captain Trask explained, since Honey Badger, the 20th had taken its new technology and trained earnestly to use it. Its focus had always been on leading the big mission, and it trained to do that for nine years. The Noriega seizure was just the latest iteration. But when that mission was cancelled, the squadron very quickly had to rerole to do whatever needed to be done. Then it was not so much the technology that the crews used; it was their basic skills as air commandos equipped with high-technology heavy-lift helicopters. "Humans are more important than hardware," Congressman Hutto had postulated back when he was an advocate for creating USSOCOM and supported the Pave Low.[25] Operation Just Cause validated that point.

The variety of missions that the crews were called upon to fly demanded the larger set of skills that they had been mentored to maintain all those years by leaders such as Bill Takacs. In many cases, they were back to doing what their predecessors in the 20th and 21st SOS had done in Southeast Asia 20 years before—only now with the ability to do it day and night, good weather and bad, if the mission demanded it. They weren't Pave Low; they were air commandos equipped with Pave Low, and the quickness with which they re-roled and carried on in Panama proved it, especially to themselves. They had been tested and had excelled. Two Green Hornets in particular were lauded for their efforts during the operation. Maj Jeff Walls received the Lance Sijan Award for 1990 in recognition of his overall performance and efforts to protect and recover a US Army Ranger team pinned down by enemy forces. Additionally, Capt Randy O'Boyle was selected as the air commando MAC pilot of the year for leading several direct-assault missions into downtown Panama City and other enemy positions.[26]

On 16 January 1990, Just Cause officially ended. USSOCOM's official history states that "JUST CAUSE clearly validated how SOF were trained, equipped, and organized: this operation showcased joint SOF capabilities, the high training standards for operators and staffs alike, and the value of interoperability procedures."[27] Bragged Colonel Weikel in the unit's biennial history for the second half of 1989, "We've developed procedures to more effectively support elite classified units, who may operate as isolated elements after our long-range infiltrations. . . . Another self-initiated development involves the innovative use of our airborne ground mapping radar to provide vectoring assistance to elite US Navy forces as well as other aerial platforms. . . . We are the recognized experts in USAF SOF helicopter operations."[28] Perhaps SSgt Dave Duffy, the left gunner aboard Jack Hester's aircraft the first night, said it best in a far simpler way. "Just Cause was the beginning of a new pace for the squadron. None of us were the same. It wasn't just training anymore."[29]

Air Force Special Operations Command

As the Airmen of the 1st SOW were reconstituting from Just Cause, MAC and USSOCOM staffs continued to work on converting Twenty-Third Air Force to a MAJCOM and component command of the latter. In March 1990, General Lindsay submitted a reorganization plan to Gen Larry Welch, the USAF chief of staff. The two staffs continued to work through the issues. When the reviews were complete and a consolidated plan had been developed that was agreeable to all parties, General Welch wrote to General Lindsay stating his approval for the requested conversion. Ever attentive to developments at Hurlburt, Congressman Hutto signaled his approval in a press release, anticipating that the development could lead to as many as 100 more permanent manpower billets in his district.

Planning proceeded apace as the transition began. One specific issue that needed to be finalized was the training of aircrews. USSOCOM formally agreed to allow MAC's 1550th CCTW at Kirtland to conduct the initial aircraft qualification training for its MC-130s and MH-53s, at least through 1991, and subject to review after that. By May all major issues had been resolved, and on the 22d, General Welch flew to Hurlburt to officiate at the redesignation ceremony as Twenty-Third Air Force became the Air Force Special Operations Command, a "testimonial to the dynamic growth of special operations," as the chief pointed out to the crowd. In supporting remarks, the MAC commander, Gen Hansford T. Johnson, said of the command MAC was losing, "The most important accomplishment of the 23d has been to build a sturdy foundation for the Air Force role as a member of the joint special operations team." General Lindsay also attended to welcome them aboard his command. He said to the proud "blue suiters" standing before him, "Air Force special operations has an especially significant role to play in dealing with terrorists, regional conflict, narcotic trafficking, insurgencies, and . . . readiness for general war. . . . Only special ops Airmen could have pulled off an operation as complex as the one in Panama. You are truly the tip of the USSOCOM spear." General Eggers, now the AFSOC commander, responded by saying that his Airmen would meet the challenges and live up to the high standards of the air command heritage. With that straightforward ceremony, all of the units under Twenty-Third Air Force were transferred to AFSOC, and once again, the Airmen of the 20th SOS, along with their worldwide brethren, changed their command patches.[30]

Another unit activation ceremony occurred just a few days before the AFSOC event. At Fort Campbell, Kentucky, the 160th Special Operations Aviation Regiment activated as an element of the US Army Special Operations Command. It was the outgrowth of the battalion-sized task force formed by the Army after the Desert One debacle and subsequently expanded into the interim 160th Special Operations Aviation Group. It trained and competed regularly with the Pave Lows of the 20th. In fact, the two units were becoming staunch competitors and even rivals in the eyes of some. The unit trained hard and had already lost 28 crew members in training accidents. Its Soldiers had also seen combat in Grenada and Panama and had flown protection missions for oil tankers in the Persian Gulf. As the first commander, Col Joseph Fucci, assumed his new post, he highlighted his unit's close bond with its companion Army ground special operations units. He said, "We live in the field with them, train alongside them, get dirty and tired and worn out, just like they do. We're not 'pretty boys' with fancy scarves. Our customers know we'll come and get them, regardless of the situation." He subscribed to the idea that "Soldiers should carry Soldiers." Indeed, the Pave Low community had some worthy competition.[31]

Pave Low Training

Under MAC/USSOCOM-approved training plans, the 1550th CCTW was tasked to produce 24 fully qualified Pave Low pilots, 20 flight engineers, and 28 gunners in 1990 to fully man the expanding Pave Low force. In the first half of 1990, the 1551st FTS finally received all of its assigned MH-53Js. However, they were still 20-plus-year-old aircraft and broke constantly. This directly impacted training, especially the production of Pave Low IPs and engineers. Colonel Holland at the 1550th formed a "tiger team" to address the problem. It suggested that the wing borrow two MH-53Js, two IPs, and two instructor flight engineers from Hurlburt; initiate several maintenance changes; request as many as 18 maintenance technicians from the 1st SOW; and dispatch current instructors and students to joint exercises.

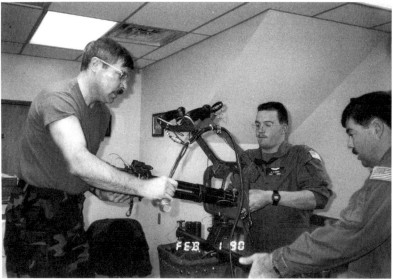

Courtesy Air Force Historical Research Agency

TSgt Clark Dawson of the 1550th Training Squadron trains Pave Low gunners SSgt R. D. Shore and MSgt P. J. Cook.

Aircrews from the 1551st also joined still ongoing mountain training with the 20th SOS. Colonel Comer was now running that program for the 20th, and he and his instructors fully qualified Lt Col John Folkerts and Lt Col Pat St. Romain from the 1551st FTS. Subsequently, Folkerts took command of the 1551st on 28 June.[32]

As these changes were instituted, training began to smooth out somewhat. In June the 1551st graduated its first fully qualified Pave Low pilot, Maj John Zahrt. By July the wing had eight fully qualified Pave Low IPs, nine instructor engineers, and five instructor gunners, and new students like Capt R. K. Williams and Capt Tim Leahy reported for Pave Low qualification. As the training program at Kirtland steadily came up to speed, Pave Low training at Hurlburt was reduced to squadron-level mission training only.[33]

The 1550th also used flight simulators in its training program and had an H-53 simulator on base. Since the H/CH-53s were now gone, technicians in the Air Training Devices Branch were able to modify it to replicate the TH-53s now being used in the qualification course. This in-house effort saved $500,000 in projected contractor costs and would allow for the substitution of simulator training time for actual flight time. Students began simulator training in March.

The next month, the wing also received a new MH-53J flight simulator from the General Electric Corporation. This $35 million visual and motion weapons system trainer (WST) was state of the art and included a worldwide terrain database that allowed the students to "fly" in varied terrain and geographical regions. Planners estimated that the realistic training the simulator provided would reduce the flight sorties each student needed by 13, a huge cost savings. Maj Ed Reed had recently arrived for instructor duty after his staff tour in the Pentagon, where he had been replaced by his longtime fellow zealot, Lt Col Donny Wurster. Colonel Holland knew that Reed had had a hand in procuring the simulator and told him to make the program work. Reed again attacked the problem with his intense, high-energy approach and purposeful vision. He called the Pentagon and talked to Wurster, who then performed more of the funding magic for which Reed and then Wurster had become adept. And the funds flowed to Kirtland AFB.

Reed also decided that he needed some more operationally experienced Pave Low crew members to help make the training realistic. He contacted Jack Kelly and asked him to join the management team for the program at Kirtland. Kelly was now retired and living in Fort Walton Beach, Florida. He had worked a few short-term projects but was otherwise not committed to anything work related. Reed was able to talk him into a visit to Kirtland. There Kelly took a senior management position and helped run the ever-improving simulators, both helicopter and fixed wing. His affiliation with the various training programs would last for the next 17 years, allowing him to help train two more generations of Pave Low crews.[34]

Students began training on the new simulator on 1 August. By December two more Pave Low IPs had been certified, and the course developers—Maj Jim Jobe and Capt Scott Pugmire—had rewritten lessons to take full advantage of the simulators. As a result, the training backlog had been substantially reduced, and the crews for the newly forming 31st SOS at Clark AB were being trained. The 1551st was well on its way to becoming a first-class training organization.[35]

20th Special Operations Squadron

One month after the AFSOC ceremony, Lt Col Mike Russell was selected to serve as the deputy DO for the 39th SOW, now in place at the Rhein-Main AB, and departed for that assignment. A few days later, Gary Weikel passed command of the 20th SOS to Rich Comer and left for a one-year student tour at the National War College in Washington, DC. There he would join other officers and leaders of recognized accomplishment and potential from all services and governmental branches and prepare for future assignments and challenges.

Weikel had much to be proud of in his tenure as a Pave Low pilot and commander. He had directly contributed to the development of the 20th SOS into a "unit of confidence," just like the ones that Joe Guilmartin had documented at Koh Tang Island. Weikel and his predecessors all the way back to Lt Col Bill Takacs had found those "aces, daredevils, barnstormers, guys who flew by the seat of their pants, hot rodders, pilots who could pick it up, turn it around on a dime, and put it back down with flair," that Col Charlie Beckwith was looking for at Desert One and turned them into a cadre of like-minded and highly motivated air commandos. It was especially fitting and perhaps poignant too that he was passing the squadron guidon to Colonel Comer, a fellow Koh Tang veteran.[36]

Almost immediately Comer decided to make a few changes. He selected Lt Col Gene Correll to serve as his operations officer. He also turned his attention to the squadron stan/eval program. As the squadron had grown, its stan/eval shop had been challenged to stay up with the expansion. Comer decided to address that issue with a personnel change. He called in Capt Paul Harmon and offered him the job as chief of the shop. Harmon had been commissioned in 1975 and was a career helicopter pilot with two overseas tours and experience as a stan/eval pilot at Kirtland AFB. He had been with the 20th since August 1988 and had received great training from Steve Otto, Randy O'Boyle, and Jack Hester. He was now a qualified MH-53J aircraft commander, waiting his turn to acquire higher qualifications. He was a little uncomfortable with the offer since he was not yet an instructor or evaluator. Comer told him, "Just go up to Dobbins [for mountain training] and get your IP checkout. We'll make you an evaluator. We need somebody who knows how to run standardization. I've got plenty of Pave Low guys, but I want somebody to run standardization. . . . You come from Kirtland. If Kirtland is good for anything, it's good for making things look good."

Harmon jumped at the job and proceeded as directed. However, he saw his charter in a larger sense. Sure, he had the stan/eval program to administer. That was no small task when he realized that he had 65 pilots, 65 flight engineers, and almost 130 gunners who had formal evaluation folders that had to be maintained to exacting standards. However, his requirement was really a larger one. Working with the commander and operations officer, Harmon's job was really to insure that everybody in the squadron could accomplish whatever he had been trained and qualified to do. Working with sharp young captains like Mike Kingsley and Tim Minish, he got to work.[37]

For Comer, however, there were so many other things to do. As he settled into his position, he was somewhat intimidated by what he was taking on. He felt that he had inherited what, at that moment in time, was the finest squadron in the entire US Air Force.[38]

☆☆☆☆☆

As the decade was ending, the Pave Low community was well into its growth spurt. The USAF now had 47 H-53s on its aircraft roster. Six were the TH-53As borrowed from the USMC and designated for use by the 1550th CCTW at Kirtland for aircrew training and qualification, along with four MH-53Js. The 21st SOS in England had four MH-53Js, with two more promised. The 20th SOS at Hurlburt had 25 of the newly modified MH-53Js and the remaining eight MH-53Hs, all awaiting conversion to the J variant. The 31st SOS in the Pacific would become the third Pave Low unit with six aircraft as the machines completed the modification line.[39]

The decade had been one of great change and challenge. Pave Low had just come to fruition for fulfilling the need for an all-weather, day/night rescue aircraft. However, the debacle at Desert One in Iran had interceded, and the Pave Lows had been diverted to special operations for a second rescue attempt. When that was cancelled, they remained with the special operations community and developed a new set of skills. When the senior Air Force leadership agreed to move them to the US Army, a relatively junior group of hard-charging officers worked closely with several congressional leaders to staunch the move. When they and other congressional leaders created the USSOCOM, the Pave Low force became an integral part, and its fleet received funding to grow sixfold. It was now fully integrated into the new command, and its leaders and Airmen identified perhaps more with their fellow special operators than they did with their fellow Air Force brethren.

Increased training produced the cadre of crews and support personnel necessary to maintain and fly those aircraft. As the personnel numbers steadily grew, Pave Low became a nascent community of highly spirited, motivated, and aggressive young air commandos who validated their creation in Operation Just Cause, where they proved that Pave Low was the sum total of the advanced technology and the "aces, daredevil, and barnstormers" to fly them to the limits of their capabilities. That capability had become the essence of the 1st SOW motto Any Time, Any Place. Lurking in the background, though—still present, still alive—was Initiative 17, held in abeyance only by eternal vigilance.

However, the world is never a static place, and events were building in other areas that, in the not-too-distant future, would necessitate the dispatch of American forces to do battle with another tyrant. For the Airmen of Pave Low, the conundrum about CSAR between USSOCOM and the ARS would rise up like a phoenix and, ironically, require the crews to perform the mission for which the Pave Low was originally modified, in addition to its new special operations taskings.

Notes

1. Stewart, *American Military History*, vol. 2, 397.
2. Ibid., 398; and Clancy, Stiner, and Koltz, *Shadow Warriors*, 302.
3. Weikel, Trask, and Hester, interviews.
4. Weikel, Joe Becker, and Trask, interviews.

5. Cole, *Operation Just Cause*, 33; and Kingsley and Weikel, interviews.

6. Waller, *Commandos*, 211; and Trask, interview.

7. Cole, *Operation Just Cause*, 40; and Trask, interview.

8. Russell, interview.

9. Kingsley, interview.

10. Hester, interview.

11. Trask and Correll, interviews.

12. Kelly, *From a Dark Sky*, 283; Trask, interview; and Trask, personal mission narrative, provided to the author.

13. Joe Becker, interview.

14. Kingsley, interview.

15. Kelly, *From a Dark Sky*, 285.

16. Weikel, interview.

17. Comer, interview.

18. Ibid.; Russell, interview; and Stewart, Sandler, and Fischer, *Command History of the United States Army Special Operations Command*, 233, 254.

19. Trask, interview.

20. Ibid.; Trask, personal mission narrative, provided to the author; and Comer, Green, and Kradel, interviews.

21. Weikel, interview.

22. Trask, interview.

23. Operation Just Cause, file 220.00, 1st/16th SOW HO; and History of 23d AF, 1 Jan–31 Dec 1989, vol. 1, 167–72.

24. History of 1st SOW, 1 July–31 Dec 1989, vol. 3, n.p.

25. Collins, *Green Berets, Seals and Spetsnaz*, xiii.

26. Cole, *Operation Just Cause*, 40; and Capt Joe Becker to 1st SOW historian, letter, 16 Sept 1993, file 220.00, 1st/16th SOW HO. Sijan data is from HQ USAF/A1SOU (Uniforms and Recognition Branch).

27. USSOCOM, *United States Special Operations Command 10th Anniversary History*, 32.

28. History of 1st SOW, 1 July–31 Dec 1989, vol. 3, n.p.

29. Duffy to the author, e-mail.

30. History of AFSOC, 1 Jan 1990–31 Dec 1991, vol. 1, 47–59.

31. Dyhouse, "Coming Home to a Changed World," 12; and Stewart, Sandler, and Fischer, *Command History of the United States Army Special Operations Command*, 225–27.

32. History of 1550th CCTW, 1 Jan–30 June 1990, vol. 1, 4, 22.

33. Ibid., vol. 1, 16–18; ibid., 1 July–31 Dec 1990, vol. 1, 14–16; and Comer and Williams, interviews.

34. Reed and Kelly, interviews.

35. History of 1550th CCTW, 1 Jan–30 June 1990, vol. 1, 27–29; and Reed and Pugmire, interviews.

36. Weikel, interview.

37. Harmon, interview.

38. Comer, interview.

39. History of 23d AF, 1 Jan–31 Dec 1989, vol. 1, 87; and MAC SON 11-84, subject: MH-53J Pave Low 3 "Enhanced," 10 Jan 1990, Pave Low file, Air Force Operational Test and Evaluation Center (AFOTEC)/HO.

PART III

From Capability to Community

Chapter 9

War in the Desert

~1990–91

Pave Low leads.

—Maj Gen Rich Comer

The Middle East

From the very beginning of Pave Low development, Lt Col Frank Pehr realized that the aircraft required a good overall navigational system to fully integrate the FLIR and TF/TA radar into a true all-weather, day/night capability. Initially, he and the design engineers tried to rely on the Doppler system, replacing that with an INS as it improved in capability. In the 1980s, the USAF developed the GPS, a quantum leap forward in accurate navigational capability. Maj Ed Reed was aware of this development and presciently pushed to procure some of the first units the USAF bought for installation on the Pave Lows as they went through the J-model conversion.

Key to the GPS system was a planned constellation of 24 satellites. They would orbit the entire globe and transmit signals 24/7, which any GPS receiver could use to determine location, accurate to within 10 meters. The first GPS satellite was launched in 1978. By the summer of 1990, 18 satellites had been launched, and 13 were operating normally. However, this array did not provide for the desired global 24/7 coverage, and several more were in preparation for launch. Controlled by the 2d Satellite Control Squadron in Colorado, another GPS satellite, #PRN-021, was successfully fired into orbit on 2 August 1990. Its area of focus was the Middle East.[1]

As the satellite was settling into its orbit, dramatic events were taking place literally below its high station. On that very same morning, heavy mechanized and special operations forces from Iraq were invading and overrunning the nation of Kuwait. "This will not stand," declared US president George H. W. Bush as he held earnest meetings with key political leaders, including the secretary of defense, Dick

Cheney; CJCS, Gen Colin Powell; and CENTCOM commander, Gen
Norman Schwarzkopf. Subsequently, President Bush directed initial
economic and political steps to punish Iraq, considered military options, and established four clear political objectives: (1) remove the
Iraqis from Kuwait, (2) eliminate production and storage of weapons
of mass destruction (WMD), (3) end Iraq's capacity to threaten its
neighbors over the next five to 10 years, and (4) ensure that the full
military capabilities of the United States would be used. The president and his key leaders also established a crucial limiting factor—
the desire to hold American military and Iraqi civilian casualties to a
minimum. This last factor was critical and put a premium on having
a CSAR capability in-theater.[2]

As the president was making these decisions, orders were issued to
military units across the land to prepare for deployment. Two aircraft
carriers, the USS *Independence* and the USS *Dwight D. Eisenhower*,
and their supporting task forces immediately sailed for the area. Air,
naval, and ground units across the land began to mobilize for deployment to the countries of the Persian Gulf to stop further aggression
and, eventually, initiate offensive operations to drive the Iraqi forces
out of Kuwait. Ultimately, the United States would deploy over
540,000 Soldiers, Sailors, Airmen, and Marines to the Gulf, where
they would join forces from 25 other nations to repel the aggression.[3]

20th Special Operations Squadron

The 1st SOW at Hurlburt Field immediately became a beehive of
activity. Most of the wing's squadrons were tasked under various contingency plans, including Operation Plan (OPLAN) 1002-90 for the
CENTCOM region. Indeed, CENTCOM had just recently completed
the war game Internal Look, and several 1st SOW and 20th SOS personnel had participated and helped update 1002-90. The 1st SOW
commander, Col George Gray, knew that his Airmen were going to
the desert—and probably very soon.

On 6 August, the 20th received its orders. Lt Col Rich Comer was
ordered to prepare eight aircraft, 16 crews, and a maintenance support package for deployment to Riyadh, Saudi Arabia. The squadron
was told to expect possible use of chemical weapons and an initial
deployment of 30 days. Obviously, not everybody from the 20th
would be deploying; one of those was Capt Joe Becker. He had been

at Hurlburt for three years now and was available for reassignment. Before Colonel Weikel gave up the squadron, he told Becker that if he would volunteer for the converting 31st SOS at Clark AB, he would upgrade Becker to flight examiner so that he could go over and fulfill that function. From a career perspective that made a lot of sense, and Becker accepted. The PCS orders were cut for an August move. However, Becker's wife, Susan, was pregnant with their first child, and he got a move delay to October. When the 20th SOS was alerted to deploy to the desert, though, Becker went to Comer and told him that he wanted to go with the squadron. Comer decided that he needed to leave a flight examiner behind to handle the ongoing training and told Becker, "Sometimes it sucks to be my friend. I need to leave an evaluator here. . . . I'm going to leave you behind." A day later, Becker went to Comer's office and tried to get the decision reversed. Comer just smiled at him and remarked that he would have been disappointed if Becker had not tried to push back, but the answer was still no. So Becker saluted smartly and helped pack the rest of the troops off to the desert. He then flew local training and evaluation flights while preparing to move his wife and new baby to Clark AB.[4]

For the deployment to Saudi Arabia, Colonel Comer split his deploying package in half. Lt Col Gene Correll would take one package over, and Comer would take the other. The Airmen loaded aboard several C-5s and C-141s and departed on 11 August. Arriving at Riyadh two days later, they were redirected to Dhahran. Arriving there, they disembarked into the blistering heat and began unloading their equipment, personal gear, and aircraft. They were now assigned OPCON to SOCCENT as part of Operation Desert Shield.

Comer was assigned a local elementary school for use as their billet and issued MREs and bottled water for his troops. He had only 26 maintenance troops, and they did not have their full complement of tools. Regardless, the Airmen hustled to get the aircraft ready to fly. However, the merciless heat took its toll on the specialists. Lt Col Mark Cunningham, the squadron flight surgeon, closely monitored the troops as they worked to near exhaustion. Fortunately, British forces on the base had a hangar that was partly air conditioned and allowed the 20th Airmen to use it for rest breaks.[5]

Despite the harsh conditions, Comer's troops had four of the aircraft in flying condition in just four days. When it became clear to all that this deployment was not going to be short term, Comer directed Correll to return home to command the rear elements and to be

A Pave Low being loaded aboard a C-5 for deployment to Desert Storm

ready to swap out with him. Arriving home, Correll was put on G-series orders as acting commander, authorizing him to take certain time-critical administrative actions for the unit. He also had to oversee ongoing training and attend to relatively mundane matters, such as the delivery of a Pave Low to Travis AFB, California, for shipment to the 31st SOS at Clark. He and Capt J. D. Clem made that flight and had to write some letters when they returned to Hurlburt concerning their transit of the Grand Canyon.[6]

At Dhahran, two aircraft and crews were put on alert to extract special forces teams stationed along the Saudi-Kuwaiti border if Iraq's forces crossed the border. Shortages of machine guns, ammunition, chaff, and flares limited further operational usage until the shortages were corrected. Within a few days, the 39th SOW dispatched weapons for the Pave Lows. Sergeant Kradel was one of the first gunners to deploy. A fully qualified instructor now, he taught the younger gunners how to maintain the weapons and coordinated with the British to use their hanger facilities to clean them.[7]

As the crews began orientation flights, it became immediately obvious that flying over the flat Arabian Desert, especially at night, was going to be a serious challenge. Moonless nights offered little ambient

Courtesy 58th SOW History Office

A Pave Low in classic desert colors

light, and the sand suspended in the air generally limited both normal visibility and use of NVGs, making it difficult to spot sand dunes. Kradel was crewed with Capt Tim Minish and Capt Ken Sipperly. They flew a night refueling mission over the trackless sands of western Saudi Arabia on an exceedingly dark night. While they were supposed to be at 500 feet, the radar altimeter did not correctly read altitudes over the sand. No one noticed that they were slowly descending, until the gunners realized that they were about to hit the sand dunes. Their "climb, climb!" calls alerted the pilots and prevented an accident.[8]

On another training mission, Comer himself lost ground visibility during a brownout landing—as the pilots came to call them—and an external tank was damaged when he did not notice the drift of the aircraft. Flying with Comer that night as his gunners were SMSgt Larry "Large Sarge" Hunter, one of the original Pave Low gunner instructors, and his newest student, A1C John Stricklin, a former armaments specialist who had requested and received a special duty assignment as a Pave Low gunner. Fortunately, neither they nor any other crew members were hurt in the accident. In response, Comer directed extra training for all crews and the development of modified procedures for landings in sand conditions. As naval ships were also made available, his crews requalified on shipboard landings.

On 18 August, Comer met with Col Jesse Johnson, the SOCCENT commander. Johnson directed the 20th to move to the newly constructed King Fahd International Airport (KFIA), 40 miles to the northwest. Two weeks later, the unit moved to King Fahd and joined several other special operations units and squadrons from the 1st SOW—the majority of the AFSOC portion of the eventual 7,700 special operations forces deploying to the theater. Colonel Gray had arrived and took over command of the deployed wing, accompanied by his DO, Col Ben Orrell. Gray was also selected to serve as the commander of the Air Force component of SOCCENT (AFSOCCENT), under Colonel Johnson, and would spend a great deal of his time in the SOCCENT command center working directly with Johnson.[9]

The 20th then received its second shipment of four aircraft and crews, along with guns, ammunition, and full maintenance kits. Now the unit had its full, designated complement of Airmen and equipment for the deployment. Two of the MH-53Js that had originally been HH-53Bs were replaced because of problems that developed with the sponson support struts, unique to those aircraft.[10]

When enough tents arrived, 1st SOW troops literally built their own compound. Unfortunately, though, they had to share the airfield with a USAF fighter wing and the 101st Airborne Division with its 300-plus helicopters. Regardless, Comer and his Airmen set up their own squadron area and began building wooden doors for the tents, plank walkways, barbeque pits, a small snack bar, and other amenities to make life a bit more bearable. As much as possible, Comer tried to keep his aircrews and support troops billeted together for unit cohesion. Unsure of how long the deployment was going to last, he also began to develop plans to rotate his troops back to home station so that everybody in the unit shared the burden of the deployment. He also wanted to expose as many of his troops as possible to combat operations and prevent a resurgence of the "A"/"B" team split that had previously existed in the unit. However, the actual initiation of any rotation policy rested with Colonel Gray and CENTCOM/CENTAF policies. Comer organized his crew members into hard crews and, as much as possible, put them together in tents. Capt Paul Harmon assumed duties as the squadron flight scheduler and began to build a comprehensive training plan. Comer began holding unit meetings, working closely with his senior NCOs—MSgt Larry Hunter and MSgt Dick Pinkowski—to ensure that the younger Airmen were being properly cared for.[11]

As other special operations forces arrived in the theater, they were also assigned to SOCCENT. The 20th was joined by the 55th SOS with its MH-60Gs. The US Army dispatched the 3d Battalion of the 160th SOAR with MH-47Es and MH-60Ks, which bedded down at the King Khalid Military City (KKMC) airfield, about 200 miles northwest of KFIA. The USAF mobilized its 71st SOS from the Air Force Reserve with its GPS-equipped MH-3s. The US Navy mobilized two special operations helicopter units from its reserve forces, Helicopter Combat Support Special Squadrons 4 and 5 (HCS-4 and HCS-5). They were assigned together in a combined unit and placed from tactical control (TACON) to SOCCENT. All told, the units provided 42 helicopters for special operations use. As the joint special operations air component commander (JSOACC) for SOCCENT, Colonel Gray, along with Colonel Orrell as his deputy, would direct their use, and they immediately began working up operations plans.

Combat Search and Rescue

However, another issue had to be resolved. All conventional USAF forces being dispatched to the Gulf were under the operational control of the CENTCOM air forces, or CENTAF, commanded by Lt Gen Chuck Horner. Functionally, he would also serve as the CENTCOM joint forces air component commander (JFACC). In that capacity, one of his assigned duties under OPLAN 1002-90 was to serve as the theater SAR coordinator and plan and coordinate a theater rescue campaign. Under then-current doctrine, each service component was obligated to provide for its own rescue capability. Horner, though, was required to develop an overall plan such that if one service could not facilitate a rescue, another service could provide the forces to do so.

The general did not have a helicopter force that could perform CSAR for his aircrews, who were expected to be shot down behind enemy lines. CENTAF was receiving large numbers of fighter, reconnaissance, surveillance, and support aircraft. Unfortunately, the realignments and reorganizations of the USAF rescue forces during the 1980s had resulted in the ultimate reformation of the USAF Air Rescue Service as a service with CSAR as its primary assigned mission, but without the necessary modern aircraft and trained crews to do it. The ARS had recently received several new HH-60s, but the crews were not fully trained, and the units were not ready for deployment. When tasked, the ARS commander, Col John Woodruff, demurred and did not dispatch any USAF helicopter rescue units for General Horner to use. Capt Fredrick Helmer, a spokesman for Woodruff, stated, "It was a command decision not to send our aircraft" to the Gulf. However, the ARS did dispatch almost 100 individuals of various specialties to augment special operations units and man rescue and command centers.[12]

Instead, the recovery tasking went to the SOCCENT. The debate within and between the USSOCOM, AFSOC, MAC, Air Staff, CENTAF, and SOCCENT was fast, furious, fractious, and, at times, bitter. However, whereas the SOCOM had recently eschewed the mission, its helicopter forces were now in a theater of operations under the control of a combatant commander. Under the revisions to military organization legislated in the Goldwater-Nichols Act passed in 1986, the theater commanders could organize their forces as they saw fit. And quite honestly, those helicopter forces—especially the MH-53s—were optimized for the mission with their equipment modifications and aircrews, many of whom had earlier been assigned to rescue units. For all of these reasons, General Schwarzkopf signed off on giving the mission of combat recovery to SOCCENT. Said Colonel Gray, "We got the rescue mission by virtue of our being the only ones left out there that had the weapons system that was capable of doing it."[13]

Through a strange twist of fate and circumstance, the Pave Lows would now be assigned the specific mission for which they were originally conceived some 23 years earlier in the bitter days of the long war in Southeast Asia.[14] To Capt Mike Kingsley, who had deployed in September, the rescue mission made sense. He said, "The Pave Low can do CSAR better than any other helicopter. We had radar; we had a GPS; we had forward-looking infrared; we had capabilities that no other helicopter had. . . . It's a very, very honorable mission."[15]

More to the point, though, was the reality of what was possibly ahead for the allied forces if they had to attack Iraq. That nation had a large and well-developed air defense capability. Based on the Soviet Union model, it was a well-integrated system of massive surface-to-air missiles—both radar and infrared guided—and 8,000-plus fixed and mobile antiaircraft guns of numerous calibers. Loss estimates varied from 40 to 60 fighter-type aircraft during a projected six-week air campaign. However, planners took close note of the fact that when Iraq attacked Kuwait on 2 August, the modern and integrated Kuwaiti air defenses shot down 39 Iraqi aircraft before they were overwhelmed by Iraqi ground forces.[16]

The Pave Low crews would fly as special operations assets vice conventional rescue assets. This was a key and critical point. General Horner was responsible for theater SAR and had OPCON of all the fighter and support forces that he needed for the mission. He would create and operate a joint rescue coordination center (JRCC) within his tactical air control center (TACC) to oversee rescue operations. But he did not have OPCON of the special operations helicopters that would do the actual recoveries. Colonel Johnson and his JSOACC, Colonel Gray, did. They readily agreed to accept the rescue tasking, even declaring it their number one mission and assigning recovery duties to their Army special forces and US Navy SEAL teams. However, both colonels made it clear that while they would do the recovery portion of CSAR, they were not equipped to do the search portion of the mission. CENTAF had the assets to do that. Colonel Orrell argued to all who would listen that helicopters had no business doing search patterns in high-threat areas. As the resident expert on the capabilities *and* limitations of helicopters, he pointed out that on the modern battlefield, the survival of any helicopter was problematic, and their use in such areas had to be carefully planned and flown. SOCCENT would maintain OPCON of the helicopters, reserving the right to make the individual launch decision and then passing TACON of the helicopters to the JFACC/JRCC upon launch. Johnson and Gray also developed a decision matrix for accepting a recovery mission that included (1) knowing the location of the survivor(s), (2) having evidence of aircrew survival via visual parachute sighting and/or voice transmission from the crew member and voice authentication, and (3) getting a favorable threat analysis.[17]

Coordinating their efforts with Colonel Orrell, Gray and Comer developed a relatively simple concept of operations for recoveries. To reduce response time, they would work with their intelligence section to develop and continuously update threat matrix templates so that they could make quick launch decisions. They wanted to push their helicopters forward as close as possible to the combat arenas. Also, they would take maximum advantage of the technology on the helicopters by operating as much as possible at night and in bad weather. Additionally, they would use their GPS navigational systems to fly at low level and avoid enemy threats. Comer then began to assign the detailed planning to his young officers. He appointed Capt Randy

O'Boyle to be the sole Pave Low representative to the CENTAF strategic planning cell, directed by Brig Gen "Buster" Glosson. There he would be "read in" to the overall Top Secret strategic air campaign plan that Glosson and his team were developing and would be able to coordinate CSAR plans with the larger directive. Captain Minish was directed to develop the squadron CSAR plan. Working with O'Boyle and Capt Corby Martin, he divided the Iraq-Kuwait AOR into four sections—west, central, east, and north—and identified possible FOLs where helicopters could sit CSAR alert, respectively, at Al Jouf and Arar, Rafha, and Ras al Mishab on the Gulf coast. The northern sector was more problematic, since it was almost 900 miles away from the southern bases. The officers realized that another recovery force, possibly stationed in Turkey, would be needed to effectively cover that area. Working with intelligence specialists, Minish and Martin designated a series of known points that became a database used to predevelop "spider routes" that the GPS-equipped helicopters could then use to enter and exit Iraqi and Kuwaiti airspace at minimum risk.[18]

Courtesy Air Force Historical Research Agency

Capt Randy O'Boyle, Pave Low pilot, who served as the SOCCENT liaison to the CENTAF staff during Desert Shield/Storm

In early September, Colonel Comer attended a meeting in the JRCC. It was his first chance to meet other key CSAR participants in the theater. He was a little shocked to discover that all of the controllers were either TDY personnel from the USAF Rescue Coordination Center at Scott AFB or random augmentees from the other services. As far as Comer could determine, none had any CSAR vice SAR experience. His concern was further heightened when he listened to the director's plan. It was simplistic and seemed to take no consideration of the threat faced by the recovery forces. Remembered Comer, "There was nothing combat about it. It was all peacetime."[19]

Over the next several months, the JRCC drafted an overall theater CSAR plan. While it was being staffed and sent out for coordination and comment, the JRCC began a series of six CSAR exercises. Using a crawl-walk-run approach, the exercises became increasingly more complicated and extensive. All service components were involved in practice missions that occurred on both land and water, day and night. They stressed communications, tactics, procedures, command and control, and intelligence integration. Scenarios were increasingly more complicated and challenging and stressed all manner of isolated personnel, from downed fighter crews to special forces teams to hostage rescues. The scenarios exercised helicopters alone and as part of large rescue task forces with A-10s and other support and fighter aircraft. All the helicopter units assigned to SOCCENT participated. The last exercise was in January 1991. Capt Tom Trask took part in the exercises and noted that the flying was just terrible. The training areas the Saudis had designated were remote and, on moonless nights, extremely dark. The sand there was very fine, which made for challenging brownout landings. However, like most crew members in the 20th, he had earlier flown rescue and was well familiar with the tactics and techniques.[20]

General Glosson and Colonel Gray dispatched Captains O' Boyle, Martin, and Minish to visit various combat squadrons and brief crews on what to expect if they were shot down. They explained the overall campaign recovery plan and stressed the importance of knowing the procedures that would be daily updated in the air tasking order special instructions. Earnest and honest with their fellow aviators, the three captains encouraged them to ensure that they were prepared to be that stranded survivor and described, in some detail, the procedures that the Pave Low crews or other special operations elements would use to recover them. O'Boyle remembered, "I said, 'This is how we are going to try to come and get you.' And I talked all about . . . some of the things that we were going to use . . . and basically gave them the plan, which was a real rah-rah speech but, I thought, realistic. I don't think that I overstated it. Before I got back, one wing commander called General Glosson and said, 'That was s--t hot. That was what the guys needed to hear.' "[21]

Eager Anvil

As the development of the strategic air campaign progressed, planners realized that they needed to include a thorough plan to overcome the Iraqi air defenses. Captain O'Boyle made a novel suggestion. Intelligence showed that the Iraqis had placed three early warning radars as close as one mile to the Saudi border. He suggested using SOCCENT-assigned Army SOF teams from the 5th SFG to attack and destroy the sites. They would infiltrate on foot and be extracted by MH-60s from the 3d Battalion, 160th SOAR, after they had destroyed the sites. SOCCENT worked up a plan to accomplish that. However, to be successful, the teams needed precision navigation gear and 72 hours to move to and penetrate the two sites. The navigational gear was certainly available, but General Schwarzkopf had already told President Bush that he could initiate combat with just 60 hours of preparation, and, in a rather heated meeting with Col Jesse Johnson, Schwarzkopf disapproved the plans.

A few weeks later, the Iraqis moved the three radar sites 20, 27, and 40 miles, respectively, back into Iraq and hardened the sites. Captain O'Boyle then suggested that MH-53s, enabled with GPS navigation capability, attack the sites with their 50-caliber machine guns. Colonel Johnson briefed this plan to Generals Horner and Schwarzkopf, who approved the concept for further planning. When Colonel Comer heard of the plan, he designated Captain Martin to be the planner flight leader for the mission, with Maj Ben Pulsifer, Maj Bob Leonik, and Captain Kingsley to serve as the other aircraft commanders. However, Comer was skeptical of the initial plan, believing that the machine guns would not be powerful enough to satisfactorily destroy the sites. A young captain from the 3d Battalion of the 160th SOAR contacted Colonel Gray and suggested that the mission be given to his battalion, which could attack the sites with its MH-60s armed with 2.75-inch rockets and 7.62 mm miniguns. Comer rejected that proposal for essentially the same reason, believing that, in reality, the Army special operations aviators were just looking for a way to block the Pave Low guys from being in the mission.[22]

Comer discussed the mission with Colonel Orrell, who suggested that the mission include US Army AH-64s with Hellfire missiles, Hydra-70 rockets, and 30 mm machine guns to do the job. Colonel Gray was briefed on the new suggestion and received permission from Colonel Johnson to talk to Lt Col Dick Cody, USA, commander, 1st Battalion, 101st Aviation Regiment, an Apache battalion assigned to the 101st Air Assault Division, also located at the King Fahd Airport.

The mission concept was relatively simple. The MH-53s would lead the Apaches, as they had been training to do for the last 10 years. Crews would use their GPSs to get them to the correct firing positions because they were much more accurate and reliable than the Doppler systems on the Army helicopters. One of the Pave Low gunners suggested to Captain Martin that they lead the Apaches to a predesignated position and then mark it with chemical night lights. The AH-64 pilots could then fly over that point and update their Doppler systems for the final run in to their targets. The idea was simple and logical, and Martin wrote it into the plan.

Kingsley was also concerned that one or some of the Apaches might get lost in the possible mayhem and run out of fuel. One of his flight engineers, TSgt Jeff Morrison, developed a procedure so that, if necessary, a Pave Low could ground transfer fuel from its tanks to the affected Apache and also made sure the necessary equipment was aboard each Pave Low.[23]

As the plan was maturing, intelligence reported that the three sites had again been moved, this time about 10 miles closer to the border, and consolidated into just two sites with several Soviet-style search and acquisition radars each. Accordingly, the 20th pilots modified the plan and then took it to Colonel Johnson at SOCCENT. He backed it and took it up to General Schwarzkopf, who approved the use of Apaches from the 101st Division and cleared them to begin training. Comer then met with Colonel Cody, and they began planning the mission in detail. The force would be called Task Force Normandy. Two flights of two MH-53s each would lead four Apaches to each site and provide combat recovery support. The two units trained for the mission through the fall. They also received permission to live-fire six Hellfire missiles in the Saudi desert.

In late October, Colonel Gray personally briefed General Schwarz-kopf that the joint team was ready to execute its mission. When Gray assured him that the mission would be 100 percent successful, Schwarzkopf replied, "Okay, Colonel, then you get to start the war." The joint team held a final rehearsal in January, and it went perfectly. "We were eager for the mission to fly," said Colonel Comer, and noted in his personal journal that "not since Desert One in Iran had special operations helicopters been given a better chance for a good mission."[24]

Gray ordered Comer and three other squadron commanders home to Hurlburt in late October. His operations officer, Colonel Correll, replaced him at KFIA. At home, Comer and the other commanders were able to attend the MAC squadron commander's course, catch up on backlogged squadron administrative items, and deal with some personnel issues. He also discovered that Hurlburt crews were training intensely with other SOCOM assets to perform a variety of missions, one of which was called Pacific Wind, a possible evacuation of the American Embassy in Kuwait that still harbored several dozen Americans and other protected personnel. He attended a training exercise focused on this mission and other possible JSOC taskings in the CENTCOM region. The exercise was directed by the JSOC commander, Maj Gen Wayne Downing.

During the exercise, Comer spoke with the USAF colonel who was assigned to the JSOC as the air component commander. Comer could not help but notice, though, that the colonel had been assigned by Downing to the plans division. Comer also noticed that Lt Col Doug Brown, the commander of the designated JSOC Army special operations aviation unit—the 1st Battalion of the 160th SOAR—did his best to insure that the aviation unit of choice was his unit vice the 20th. Comer tried to highlight the differences in capabilities of the aircraft in the units to Downing. However, the JSOC commander preferred Brown's unit and was functionally using Brown as his aviation component commander.[25]

At Hurlburt, though, Comer had some more immediate unit concerns. Many unit families were upset about the extended deployment and were filing complaints. Working with his wife, Stephanie, he tried to address every one of them and to assure the family members that their loved ones were doing important work and would not be kept away from home any longer than needed.[26]

As part of the rotational flow, SSgt Jim Kradel returned home in December. However, while there, he received orders to transfer to

Kirtland AFB to serve as a gunner instructor. The school was increasing the size of the training classes to fill the growing 21st and 31st SOSs. Consequently, he did not rotate back to Saudi Arabia.[27]

While Colonel Comer was back in the United States, President Bush was beginning to doubt that the diplomatic and economic measures being taken against Iraq were going to be sufficient to force Sadam Hussein to withdraw his troops from Kuwait. Accordingly, he directed General Schwarzkopf to prepare for offensive action and authorized him to increase his force with an entire US Army–heavy corps. In parallel, General Horner increased the size of his force, called for the deployment of another aerial force into Turkey, and directed his planning staff to finalize its overall air campaign plan. By December General Glosson had it completed. It directed an air campaign of four phases:

1. *Strategic air campaign*—to gain control of the airspace and attack Iraqi leadership, strategic weapons, long-range missiles, and electric-generation capability.

2. *Superiority over the Kuwaiti theater of operations*—to support phase 1.

3. *Battlefield preparation*—to direct attacks on Iraqi fielded forces to degrade fighting morale and destroy 50 percent of Iraqi equipment.

4. *Ground war*—to provide direct support to the massive coalition ground units as they destroyed the Iraqi army.[28]

In readying for the campaign, General Glosson visited the combat air bases and gave the combat crews an overall brief on the theater campaign plan. Like Captains O'Boyle, Martin, and Minish, he also addressed CSAR. However, his discussion was a bit different than that of the three Pave Low pilots. He was much more sanguine about rescue and assured the aircrews that "if you get shot down, you [won't] have to spend the night. . . . You are not going to spend 24 hours on the ground. . . . We will pick you up if we have to stack helicopters on top of each other and get them all shot down. But we are not going to leave you out there." Glosson was a veteran of air combat in Southeast Asia and was thinking back to that paradigm. On the issue of CSAR, he and the men of AFSOC were on different intellectual frequencies. In a few short weeks, this difference would lead to a contentious misunderstanding between USAF conventional and special operations forces.[29]

Courtesy Col Corby Martin, USAF, Retired

Task Force Normandy crew. *Left to right*: (*standing*) Sgt Phil Carroll, Capt Corby Martin, Capt Bill Lemenager, and MSgt Mike Lael; (*kneeling*) SSgt Mike Harte and Sgt Barrett Harrison.

Comer returned to the squadron at KFIA in early December with Maj Mike Homan, who would serve as his deployed operations officer and oversee current operations and scheduling. Homan had just completed his Pave Low requalification and wanted to go to the Gulf. He would fly as a copilot for his first few missions and then lead his own crew, in addition to his larger duties.

Back with his deployed Airmen, Comer found a few things that concerned him and required his immediate attention. Fortunately, he had the unit flight surgeon, Maj Mark Cunningham, with him. Cunningham worked daily with the officers and Airmen of the unit to address their medical needs and keep them fit for the rigors of their mission and life in the desert. However, the Army aviators from the 3d Battalion, 160th SOAR, were still trying to get the Eager Anvil mission. While he was gone, Colonel Johnson had directed the 20th to provide him with an MH-53 for VIP support as he took several of his subordinate commanders to Al Jouf in central Saudi Arabia to inspect that area as a possible forward deployed site for his forces. Capt Brad Webb served as the aircraft commander on the week-long mission and took a small maintenance team to support him. While out in the harsh desert environment, though, the Pave Low suffered a complete loss of its navigational system, making navigation over the flat desert much more difficult. Colonel Johnson was very disappointed in the Pave Low's performance and believed that the aircraft might not be able to handle the radar site mission. He spoke to Lt Col Dell Dailey, the 3d Battalion, 160th SOAR commander, about this situation. Dailey had just received GPS receivers for his MH-60s and suggested that his crews could provide the precision navigation needed for the mission. Comer talked to Colonel Cody and asked that they hold another mission rehearsal to revalidate the capabilities and reliability of the Pave Lows. Within a week, they did so satisfactorily, and the arguments ended. However, Comer was surprised that such "blue-green" bickering and competition that had evolved from the Initiative 17 debate could extend forward into a combat theater when the lives of so many were at stake. He realized, though, that he would always have to deal with Army aviators who believed that "Soldiers should fly with Soldiers." He was determined that his unit would fly the Eager Anvil mission.[30]

Proven Force

When President Bush first considered responding with military force, Secretary Cheney and General Powell envisioned deploying US and possibly NATO forces into Turkey to attack Iraq from the north. Over the next several months, planning took place at the United States European Command (USEUCOM) headquarters to build a task force primarily based upon the 52d Tactical Fighter Wing (TFW) at Spangdahlem AB, Germany. Consisting primarily of F-111s, F-15s, and F-16s accompanied by a large fleet of supporting aircraft, this contingent would be known as Proven Force and would deploy to several air bases in Turkey to operate from there, subject to approval of the Turkish government. It would also include a small SOCEUR contingent of aircrews and support personnel flying MC-130s and MH-53Js from the 67th and 21st SOSs of the 39th SOW, along with special forces Soldiers from the 10th SFG, to perform CSAR duties and SOF missions as assigned. This JSOTF would be called Elusive Concept and be directly commanded by the SOCEUR commander, Brig Gen Richard Potter.[31]

21st Special Operations Squadron

The 21st SOS was ready for the mission. Now in possession of five of its six designated MH-53Js, throughout 1990 the squadron had continued to receive new personnel as they completed their training at Kirtland AFB. Taskings steadily arrived from SOCEUR, directing the unit to participate in training with other US and NATO special forces elements in several countries. The unit also accepted SAR taskings, launching one aircraft in February to search for the bodies of two F-111 crew members killed in a crash off the east coast of Great Britain. In March the unit deployed three aircraft and crews for Exercise Cold Winter '90 in Evennes, Norway, to train with other special forces units. While there, two Norwegian paratroopers had a midair collision while conducting a night jump onto a frozen lake and were injured—one critically. A 21st SOS Pave Low, flown by Capt Bill Bassett and Capt Brendan Clare, diverted to medically evacuate the soldiers. They had to be very careful as they gently set the heavy aircraft down on the frozen lake without melting the ice or cracking through it. As the aircraft settled on the ice and snow, medics quickly loaded the two injured soldiers aboard, and the pilots lifted off and headed for a local hospital. Landing there on its helipad was a challenge because it was built for much smaller helicopters. Regardless, the crew was able to land safely, and the soldiers were quickly taken inside for immediate medical care. In the opinion of the doctors who treated the more severely wounded soldier, the quick actions of the Pave Low crew saved his life. The Norwegian army Jaegers honored the crew members for their lifesaving mission.[32]

In May, the 21st deployed to Pisa, Italy, to participate in Exercise Flintlock '90. While there, the unit received an ORI conducted by the MAC inspector general. Overall, the unit was rated outstanding, testimony to the hard work of all those assigned to it.

On 24 June Lt Col Robert Zdenek succeeded Lt Col Steve Connelly as the commander of the 21st SOS. Zdenek selected Lt Col Russell Rakip, the sole USAF helicopter pilot veteran of the disaster at Desert One, as his operations officer. The squadron was ready for any operational challenge.[33]

Later that summer, as the Airmen of the 21st SOS observed the events occurring in the Gulf, they sensed that they, too, would become involved. In October Capt Steve Otto transferred to the unit from the 20th. He had initially deployed to Saudi Arabia with that unit and shared his limited experiences with his new squadron. He explained to them how the Pave Lows were being tasked for both combat rescue and SOF and that the helicopters based in Saudi Arabia could not easily cover northern Iraq.

When the OPLAN for Proven Force and then Elusive Concept arrived, Zdenek put his troops to work getting ready for possible deployment to the small Turkish base at Batman, 35 miles east of the big air base at Diyarbakir but still 110 miles from the Iraqi border. By November they were ready to deploy and perform whatever duties they were assigned. However, their deployment depended upon the willingness of the Turkish government to allow them to enter and operate from its country.[34]

Somalia

As 1991 began, Saddam Hussein still showed nothing but intransigence against the demands leveled at his actions. Accordingly, all units in the Gulf were finalizing their plans for eventual offensive action. Almost completely ready now to meet its rescue tasking and fly the preplanned Eager Anvil missions, the 20th SOS received another tasking from another completely unexpected quarter.

For some time, serious internal unrest had been sweeping the nation of Somalia on the eastern coast of Africa. On 10 January, CENTCOM alerted the 20th to be ready to fly to two locations there to evacuate US and coalition personnel. This threw the unit into chaos since it was now faced with the possibility of having three simultaneous missions in three different parts of the world. Fortunately, the orders were changed. The Pave Low crews were about to start engines when their participation was cancelled. CENTCOM decided to send a Marine expeditionary unit (MEU) instead. A rescue force of 55 Marines and Navy SEALs launched off of the USS *Trenton* recovered 281 Americans and other nationals from the US Embassy. The Airmen of the 20th stayed focused on their two assigned missions. Said Colonel Comer, "As it turned out, [the deployment] didn't happen. The marines got the mission . . . . It was a good thing."[35]

Proven Force

As the United States was completing the Somalia mission, US and other national leaders were still trying to diplomatically resolve the crisis as the allied force in the Gulf region, now over 600,000 strong, made final plans for the initiation of combat operations to force Saddam to withdraw his troops and honor the sovereignty of Kuwait. On 13 January, US government representatives met with Turkish government officials and presented them with a formal full briefing on Operations Proven Force and Elusive Concept. Some aircraft were already in place under previously existing agreements, and Turkish president Turgut Özal approved the full deployment. Almost immediately the larger deployment commenced, and, eventually, the full complement of 24 F-16, 22 F-15C, 18 F-111E, eight F-4G, six RF-4, six EF-111, three Airborne Warning and Control System (AWACS), and 14 KC-135 aircraft moved onto Incirlik AB.

The 39th SOW deployed its assets four days later. They consisted of two MC-130Es, four HC-130N/Ps, and three MH-53Js from the 21st SOS. The Pave Low's primary mission was to support joint search and rescue (JSAR) vice CSAR because the Turks did not want to say overtly that anybody was flying combat missions out of Turkish bases. Arriving in Turkey during the coldest and shortest days of winter, the MH-53s were moved forward to the small, austere air base at Batman, where the crews were literally given an open icy, muddy field to work from and had to provide totally for themselves. The senior gunner, TSgt John Sprouse, was not impressed with the accommodations. He remembers that "they dropped us off on a taxiway . . . and said, 'There is your home.' They had a little row of tents set up—no lights, no heat. We went three weeks without any running water. You get to know people very well."[36] A few days later, the 20th at Hurlburt flew over two more MH-53Js with three more aircrews. Regardless of the primitive conditions, the Airmen of the 21st made the best of the situation and within two days were able to assume JSAR alert as a supporting force to SOCCENT, with the tasking worked through a JRCC set up at Incirlik that was directly linked to the JRCC in Saudi Arabia. However, the use of Proven Force elements in action against Iraq was still subject to the Turkish government's final approval.[37]

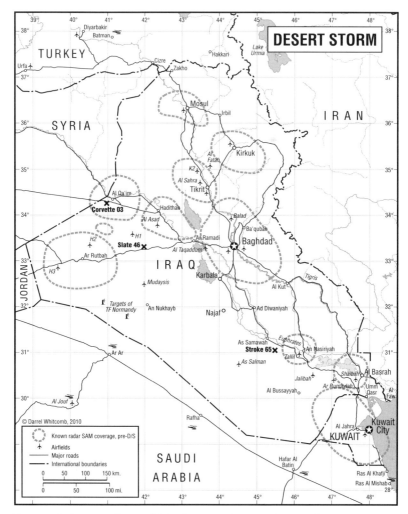

Figure 4. **Desert Storm/Shield area of operations**. (Copyright Darrel Whitcomb, 2010.)

Eve of Combat

On 11 January, SOCCENT activated an FOL at Al Jouf, and Colonel Comer was ordered to move his unit with all MH-53s there. Three days later, he and his Airmen completed the move. Colonel Cody and his Apaches also deployed forward. On 16 January, it was obvious that all nonmilitary efforts to resolve the Kuwaiti occupation had failed, and President Bush directed that military operations begin. SOCCENT notified all of its forces that the war would start the next morning at 3 a.m. Comer alerted his personnel that Eager Anvil would be going that night. To cover his rescue taskings, he dispatched Captains Minish and Trask and crews to Rafha to sit alert for the central sector. The western sector would initially be covered by SH-60s from HCS-4/5 and then by the MH-53s from Task Force Normandy when that mission was complete. Since the 21st had not yet arrived in Turkey, there was no immediate coverage in the north. The eastern sector was covered by MH-3s from the 71st SOS, now located at Ras al Mishab on the Persian Gulf coast.[38]

At 9:30 p.m., Colonel Comer held a final flight briefing for his Pave Low and the Apache crews. There really was nothing more to say. All recognized that they were about to take part in a significant event and, while nervous, were extremely confident that they were the right force at the right time and place. All used the short time available before proceeding to their aircraft for private moments, actions, and prayers. Captain Kingsley felt the gravity of the moment, noting that "I immediately had 'butterflies' in my stomach. [I thought,] oh my gosh, the weight of the world is on this mission. A lot of people could die if we fail." He grabbed Capt Corby Martin and went over the details of the mission for the "hundredth" time before heading out to the aircraft.[39]

The crews coordinated their engine starts so that the entire formation lifted off at Al Jouf at 1 a.m. The "Red Team" Pave Lows led by Martin and Major Pulsifer and crews were joined by their four Apaches and set course for the western target now designated "Nevada." Capt Newman Shufflebarger led the Apaches. The second section of "White Team" Pave Lows led by Captain Kingsley and Major Leonik and crews did likewise and proceeded to the eastern target, now designated "California." Colonel Comer flew as Leonik's copilot and maintained communications contact with the SOCCENT command center, where Colonels Gray and Johnson were closely monitoring the mission. Lt Col Dick Cody led their accompanying Apaches. Trailing in combat rescue support were the two SH-60s from HCS-4/5—led by their skipper, Cdr Neil Kinnear; they took up an orbit just north of Arar.

At 2:12 a.m., the Task Force Normandy helicopters crossed into Iraq, varying their flight path as necessary to avoid known or suspected enemy observation posts or Bedouin locations. The western target was 13 miles farther; the eastern target, 23 miles. The Pave Lows used their TF/TA radar and FLIR to stay less than 50 feet above the ground. At one point, the navigational system on Leonik's Pave Low failed, and the crew had to scramble to reset it. All crews observed some small arms tracers, but they were inaccurate and of no consequence. The Pave Lows flew to the prebriefed drop-off points, where the gunners and engineers threw out bunches of green chemical sticks, and the pilots then turned south. As they departed, the Apaches slowly passed over the chemical lights and updated their Doppler navigational systems for the final 10-mile run to their individual targets. Slipping through the clear, dark night, they pulled into firing position exactly 90 seconds early. The Apache crews could see the sites, which matched the intelligence pictures they had been shown. The Apache crews also saw enemy troops around the structures.

Suddenly, the lights began to go off. One of the pilots mused, "I think they know we are here." Thirty seconds prior, the Apache crews turned on their ranging lasers. At exactly 2:37:50 a.m., White Team Apache pilot 2d Lt Tom Drew keyed his radio and broadcast, "Party in 10." Precisely 10 seconds later, all crews began firing their Hellfire missiles. Twenty seconds later, the deadly weapons began to detonate against the structures. The generators were first, then the command bunkers, and, finally, the radar dishes themselves. The enemy soldiers died in the melee.

Once the Hellfires were totally expended, the helicopters flew toward the sites and ripple-fired their rockets. Two thousand meters from the sites, they opened up with their 30 mm chain guns and riddled what remained of the compounds with every bullet they had. Four minutes after it started, it was over. The Apaches had expended 27 Hellfire missiles, 100 Hydra-70 rockets, and 4,000 rounds of 30 mm cannon fire. They turned south, rejoined with the Pave Lows, and headed home. En route, Captain Martin's crew observed what appeared to be the launch of two SA-7 missiles. Utilizing onboard defensive systems and some aggressive maneuvering, the crew managed to escape them.

Outbound, Comer radioed a code-word message to SOCCENT headquarters reporting their complete success: "SOF targets destroyed." Colonel Johnson personally reported the results to General Schwarzkopf's command center. "Thank God!" the general responded.[40]

The combination of the Pave Lows and Apaches had worked as hoped. All of the planning, calculating, and training had paid off. As

Martin was leading his formation back to the south, he could see in the clear night air above the massive formations of allied aircraft heading for the radar gap. He remembered how "you could look off to the south, and there were blinkers lined up. You could see a long way on goggles. And it's also desert, so it's clear. There were anticollision lights lined up; it looked like an LA freeway, . . . and they were all chasing these big blinkers . . . [the] tankers. Then, all of a sudden, there was a point where there were no more lights. So they would get gas, drop off, turn lights off, and head north."[41] One F-15E fighter pilot who was in that massive gaggle of firepower wrote a thank-you letter to the men of Task Force Normandy that said, "During our [flight intelligence] brief, we noticed our route of flight took us right over an active [radar] site. . . . We were told not to worry about it! We saw the explosions and your helicopters in our FLIR as we flew over you. There was immense relief!"[42] Capt Mike Kingsley noted their contribution to the operation when he said, "We were the logical choice because we have an advanced navigational system. . . . They had the confidence in us to lead them in so that when it was time to destroy these radar sites they were fresh and ready to go."[43] "Pave Low leads," declared Colonel Comer. The task force of Air Force and Army Airmen had blown open the door for their fellow combat aviators to begin the air campaign against Iraq. They were the right force, at the right place, at the right time.[44]

Approaching Arar, the four Pave Lows of Red Team and White Team assumed rescue alert duties as their Apaches proceeded back to Al Jouf. The Pave Low crews monitored the CSAR SATCOM frequency, along with the two Pave Lows at Rafha and the H-3s at Ras al Mishab. They were backed up by the entire SOCCENT helicopter fleet, if necessary. However, throughout the night, the frequencies were eerily quiet. In contradiction to the best estimates, only one manned aircraft was lost, an F-18 from the USS Saratoga. However, the pilot, Lt Cdr Michael Speicher, had not been heard from since his strike package had departed its target, the Iraqi airfield at Al Taqaddum, and rescue forces were not dispatched. Subsequently, Secretary of Defense Cheney announced that Speicher had been killed. Throughout the night, the rescue crews monitored the frequencies, making occasional radio checks to insure that the relative silence was not because of communications problems. The predictions of horrendous losses were obviated by years of technological development and hard training.[45] General Horner was most pleased.

The strategic portion of the air campaign was now in full swing as allied aircraft swarmed over Iraq and Kuwait. On 17 January, the Turkish government finally gave its approval for Proven Force to begin combat operations. Colonel Gray was relieved that he now had a recovery force for the northern part of the country. He divided Iraq at latitude 33 degrees and 30 minutes north, assigning the 21st SOS any recoveries above that demarcation. His SOCCENT assets in the south would continue to handle their three sectors. On that day and the next, though, the Iraqi air defenders began to strike back, downing eight fighter aircraft. Most crews went down directly over enemy airfields or ground units and were either killed in the downing or immediately captured. There were no calls for rescue.[46]

Stroke 65

On 19 January, thick clouds enveloped the region as several large packages of fighter aircraft attacked targets in the Baghdad area. Iraqi SAMs shot down two USAF F-16s. One pilot, Capt Harry Roberts, ejected over enemy units and was immediately captured. The second pilot, Maj Jeff Tice, call sign Stroke 65, was able to fly halfway back toward Saudi Arabia before he had to eject. While descending under his parachute through the thick clouds, Tice was able to report his status to an orbiting AWACS aircraft, which then passed the information to the JRCC. When Tice landed, though, he was immediately taken prisoner by Bedouin tribesmen and was not able to report his capture to those orbiting above.

Unaware of his status, his wingmen reported his location to the AWACS aircraft and then had to depart the area. The AWACS crew directly forwarded that information to the JRCC, which passed the mission to SOCCENT. Colonel Gray and his staff did a quick mission analysis and determined that a rescue using Pave Lows was possible. Two 20th SOS Pave Lows, commanded by Captains Minish and Harmon, were en route from Al Jouf to Rafha. On board with Harmon was the unit flight surgeon, Maj Mark Cunningham. Colonel Comer contacted them and gave them the mission and available data. While refueling at Rafha, Minish used his spider-route matrix and latest intelligence updates to design a path to the survivor's location. Harmon was directed to unload the flight surgeon. Major Cunningham would have none of it and refused to leave the aircraft. He was assigned scanner duties, and, when the refueling was complete, the two aircraft took off and headed north.

Approaching the border, the two helicopters descended to 80 feet above the ground and entered low clouds. Minish began navigating with his TF/TA and FLIR as Harmon maintained position off of his aircraft. Encountering especially thick fog, though, Harmon lost visual contact with the other aircraft and had to pull away for safe separation. He and his crew then used their radar to maintain a trail formation on the lead aircraft as they continued through the weather, which was now providing a cover for the two aircraft. As they continued north, fighter aircraft contacted them on the radio and offered their support. The fighters were able to provide airborne protection above the helicopters. However, they were never able to see the Pave Lows and could not risk dropping ordnance without visual identification and deconfliction.

Courtesy Col Paul Harmon, USAF Retired

The Pave Low crew that made the attempt to recover Stroke 65. *Left to right:* (*standing*) Sgt Rob Turner, Capt Paul Harmon, Capt Ken Sipperly, Sgt Jeff Mucha, SSgt Mike Hulin, and TSgt Troy Arce; (*front*) Sgt Ismael Gonzalez and SrA Martin Brown.

About 10 miles from the survivor's reported location, Minish called for the survivor on the rescue radio frequencies. When Tice did not respond, the two helicopter crews coordinated a sector search. For 30 minutes, they fruitlessly swept the area, flying over several Bedouin encampments—one of which was holding Tice, who heard them fly over. The AWACS crew then gave them another set of coordinates, which was the F-16 wreckage site. Flying to that site, Pave

Low crews were notified that Iraqi forces in the area were aware of their presence and actively searching for them with radar and direction finding devices. The AWACS monitoring their progress then ordered them out of the area, which was very satisfactory with the crews since they were low on fuel. Still enshrouded by the low clouds, the two aircraft turned south and left the area after logging over five hours in enemy territory.

The recovery attempt for Maj Jeff Tice had been unsuccessful but not because of the efforts of the two Pave Low crews or their aircraft. Both had done exactly what had been asked of them. The crews proved that the aircraft could overcome the limitations of weather and low visibility conditions that earlier rescue forces had faced. Furthermore, they had operated in hostile territory against a fully alerted enemy force and had used the formerly restrictive weather as a defensive cover. Captain Harmon recalls that "this was the first time that the Pave Low had been fully used as designed—Vietnam lessons learned, adverse weather, night capability, etc. It was actually the first time the airplane had ever done what it was designed to do. We never considered turning around because of the weather. We just continued north. Tim [Minish] had already configured his airplane to set up his hover coupler to descend through the weather had he needed to once we got into the area, had Tice come up on the radio."[47]

Comer was pleased, too. He shared Harmon's satisfaction. However, it was more tempered, for he felt that his crews would be spending a great deal more time in enemy territory, and he was concerned by the capabilities that the enemy forces had displayed in trying to track the Pave Lows. He knew that war was a process of tactic-countertactic, and only the quickest survived.

Regardless, the war went on. As the large force packages were attacking near Baghdad, Saddam Hussein ordered his forces to launch intermediate range missiles against Saudi Arabia and Israel from sites in western Iraq. Fearing an Israeli intervention, General Schwarzkopf directed General Horner to attack the suspected launch positions. On short notice, strike flights were refragged from well-planned targets to hit hastily identified potential missile locations near the Iraq-Jordan border.

Corvette 03

One of the strike flights so redirected was the Corvette 01 flight from the 4th TFW. That wing was the first to be assigned the new strike version of the premier air-to-air fighter; it was one of Horner's key USAF units in the war. Corvette 01 was dispatched as a flight of six aircraft to hit sites near the Iraqi city of Al Qaim, an area heavily defended by multiple SAM and AAA batteries.

Flying as the crew of Corvette 03 were Col Dave Eberly and Maj Tom Griffith. As they entered the target area, a SAM struck and mortally wounded their aircraft. Both men ejected. Arriving on the ground, they were able to join up, move away from Al Qaim, and make some radio calls.

The Corvette 01 crew immediately notified the AWACS that their wingman had gone down. The AWACS crew notified the JRCC. Rescue specialists in the JRCC began working with intelligence and other sources to determine an accurate location of the survivors while also passing a warning order to SOCCENT. Colonel Gray got the message and alerted the crews at Arar. Captain Martin and crew were first on alert and quickly began planning as they awaited location data and intelligence updates. However, initial reports indicated that the crew of Corvette 03 was down near Al Qaim, an extremely dangerous area and north of the sector dividing line. While his intelligence section began a threat analysis, Gray pressed the JRCC for an accurate location and also got Colonel Johnson's approval to contact the 21st SOS guys at Batman.

For the next several hours, the AWACS, Rivet Joint RC-135s, and SAR satellites attempted to gain an accurate location of the PRC-90 radio being used by Eberly and Griffith. However, they were not able to provide anything but a general location. The JRCC suggested that Gray dispatch Pave Lows into the area to do a search. Colonel Orrell was adamantly against that, recalling his experiences flying HH-53s in Southeast Asia. He wanted a good location so that the Pave Low crews could take advantage of their precision GPS navigational capability to get in and out quickly at low level, and preferably at night, giving the crew the best chance at success and survival.

Unfortunately, the fighter crews of the 4th TFW did not know all of that. General Glosson had told them that if they were shot down, the helicopters would be there regardless. Now their buddies were on the ground, and they could hear them on the radios. Yet, apparently, the rescue forces were doing nothing. Captain O'Boyle in the TACC was accosted several times by fighter guys who did not understand the delays. At one point, O'Boyle tried to explain by saying, "You just can't go trundling into some place in a high-threat environment without knowing exactly where the guy is."[48]

Despite the situation, the pressure was building on Colonel Gray to make an attempt—at least for morale purposes. He asked the JRCC for its best position on the two men. When it provided that, he realized that the 21st crews were the obvious choice and, with Colonel Johnson's approval, passed the mission to them.

Colonel Zdenek and his crews seized the opportunity. Two helicopters, commanded by Capt Grant Harden and Capt Steve Otto, would go in, accompanied by an HC-130 tanker. The crews had already tasked intelligence for the latest possible data and the JRCC for supplemental information. However, they had some practical problems based upon their location in Turkey. First of all, the crews had to make sure they could get clearance through Turkish airspace to fly their missions. Next, in doing threat analysis, they determined that their best approach to the Al Qaim area was directly through Syria. They had already requested permission to fly through Syrian airspace. However, the necessary clearances were not forthcoming to allow them to fly that night, and they had to delay until the next evening.

The next day, several aircrews flying through the Al Qaim area heard Eberly and Griffith on the radio, adding to the frustration building in the fighter community. Unsure of what was happening with the rescue forces, the two Airmen decided to try to walk into Syria. Later that evening, they stumbled into some enemy soldiers and were captured. US intelligence sources and commanders did not know that.

At Batman, the Pave Low crews got ready. The three aircraft would fly due south through Syria. The tanker would refuel them en route. Besides the crew of six, the Pave Lows would carry two PJs, a combat controller, and six US Army special forces Soldiers. General Potter, the SOCEUR commander, determined this because he wanted the rescue crews to be able to insert the team for a short overland recovery. It was a calculated way to generate another rescue tactical option if the threat in the immediate area of the survivor precluded the helicopter from getting in.

At launch time, approval to fly through Syria had still not been granted. Regardless, the three aircraft took off and turned south.

Twenty minutes into Syria, the crews finally received their clearance. The two helicopters then refueled from the HC-130, separated from it, and proceeded to a holding point near Al Qaim. Crews were instructed to make no attempt to pick up the two Airmen unless they had voice contact with them. The recovery forces would be supported with an air strike that would bomb SAM and AAA sites as they made the pickup. Additionally, one of the fighter flight leads would contact the survivors and authenticate them for the pickup.

The helicopter crews were right on time. But the air strike was late and hastily conducted. The Pave Low pilots watched the bombs explode and the enemy guns and SAM sites return fire. They heard a few radio calls to Corvette 03, with no response. Then the fighters were gone. Captain Harden and his copilot, Capt Matt Shazda, called on the PRC-90 radio frequencies for the two Airmen. As they did, they could not help but notice that the calls drew ground fire. The pilots suspected that the enemy was trying to direction find against their radio calls, and this seemed to confirm it. Capt Shazda relates,

> I got on the radio and started trying all the different frequencies to contact him. . . . We realized that the SAR net was nothing more than a . . . pilot-controlled AAA. We would key the mike, and they would start firing. I told Harden, "Look! They're DFin' [direction finding] us. Watch this!" So I made a radio call, and they started shooting again. He told me, "Cut that out!" They definitely had a trap set up for us. They were waiting for us, because the final location that we got [was] where all the AAA was coming from.[49]

With no contact, the crews departed the area and proceeded back to Batman. They went back into crew rest, anticipating another attempt the next night. Colonel Gray also planned another attempt from the south using a task force of MH-53s, MH-60s, and an HC-130. Captain Martin would plan and lead the mission. However, without a solid location and contact with the survivors, Gray would not commit to another attempt. The operation was subsequently cancelled when he received confirmation that the men had been captured. Unfortunately, the fighter crews were not aware of the efforts of the Pave Low crews or the difficulties that CENTAF was having in trying to locate its downed crew members. They just knew that their buddies had not been rescued. It caused a significant morale problem among those who bore the biggest burden of combat.[50]

Slate 46

On 20 January, in the midst of the Corvette 03 effort, 20th SOS crews at Arar were alerted for two more possible CSAR missions. SOCCENT reported that enemy missiles had downed an A-6 and an F-14 from the USS *Saratoga* while they were conducting early morning strikes in western Iraq. The SOCCENT force at Arar also included four US Navy SH-60s from the HCS-4/5 detachment, and, understandably, those crews wanted to rescue their service brethren. Unfortunately, the airfield was enshrouded in heavy fog and below the takeoff minimums for those aircraft. Since the Pave Lows could launch in those conditions, the local SOCCENT element commander, Lt Col Jerry Garlington, gave them the mission. He selected Captain Kingsley as lead and Capt Mike Beard as copilot for one crew, and Captain Trask and Major Homan, respectively, for the other. Both crews began planning their missions right away. Within a few minutes, though, the A-6 landed at an airfield in Saudi Arabia, and Kingsley's mission was cancelled.

Flying with the call sign of Moccasin 05, Trask and his crew lifted off into the weather and, using their Pave Low navigational gear, headed north into Iraq to recover the pilot, Lt Devon Jones, and the radar intercept officer, Lt Larry Slade, of the downed F-14, Slate 46. The fog ended at the border, and the crew members found themselves traversing an almost completely flat and trackless region of Iraq with almost unlimited visibility. Trask descended to just 20 feet above the ground and utilized the best spider route for the area. As they flew, the crew received constant threat updates from an AWACS aircraft that was watching them. Additionally, the AWACS crew arranged for F-15s to provide combat air patrol and A-10s to support them on the recovery.

As the Pave Low crew cruised to the reported location of Lieutenant Slade and tried to make contact with him, the AWACS warned them that Iraqi fighter aircraft and helicopters were headed in their direction. The crew avoided them by flying just above the ground and using what little terrain masking was available. But flying at such low altitudes prevented them from making radio contact with either Jones or Slade. An orbiting EA-6B that had been part of the strike package with Slate 46 contacted Moccasin 05 and told them that the survivors were about 50 miles to the north of their position. After checking with AWACS and SOCCENT, Trask widened their search

The crew of Moccasin 05. *Left to right*: TSgt Jim Peterson, Sgt Craig Dock, MSgt Tim Hadrych, Capt Tom Trask, Maj Mike Homan, and TSgt Greg Vanhyning.

area, which was dangerously close to the Mudaysis AB. Their best efforts were unsuccessful, and Moccasin 05 returned to Arar for fuel and better survivor data. Unbeknownst to them, Slade was subsequently taken prisoner by Iraqi troops.

As Moccasin 05 headed for Arar, a flight of A-10s—Sandy 57 and 58, Capt Paul Johnson and 1st Lt Randy Goff—was diverted to the CSAR effort. Johnson heard Jones calling on his survival radio and was able to contact him and fly to his location. When the survivor said that he could see the A-10 over his location, Johnson marked his location with his INS and reported it to AWACS.

At Arar, Trask and his crew were refueling. They were instructed to take off and fly to Al Jouf so that their aircraft could receive some needed maintenance. However, they had been monitoring the emergency radio frequency and could hear Johnson talking to Jones. Believing that Pave Low best operated when utilized with an "assault mentality," Trask asked Colonel Garlington for permission to relaunch for the recovery. With the weather now clear, the US Navy crews of HCS-4/5 concurrently were again asking for the mission to rescue their service-mates. Since Trask and his crew had just flown through that area, Garlington believed they had a tactical advantage.

He directed Moccasin 05 to go, accompanied this time by Moccasin 04, with Kingsley and crew flying as wingmen.[51]

As the two Pave Lows headed north, they could still hear Captain Johnson talking to Lieutenant Jones. Moccasin 05 contacted Johnson directly. He reported that he was in the area of the survivor but needed to depart to refuel. "Just give me the survivor's location," responded Trask. Using a secure means of communication, Johnson gave them the survivor's coordinates as determined by his INS, and then he and Lieutenant Goff departed to find a tanker.

Trask and Homan quickly loaded the location into their enhanced navigational system and plotted it on their maps. They realized immediately that the survivor was in the northern sector, which was supposed to be covered by the 21st SOS troops at Batman. Regardless, they reported to SOCCENT via SATCOM that they were pressing on to his location. But they would have to cross the main east-west highway from Baghdad to Jordan. The road was heavily used and guarded, and Trask instructed Kingsley to hold south of it while he proceeded to the survivor.

After crossing the road, Trask and crew steered directly for the survivor's location. As they did, the AWACS crew informed them that a Roland SAM site ahead of them had become active and gave them its coordinates. Homan plotted its location and determined that it was at almost the exact same position as the survivor. When the Roland site was displayed on the MH-53J's radar warning receiver, Trask maneuvered his aircraft to stay out of its engagement zone as the AWACS controller shouted at them to turn to the east. A few minutes later, Sandy 57 and 58 returned full of fuel and contacted Moccasin 05. Trask reported that he was in the vicinity of the survivor. Johnson could not see him. Trask realized that the INS on the A-10s had probably drifted quite a bit, since Johnson and Goff had now been airborne for almost eight hours, and he used his main radio to home in on Johnson's transmissions.

Johnson and Goff spotted Moccasin 05 and dropped down to escort it to the survivor. Johnson contacted Lieutenant Jones and told him to get ready for the pickup. Then Jones saw the helicopter, and he remembers, "I . . . saw the Pave Low, about five feet off of the ground. I started talking to him. I have never seen such a beautiful sight as that big brown H-53."[52]

Very excited now, Jones started giving Trask vectors. Unfortunately, Iraqi forces in the area were also monitoring his transmissions and began homing in on his location in two trucks. The left gunner on Moccasin 05, MSgt Tim Hadrych, spotted them and called them out to the rest of the crew. Homan called Sandy 57 and 58 and told them to "smoke the trucks!" Sandy 58, Lieutenant Goff, hit the lead truck with several rounds of 30 mm fire, stopping it and setting it on fire. Captain Johnson also shot it with more 30 mm fire for good measure. The second truck turned around and fled. Throughout the engagement, Trask continued his approach to the survivor, who was now standing and quite visible. Trask set the Pave Low down between Lieutenant Jones and the now furiously burning enemy vehicle. He cleared his two PJs to disembark and secure Jones.

The burning truck as seen by the crew members of Moccasin 05 as they approached Slate 46 Alpha's position

When all three were aboard, he lifted off and, with the A-10s again providing escort, turned south. He was immediately joined by Captain Kingsley and crew in Moccasin 04, who had crossed the main road to provide assistance if needed. The A-10s guided them back across the busy highway and stayed with them until they crossed the Saudi border. Captain Johnson and Lieutenant Goff then headed off to find another tanker before flying back to their base at KFIA. The two Pave Lows headed for Al Jouf and a thunderous welcome.

Courtesy USSOCOM Public Affairs

The actual rescue of Slate 46 Alpha, US Navy lieutenant Devon Jones

As Lt Devon Jones stepped off of the helicopter, his recovery as well as the unsuccessful attempts for Stroke 65 and Corvette 03 made it obvious to all that the Pave Lows could finally perform the mission for which they had been modified. However, the astounding capabilities of the Pave Low also highlighted a larger CSAR deficiency. While a precision day/night, all-weather recovery capability now existed, the USAF had a larger problem. For optimal use, the Pave Low needed precision GPS coordinates for its survivors. In the years since Southeast Asia, the USAF had not developed the capability either with its survival radios or intelligence collection platforms to provide those coordinates. As good as Pave Low was technologically, it was only as good as the system that supported it. On all three missions, the crews flew the aircraft to the limits of its capabilities. Of the five Airmen awaiting rescue, though, only one was recovered—in large part because the crew of Moccasin 05 was able to overcome the larger limitations in the USAF's CSAR capability at that time. Lamenting that revelation, Colonel Comer later noted, "We didn't have the technology on our people . . . to know their location. We had GPS, but GPS was brand new. We didn't understand that it changed the world."[53]

About that same time, Colonel Comer received a call from Col Ben Orrell informing him that Colonel Johnson wanted him to move four of his aircraft and crews back to KFIA to better support the SOCCENT ground SOF elements. Comer was somewhat concerned that his unit's initial emphasis on rescue might provoke some USAF officers to suggest that the 20th focus exclusively on that mission. He did not want to have to engage in a repeat of the endless debate on that issue and welcomed Johnson's directive. However, he did not want to split his aircraft maintenance element and suggested that he be allowed to provide a planning staff for duty at KFIA with the SOCCENT command element, but keep his aircraft at Al Jouf for better maintenance. When necessary, aircraft and crews could be provided for missions.

Colonel Johnson did not concur with Comer, and on 25 January, four aircraft and crews, and a portion of the 20th SOS maintenance team, flew to KFIA. Comer was not happy with the arrangement. However, he had come to realize that in the Army, the primary emphasis was on directly supporting the combat forces, and all other considerations were secondary. Colonel Johnson was the SOCCENT commander and had OPCON of the deployed element of 20th SOS. It was his call. However, he never developed a feel for the needs of his highly specialized AFSOC aviators. Gradually, Comer realized that the best way to deal with him was to use Colonels Gray and Orrell as conduits of sensibility and sound reason.[54]

Special Operations Missions

Colonel Comer's concern about his overutilization for rescue was also inadvertently addressed by events in the war. The diversion of the air campaign to attack the Iraqi surface-to-surface missile (Scud) did not completely dissuade Iraq from firing its missiles into both Saudi Arabia and Israel. When Israeli intervention with special forces and possibly air strikes looked imminent, the senior British commander in the Gulf, Sir Peter de la Billière, suggested to General Schwarzkopf that he be allowed to insert several British Special Air Service (SAS) teams into the western portions of Iraq to find and destroy the missiles. Schwarzkopf agreed and on 20 January, as both the Corvette 03 and Slate 46 efforts were under way, several teams entered Iraq—some by vehicle and some by insertion via RAF CH-47s.

Almost immediately the teams began harassing Iraqi forces and interdicting supply convoys. At SOCCENT headquarters, Colonel Gray suggested that the British elements provide a direct liaison officer to them for operational deconfliction. He also believed that the aviation support package sent with the British force was not sufficient to support their teams if they got in serious trouble and wanted to be able to provide support quickly with his larger force if it were needed.[55]

That need quickly appeared. The Iraqis reacted violently to the intrusions and engaged the British SAS teams in numerous stiff battles. One team, Bravo 20, was hit especially hard and had to evade. In the process, the team was split up as it tried to make its way to the Syrian border. On 27 and 28 January, Capt Corby Martin, Capt Bill Lemenager, and the crew flew two long missions with a British CH-47 from the RAF 7th Squadron in an attempt to find the remnants of Bravo 20. The Brits provided them the planned route that the team was supposed to follow, and Martin and crew led them along it using their Pave Low equipment. At one point, USAF F-15 pilots tracked the aircraft, but they left the rescue crews alone once they determined who they were. Regardless, both missions were unsuccessful. The crews learned later that only one troop from Bravo 20 made it to safety in Syria. The rest were either killed or captured.[56]

When the 20th moved its four helicopters and crews back to KFIA, Colonel Comer accompanied them so that he could deal directly with the SOCCENT leadership. Maj Mike Homan remained at Al Jouf to run the unit operation there. But Comer found himself with a significant challenge. His squadron was spread over a vast distance. He still had aircraft and crews back at Hurlburt working directly with other JSOC elements to develop contingency capabilities for operations in other areas of the world. He had two aircraft and three crews at Batman with the 21st. Now his unit element in Saudi Arabia was split between two locations, still sitting rescue alert as its primary mission but also supporting ongoing British SAS operations and now planning to operate with other SOCCENT elements. Comer had to rely on his young majors, captains, and NCOs to provide the necessary leadership for each of these dispersed teams. At KFIA he put Captain Harmon to work developing plans to work with SEALs on water operations in the Gulf. Harmon talked to the commander of the 71st SOS, the USAF Reserve unit activated and deployed to Saudi Arabia with its MH-3s. The aircraft had been modified with GPS receivers, and its pilots were trained to operate with NVGs. Harmon recalled that the aircraft were capable of landing on the water and suggested that they support the SEALs. The SEALs concurred, and Harmon designed a plan to utilize mixed flights of MH-53s and MH-3s to insert and cover the SEALs for missions in the northern Gulf region. On 6 February two Pave Lows, commanded by Harmon and Capt Jeff White, led a mission with H-3s from the 71st SOS to insert SEALs in the northern Gulf as planned. Comer also assigned White to work with Kuwaiti special forces and US Army Operational Detachment Alpha (ODA) special forces A-Team units to plan operations to insert their teams into Kuwait and possibly the adjoining areas of Iraq.[57]

As additional support for the anti-Scud effort in western Iraq, the SOCCOM commander, Gen Carl Stiner, recommended to General Schwarzkopf that SOCCOM deploy a JSOTF to Saudi Arabia for that purpose. Schwarzkopf was not a huge supporter of special forces and had been hesitant to allow such a force into his theater unless it was under his direct control. When the details were worked out, he allowed a task force of 400 operators—including two squadrons from the Delta Force, a company of Rangers, a small detachment of SEALs, and a portion of the 1st Battalion of the 160th SOAR commanded by Colonel Brown—to deploy to Arar. There they would be supported by a detachment of A-10s, the MH-47s from the 3d Battalion of the 160th SOAR, and possibly the Pave Lows of the 20th SOS.

The JSOTF package began to arrive on 30 January. As troops were unloading from the C-141s, the base was rocked by a large explosion and alarm warnings. Assuming it was a Scud attack, they scrambled for cover. The alarm was cancelled when the commanders there determined that the explosion was actually caused by a US Navy antiradiation missile that had erroneously homed in on the base TACAN station.

The JSOTF was led by Maj Gen Wayne Downing. He and his staff promptly began working with the British to learn from their successes and failures and to establish clearly defined areas of operation for deconfliction and maximum effectiveness. By mutual agreement, the British would work in areas close to the Saudi border, while US forces would utilize their aviation assets to operate farther north around the ever-dangerous city of Al Qaim.[58]

When General Downing discovered that the MH-47s of the 3d Battalion of the 160th SOAR lacked IRCM countermeasure equipment to protect them from the dangerous shoulder-fired, heat-seeking missiles like the SA-7, he requested that the 20th SOS support his operation. SOCCENT approved the request, and the 20th was so tasked—its fifth concurrent commitment. The aircraft and crews at Al Jouf would now have to maintain their rescue commitment while also supporting the JSOTF. Colonel Comer shuttled every other day between KFIA, Al Jouf, and Arar as he tried to keep a handle on the now scattered and separate operations of his unit. At one point, Colonel Gray, in looking forward to the evolution of the overall campaign, suggested that the unit might need to be able to move forward into Kuwait City to set up an operation there. Comer quickly pointed out that such a move would definitely require more aircraft and personnel from Hurlburt.

The first insertion mission for the JSOTF was conducted on 7 February. Captain Martin and crew led the mission, which also included Pave Lows commanded by Major Homan and Captain Kingsley and two MH-60s from the 1st Battalion, 160th SOAR. The Paves carried specially modified Pinzgauer fighting vehicles to be used by the teams. They were covered by an extensive support package of electronic jamming and strike aircraft. Because of the tactical needs of the inserted teams, the helicopters were loaded to their absolute top tactical weight of 50,000 pounds. Colonel Comer authorized this procedure based upon operational necessity and earnest discussions with his crews and maintenance personnel. Additionally, the length of the mission was such that the Pave Lows required an in-flight refueling from MC-130s from the 8th SOS. Arriving at the landing zone, the Pave Low pilots discovered that the aerial photos used to plan the mission had not shown some distinctive, dangerous variations in the terrain, forcing them to modify their procedures to safely deliver the team and its vehicles.[59]

Over the next three weeks, the 20th SOS Pave Lows and crews flew eight missions in direct support of the JSOTF, leading and sometimes being led by the helicopters of the 1st of the 160th. Frequently operating at their maximum weight of 50,000 pounds, they inserted teams and their fighting vehicles and necessary supplies as the special troops attacked Iraqi facilities, searched for Scud missiles, disrupted Iraqi communications, and generally wreaked havoc on the enemy forces and bases. Reminiscent of their training missions in the 1980s, the Pave Low crews—commanded by Major Homan and Captains Corby Martin, Mike Kingsley, Tim Minish, and Kevin Ewing—became adept at doing detailed planning with the ground and aviation elements and flew with flights of MH-47s and MH-60s over the trackless desert, wadis, and hills through the dark night.

Captain Minish and Capt Tim Brown and crew led another mission on 17 February with three MH-47s and two MH-60s to insert a ground team and vehicles deep into Iraq. The delivery flight was uneventful, but they had difficulty getting the heavy helicopters into the landing zone because of brownout conditions that forced two crews to abort their initial landing attempts and circle for another approach. Upon landing, the back ramp on the Pave Low would not properly lower so that the vehicle being carried could be unloaded. Fortunately, the flight engineers and gunners were able to resolve the problem and unload the special vehicle so that the ground team could execute its mission.[60]

The JSOTF senior Army officers were impressed with the performance of the 20th crews, displanting years of misunderstanding and distrust. They were especially impressed with Martin. He was already lean and mean-looking and flew in BDUs instead of the darker flight suit. Additionally, he had grown a thick, bushy mustache that the grunts all wanted to copy. However, they were most taken with his self-confidence. It was a confidence based on mastery of his aircraft, mission experience, and nine months in-theater—all leavened with a steep dose of a direct-assault mentality. Said Martin,

> You get so you are part of the machine. . . . I felt that I was part of the helicopter. It was part of me, part of my body. When I scratched my nuts, it scratched its nuts. I felt that way. I was a captain. I was impervious—bulletproof! . . . Young to senior captains—all we did was fly. When you do that every day for almost a year, you get very good at it.

> [We had] the mentality "let's get the mission done. Let's do it right. Let's do it the way it's supposed to be done."[61]

Comer continually shuttled back and forth from KFIA to Al Jouf and Arar to maintain contact with his crews and liaise with Colonel Brown, the commander of the 1st of the 160th, concerning the aviation support of the JSOTF. Brown was now assigned as the air component commander for the JSOTF and was also a firm member of the "Soldiers should fly with Soldiers" clan. Comer believed that Brown constantly looked for ways to push his aircraft and crews vice the Pave Lows for missions. Strangely enough, he also found among many of his Air Force brethren a belief that the USAF should just go with the flow and let the Army have the SOF aviation mission à la

Initiative 17. Comer found such talk infuriating, believing that "we had the best machines and the best thinkers about how to execute long range missions. . . . Our doctrine had given us the aircraft and trained us to do this job in DESERT STORM better than anyone else could."[62] He was resolved that he would fight tirelessly to insure that his unit and troops got the missions for which they were uniquely and best qualified. That disparity was put on graphic display in the dark night of 21 February. A special forces Soldier was injured in the western area and needed to be evacuated. An MH-60 from the 1st of the 160th was dispatched to pick him up. When the aircraft returned to Arar, the field was blanketed in a thick shroud of fog. The Pave Lows routinely operated in and out of it; unfortunately, the MH-60 was not so equipped. While trying to land in the restricted visibility, the crew crashed, killing all seven Soldiers on board.[63]

As the missions with the JSOTF were proceeding, Colonel Comer was spending more and more time working with the commanders at SOCCENT as they developed ground and sea special operations forces missions to support the planned ground campaign designed to drive the Iraqi forces out of Kuwait. He spoke several times with Colonel Correll back at Hurlburt and discovered that the squadron there had just received new chemical warfare flying suits, and several crew members had certified flying with them. Comer approached Colonel Gray about bringing over Correll, two more Pave Low aircraft, and several of the crews trained on the chemical warfare suit as reinforcements for the ground campaign. Gray concurred and arrangements were made to do so. Comer also asked that the two 20th SOS aircraft and crews at Batman be transferred down south with his detachment. He received one of the 20th crews but not the aircraft.

Additionally, Comer observed the planning that Capt Paul Harmon and Capt Jeff White were doing to involve the Pave Lows in SEAL operations in the Gulf and deep penetration strategic reconnaissance missions into Kuwait and Iraq with Army ODA teams. He also developed an excellent relationship with CW3 Vernon Ward, the ground liaison supervisor in SOCCENT, who helped him understand the needs of the special teams who would perform these missions. Ward had an uncanny understanding of Army internal politics and mentored Comer on that minefield too.

Captain Harmon's detailed planning paid dividends when, on 12 February, a Pave Low led a 55th SOS MH-60G and two 71st SOS MH-3s on a mission to insert SEAL elements into the waters of the northern Gulf. The teams were being inserted for several covert missions preparatory to the massive ground campaign designed to eject Iraqi forces from Kuwait. Over the next 11 days, Captains Harmon, White, and Sipperly led crews several more times to repeat this mission as the SEALs collected intelligence data and helped support the deception plan designed to convince the Iraqis that a large amphibious landing would be conducted upon the shores of Kuwait. On 22 February another crew, led by Capt Joe Turnage and copilot Capt Brad Webb, flew as part of a joint four-ship formation to insert more allied teams in support of this operation.[64]

Captain Trask and his crew were assigned a mission to place an Army ODA deep into Iraq to intercept and stop a train by setting off a charge under the engine. They derisively titled it the "Throw Mohammed from the Train" mission, hijacking the title of a Hollywood movie then popular. But the Army team members would not completely destroy the train. Instead, they would board it and search for specific pieces of equipment. Once the equipment was found, they would abandon the disabled train, blocking the tracks for several days. The team rehearsed the mission several times near KFIA before repositioning to Al Jouf for the execution order. However, it was never ordered to go. Instead, after 10 days the mission was cancelled, and Trask and his crew were released for general tasking—after missing several opportunities to fly other missions.[65]

Also working closely with Chief Warrant Officer Ward in the SOCCENT command center, Captain White formulated the plans to support the infiltration of Army special forces deep into Iraq to support the allied ground campaign, now slated to start on 24 February, to pressure the Iraqi forces out of Kuwait. On 23 February, Captains Mike Kingsley, Frank Gray, Jeff White, Joe Turnage, Mike Beard, Kevin Ewing, and Ken Sipperly led crews that flew up to 150 miles into Iraqi territory to deposit Army ODA teams. Their mission was to overwatch key roads for possible movement of Iraqi forces as they reacted to the movements of the VIIth Corps and XVIIIth Airborne Corps preparing to sweep into Iraq to envelop and trap the Republican Guard forces of Iraq ensconced in Kuwait. Each mission was challenging in its own way. When one of the aircraft experienced a severe hydraulic malfunction, its flight engineers were able to repair it at the team site while the Soldiers provided security. The special forces team that Kingsley and crew inserted was compromised as it began to set up its hide site and had to be immediately extracted. In

WAR IN THE DESERT | 327

the confusion that ensued, Kingsley and crew became critically short on gas and had to arrange for an in-flight refueling in enemy territory. Overall, the crews averaged over two and a half hours behind enemy lines.[66]

The next morning, General Schwarzkopf unleashed his allied ground forces. As the battle was unfolding, the Pave Low crews of the 20th were also constantly supporting the British and JSOTF forces in the west with resupply, infiltration, and extraction missions. On 24 February, Captain Harmon and Major Homan and crews led two MH-47s and two MH-60s on another mission deep into western Iraq to insert another 20-man special forces team and four special vehicles. Both Pave Lows were, again, over their authorized maximum gross weight. They proceeded to their assigned landing zone as supporting air strikes hit known enemy locations around which they had to maneuver. The mission proceeded normally until the helicopters departed to return home. En route, Harmon's Pave Low developed a fuel transfer problem. An MC-130 tanker was able to rendezvous with the flight just north of the Saudi-Iraqi border and provide it with enough fuel to return to Arar.[67]

On another mission on 26 February, Capt Tom Trask and crew planned and led a joint flight of Pave Lows and several helicopters from the 1st Battalion of the 160th SOAR on a mission to deliver two teams of Army Rangers to neutralize a communications center near the Jordanian border. The site was heavily defended, and the attack had to be coordinated with significant covering air strikes to neutralize the enemy AAA and SAM positions in the area. The Rangers were able to destroy the facility and collect a great deal of significant intelligence data. During the egress back to Saudi Arabia, the helicopters had to take extensive evasive actions to avoid enemy air defense sites.[68]

The next day, three Pave Lows, flown by Captains White, Webb, and Minish and crews, led six other helicopters on two sorties into the Kuwait International Airport, just south of Kuwait City. Flying at maximum weight through the thunderstorms and thick smoke created by the burning oil heads set alight by the now retreating Iraqi forces, the crews had to use their NVGs. They also had to maneuver around the massive allied forces sweeping through the area and then land on the airfield, littered with wrecked aircraft and vehicles, mines, and unexploded ordnance. Regardless, they delivered their teams, who were then able to secure the field for immediate use by allied aviation forces. Lt Col Gene Correll had recently returned to the theater and flew the first mission with Webb. He then remained at the airfield to determine if the Pave Lows could use it as an FOL.[69]

Flying over the devastated landscape, the crews encountered an unusual problem. The slimy oil sludge from the plumes of smoke coated the aircraft and was difficult to scrub off. The sludge collected grime and began to build up on the aircraft. Fortunately, it did not affect the FLIR radar or navigation systems, and the crews carried on with their missions, deferring any significant sludge removal until hostilities ended—hopefully soon. Through this mess, Webb and his crew also flew two missions directly supporting US Navy SEALs working along the coastlines.[70]

By 28 February, the allied coalition forces had achieved all of their objectives, and President Bush declared a cease-fire, effective at 8 a.m. Kuwaiti time. Regardless, the Pave Lows continued to fly. Just before the cease-fire, Captain Webb and crew helped deliver the first US forces to the American Embassy so that it could be returned to US control. Three Pave Lows led by Capt Doug Moore and crew flew to the Kuwait International Airport carrying 13 personnel. Two of the crews were then put on rescue alert there. Two hours later, Moore and his crew were launched to search for an emergency beacon that had been heard about 40 miles north of Kuwait City, near where a US Marine had gone down a few days earlier. They flew through poor weather mixed with the sooty oil smoke over Iraqi fortifications and abandoned equipment but did not observe any hostile actions by enemy forces. The next day, those two Pave Lows were tasked to fly a search for an F-16 pilot shot down in Kuwait on 27 February and an Army helicopter crew also shot down while trying to rescue him. They did not find the pilot or helicopter crew, discovering later that all had either been killed or taken prisoner. That afternoon another Pave Low led seven other helicopters as they flew to western Iraq and recovered members of the JSOTF. Three days later, three Pave Lows flew deep into Iraq to recover more JSOTF teams and their vehicles and ODAs emplaced to support the ground campaign. Capt Jeff White led one of the flights. His copilot, Capt Tim Leahy, was a brand new Pave Low pilot. He had finished his Pave Low course at Kirtland in January and, after reporting to Hurlburt, was shipped directly to the 20th detachment in the Gulf, where he quickly received his initial aircraft mission qualification and was inserted into the flying schedule. His transition went well—a testimony to the excellent training that the 1551st FTS was conducting. These were the last Pave Low sorties of the conflict.[71]

With the cease-fire, General Schwarzkopf began to release units for return home. He decreed that units would redeploy based upon their arrival dates in the theater. The 20th would be one of the first units released, and that evening, Comer let Captain Martin and Captain Kingsley and several enlisted troops catch a C-141 for home. However, Comer was directed to leave three Pave Lows and four crews in Saudi Arabia for what would ultimately become Southern Watch. They subsequently flew humanitarian missions to several locations in Kuwait and southern Iraq and also flew support to recover the bodies of the crew of Spirit 03, an AC-130 shot down on 31 January 1991 off the coast of Kuwait.[72]

Throughout the period of the conflict, Comer insisted that all crew members got an equal opportunity to fly in combat. In all, 39 pilots, 35 engineers, and 35 gunners logged combat sorties. During the Desert Shield/Storm deployment between August 1990 and March 1991, the 20th SOS flew 1,946 hours on 920 sorties, of which 806 hours and 360 sorties were in combat. Of those, 49 sorties were flown into enemy territory. Several unit members received key recognition for their time in the Gulf: Capt Corby Martin was selected as the AFSOC pilot of the year as well as the Col James Jabara Award recipient for 1992; Capt Mike Kingsley, the AFSOC company grade officer of the year; Maj Mark Cunningham, the AFSOC and USAF flight surgeon of the year; and Capt Tom Trask and his crew, the Cheney Award recipients for 1991. Additionally, Comer began working with his commanders and the personnel assignment system to move some of the exceptionally high performers into key positions within the wing, AFSOC, and even the larger USAF.[73]

The outstanding squadron that Lt Col Rich Comer had taken over from Lt Col Gary Weikel had just gotten better. And some of the members of the unit had learned some immutable truths applicable to their trade. Trask felt that some of his Pave Low brethren had developed a cockiness bordering on rashness that was held in check by communal self-policing. He observed,

> I think that there was an element of the Pave Low community that was really done right. . . . You got forced by your peers to focus on where you were and what you were doing right at that moment. Anybody who ever tried to get too grandiose . . . was put back in his place pretty quickly. . . . You could tell if guys were getting out in front of their headlights a lot. You weren't allowed to do

that in our business. It became part of our culture . . . the way you trained [to] focus on the task in front of you and make sure that every day you are preparing and training as thoroughly and realistically as possible.[74]

Martin offered a similar view but one more focused on working with the various "customer" groups in JSOC, a critical element of Pave Low operations. He remarked that "if they [JSOC] know who you are and know that you are not an idiot, they'll work with you. If they think you are an idiot, they won't even talk to you. You'll never get in the door."[75]

These were two lessons passed down to these young captains by the men of that earlier generation who mentored them. Such lessons were validated by the experiences of hard combat and then passed on to those who would follow in the business of Pave Low. They were staples of a "unit with confidence," just as they were for those units at Koh Tang Island.[76]

Three months after the unit returned to Hurlburt Field, Trask and crew had an opportunity to fly a Pave Low to the Air Force Academy for a recruiting visit. They landed their helicopter in the middle of the grassy area between the chapel and other buildings. Many cadets paid the crew a visit. Several young cadets—Mike Grub, Shawn Cameron, Steve Plumhoff, Leighton Anderson, Pete Doty, Joe Michalek, and others—were quite impressed with the aircraft and intrigued with the mission. Michalek got the opportunity to take an incentive ride along the face of the mountains, quite a treat for a cadet third class—as it was for cadet Rich Comer, who also received such a ride 21 years prior. The three cadets decided that they wanted to fly Pave Lows. Little did they know that this choice would take them on a journey that would fulfill their desires in places and ways that, at that moment, they could not even imagine.[77]

21st Special Operations Squadron

While the tactical assets in Proven Force were quite active, attacking targets in Iraq on a daily basis, the operations schedule for the special operations forces was much more benign. After the Corvette 03 nonrecovery, the 21st SOS crews maintained 24/7 JSAR alert. A Pave Low was launched on 20 February for an F-16 that missed a tanker and was critically short of fuel. The aircraft flamed out short of Incirlik, and the pilot ejected. He was recovered by Turkish forces before the Pave Low could arrive. On several occasions the crews also planned and practiced missions with the troops from the 10th SFG. However, no special operations missions were executed. One crew did fly in support of a classified mission for another governmental agency, and several flew in support of explosive ordnance disposal taskings. Regardless, the crews of the 21st did log 196 sorties for 381.9 flying hours during their deployment. By 18 March, all members of the 21st SOS returned to their home station at RAF Woodbridge.[78]

Provide Comfort

Their homecoming was short-lived. After the crushing defeat of Iraq's military forces, minority groups within the country rose up in open rebellion against Saddam Hussein. He used his remaining military forces to crush them. One of the groups was the Kurds, located essentially in the northern quarter of Iraq. As Saddam's forces attacked, an estimated 700,000 fled for their lives into the cold and snow-covered mountains along the northern Iraq-Turkey border. They lacked all basic necessities of life. It was a potential humanitarian disaster of the first order. On 5 April, the United Nations Security Council passed Resolution 688, calling upon Iraq to stop its repression and asking other nations to assist the Kurds. President Bush ordered US military forces to do so. The orders quickly flowed to USEUCOM and USAFE, and the 39th SOW was directly tasked to again deploy M/HC-130 and MH-53 aircraft, crews, and support personnel to southeastern Turkey for Operation Provide Comfort. The second week of April, the 21st SOS shipped all five of its MH-53s aboard C-5s to Incirlik, with 47 personnel. When the scope of the tasking became clearer, the 39th SOW commander, Col Byron Hooten, requested augmentation of his helicopter forces and received two more MH-53s from Hurlburt and 13 more aircrewmen and support personnel from Hurlburt and Kirtland.

The forces of the 21st SOS joined what eventually became a combined joint task force (CJTF) of personnel from 13 different nations, including a force of 52 helicopters and almost 21,000 personnel, military and civilian. They supported a sprawling mass of refugees sequestered in an area centered on the small city of Zakho, approximately 150 by 40 kilometers. The 21st SOS crews were assigned duty as the CJTF rescue force and assumed 24/7 alert. A 21st SOS crew did perform a SAR mission when a US Marine CH-53E crashed.

In addition, their capabilities as heavy-lift helicopters were constantly put to good use as they ferried VIPs and task force personnel, moved huge loads of supplies and materiel, performed area reconnaissance, and accomplished medical evacuation missions that resulted in seven saved lives. In many cases, it was the same types of missions that their predecessors with the 21st SOS in Thailand had performed over 20 years prior.

With the coming of spring, though, allied leaders felt that the situation was stabilizing and began to withdraw the coalition forces. Additionally, ground vehicles were able to take over for the aircraft, and the 39th SOW elements were released to return to their bases. All of the MH-53 aircraft, personnel, and augmentees were home by 10 June 1991.[79]

Sensing allied weakness, Saddam Hussein ordered his forces to intimidate the Kurds. As a show of force, allied fighter aircraft began patrolling the airspace over the region to enforce a cease-fire as part of Provide Comfort II. On 23 July, four MH-53s, crews, and support personnel from the 21st SOS again returned to Incirlik to assume JSAR alert in support of the fighters now flying in the no-fly area. A few days after arriving, though, maintenance technicians inspecting one of the MH-53s discovered serious cracks near the hinge point on the tail boom. The aircraft was immediately grounded and flown by C-5 to Pensacola. There technicians determined that airframe vibrations caused the cracks. Inspections of several other MH-53s found the same problem, and all MH-53s were inspected and identified for repair as necessary. However, the repairs had to be done at Pensacola. All of the 21st SOS aircraft had the same cracks and were grounded for an unspecified period pending repair. Consequently, the 39th SOW had to request augmentation to fulfill the JSAR mission at Incirlik. The 55th SOS at Hurlburt received the tasking and dispatched four MH-60G "Pave Hawk" crews and support personnel to assume the JSAR role for the task force. 21st SOS personnel returned to RAF Woodbridge but were not able to fly again until their aircraft were repaired and returned to the unit in December 1991.[80]

Notes

1. Rip and Hasik, *Precision Revolution*, 75; and Whitcomb, *Combat Search and Rescue in Desert Storm*, 44, 248.

2. Murray and Thompson, *Air War in the Persian Gulf*, 32; and Whitcomb, *Combat Search and Rescue in Desert Storm*, 43.

3. Ibid.

4. Joe Becker, interview.

5. Comer, "History of Desert Shield / Desert Storm," 1–5, 1st/16th SOW HO.

6. Correll, interview.

7. Kradel, interview.

8. Ibid.

9. Comer and Gray, interviews; and Stricklin to the author, e-mail, review comments, 23 Jan 11.

10. Bergeron, *Desert Shield / Desert Storm*, 13, 25–26, AFSOC/HO.

11. Comer, "History of Desert Shield / Desert Storm," 10–18, 24, 1st/16th SOW HO.

12. Whitcomb, *Combat Search and Rescue in Desert Storm*, 46–47; and Schemmer, "No USAF Combat Rescue Aircraft in Gulf," 37.

13. Gray, interview by the author, 3 May 2001, for Whitcomb, *Combat Search and Rescue in Desert Storm*, 48.

14. Ibid., 47–48; and Clancy, Stiner, and Koltz, *Shadow Warriors*, 47–48.

15. Kingsley, interview.

16. Whitcomb, *Combat Search and Rescue in Desert Storm*, 68–69.

17. Ibid., 62.

18. Ibid., 62–63.

19. Ibid., 58–59.

20. Ibid., 67–68; and Trask, interview.

21. Whitcomb, *Combat Search and Rescue in Desert Storm*, 82–84.

22. Comer, "History of Desert Shield / Desert Storm," 45–46, 1st/16th SOW HO; and Kingsley, interview.

23. Kingsley, interview.

24. Bergeron, *Desert Shield / Desert Storm*, 77–83, AFSOC/HO; and Comer, "History of Desert Shield / Desert Storm," 23, 1st/16th SOW HO.

25. Comer, interview.

26. Comer, "History of Desert Shield / Desert Storm," 28–32, 1st/16th SOW HO; and Clancy, Stiner, and Koltz, *Shadow Warriors*, 410.

27. Kradel, interview.

28. Whitcomb, *Combat Search and Rescue in Desert Storm*, 67.

29. Ibid., 82–83.

30. Comer, "History of Desert Shield / Desert Storm," 23, 48–49, 1st/16th SOW HO; and Comer and Webb, interviews.

31. Whitcomb, *Combat Search and Rescue in Desert Storm*, 73–74; Thigpen, *Praetorian Starship*, 357; and Bergeron, *Desert Shield / Desert Storm*, AFSOC/HO, 41.

32. History of 39th SOW, 1 Jan–30 June 1990, vol. 3.

33. Ibid.

34. History of 39th SOW, 1 July 1990–31 Dec 1991, vol. 1, 20–34.

35. History of AFSOC, 1 Jan 1990–31 Dec 1991, vol. 1, 316.

36. Sprouse, interview.

37. Whitcomb, *Combat Search and Rescue in Desert Storm*, 85; and History of AFSOC, 1 Jan 1990–31 Dec 1991, vol. 1, 299–301.

38. Whitcomb, *Combat Search and Rescue in Desert Storm*, 86; Bergeron, *Desert Shield / Desert Storm*, 76–77, AFSOC/HO; and Trask, interview.

39. Kingsley, interview. Pave Low aircraft and crews on the Eager Anvil mission were as follows:

White Team

Lead–MH-53J #68-10356

Pilot	Capt Mike Kingsley
Copilot	Capt Mike Beard
Flt. Eng.	Sgt Todd Corey
Flt. Eng.	MSgt Robert Pinkowski
Gunner	MSgt Robert Jensen
Gunner	SSgt Dennis Shindle

Chalk 2–MH-53J #68-10367

Pilot	Maj Bob Leonik
Copilot	Lt Col Rich Comer
Flt. Eng.	TSgt Dan Sherriff
Flt. Eng.	SSgt Bob Rice
Gunner	Sgt Mike Pearce
Gunner	Sgt John Summers

Red Team

Lead–MH-53J #70-1630

Pilot	Capt Corby Martin
Copilot	Capt Bill Lemenager
Flt. Eng.	MSgt Mike Lael
Flt. Eng.	SSgt Mike Harte
Gunner	SSgt Barry Harrison
Gunner	Sgt Phil Carrol

Chalk 2–MH-53J #68-10369

Pilot	Capt Ben Pulsifer
Copilot	Capt Penny Woodson
Flt. Eng.	Sgt Tom Hinson
Flt. Eng.	SSgt Melvin Wells
Gunner	TSgt Phillip Taylor
Gunner	TSgt Terry Null

40. Comer, Kingsley, and Martin, interviews.

41. Martin, interview.

42. Headquarters, 1st Battalion, 101st Aviation Regiment (AH–64), Eager Anvil, after action report, file 500.600, TF Normandy, 1st/16th SOW HO; and Martin, interview.

43. Kingsley, interview.

44. Whitcomb, *Combat Search and Rescue in Desert Storm*, 90–92; Bergeron, *Desert Shield / Desert Storm*, 85–87, AFSOC/HO; Schemmer, "USAF MH–53J Pave Lows Led Army Apaches"; and Comer, interview.

45. Whitcomb, *Combat Search and Rescue in Desert Storm*, 99. The story of the sad loss of Lt Cdr Michael Speicher is told in *No One Left Behind* by Amy Yarsinske. His remains were repatriated in 2009.

46. Whitcomb, *Combat Search and Rescue in Desert Storm*, 100–110, 260.

47. Ibid., 117–18.

48. Ibid., 127.

49. Whitcomb, "Nonrescue of Corvette 03," 111.

50. Ibid.; Whitcomb, *Combat Search and Rescue in Desert Storm*, 122–37; and Martin, interview.

51. Trask, interview.

52. Whitcomb, *Combat Search and Rescue in Desert Storm*, 151.

53. Ibid., 142–52; Paul Johnson, "Desert Rescue," essay 22, in Vriesenga, *From the Line in the Sand*, 177–84; and McConnell, "Rescue in Iraq!," 75–82.

54. Comer, "History of Desert Shield / Desert Storm," 58–59, 1st/16th SOW HO.

55. Waller, *Commandos*, 340; and Gray, interview.

56. Waller, *Commandos*, 431; "Chronology of Desert Storm Missions," n.d., 1st/16th SOW HO; and Martin, interview.

57. Comer, "History of Desert Shield / Desert Storm," 62–64, 1st/16th SOW HO; and mission narrative for both events, n.d., 20th SOS, historical files, 1st/16th SOW HO.

58. Gordon and Trainor, *Generals' War*, 244.

59. Comer, "History of Desert Shield / Desert Storm," 65–67, 1st/16th SOW HO; and Martin and Kingsley, interviews.

60. Mission narrative, n.d., 20th SOS, historical files, 1st/16th SOW HO.

61. Martin, interview.

62. Comer, "History of Desert Shield / Desert Storm," 65–67, 78–79, 83, 1st/16th SOW HO.

63. Ibid., 65–67, 78–79, 83; Gordon and Trainor, *Generals' War*, 246; "Chronology of Desert Storm Missions," n.d., file 500.608, 1st/16th SOW HO; Waller, *Commandos*, 345; and Martin, interview.

64. "Chronology of Desert Storm Missions," n.d., file 500.608, 1st/16th SOW HO; Gordon and Trainor, *Generals' War*, 368–69; Clancy and Horner, *Every Man a Tiger*, 319; and mission narrative, n.d., 20th SOS, historical files, 1st/16th SOW HO. Col Corby Martin, USAF, retired, supplied mission data.

65. Trask, interview.

66. Kingsley, interview.

67. Mission narrative, n.d., 20th SOS, historical files, 1st/16th SOW HO.

68. Trask, interview.

69. Correll, interview.

70. Webb, interview.

71. "Chronology of Desert Storm Missions," n.d., file 500.608, 1st/16th SOW HO; Col Corby Martin, USAF, retired, Desert Storm log, provided to the author; Comer, "History of Desert Shield / Desert Storm," 85–88, 1st/16th SOW HO; mission narrative, n.d., 20th SOS, historical files, 1st/16th SOW HO; and Williams to the author, e-mail, 24 Jan 2011.

72. Kingsley, interview.

73. Trask, interview.

74. Ibid.

75. Martin, interview.

76. Guilmartin, *Very Short War*, 41–42.

77. Grub to the author, e-mail.

78. Whitcomb, *Combat Search and Rescue in Desert Storm*, 200; and History of 39th SOW, 1 July 1990–31 Dec 1991, vol. 3, 2–43.

79. History of 39th SOW, 1 July 1990–31 Dec 1991, vol. 1, 35–42.

80. Ibid., 43–44, 66.

Chapter 10

Interim Years—Volcanoes, Challenge, and Change

~ 1991–93

As air commandos, we stay a step ahead of any adversary by anticipating and responding to changing demands.

—Maj Gen Bruce Fister

31st Special Operations Squadron

On 5 August 1990, as the 20th SOS was packing up to deploy to the Gulf, the 31st SOS at Clark AB, Philippines, received its first two MH-53Js. It had already received several fully qualified crew members from Kirtland, although several key maintenance personnel were yet to arrive. Regardless, the squadron recorded its first Pave Low flights just three days later. The next week, Lt Col Dale Cook relinquished the unit to Lt Col Lee Massey, and the unit flew a mixed fleet of MH-53s and H-3s until 26 September, when two more MH-53s arrived. The H-3s were then shipped back to the United States, and the 31st was a full-fledged MH-53 squadron. The unit began a steady training program to qualify its crews for the panoply of missions assigned to them. For the next several months, the crews deployed to various joint and coalition training exercises, such as Extended Knight and Aqua Wally II in the Philippines, Thailand, Malaysia, Japan, and Korea. They focused on day/night water infiltration and exfiltration procedures utilizing inflatable boat drops, fast rope and rope ladder procedures, hoist operations, and short-field landings, especially with US, Philippine, and Thai Navy SEAL teams and US Army ODAs. The crews also maintained alert for peacetime emergency rescue and humanitarian operations and provided VIP transport when requested by Headquarters Thirteenth Air Force, also at Clark AB. By the end of the year, the unit had several crews trained but had only 45 of 64 authorized personnel.[1]

Capt Joe Becker arrived at Clark AB in October for his assignment as the flight examiner for the 31st SOS. However, he did not bring his wife and new daughter, Emily. Before departing he was notified that because of an increased threat to US personnel in the Philippines, he could not take his dependents for an accompanied tour. Becker tried to change his orders but could not. He also tried to resign from the Air Force but was denied that because Pave Low crew members were blocked from leaving by "stop-loss" policies initiated as part of the military response for Desert Storm.

When Becker got to Clark AB, he was met by his squadron commander, Colonel Massey, who also expected to see Becker's wife and child. Becker explained what he had been told. Massey checked and found out that as soon as Becker had on-base housing, he could bring them over. Becker arranged their travel, and the personnel office at Clark amended his assignment to an accompanied 24-month tour with the 31st.[2]

By January 1991 Captain Becker had housing, and his family joined him. While awaiting their arrival, he joined the 31st SOS and integrated into the operation. The training and deployment pattern continued as the Airmen of the 31st worked to develop full mission capability and integrate their skills into those of the 353d SOW. This routine was soon to be interrupted by events from an entirely unexpected quarter, changing life irrevocably for everyone at Clark AB.

Mount Pinatubo

Clark AB, located on the Philippine main island of Luzon, had been in existence in some form since US forces arrived in the area in 1898. From that simple beginning, it had grown into the largest US military facility outside of the United States. It was home to the Thirteenth Air Force, the 3d TFW, the 353d SOW, and many subordinate units; an estimated 20,000 US active and retired military lived in the immediate area.

Unfortunately, that region of Luzon was seismically active. In July 1990, the area suffered a severe earthquake that killed almost 2,000 people. The 31st launched numerous humanitarian relief missions as part of the recovery efforts. More ominously, though, Mount Pinatubo—a rather unobtrusive 5,700-foot-high peak located just 10 miles southwest of the air base—began to spew white smoke on 2 April

1991. US Geological Survey (USGS) scientists indicated that an accompanying explosion had spread out ash as far as six miles. They quickly installed monitoring equipment and determined that molten lava was rising below the mountain: a major eruption could be expected within one year.

Over the next month, the seismic activity steadily increased. USGS specialists dramatically advanced their estimates, now stating that the mountain could erupt at any time. Unit commanders scrambled to develop evacuation plans for personnel and equipment. The 3d TFW was already in the process of drawing down, and most of its assigned F-4 aircraft had been ferried back to the CONUS. However, all residual aircraft and assigned personnel had to be cared for. Col Lee Hess, the 353d SOW commander, worked closely with Maj Gen William Studer, the Thirteenth Air Force commander, and Col Jeff Grime, the 3d TFW commander, to coordinate the mass move of their equipment and personnel to NAS Cubi Point, Subic Bay Naval Base, and other smaller locations throughout the Philippines. As information became available, it was broadcast to all US personnel through the base television station and printed media. Detailed evacuation planning guides were developed and passed out to all. Personnel were told to expect a short-duration evacuation and then a return to Clark.

In the early morning hours of 9 June, USGS technicians observed that pressure was building up below the mountain so rapidly that a major explosion could be expected within 24 hours. When briefed, General Studer directed the evacuation of all aircraft and personnel. As base personnel gathered, with only a minimum of personal items, to form preplanned convoys, the 31st SOS launched three of its Pave Lows to Cubi Point. A fourth, undergoing heavy maintenance, flew out the next day. Crew members on unaccompanied tours were assigned to fly the aircraft out. Per Colonel Massey's directions, the rest of the 31st personnel rallied at the squadron building at 5:30 a.m. They were in 30 vehicles, and Captain Becker organized them into groups of 10, each group equipped with short-range radios for coordination. They then joined 14,000 other base personnel on the 52-mile, six-and-a-half-hour journey to NAS Cubi Point and a few other smaller locations, as the 31st SOS Pave Lows flew traffic escort. Arriving at their destinations, the Clark Airmen were met by local personnel, who scrambled to find whatever space they could for so many short-notice "guests." All 31st SOS personnel went to Cubi Point. Joe

Becker knew several members of the USN SEAL detachment there, including the unit executive officer, Lt Cdr Bob Harward, who made arrangements for the group to move into the air-conditioned unit classroom and use the facility bathrooms until something better could be arranged with Navy families on base. Within a day, Becker and his family moved in with the family of a USN warrant officer.[3]

A predesignated group of 1,500 Airmen, mostly security personnel and engineers, stayed behind at Clark. At Cubi, all four Pave Lows were put in one of the hangars and protected as much as possible from the looming threat.

Courtesy 353d SOG History Office

Mount Pinatubo explosion

At 8:50 a.m. on 12 June, Mount Pinatubo erupted. A horrendous column of thick brownish-gray ash began climbing skyward, eventually reaching 70,000 feet. The 31st SOS put two aircraft and crews on alert for possible rescue duty. Collateral explosions continued until the morning of 15 June, when, in one huge multihour, climactic eruption, a pyroclastic lava mass began to flow down into the valleys. More than six miles of the mountain ridgeline rose simultaneously and dissolved into a massive blanket of ash, twice as large in volume as the Mount St. Helens explosion in Washington State in 1980. The ground shook violently in tune with the eruptions. Unfortunately, as the mountain was going through its angry spasms, a tropical storm,

Typhoon Yunya, swept the area and dumped seven inches of rain. It mixed with the ash and fell to the ground as a sticky goo that covered everything. At times Becker went outside and was shocked to see that it was almost as dark as night. Clark AB was now blanketed under up to 10 inches of the muck. Many buildings collapsed under the weight or were damaged by the flooding caused by the rainfall. Clark AB was no longer a functioning facility.

The ash also covered Subic Bay and Cubi Point, in some places eight inches thick. Power lines were down, and the electricity was off. As base personnel began to dig out from under the gooey mess, the damage was immediately obvious. At the direction of the US Embassy, all Clark dependents would be evacuated to the CONUS or other Pacific USAF bases. They would not be allowed to return to Clark, even to retrieve their personal belongings or pets. Several US Navy ships—including the USS *Midway*, USS *Abraham Lincoln*, and USS *Long Beach*—pulled into Subic and loaded the evacuee families for transport to the island of Cebu, where they were met with MAC and charter aircraft to fly them back to the CONUS. The troops of the 31st SOS were declared mission essential and would remain at Cubi with their aircraft, pending relocation decisions. Consequently, the 31st SOS dependents were processed for return to the United States through Guam. Becker and his squadron mates delivered their dependents and pets and what little they were able to carry for movement to the ships. Susan and Emily Becker traveled to her parents' home in Portland, Oregon, where both arrived sick. They also had to ship their dogs. Unfortunately, all animals had to go through inspection at Guam, and their dogs finally arrived in Portland after a lengthy delay, and much the worse for wear. Many other 21st SOS, 353d SOW, Air Force, and Navy families shared the same fate.[4]

The Pave Lows were safely ensconced in their assigned hangar and were not harmed. Colonel Hess was notified that the 353d SOW would be temporarily relocating to Kadena AB, Okinawa. He submitted a request through channels for sealift to move the Pave Lows to Okinawa. On 26 June, the USS *Midway* steamed back into Subic Bay, and three of the Pave Lows were flown aboard. The fourth was not flyable because of missing parts. Three days later, the three aircraft were flown off of the *Midway* to USMC Air Station Futenma, located six miles south of Kadena. When the fourth aircraft was finally flyable six days later, its crew flew it to Futenma with an HC-130 escort from the 17th SOS.

The Airmen of the 31st SOS were somewhat taken aback about being placed at Futenma vice Kadena. However, the placement was determined by the 313th Air Division commander, Brig Gen Joseph Hurd. He commanded the USAF units on Okinawa and was very concerned about anti-US sentiment among the population around Kadena. He believed that while the MC-130s would blend in well at Kadena, the MH-53s would be noticeable and potentially antagonizing. He further reasoned that the MH-53s would more easily blend in with the USMC helicopters at Futenma and received permission from the commander there to place the Pave Lows on the parking ramp temporarily. Henceforth, the 31st Airmen were designated "Hurd's Kurds."[5]

As the eruptions of Pinatubo abated, recovery teams began to return to Clark to assess the damage and begin the cleanup on base—the recovery of hundreds of pieces of equipment and the salvage of whatever supplies possible. Because of the widespread destruction, Clark would no longer be an active USAF base. The Philippine government decided not to renew the US lease of the base, and by July, US and Philippine officials signed documents directing the United States to withdraw all forces from Clark. Like other units, personnel from the 31st went to the homes of their evacuated members and shipped their hastily left-behind personal belongings and pets to wherever the Airmen and families had been reassigned. By November all 353d SOW personnel either had relocated to Okinawa or had been returned to the CONUS, as Clark AB was formally returned to the government of the Philippines. Having recently replaced Colonel Hess as the 353d commander, Col Robert Stankovich (the first Pave Low pilot to achieve wing command), returned to Clark for the transfer ceremony aboard one of the 31st SOS MH-53s and lowered the wing flag for temporary transfer to Kadena. Many 353d personnel flew down on MC-130s from the 1st SOS for the ceremony. However, AFSOC had not yet made a decision on a permanent location for the 353d. Pending that decision, the TDY costs for its personnel at Kadena were rapidly depleting command travel funds.

While the multitudinous details attendant to the evacuation had to be steadily worked out, the 31st SOS tried to regain its operational footing. Most of the unaccompanied officers and Airmen stayed. They were drawing full per diem at Futenma and collecting a sizeable sum of money. However, those there on accompanied tours were allowed to return to the CONUS to be with their families. Several Pave

Low troops went back to Hurlburt. Captain Becker received orders to the 551st FTS at Kirtland AFB and departed Futenma in December 1991.[6]

Since the unit did not currently have a permanent assigned station, it could not receive PCS replacements. Consequently, the unit required TDY manning, primarily from the 20th SOS, to maintain any mission capability. AFSOC addressed this need with Operation Scimitar Sweep, which provided enough personnel on TDY status to the units of the 353d. By September, the 31st was manned with sufficient personnel on varying 60-day orders to initiate a steady flying and training schedule, initially taking advantage of US Navy ships in the area to do shipboard training. The next month, squadron aircraft and crews deployed to Korea to participate in Foal Eagle 91 with US and allied special forces units. On 18 December, Colonel Correll arrived from Hurlburt Field and took command of the squadron from Lt Col Lee Massey in a ceremony at Futenma. A few days later, Correll was notified that the 353d would be assigned provisionally to Kadena AB, but the permanent location for the wing or any of its squadrons was still undetermined.[7]

Courtesy Col Gene Correll, USAF, Retired

31st SOS change of command from Lt Col Lee Massey to Lt Col Gene Correll

That fall SSgt John DeSalle arrived at the 31st SOS as a new gunner. He had enlisted in the USAF in 1981 and had served several tours as a weapons loader on F-111s and F-15s. During Desert Storm, he was at Luke AFB when he saw a message soliciting volunteers for duty as gunners on the Pave Lows, and he submitted a request. His transfer was approved, and after attending the necessary survival schools, he reported to Kirtland AFB in May for his crew and gunnery training. He found the academics to be challenging but enjoyed the actual flying as he learned his scanning duties and overall crew member obligations. DeSalle also enjoyed learning to fire the .50-caliber machine gun and the 7.62 mm minigun, qualifying on live-fire missions to the Red Rio and Melrose Ranges in central and eastern New Mexico. At the completion of his training, he flew over to Kadena, arriving in September 1991. He was quickly inserted into the exercise rotation schedule and did his share of trips to Thailand, the Philippines, and Korea before leaving in April 1992 to transfer to the 21st SOS in the UK.[8]

Kirtland AFB, New Mexico

As the 20th and 21st SOSs were participating in the turbulent events in the Middle East, life was a bit more mundane at the 1550th CCTW. Its 1551st FTS continued to qualify aircrew members utilizing its assigned MH-53J and CH-53A aircraft and the newly received/modified simulators owned by the 1550th Technical Training Squadron (TCHTS). That unit also took possession of new equipment that facilitated self-guided training and a part-task trainer, which provided focused training for the students on the enhanced navigation system, map display functions, utilization of the FLIR and radar systems, and cockpit procedures. The equipment was also instrumental in teaching crew coordination and saved several flight hours.

The 1551st FTS was also called upon to provide operational support to the deployed units in the Middle East for Desert Shield/Storm. It dispatched 10 Pave Low crew members, who flew with both the 20th and 21st SOSs. They were joined by a larger group of 30 maintenance technicians drawn from other 1550th CCTW squadrons, which provided augmentation to the two units. Two more Pave Low pilots, Maj Dave Harris and Capt Paco Burrell, were sent to Fort Bragg to work with the JSOC. They both deployed with the JSOTF that it dispatched to conduct operations in western Iraq.

Throughout Desert Shield/Storm, the 20th SOS was also required to maintain a capability at Hurlburt to support other JSOC taskings that might arise. To support that contingency, the 1551st dispatched

Courtesy 58th SOW History Office

The flight simulators at Kirtland were an integral part of Pave Low training.

two of its MH-53s to Hurlburt. They were accompanied by another team of four maintenance technicians, who augmented the residual 20th SOS maintenance element. While there, they also provided some support at the NARF, NAS Pensacola, where MH-53s were still being modified or going through the SLEP upgrade.[9]

After the termination of combat, the 1551st was tasked to provide another Pave Low crew to augment the 21st SOS on Operation Provide Comfort. Capt Bill Bassett had recently joined the unit after completing his tour with the 21st in England. He volunteered to lead a crew with Capt Keith Kollarik, MSgt Ben Wilhelm, TSgt David Smith, SSgt David Dean, and SSgt William Nelson. They joined the unit in Turkey and subsequently flew 36 missions, carrying supplies to the refugees, surveying relocation sites, and moving displaced Kurds and Iraqis.[10]

On 2 March, two 1551st crews received real-world experience at Kirtland when they were dispatched to a wilderness area 180 miles southwest of Albuquerque to recover a group of 26 lost backpackers. As the two aircraft arrived in the area, the crews immediately located and extracted 11 members of the group. However, the rest were not found until after nightfall. They were in a much more remote area where the Pave Lows could not land or safely perform night hoist operations. Instead, the crews directed the backpackers to move to a more open area, where they were subsequently recovered. This was not only the second largest single rescue in the history of the 1550th CCTW but also good training for the Pave Low crews.[11]

On 1 July 1991, Colonel Folkerts passed command of the 1551st to Lt Col Mike Planert and departed to attend the National War College in Washington, DC. Four months later, MAC directed the 1550th CCTW and collocated the 1606th ABW to consolidate and reorganize as the 542d Crew Training Wing (CTW). In the change, the 1551st FTS was redesignated as the 551st FTS and the 1550th TCHTS as the 542d TCHTS. Both units continued with their assigned missions. Through the remainder of 1991 and 1992, the 551st steadily provided flight training to Pave Low crews utilizing its six assigned TH-53As (augmented with two NCH-53As received from AFSC) and six MH-53Js. All aircraft rotated to Pensacola at least once for modifications, upgrades, or SLEP. The TH-53As were modified to carry guns and became the primary aircraft used for gunnery training.

Courtesy Wayne Mutza

CH-53A #66-14470, one of the training aircraft at Kirtland

In March 1992, the building housing the weapons system trainer suffered a power surge, seriously damaging the trainer and disrupting the training schedule. It took a month for the maintenance technicians to fix the problems. By the end of 1992, the WST was joined by a fully operational TH-53A simulator, all requested computer-based training units, a night-vision training laboratory, several part-task trainers, and the ultramodern Mission Rehearsal System (MRS). All of these integrated training devices dramatically reduced needed actual aircraft flight time and provided excellent training, as evidenced by 99 percent of students passing their crew qualification check rides with no major discrepancies over this training period.[12]

Arriving at the 551st FTS in January 1992, Capt Joe Becker took over as the MH-53 flight commander. To his delight, he found that he now had several operationally experienced guys like Capt Bill Bassett from the 21st SOS and Capt "Paco" Burrell and Capt Jim Billings on board. That pleased him because his first impression was that the training squadron lacked an operational focus, and he took that issue as his personal "windmill" to attack. He convinced the squadron commander, Colonel Planert, to allow crew members to volunteer to go forward on occasion to augment the operational squadrons, as well as to establish a program to deploy an operational crew to Saudi Arabia on a continuing basis to augment the still-deployed 20th SOS there, seeing it as a gain for both units. Planert supported both initiatives. In reviewing the overall pilot and flight engineer programs, Becker discovered that very few were graduating as scheduled. He worked with his instructors to restructure the courses and flying schedule and eliminate outdated material, significantly reducing the late graduation rate. However, his goal was not just to train MH-53 crews but to train crews who could leave Kirtland thinking like special operators. That was why he was so pleased to have instructors with operational experience. He wanted his students to adopt the special operations frame of mind—the "aggression in the attack" mode that made them so effective—and pushed his instructors to instill that in every student. Becker put his heart into training students and thoroughly enjoyed the year, especially flying the TH-53As, or "sports cars," as he called them. He also remembered, in particular, two first lieutenants—Jim Slife and Carlos Halcomb—who came through. Both were mature for their rank and showed great potential, seeming to take to the aircraft and mission naturally.[13]

Jim Slife was commissioned as a second lieutenant out of the ROTC program at Auburn University in 1989. He proceeded directly to pilot training at Fort Rucker, graduating at the top of his class. Jim had heard about Pave Low and really wanted to fly it, but his class received an HH-60 assignment. Although he had first pick, he reasoned that if he took it, he would stay in HH-60s forever. Consequently, he agreed to stay as an instructor and ask for Pave Low after Rucker. Six months later, though, the USAF training unit at Fort Rucker was shut down, and Slife did not have an assignment. He asked for Pave Lows since it would be his "second" flying assignment. He got the assignment, reported to Kirtland in the fall of 1991, and fell under the wise guidance of Joe Becker. Slife recounts that

> Joe Becker was probably the most credible instructor pilot out there. He had been in the 41st; he was in the 20th for a long time; he had been in the Philippines and stood up the 31st. He was a very credible guy. . . . We just really idolized Joe. The thing that made Joe stand out was (a) he was a good instructor, but (b) frankly, he treated us like human beings. . . . Joe started right there imparting the history of Pave Low to me. . . . I mean, I could tell you all the Pokeweed stories and all that stuff. . . . So I knew the "who begat whose". . . . I really felt connected to the generation who had just preceded me.[14]

Another Pave Low student who flew with Joe Becker was Capt Scott Howell. He was a classic case of the value of mentoring. Howell attended the Air Force Academy, graduating in 1987. While there, one of his direct supervisors was Capt Art Schwall, who had flown on one of the MC-130s at Desert One. Schwall spoke to the young cadet about special operations and helped him arrange a summer visit to Hurlburt in 1985. Howell loved it, especially the helicopter operations. Two years later, another officer, Maj Mike Collins, an early HH-60 pilot, helped him get one of the four helicopter training slots available to his class. After commissioning in 1987, he proceeded to Rucker, where he learned to fly helicopters. Graduating from there, he went to Fairchild AFB, Washington, to fly the UH-1N. His commander for a while was Maj Roger Smith, who had flown UH-1Ns with the 20th SOS in Vietnam and further encouraged Howell to consider special operations and Pave Lows.

Unfortunately, though, young pilots like Howell had a large systemic problem that lurked in the background. With the cancellation of the purchase of the UH-60D, the USAF now had a glut of young helicopter pilots. Working with the Army, the USAF was able to establish an exchange program whereby the Army would accept 50 USAF helicopter pilots for a period of three or four years as a way of utilizing them instead of moving them all into nonrated jobs or releasing them outright. Hearing about the program, Howell believed that it was a chance to fly the UH-60 and volunteered. He was sent to

Fort Hood, Texas, to fly with the 2d Armored Division in early 1990. As luck would have it, as he arrived, the 2d was slated for inactivation, and he was moved to the 1st Cavalry Division to fly UH-1Hs. Arriving there, he was qualified to fly with NVGs and assigned to Echo Company of the 227th Aviation Regiment, a utility lift unit. That summer, Saddam invaded Kuwait, and in September, Captain Howell deployed with his unit to Saudi Arabia.

Howell flew with his unit through all of the movements and operations in which the 1st Cavalry was involved. During the ground campaign in February 1991, he served as the pilot for the aviation brigade commander, flew in several major engagements, and watched the allied "Big Army" maul the Iraqi forces. He also learned how dark and dangerous night flying over the open desert could be. Returning to Fort Hood in April, he visited the USAF Personnel Center in San Antonio and inquired about the "early out" program now in effect because of the post–Cold War and Desert Storm force reductions. He was informed that his referential year group was not considered in that program, so he asked for reassignment back into the USAF. That looked very good. He asked if he had any choices of assignment. He was told that with his level of experience, he could have an HH-60 at Iceland or an MH-53 at Hurlburt. That was not really a choice, and in 1992 he reported to Kirtland AFB for his MH-53 qualification training with Jim Slife.[15]

From the very beginning, he just loved it. He had some outstanding instructors/evaluators, Maj Scott Pugmire and Maj Jim Eustace. Both helped him learn how to fly the beast and use all of the special systems that made Pave Low so unique. Eustace, especially, taught the TF/TA radar. He made the students learn it and then use it until they developed the confidence to truly rely on it. From Joe Becker, though, he learned something different. Paralleling Slife's experiences, Howell added that "he was the first guy who kind of took it away from the nuts and bolts of flying and learning the machinery to [explaining]: 'There's a reason we have these machines, and the reason is the guys we put in the back.' He was the first one who started talking about the customer focus and what these guys were trying to accomplish. 'How can we support their plan?' Which was good; I got a lot out of it."[16] Finishing his Kirtland training in July 1992, Howell drove to Hurlburt to join the 20th SOS, just a few weeks behind 1st Lt Jim Slife.

In the spring of 1993, Captain Becker moved over to the wing safety office for some broadening. He still instructed but only as an adjunct to the squadron guys. This duty was fairly straightforward, and he began to look for another assignment back somewhere in operations. He was subsequently selected to transfer to the AFSOC Air Support Operations Squadron at Fort Bragg in 1994 as a newly selected major.[17]

Throughout 1993 operations were fairly mundane at the training squadron. To expedite requalification training for aircrew members returning to the aircraft, MAC granted a training waiver to reduce the course length to a maximum of 99 days. This obviated the need for a PCS assignment for training. Also, each student could influence his course length based upon his course performance and individual training needs. The first student through under this program finished his training in February and needed only 38 days of school time. By June the unit had qualified 10 pilots, four IPs, 10 flight engineers, and four gunners. On 11 June, Lt Col Michael Planert gave up command of the 551st to Lt Col Michael Damron.[18]

Air Force Reorganization

In late 1991, while the Airmen of the 31st SOS were battling with the aftermath of the Mount Pinatubo eruption and subsequent relocation of the unit, the Air Force leadership was contemplating a wholesale reorganization of the entire service. Noting the stunning collapse of the Soviet Union and Warsaw Pact and the recent victory in the Persian Gulf, the CSAF, General McPeak, and Air Force Secretary Donald Rice realized that the nation would now demand significant cuts in its military forces. They both accepted that the USAF would be required to reduce its force structure and personnel by perhaps as much as 25 percent. They directed a top-to-bottom restructuring analysis focused on maintaining as much combat capability as possible as the cuts took effect.[19]

Additionally, McPeak tasked his staff members to take a back-to-basics approach. He wanted them to look at all levels of the service and accomplish several things: (1) decentralize power and authority down to the working Airman level; (2) strengthen commanders so that they have the authority to achieve results; (3) streamline and flatten the organizational structure; (4) consolidate where practical to bring resources under a single field commander; and (5) clarify functional responsibilities. McPeak recognized that the squadron was the basic combat or operational organization of the Air Force. He directed that the traditional wing organizational structure—which had squadrons assigned to three colonels serving as deputies for operations, maintenance, and resource management—be reorganized. Flying squadrons would be reassigned to an operations group, and the various maintenance, supply, and logistics units would be reassigned to a logistics group. Other units, such as medical groups and so forth, would also be so organized.

McPeak also mandated that, as much as possible, the USAF would have on any base "one base, one wing, one boss"; this new structure would be known as the "objective wing." He also wanted most wing commanders to be general officers, and he realized that such wings would probably end up as composite units with possibly more than one operations group or logistics group. The wings would be very flexible organizations. Additionally, McPeak directed that as part of the overall restructuring of the USAF, his staff would examine the heritage and lineage of all the USAF wings to insure that there was no duplication of numbers and that units with the longest periods of service or most distinguished combat honors were retained.[20]

Above the wing level, McPeak decided to eliminate air divisions and strengthen the numbered air forces. He also decided to consolidate several major commands to reduce staff duplication, save manpower spaces, and improve operational efficiency. Specifically, AFSC and the AFLC would merge into the Air Force Materiel Command (AFMC). SAC, TAC, and MAC would be consolidated into two new commands: Air Mobility Command (AMC) and Air Combat Command (ACC). All of these changes were slated to take place on 1 July 1992. Subsequently, the Air Training Command and Air University would combine at a later date to become the Air Education and Training Command (AETC), which would improve overall training and education effectiveness and standardization.[21]

AFSOC was not dramatically affected by these structural changes, other than eventually taking possession of Hurlburt Field and being required to change some unit numerical designations. However, it was directed to develop a proposal to revamp its wings as objective wings. As 1992 began, the AFSOC staff worked with its three wings to develop their plans. When AFSOC presented them in April to the Air Staff, though, AFSOC was informed that only the 1st and the 39th SOWs would reorganize as objective wings under the wing–subordinate group structure. The 353d SOW would realign as the

353d Special Operations Group (SOG) and be attached to a larger wing to be determined.[22]

Air Force Special Operations Command

That was just one of many items that the AFSOC had to deal with as the new year began. With the demise of the Soviet Union and Warsaw Pact, a large theater war was now seen as highly unlikely. Instability in many regions of the world pointed to smaller or low-intensity actions across the full spectrum of conflict, which would put a high demand on special forces. The AFSOC mission was to organize, train, and equip forces for worldwide deployment and assignment to regional unified commands to conduct the five special operations missions: unconventional warfare, direct action, special reconnaissance, counterterrorism, and foreign internal defense. Collaterally, they would also be prepared to provide humanitarian assistance, psychological operations, counternarcotics, and personnel recovery operations.[23]

Maj Gen Bruce Fister had taken command of AFSOC from General Eggers on 21 June 1991. He believed that his command needed to be proactive in addressing its mission and capabilities. To his Airmen, he explained, "As air commandos, we stay a step ahead of any adversary by anticipating and responding to changing demands. Our strategy remains to provide specialized air power for special operations forces and, where appropriate, act as a conventional force multiplier."[24]

The personnel recovery tasking was a bit contentious. The term itself was an updated but more inclusive moniker for CSAR and referred to all of the actions, training, equipage, and actual missions flown to recover personnel trapped or isolated in enemy or neutral territory. Lessons learned from Desert Storm reaffirmed the need for a dedicated rescue force, and the ARS was in the midst of a program to redevelop its force structure to reassume the mission. However, AFSOC still had the 21st SOS and the 55th SOS providing rescue alert forces in Turkey for Provide Comfort II and 20th SOS assets in Saudi Arabia supporting residual forces in that area for Operation Desert Calm. Later that fall, the 20th's assets would reposition to Kuwait International Airport to support Operation Southern Watch.

To cleanly address this issue, AFSOC published the white paper *Combat Rescue—Bridging the Gap.*[25] Reviewing the history of combat rescue and the more recent events of Desert Storm, it concluded that the USAF could not afford to build a fleet of fully mission-capable helicopters to adequately perform the mission. It recommended that AFSOC be given additional aircraft and personnel to do the mission, either as an additional reinforcement force to the ARS or with a complete change of doctrine to assign the mission to AFSOC with a wholesale transfer of CSAR force structure from MAC/AMC to AFSOC. In support, the Air Staff developed a cost estimate for the conversion of mothballed USMC CH-53A aircraft to the Pave Low IIIE configuration. The USAF had taken possession of 34 of the aircraft, including two NCH-53A aircraft initially modified to test the special retrieval gear subsequently installed on the HH-53s assigned to the 6594th Test Group at Hickam. These 34 aircraft could be modified to the MH-53J configuration for $15 million each.[26]

However, that debate was sidetracked by a larger issue when, in July, Senator Sam Nunn, in a speech on the Senate floor, asked why the US military had "four separate air forces—one for each service." He suggested that since the US Army owned and maintained a fleet of over 5,000 helicopters, it was more than capable of managing and operating all Army and USAF helicopters, including the AFSOC MH-53s. His position was a reincarnation of the dormant—but not dead—Initiative 17. The AFSOC staff dusted its off position papers on the issue and again provided the convincing logic against such a move. Two months later, the new SOCOM commander, General Stiner, reviewed the issue and informed AFSOC that any discussion of transferring the helicopters to the Army was dead.[27]

Several other issues of a more general nature arose concerning the Pave Low force that required AFSOC actions. During the year, the aircraft entered another SLEP program. This one directed 14 different modifications to various aircraft systems. It also called for blade and tail modifications to allow for folding so that the aircraft could be carried aboard naval ships. Lastly, engineers validated the procedures adopted by Colonel Comer and his crews in Desert Storm to operate the aircraft up to a maximum takeoff weight of 50,000 pounds vice their previous 42,000-pound limit.

Some personnel issues were also developing. As the Pave Low fleet was expanding in the 1980s, pilots were essentially drawn from the inactivating tactical air support or rescue squadrons. That infused the Pave Low community with a strong cadre of experienced aircrew members. However, that source had dried up; consequently, AFSOC coordinated with the Air Staff to begin drawing experienced fixed-wing pilots to cross-train to rotary-wing qualification and enter the Pave Low program.

Debriefs coming in from the operational squadrons and the training squadron at Kirtland indicated that an uncomfortably high number of flight engineer candidates did not have the requisite skills necessary to qualify in that position. As the Pave Low became more technologically advanced, the flight engineers were increasingly tasked to perform duties that were not classically taught to flight engineers, including mission planning, navigation, systems integration, electronic warfare, and flight gunnery. On the six-man Pave Low crew, the flight engineer was the key focal point who needed to be able to recognize quickly what needed to be done, work directly with the pilots to set priorities, and, if necessary, direct actions. A Pave Low flight engineer needed to have skills well beyond the initial mechanical skills that had been the traditional qualifiers to become a generic flight engineer. Consequently, AFSOC took necessary actions to increase the required Aptitude Qualification Examination scores to qualify for the position and worked with the instructors at the 1551st FTS to better focus what was already the longest flight engineer course in the USAF to better train the young Airmen volunteering for this critical job.

Additional feedback coming from the AFSOC operational units indicated that many of the now combat-experienced aircrews in all aircraft had become quite cocky about their flying skills and displayed a willingness to disregard regulations and sound safety processes to complete missions.[28] These concerns were doubly reinforced on 29 October 1992, when an MH-60 from the 55th SOS crashed while taking part in a classified joint training exercise southwest of Salt Lake City, Utah. The operation involved 11 aircraft, USAF and Army, including one 20th SOS MH-53, flown by Capt Brendan Clare and Maj Richard Kianka, and three AFSOC MH-60s. The Army aircraft were from the 160th SOAR. While maneuvering at night to insert assault elements into a simulated denied area, one of the AFSOC MH-60s descended and hit the shallow water on the west side of the Great Salt Lake. Twelve Airmen and Soldiers aboard were killed, and one crew member, copilot Maj Steve Laushine, was wounded. Clare and his crew were not airborne when the accident occurred because they had a maintenance problem with their aircraft. However, when notified of the accident, Clare determined that his aircraft was safe to fly and launched to the crash site with two USAF PJs onboard. Arriving overhead, he inserted his PJs by hoist so that they could assist ground elements who had recovered Laushine and were now recovering the bodies from the horrible crash scene.

The subsequent accident report was very disturbing. It pointed to problems with joint flight standards, a breakdown in MH-60 crew integrity, cockpit crew loss of spatial orientation, and poor intraflight coordination. Corrective actions pointed to the need for intraformation positioning lights, better joint operating procedures, and more emphasis on aircrew professionalism. Additionally, the MH-60s received some mission restrictions, but none were placed on the MH-53s.[29]

Concerned that the AFSOC Airmen were pushing the careful balance between risk and reward, the AFSOC DO, Col Lee Hess, wrote a letter to all AFSOC operational flying units. In it, he reemphasized the duties and responsibilities of the aircraft commanders and flight leaders to properly and fully plan their missions and conduct thorough flight briefings. He admonished them to insure that all participants were present for the complete briefing. Additionally, he told his staff, "It's up to all of us to fight off that 'cowboy image.' " He instructed his stan/eval team to emphasize crew coordination, aircrew discipline, and situational awareness on all check rides. He needed to raise the standard for the entire command and determined that his standardization and evaluation process was the most efficient way to quickly and effectively change ingrained attitudes. The aircrews flying the 28 Pave Lows with the 20th SOS, the six with the 21st SOS, and the four with the 31st SOS quickly got the message. However, this change had unintended consequences. The amount of time that the Pave Low crews and 160th crews worked together now was dramatically reduced, and an air of insolence seemed to shade the relationship. Said one anonymous Pave Low pilot of that period, "The 160th would lie, cheat, or steal to make the Air Force look bad."[30]

Colonel Hess also started another initiative called Commando Look. This program was designed to screen volunteers for Pave Low to determine if they had the true determination to handle the aircraft and mission. It addressed a specific concern that General Fister had about the Pave Low crews. He had encountered several who he felt were either not fully committed or simply unsuited for the demands of the Pave Low program. Some recent flight engineer classes had suffered 33 percent washout rates. He noted that several other USSOCOM components had very successful screening programs and directed Hess to ascertain whether such a program would prove useful for

Pave Low. Working with his staff and the 20th SOS, Hess designed a four-day orientation at Hurlburt. Prospective volunteers would attend an orientation at the 20th and mingle with members of the unit. They would receive a psychological screening, go through underwater egress survival training, and take a night NVG flight on a Pave Low. Sponsor personnel within the 20th would shepherd them through the screening process and then help determine which candidates were selected for the program. The 1st SOG commander, Col Norton Schwartz, reviewed the recommendations from the 20th and approved them, with the suggestion that the program should be expanded to the other AFSOC aircraft. Colonel Hess noted that request but initially limited the program to Pave Low. He believed that as many as 108 candidates could be screened per year, enough to select sufficient new personnel to fulfill Pave Low aircrew needs through 1999.[31]

20th Special Operations Squadron

The new year of 1992 started off well for the 20th when it was notified on 17 January that the unit had been selected as the AFSOC squadron of the year for 1990, the award delayed because of the war in the Gulf. Considering the tough competition from so many units that had performed well during that difficult time, it was a tremendous honor. The 20th troops were also involved in the lessons-learned process for Desert Storm as all of the operational squadrons had to record and send in their findings and larger histories. Additionally, several unit members—Captains Trask, Kingsley, and Martin in particular—were in high demand for presentations on their exploits in the conflict.[32]

The 20th also watched as the 1st SOW prepared to convert on 1 October to the objective wing structure. The 20th would be assigned to the newly forming 1st Special Operations Group, a simple change from its perspective. Additionally, the collocated 834th ABW that commanded most of the support functions on the base would combine with the 1st SOW sometime within the next year, as the AFSOC formally took control of Hurlburt Field.

On 8 June, Lt Col Rich Comer passed command of the 20th SOS to Lt Col Russell "Rotor" Rakip and departed to attend the US Marine Corps Senior School at Quantico, Virginia. As he was preparing to leave, the squadron was notified that it had also been selected as the

AFSOC squadron of the year for 1991 for its performance in Desert Storm. Comer was extremely proud of his unit and very well satisfied with his command tour. His one regret was that he had never had his unit all in one place, at one time during his entire tenure. In fact, as he signed out of the 20th, the squadron had aircraft and crews operating in four different countries. But that was what the 20th SOS did.[33]

Rakip was well qualified for the job. He had flown CH-53s in SEA with the 21st SOS at Nakhon Phanom AB, Thailand, and later was the sole USAF helicopter pilot in the ill-fated 1980 hostage rescue attempt in Iran. He took over a squadron that had just about recovered from its challenging experiences in the desert, although some of the helicopters were still carrying maintenance discrepancies from that hard duty. The unit also still had personnel deployed to Saudi Arabia and Kuwait sitting rescue alert for Operations Desert Calm and then Southern Watch. In August, the 20th dispatched one aircraft and crew to Aviano AB, Italy, to support the 21st SOS on a short-notice tasking. That same month, the squadron dispatched two aircraft from home station to transport a CCT to Homestead AFB to support recovery operations in the aftermath of Hurricane Andrew that devastated southern Florida. While there, the control team provided critical traffic control. The Pave Lows, led by Capt Brad Webb, participated in the rescue and recovery operations in the ravaged area. The Green Hornets also routinely participated in classified exercises with other special operations forces, similar to the one at Salt Lake. Even though the squadron was essentially in-garrison for the year, it was still a busy unit.[34]

In June 1992, 1st Lt Jim Slife reported to the 20th SOS. He was the youngest officer there. Being well versed in the Pave Low history, he was blown away to be part of something so consequential with guys such as Captains Tom Trask, Mike Kingsley, Corby Martin, Grant Hardin, Brendan Clare, and Matt Shazda and the new generation, such as Capt R. K. Williams and Capt Tim Leahy, and he turned his junior rank to advantage by soaking up all he could from the older types. However, he also determined that there was a downside to being the sole unit lieutenant. Slife noticed that most of the guys in the unit, officer and enlisted, just ignored him. Fortunately, R. K. Williams took him under his wing and helped work him into the social and professional structure of the squadron. At the time, Williams was serving as the squadron flight scheduler and within a few months had himself and Slife paired up for a deployment to Kuwait for Southern

Watch. While there, Slife was able to log some serious tactical training. He also learned to never leave his personal camera unattended whenever gunners were present.[35]

Two months later, Captain Howell reported to the 20th SOS. He was impressed when Colonel Rakip walked up from behind and said, "Hello, Scott."

"Gosh," he thought, "the squadron commander knows my name." He was put to work in current operations and scheduling. However, he remembered Becker's words about planning and asked to be put in that shop. Like Slife, he was overwhelmed by the caliber of men in the unit, who had been out in the operational squadrons and in combat and had done what Pave Low was all about. They had done the Big Mish and so much more.[36]

21st Special Operations Squadron

The beginning of 1992 also heralded the start of a busy year for the Airmen of the 21st SOS. In January their parent unit, the 39th SOW, moved its headquarters from Rhein-Main AB to RAF Alconbury, UK. Colonel Zdenek was still in command of the 21st and had his hands full preparing the unit to move from RAF Woodbridge to join the 39th at Alconbury. In March he dispatched three Pave Lows and crews to Norway to support Exercise Teamwork 92, an opportunity to work with special forces from several countries in arctic conditions. On 15 May, Zdenek passed command of the squadron over to Lt Col Mike Russell, who completed the move a week later.

The next month, Russell deployed his helicopters and crews to Rota, Spain, to conduct deck qualification training aboard US Navy ships. In May, the 21st received a request from the 20th to augment that unit in Saudi Arabia for Operation Desert Calm. Russell had to turn that down; he had to deploy crews to participate in Operation Ellipse Bravo, a classified training exercise with special forces units in Europe. He had been notified that the 21st would again deploy to Turkey in August to support Provide Comfort II as rescue assets. Additionally, the unit was directed to deploy two aircraft and a support package to Aviano AB in northern Italy for a classified tasking.[37]

That spring SSgt John DeSalle reported to the 21st SOS from his short tour with the 31st. He upgraded to instructor gunner and was promoted to tech sergeant and assigned duty as the technical orders

NCO. His job was to ensure that the unit was receiving and using the latest versions of all flight and training manuals and aircraft technical orders, an onerous job but crucial for safe and efficient operations. On rotations to Turkey and Italy, he also worked with crews from other allied nations to insure operational standardization on coalition operations and was subsequently upgraded to aerial gunner evaluator. While with the 21st, he met and married a woman who was also in the USAF.[38]

On 19 August, the 21st SOS flew four of its Pave Lows and support personnel to Incirlik, Turkey, for another tour of CSAR support for Provide Comfort II. The next month, a 21st crew assisted in the recovery of the wreckage of a US F-16 in Turkey. However, the tour was relatively uneventful, and the 21st crews returned home at the end of the year.

In mid-September, AFSOC notified the 39th SOW that it had been authorized to reorganize as an objective wing. This was accomplished on 1 October, when the 39th activated its operations and logistics groups as provisional units, pending final approval from AFSOC for the reorganization. Five days later, though, AFSOC announced that the 39th would *inactivate* on 1 December and that the 352d Operations Group—drawing its personnel and assets from the 39th and deriving its lineage from the 2d Air Commando Group from World War II— would activate to replace the 39th SOW. The 21st SOS would be one of its four operations units, all finally together at RAF Alconbury.[39]

31st Special Operations Squadron

As 1992 began, the commander, Lt Col Eugene Correll, was not happy. His squadron was in messy disarray, sequestered at MCAS Futenma on Okinawa while his parent 353d SOW was still in provisional status at the Kadena base, several miles away. Most of his original Airmen from Clark had returned to the CONUS, and he faced constant turnover of TDY personnel who now filled the unit under Scimitar Sweep. However, this situation did allow the unit to stay functional, pending the decisions necessary to find permanent locations for the 353d SOW and its component units.

Opportunities for good tactical flying on the island of Okinawa were limited. To address the need for mountain flying, access to weapons ranges, and day/night low-level flying, the 31st SOS established an FOL at Osan AB, Korea. Correll dispatched two of his aircraft to the base and began rotating his crews to reacquire their skills. The 31st also deployed aircraft, crews, and a support package to exercises in Thailand.[40]

By February the necessary political agreements between the United States and Japan had been resolved, and AFSOC announced that the 353d SOW would be permanently assigned to Kadena AB, except for the 31st SOS, which was still being considered for location elsewhere. The effective date of the directive was 5 February. As of that date, personnel were assigned PCS to the wing at Kadena, and as they steadily arrived over the next several months, they replaced the TDY personnel, who then returned to their permanent units.

Through the spring, the Airmen of the 31st SOS continued to travel to the Osan FOL for training and to exercises from Korea to Malaysia, working with the special forces of other nations. The location at Osan was working well, and representatives from the US government formally requested that the Korean government allow the USAF to permanently assign the 31st to that base. By April the Korean government agreed, and in a formal announcement, the US State Department declared that the 31st SOS and a maintenance support team would permanently move to Osan in July. Surprisingly, some of the strongest resistance to the movement of the 31st to Osan came from the current residents, the 51st Fighter Wing (FW). Quite simply, they did not want a helicopter unit on their base, citing operational and safety concerns. General Fister visited the base and had an office call with the wing commander and the Seventh Air Force commander, Lt Gen Ron Fogleman, to iron out any differences of opinion. Soon after, the 353d SOW commander, Colonel Stankovich, signed a memorandum of agreement with the Osan AB commander in June, and, on schedule, the 31st SOS relocated to Osan.[41]

As the 31st SOS settled into its new home, it was immediately tasked to support another series of exercises, classified and unclassified, in Korea and other Asian nations. Colonel Correll had to work through a series of personnel challenges as his TDY personnel departed and he finally received PCS troops for one-year tours. He discovered that the majority of his new maintenance troops were not fully qualified to work on the complex Pave Low systems. Working through the 353d SOW and AFSOC, he was able to arrange for all minimally qualified technicians being assigned to the 31st SOS to receive a short TDY tour to the 20th SOS for several weeks to acquire

Courtesy SSgt Glen Fleming, USAF

The flight line for the 31st SOS at Osan AB

some of the specific training they needed to be fully qualified before coming to Korea. Additionally, the two headquarters agreed to insure that, from then on, a minimum of 50 percent of his maintenance technicians would arrive fully qualified in their specialties.[42]

One of the new pilots to join the rebuilding 31st SOS was Capt Greg Lengyel. The son of a USAF flyer who had been a POW in SEA, he had attended Texas A&M and was commissioned through ROTC in 1985. He had a burning desire to be a fighter pilot and was accepted into the Euro-NATO joint jet pilot training program at Sheppard AFB, Texas. Unfortunately, the doctors there determined that he had a spinal defect that precluded him from sitting on an ejection seat, and he was assigned to nonflying duties in Colorado. With perseverance, Lengyel was able to obtain a waiver to fly in non-ejection-seat assignments. Since helicopters were the only way to do that, he volunteered and was accepted and sent to Fort Rucker with Capt Scott Howell. Graduating from there with his pilot wings, he went to Fairchild AFB to fly UH-1Ns in support of the USAF Survival School, again with Howell. Lengyel learned quickly and upgraded to instructor and then flight evaluator. At one point, he flew to Nellis AFB for some training and met Capt Brad Webb from the 20th SOS. They had a long talk, and afterwards Captain Lengyel applied for Pave Lows. He was accepted and reported to Kirtland in July 1991 for the long course.

Lengyel found the program to be challenging. While the flying was similar, there was just so much to the aircraft itself, especially all of the Pave Low gear. He also found that working with a larger crew than he had on the UH-1N took some adjustment. The pilot quickly got used to the cockpit cadences and rhythm necessary to maneuver the aircraft, especially into challenging landing zones both day and night.

Impressed with the role that the flight engineers played on the crew, Lengyel remembers that "[their] position is tough, it really is. We asked a great deal of the Pave Low engineers, especially the guy in the seat. The guys who made it through [training] were worth their weight in gold." Lengyel also began to form definite opinions about the Pave Low gunners. He chronicles how

> the gunners tended to be more of the happy-go-lucky, free-spirited, party members of the crew. . . . Gunners were an important part of the crew; they could kill you as much as anybody could by talking your tail rotor into the trees or something like that. They had that crucial role on the crew. The whole cadence of the approach, where the pilots are so restricted—particularly at night—on visibility, that they are so dependent on the flight engineer calling out altitude and air speed, and then the rest of the crew calling you in to a landing zone. Right, left, tail. Left and tail are gunners; they are two-thirds of that call. . . .
>
> They were definitely a different tribe than the flight engineers just because they could get away with being a little more carefree. . . . Sometimes if there is a little too much tension, they would be the ones who'd try to crack a joke or do something silly.[43]

Lengyel finished his training in April 1992 and qualified as a mission pilot, which meant that he would not need to come back to Kirtland to achieve aircraft commander qualification. That could now be done in his tactical squadron. Lengyel received a remote assignment to the rebuilding 31st SOS and prepared to travel to Osan.[44]

Anticipating a follow-on assignment to the 20th SOS, Lengyel first went to Hurlburt to procure housing for his wife and new baby before crossing the Pacific. He arrived at Osan before the squadron did. After in-processing, he was sent down to Futenma to join the units. There he was put on a C-5 and deployed with the unit to an exercise in Thailand. A few weeks later, he helped the unit move to Osan. Once the move was complete, he deployed to Marine Corps Air Station (MCAS) Kaneohe Bay, Hawaii, to train for a possible real-world mission. There he was crewed with Capt Bill Bassett, a TDY augmentee from the 551st at Kirtland AFB, with whom Lengyel had recently trained. They worked for several days on rehearsals with special forces elements. The missions involved long legs over water, lots of air refuelings, and use of the TF/TA in real weather conditions to deliver their units to precise locations. Lengyel learned a great deal on that exercise. During his one-year tour, he was able to upgrade to aircraft commander and spent more time on the road than he did at Osan. He left the 31st SOS in May 1993, with orders to report to the 20th SOS at Hurlburt Field.[45]

On 1 December 1992, as per AFSOC direction, the 353d SOW was officially redesignated the 353d SOG. Colonel Stankovich remained in command of the now downsized unit as it became a tenant of the 18th Wing, also at Kadena. Regardless of the unit designation change, though, little was different. The Airmen of the 353d continued to conduct their day-to-day missions and activities, and Stankovich had to admit that he felt much more comfortable as a group as opposed to a wing commander on such an active and essential air base in the western Pacific. The change also meant little to the Airmen of the 31st SOS at Osan. A few days later, they were launching sorties to participate in Exercise Foal Eagle, a joint and combined exercise in Korea. They were just happy that they had finally found a permanent home that would serve the unit well for the next nine years as they finally settled into a steady operational rhythm.[46]

Air Force Special Operations Command

At times it seemed that certain issues would just never go away. Just two weeks before 1992 ended, the CJCS, General Powell, released a draft roles and missions modification proposal and sent it to all of the services for comments. It was intended to initiate a series of force reductions facilitated by the demise of the Soviet Union and the end of the Cold War. In it was a proposal to transfer all of the USAF's helicopters to the Army and all of its HC-130s to the Marines. It was Senator Nunn's proposal all over again. It was Initiative 17 on steroids, now including all utility helicopters and those assigned to the ARS for rescue duty, plus all the tankers. The transfers would begin within six months.

For the second time in less than a year, the AFSOC staff pulled out all of its briefing papers on Initiative 17, including justification for keeping the HC-130s, and rebutted the proposals. The countereffort had the desired effect; eight weeks later General Powell issued a revised plan. Directly addressing Senator Nunn, Powell said, "America has only one air force, the United States Air Force." The revision lacked any mention of any reassignment of USAF helicopters or HC-130 tankers. In fact, budget projections showed a steady increase in spending for SOCOM and its components. James Locher III, the assistant secretary of defense for special operations, pointed out that since 1986, special operations forces had doubled in size with no cuts anticipated. Increasingly, in a world devoid of any significant major threat, uncertainty abounded, and the SOF became the force of choice.[47]

One week later, AFSOC received some relief for a long-standing commitment when the 66th Rescue Squadron (RQS) of the ARS deployed to Kuwait to replace the 20th SOS from its continuous combat recovery tasking since the termination of combat in Desert Storm. When the 20th helicopters and personnel departed, the 30-month presence of the Green Hornets in the region ended. Wishing them a warm farewell, the commander of Joint Task Force Southwest Asia said, "Bravo Zulu [outstanding] to all AFSOC personnel involved. You did an outstanding job in carrying out a difficult mission under challenging circumstances. . . . You provided a blanket of security for coalition aircrews. . . . Be proud of the role you have played in this long watch."[48]

21st Special Operations Squadron

Into 1993 the 21st SOS was still supporting Provide Comfort II in Turkey. In early January, 21st crews flew medevac missions to recover injured coalition personnel. On one of the missions conducted on 5 January, Colonel Russell and Maj John Brainerd and crews flew their Paves into northern Iraq to recover an injured French officer. Because of recent hostile incidents between coalition and Iraqi forces, the mission was politically sensitive. The two aircraft flew at night through snowstorms and icing conditions to Zakho, Iraq, where the patient was located. They had to fly at low level through the mountains and utilized all of the special navigation equipment on their aircraft to safely do so. At one point, they received ground fire from enemy forces. Regardless, they recovered the French soldier, reversed their course, and delivered him to critically needed medical care at

Incirlik AB. The two crews logged 6.3 hours of flight time in some of the worst flying conditions possible, tasking the aircraft and crews to their limits. For their efforts, Russell and Brainerd were awarded the Cheney Award for 1993. Over the next several months, 21st crews also flew a rescue mission for a Turkish pilot who went down in the Mediterranean Sea and two missions to secure aircraft crash sites. That long-term Pave Low commitment ended in mid-July, when the 21st SOS completed its rescue alert mission as part of Provide Comfort II at Incirlik. MH-60s and personnel from the 55th and 71st SOSs replaced the Pave Lows and crews in that role. The Airmen of the 21st packed up their equipment and flew their aircraft back to RAF Alconbury, completing an almost uninterrupted 27-month TDY commitment.[49]

Also during 1993, the congressionally mandated Base Realignment and Closure Commission announced the shutdown of the Naval Aviation Depot (NADEP) at Pensacola. This would directly affect the Pave Low community since all of its major maintenance and modifications were still being accomplished there. AFSOC staff members had to modify their long-term logistics plan to support the aircraft. Working with USMC planners, they began to develop a logistics and funding program to transfer the work to the large H-53 depot at Cherry Point MCAS, North Carolina. However, interruptions to modifications were inevitable as the highly skilled technicians who were the heart of the NADEP began to retire or transfer to other locations.[50]

Notes

1. History of 353d SOW, 1 July–31 Dec 1990, vol. 4, 1–19.
2. Joe Becker, interview.
3. Ibid.
4. Ibid.
5. Anderegg, "Ash Warriors," 1, 43–52; Grier, "Last Days of Clark," 56–60; History of AFSOC, 1 Jan 1990–31 Dec 1991, vol. 1, 197–200, 209; History of 353d SOW, 1 Jan–30 June 1991, vol. 1, viii–ix, 8–9; and History of the 353d Special Operations Group (Formerly 353d Special Operations Wing) (hereafter referred to as History of 353d SOG [Formerly 353d SOW]), 1 Jan–31 Dec 1992, vol. 1, 84.
6. Joe Becker, interview.
7. Crawford, "Nomads of the Pacific," pamphlet, 16–18, Heritage File, AFSOC/HO; and Marion, "Ash Warriors," 23.
8. DeSalle, interview.
9. History of 1550th CCTW, 1 Jan–30 June 1991, vol. 1, 15, 22.
10. Bassett, interview.
11. History of 1550th CCTW, 1 Jan–30 June 1991, vol. 1, 8, 15, 22, 25, 39.

12. Ibid., 1 July–30 Sept 1991; and History of the 542d Crew Training Wing (hereafter referred to as History of 542d CTW), 1 Oct 1991–31 Dec 1992, vol. 1, xxi, 1, 4, 25–27, 52–54.

13. Joe Becker, interview; and Waller, *Commandos*, 176.

14. Slife, interview.

15. Howell, interview.

16. Ibid.

17. Joe Becker, interview.

18. History of 542d CTW, 1 Jan–30 June 1993, vol. 1, 7, 15, 18, 23, 56–58.

19. McPeak, *Selected Works*, 52.

20. Ibid., 247–51.

21. Ibid., 53–57.

22. Thigpen, *Praetorian Starship*, 378–79.

23. History of AFSOC, 1 Jan–31 Dec 1992, vols. 1, 2.

24. Ibid., 34.

25. AFSOC, *Combat Rescue—Bridging the Gap*, white paper.

26. History of AFSOC, 1 Jan–31 Dec 1992, vol. 3, supporting doc. 1–19; and Lt Col Donny Wurster, SAF/AQQU, point paper, Conversion of Additional MH–53Js, n.d.

27. History of AFSOC, 1 Jan–31 Dec 1992, vol. 1, 4.

28. Ibid., 104.

29. HH–60G Class A Flight Mishap Report, AFSOC/HO.

30. Colonel Hess to AFSOC operational flying units, letter, subject: Duties and Responsibilities of the Aircraft Commander, 11 Dec 1992, AFSOC/HO; History of AFSOC, 1 Jan–31 Dec 1992, vol. 1, 55–56, 104, 221; and anonymous Pave Low pilot.

31. History of 1st SOW, 1 Jan–31 Dec 1992, vol. 1, 94–98.

32. Martin, interview.

33. Comer, interview.

34. History of 1st SOW, 1 Jan–31 Dec 1992, vol. 1, x, 4, 8, 40, 108, 199.

35. Slife, interview; and Slife to the author, e-mail, concerning the retirement of Col R. K. Williams.

36. Howell, interview.

37. History of 39th SOW, 1 Jan–31 Dec 1992, vol. 1, xi, 26, 76.

38. DeSalle, interview.

39. History of 39th SOW, 1 Jan–31 Dec 1992, vol. 1, xiv–xv, 20–21.

40. History of 353d SOG (Formerly 353d SOW), 1 Jan–31 Dec 1992, vol. 1, 32; and Crawford, "Nomads of the Pacific," pamphlet, 18, Heritage File, AFSOC/HO.

41. History of 353d SOG (Formerly 353d SOW), 1 Jan–31 Dec 1992, vol. 1, xi, xii, and 32; Crawford, "Nomads of the Pacific," pamphlet, 20, Heritage File, AFSOC/HO; and Stankovich and Correll, interviews.

42. History of 353d SOG (Formerly 353d SOW), 1 Jan–31 Dec 1992, vol. 1, 64, 80.

43. Lengyel, interview.

44. Ibid.

45. Ibid.

46. History of 353d SOG (Formerly 353d SOW), 1 Jan–31 Dec 1992, vol. 1, 21; and Crawford, "Nomads of the Pacific," pamphlet, 20, Heritage File, AFSOC/HO.

47. History of AFSOC, 1 Jan–31 Dec 1993, vol. 1, 2; William Matthews, "Powell Calls for Consolidation, but No Major Overhaul," *Air Force Times*, 22 Feb 1993, 4;

and George Wilson, "Special Operators, Losers Now Winners," *Air Force Times*, 22 Feb 1993, 14.

    48. History of AFSOC, 1 Jan–31 Dec 1993, vol. 1, 101.

    49. Ibid., xvii, xix, 103; and ibid., 1 Jan–31 Dec 1994, vol. 1, v, supplemental docs. II–35, II–37.

    50. Ibid., 1 Jan–31 Dec 1994, vol. 1, 212.

Chapter 11

Into the Balkans

~1993–96

We were all sweating bullets, and it was the hardest flying that I have ever done in my life.

—Capt Steve Kelly

RAF Alconbury

As the 21st SOS settled back in at its home base, Lt Col Mike Russell gave up command of the unit to Lt Col Donny Wurster on 9 July 1993. Wurster had been serving as the squadron operations officer since the summer of 1991. Although relatively new to the Pave Low, he brought to the job a wealth of operational experience flying the HH-3 and MH-60. That experience was leavened with his staff tours at MAC and then the Pentagon, where, in tandem with Maj Ed Reed, he had fought tirelessly for the modification of the MH-53s and MH-60s for both SOF and CSAR use.

On his Pentagon tour, Wurster replaced Reed in the OSD's acquisition division when Reed departed for Kirtland AFB and the challenges of building a world-class flight and simulator training facility. In the Pentagon, Wurster fought for the programs in the incessant daily give-and-take of staff duty. In doing so, he developed a reputation as an even-tempered and highly effective staff officer. His efforts also earned him an unusual nickname. After one particularly contentious staff session, he stopped by the Office of the Assistant Secretary of Defense for Special Operations and Low-Intensity Conflict and encountered Col Gary Weikel and Army colonel Mark Lewis, to whom he expressed some firm comments about the recent session. After he left, Lewis remarked, "You could misjudge that guy because he looks like Mr. Peepers but could easily sidle up next to you, and you would find yourself bleeding from multiple stab wounds before you knew it."[1] Completing that tour, Wurster received orders to Kirtland for Pave Low transition and then onto the 21st SOS. Arriving in

Courtesy Lt Gen Donny Wurster, USAF

Lt Col Donny Wurster as the commander of the 21st SOS

England, he was thrilled to be back in an operational unit and joined a squadron well founded and full of young, aggressive officers such as Capt Steve Otto, Capt J. D. Clem, and Capt Grant Harden.[2]

Taking command of the 21st, Wurster's attention was squarely drawn to events occurring in the Balkans region of Europe. Long-dormant ethnic tensions were simmering to a boil there as the former nation of Yugoslavia disintegrated and violence broke out in several areas among different ethnic groups. Relations were also strained between Serbia—which wanted to maintain some semblance of the former Yugoslavia but under its control—and the other areas, including Slovenia, Croatia, and Bosnia-Herzegovina, which wanted to be independent nations. In an attempt to staunch the fighting, the United Nations in July 1992 inserted a Protection Force (UNPROFOR) of 23,000 troops from over 20 nations to attempt to separate and protect the various factions. To sustain that mission, NATO initiated Operation Provide Promise, a joint and coalition airlift campaign to deliver supplies by air through landing or airdrop.

In February 1993, the 21st SOS was tasked to support the operation as part of a larger SOCEUR joint special operations task force, designated JSOTF2. It moved three of its aircraft, crews, and a maintenance support package from Turkey to Brindisi AB, located on the heel of Italy. Initially, the squadron was assigned CSAR alert, a legitimate precaution since an Italian cargo aircraft had been shot down and several other coalition aircraft had been damaged by enemy ground fire. As available, the Pave Lows could also be used for some precision cargo delivery or the movement of key US or allied leaders. However, as the Airmen from the 21st SOS settled in at Brindisi, they did not realize that this commitment would last over six years and also involve Pave Low personnel from all four of the units.[3]

Courtesy Lt Col Jim Breck, USAF

The 21st SOS home away from home for seven years

Courtesy Col Bill Bassett, USAF, Retired

Flight line at Brindisi, 1994

A few months after Wurster took command of the 21st SOS, TSgt Jim Kradel reported to the 352d SOG as a gunner evaluator in the stan/eval office. He flew with the 21st crews and also deployed on a few training exercises before he and TSgt John DeSalle attended the same NCO Academy class at RAF Upwood, graduating in the summer of 1994. Both enjoyed and appreciated the course, which, unfortunately, was the last USAF course conducted at that RAF base.[4]

While Kradel and DeSalle were in school, Serbia tried to interfere with the support missions that the USAF and coalition forces were flying and unleashed its ground and air forces to attack Croatia and Bosnia-Herzegovina. After the UN passed a series of resolutions that failed to force the Serbians to desist, it asked NATO to enforce a no-fly zone for Serbian aircraft over Bosnia. NATO accepted the task and began dispatching AWACS aircraft and allied fighters from several nations to patrol the area, starting on 12 April 1993, as Operation Deny Flight. To support this additional operation, the 21st SOS team at Brindisi was tasked to provide CSAR cover for the aircraft on patrol. The squadron dispatched two more of its aircraft to meet the minimum five-aircraft tasking. Additionally, the 21st SOS was tasked to provide personnel to serve on the JSOTF2 staff and at other headquarters. By midsummer, the operations tempo was so high that it was obvious the 21st SOS would not be able to honor this tasking without AFSOC providing substantial augmentation.[5]

Air Force Special Operations Command

As 1993 continued, in addition to the developing crisis in the Balkans, AFSOC monitored the participation of Pave Low crews and support personnel as they also joined exercises and training events literally all over the world. The Pave Lows were in high demand. The AFSOC staff also had to monitor and balance the aircraft fleet among the units as the Pave Lows went through their SLEP updates and other required maintenance inspections. Of the 37 MH-53Js available—26 with the 20th as the national reserve, six with the 21st, and five with the 31st—on average, 13 were off of the flight line for these two processes at any one time.

The AFSOC DO, Colonel Hess, continued his efforts to better standardize the crews. He directed his safety office to build briefings for all crew members on operational risk management and human factors. He also drafted a directive ordering the operational squadrons to form hard crews of individuals who would train and fly together and, where possible, to organize their units into formal flights for better personnel management and officer and NCO leadership development.[6]

Under Hess's guidance, the Commando Look program received funding. The project leader, Lt Col Douglas Layne, and his senior NCO, MSgt Leonard Sullivan, traveled to Fort Campbell to watch the 160th SOAR do its "new guy" assessments and left with a number of ideas. Working with Colonel Hess, they drafted a proposal to be forwarded to the USAF Personnel Center requesting that Pave Low assignments be considered special-duty assignments and that more fixed-wing aviators be directed to the program. During the year, they held two Commando Look assessment sessions. At the first one, Lt Col "Rotor" Rakip, the 20th SOS commander, told the aspirants, "Being in special operations requires a total commitment. . . . Sure, the job is exciting and rewarding, but we need people who accept the risks and sacrifices as well. Special operators have to have candor in knowing that when needed, they'll respond. . . . Special operations is high-risk, high gain, the most demanding [missions] I have flown."[7]

One of the candidates was 1st Lt Mike McKinney, currently flying UH-1Ns at F. E. Warren AFB, Wyoming. He and the other candidates also met with retired colonel Bill Takacs. The now silver-haired but still cigar-chomping Pave Low icon was even more blunt: "I can remember leaving on Christmas Eve, not being able to tell the wife and kids where we were going to or when we'd return. It is going to be that kind of life. . . . Staying alive in Pave Low means having crew coordination—everyone has to do his job to keep the airplane away from trouble. That takes dedication and professionalism. You've got a responsibility to everyone else on that helicopter. There aren't any Lone Rangers in this business."[8]

The messages were well received by the attendees. "There is no doubt that I want to be a special operator," said 1st Lt Eric Braganca, as he and flight engineer SSgt Mark Pryor joined McKinney and the other Airmen who applied and were accepted for Pave Low duty in the initial iterations of Commando Look.[9]

A few female Airmen also expressed an interest in the program. At the time, service opportunities were being vastly expanded for females. In April 1993, Secretary of Defense Les Aspin issued a new policy allowing women to serve in most career fields, including pilot, navigator, and enlisted aircrew, on almost all USAF aircraft. That policy applied to the AFSOC C-130s of all variants. Conspicuously absent on the list, however, was the MH-53. Women were not accepted for crew duty on the Pave Lows because doing so would put them at too high a risk of being engaged in ground combat. Pave Low crew duty would remain all male.[10]

31st Special Operations Squadron

The 31st SOS, now fully settled at Osan, received the mandates on the hard crews and flight system with mixed reviews. The guidance was clear. AFSOC wanted to realign the structure so that (1) the best possible crews could be sent to supported operations, (2) leadership opportunities for aircrew members could be improved, and (3) aircrew members would begin to think and operate as a crew vice as a specific position on the crew. The guidance further postulated that "the crew that trains together as a team, better understands each other's capabilities, strengths, and weaknesses, thus maximizing their chances for success when called upon." The squadron was directed to form one crew per assigned aircraft by 30 September 1993.[11]

Some 31st SOS crew members had served on other aircraft and understood the concept. Others questioned the efficacy of doing it in a small squadron, with everybody on one-year tours. Every month, about 10 percent of the squadron turned over; the only personnel constant was change. Additionally, the crews were to form into flights, with the officers now doing efficiency reports for the enlisted. Several of the NCOs resented losing their opportunities to be supervisors of the younger Airmen. Regardless, the squadron did its best to comply as the 31st SOS "nomads" traveled far and wide across the Pacific—Australia, Thailand, Malaysia—to participate in an endless spate of exercises and adjust to the challenges of flying in Korea, where the airspace and ranges were limited and in high demand. Behind all of the training, too, was the sobering thought that North Korea still posed a threat to the south and still served as one of the main reasons for the existence of the 353d SOG. In November the entire 353d deployed to Korea and was given an ORI based on the Korean scenario. The unit received an "excellent" rating, clarion testimony to the great work that the 352d and 31st SOS did to reconstitute themselves after the debacle of Mount Pinatubo. Colonel Correll was certainly pleased. On 20 December 1993, he gave up command of the 31st to Lt Col Craig Jensen and returned to Hurlburt to serve on the AFSOC staff.[12]

20th Special Operations Squadron

The 20th SOS troops who had been the last ones in Kuwait had been home only 10 days when another team was dispatched to support the 21st SOS in its two deployments. One aircraft, crew, and small maintenance team went to Incirlik for Provide Comfort II, and two aircraft, three crews, and another maintenance team went to Brindisi, Italy, to support the growing Provide Promise operation. Most of the 20th and 21st personnel knew one another, either from their Pave Low training or from previous tours, and they blended well. The 20th guys also could not help but sense that the 21st guys really appreciated the support since they had been tasked to carry such a heavy dual deployment load for quite a while by now.

Back at Hurlburt, the 20th began deploying to Asheville, North Carolina, for continuation mountain training in June. This training gave the squadron an excellent opportunity to begin tactical flying under the AFSOC-mandated hard crew concept. Each crew was formed with nine members: three pilots, three flight engineers, and three gunners. This allowed for the maximum flexibility in scheduling. However, there were still growing pains as the squadron adjusted to the new system. Capt Scott Howell was crewed with Capt Tom Trask, in charge of the stan/eval section; flight engineer TSgt Eddie Parris; and gunner MSgt Willie Taylor, both also from stan/eval. For a year, Howell flew almost exclusively with them—learning the finer nuances of the aircraft, tactics, and crew management through their mentorship—as they traveled to various exercises and worked with the standard customers. He was able to work his way into the plans section and then began to see the big picture of what the 20th could be called upon to do worldwide. That was a very sobering discovery. Similarly, 1st Lt Jim Slife was hard crewed with Capt Matt Shazda and found that experience to be most enlightening, enjoyable, and professionally enhancing.[13]

In May 1993, Capt Greg Lengyel reported to the 20th from his tour at the 31st SOS. Like Capt Scott Howell earlier, Lengyel was also a bit intimidated by what he found. First of all, the squadron commander, Colonel Rakip, was a legend within the Pave Low community. Additionally, the squadron was still full of guys who had flown hard combat in Desert Storm. Third, it had its own assigned organizational maintenance section, growing the squadron to over 600 officers and Airmen. Perhaps most importantly, though, it was literally the Pave Low place to be—the "show," using the term made famous by the movie *Bull Durham*. It was the unit that worked with all of the best special forces elements, got the really important national force missions, and stood to a global commitment. These were the crews that flew the Big Mish.

Additionally, Lengyel could tell that the unit had exceptionally high standards. It expected more of its officers and Airmen, although he sensed that it could be rather impersonal at times because it was so large. Regardless, he liked being in a unit that self-policed to high levels of performance and standards. Overall, he found it to be a "very impressive" unit.[14]

The 20th was not affected in any significant way when on 1 October 1993 the 1st SOW was redesignated the 16th SOW, per General

McPeak's desire to restructure the USAF. As part of that process, he stipulated that wings would not hold identical numerical designations. At that time, there were three 1st wings: the 1st Fighter Wing, the 1st Space Wing, and the 1st Special Operations Wing. The 1st Space Wing was scheduled to inactivate. However, McPeak specifically wanted the heritage of the first 13 pre-USAF wings protected. The 1st FW was one of those, and the 1st SOW was not. The 1st SOW certainly had a long and distinguished heritage; however, when compared to the 1st FW using a formula devised by the historical analysts at the Historical Research Agency, the 1st SOW lost. Consequently, the 1st SOW was designated the 16th SOW, derived from the 16th Pursuit Group, a unit that had been one of the 13 originals and had a heritage dating back to 1923. Its subordinate groups and support squadrons also changed their designations to the 16th, and life went on.[15]

Just a few days after the wing designation change, the 20th SOS was directed to fly nine MH-53s to Guantanamo Naval Base, Cuba, for a classified contingency operation. Rakip led the formation—airborne within 16 hours of notification—and landed in Guantanamo without incident. Crew members remained there for five days and then returned to Hurlburt, also without incident. While at Guantanamo, they worked directly with the 1st Battalion of the 2d Marine Regiment. After the deployment, the regimental commander wrote to the 16th SOW commander, Brig Gen Maxwell Bailey, "The spirit of cooperation, teamwork, and motivation exhibited by Lt Col Rakip and his staff and aircrews was simply outstanding."[16]

Two months later, the 16th SOW and 20th SOS held another Commando Look screening. One of the candidates was SSgt Robert Dinsmore, who had enlisted in 1988 and had trained as a weapons loader. After two tours loading bombs, missiles, and 20 mm ammunition on B-52s and F-4s, he was ready for something new. After hearing about Pave Low, he signed up for the evaluation as a gunner and traveled from his current assignment at Kadena to Hurlburt. He liked the program, and the evaluators found him compatible. Consequently, he received an assignment to the 20th SOS as a gunner. During the summer and fall of 1994, he went TDY to the 551st SOS for his gunnery and crew training. While there, he logged 17 training flights and qualified with both the .50-caliber machine gun and the 20 mm minigun on the great Red Rio Bombing Range. He also learned his manifest duties as a scanner and overall Pave Low aircrew member. However, he broke a thumb while at Kirtland and was not able to finish his training until he returned to Hurlburt. By early 1995, though, he finished his qualification and, when certified as combat ready and proudly wearing his red scarf, immediately left on a series of training exercises with the various customers with whom the 20th routinely trained.[17]

Air Rescue Service

The realignment of all USAF units as directed by General McPeak had one perhaps unintended consequence. With the dissolution of MAC, the Air Rescue Service was initially reassigned to the AMC. Since its reactivation on 1 August 1989, it had worked steadily to re-establish its CSAR capability and by 1992 had seven combat-ready rescue squadrons equipped with HH-60G and HH-3E aircraft. Regardless, on 2 July 1993, the ARS was reassigned from AMC directly to the DO at ACC and transferred all of its squadrons to the host units at their assigned bases. Operational control would be exercised by the affected overseas command or ACC. The ARS staff was absorbed under the ACC/DO, and the ARS was redesignated the USAF Combat Rescue School at Nellis. For the first time since it was formed as a separate service, the USAF did not have an operational rescue command. There was no clarity of mission or even one individual in any high position as the overall leader of its rescue forces. Rescue was now a dispersed set of squadron-level units, all under the command of officers who had other priorities.[18]

Kirtland AFB

On 1 July 1993, AETC was finally activated. Reflecting this consolidation, the 542d CTW was reassigned from the AMC to AETC effective that same date. In accordance with McPeak's desire to renumber the wings to best preserve unit lineage and historical honors, the 542d was notified that within a year, it would receive a new designation, to be determined.

These changes had little impact on the 551st. For the rest of the year, it continued to qualify crew members for the Pave Low units, although it did have several individuals, especially flight engineers, either fail the course or self-eliminate from the program. Unit crews were also allowed to participate in training exercises with US Army special forces units and move outsized containers for other organizations on Kirtland. Weapons training for the gunners and flight engineers was improved when the 542d TCHTS began using inert ammunition to teach proper weapons procedures in the helicopter part-task trainer.

On two occasions, crews were again called out to perform local rescue or humanitarian missions. They were dispatched to perform SAR missions and humanitarian relief for remote towns cut off by heavy snows, especially on the Navaho Indian reservations. A 551st crew was also launched to recover an F-111 crew that ejected while on a tactical mission in eastern New Mexico. Lt Col Mike Damron commanded the crew that picked up the two Airmen and returned them to their unit at Cannon AFB, New Mexico. Even the training crews occasionally got to perform real-world missions.[19]

As 1993 was drawing to a close, the Airmen of the 542d CTW were notified that their unit would inactivate, as per the McPeak reorganization/restructuring of the USAF, on 1 April 1994. It would be replaced by the newly activated 58th SOW, which would be assuming the numerical designation from the 58th FW formerly at Luke AFB. The 58th SOW would still be assigned to AETC's Nineteenth Air Force. The subordinate 58th SOG would have assigned to it the 551st which, along with the 550th FTS, would change from a flying training squadron to a special operations squadron. Additionally, the 542d TCHTS would convert to the 512th SOS and become the training squadron for the UH-1s and H-60s.[20]

On 1 April 1994, the changes took place as scheduled as the various unit flags were furled and unfurled and the various commanders rendered their salutes and then made the obligatory speeches. However, the mission for the wing and the flying squadrons remained the same. The 551st, with its six assigned TH-53As and four MH-53Js, continued to produce new pilots, engineers, gunners, and instructors for the operational squadrons. At the time, the TH-53s were being modified with air refueling gear so that they could be used for that phase of training. Throughout the year, the squadron also accomplished some operational training as it participated with aircraft and crews in the latest series of Chili Flag exercises with US Navy SEALs, Army special forces units, and USAF CCTs and PJs. Its crews also responded to statewide SAR calls when they happened—quite a service for the state of New Mexico. Additionally, the 551st deployed maintenance personnel to support the ongoing operations in Saudi Arabia and Turkey.[21]

Clear and Present Danger

In 1994 Paramount Pictures produced and released the movie version of Tom Clancy's *Clear and Present Danger*. Harrison Ford played the arch-hero Jack Ryan in the widely viewed and acclaimed narco-thriller. Members of the Pave Low community initially flocked to theaters to see the film, anticipating a key role for the Pave Lows, since they had been so well featured in the book. However, they were sorely disappointed because the Pave Low helicopters were not included in the script. Instead, the movie used US Army special operations helicopters similar to those in the 160th SOAR. Ed Reed, in particular, was upset with the substitution since he had been part of the initial effort to get the Pave Lows in the book. He did some checking, only to discover that apparently some skullduggery had taken place. Production representatives from Paramount had contacted USSOCOM for production assistance. The Army officers who received the request did not contact AFSOC for help. Rather, they peremptorily approved the use of the Army 160th SOAR helicopters versus the Pave Lows for the movie.[22]

Air Force Special Operations Command

On the same day that the 58th SOW was activated at Kirtland AFB, one of the very last unit changes dictated by the McPeak realignment took place at Hurlburt Field. The Special Missions Operational Test and Evaluation Center was inactivated, and all of its personnel, facilities, and funds were transferred to the newly activated 18th Flight Test Squadron (FLTS). The 18th also inherited a long list of ongoing SOF-specific projects. With the unit change, though, came added responsibility. In 1993, as part of a tactics review process, General Fister questioned how the AFSOC developed proper and current defensive maneuvers. To address that shortfall, the 18th FLTS would also be given the responsibility to develop, test, validate, and disseminate new tactics for AFSOC. Consequently, the 18th grew from 98 to 142 personnel to address these new tasks.[23]

Many of the ongoing projects dealt with the Pave Low helicopters, such as testing related to the almost continuous SLEP modifications, installing folding blades for shipboard operations, and increasing gross weight limits to 50,000 pounds for emergency war-plan contingencies. The 18th assumed responsibility for initial testing begun in 1993 on a new proposed modification to the aircraft called the Interactive Defense Avionics Systems/Multi-Mission Advanced Tactical Terminal (IDAS/MATT). This sophisticated and highly classified concept would integrate several onboard sensor systems with the overall enhanced navigation system and existing ECM and flare/chaff dispenser systems. Additionally, the system would be able to receive real-time intelligence and operational data that could then be displayed on both existing and newly proposed display screens, providing the aircrews greatly increased tactical situational awareness and an improved capability of dealing with threats. It was an exciting concept and one that could add to the technological brilliance of the Pave Low aircraft. However, the concept needed to be fully matured and refined before it could be accepted for the fleet, and the 18th was given responsibility to accomplish the necessary testing to make it work.[24]

Commando Vision

In early 1994, the AFSOC commander, General Fister, directed a review of the readiness posture of the command as the long-standing Soviet threat disappeared and the "new world order" of dispersed regional and ethnic threats and potential humanitarian needs became the primary concerns. His planners reviewed the current AFSOC force structure initially developed under the Twenty-Third Air Force Forward Look program 10 years earlier. They concluded that it had been structured to support two theaters simultaneously but was now being called upon to support contingencies in all six foreign theaters. The command TDY rate around the globe had increased 100 percent since the pre–Desert Shield days. In response, the planners developed "Commando Vision," designed to consolidate AFSOC forces in the CONUS and establish a theater orientation in line with regional defense concepts that could more equitably provide special operations aviation assets to theater commanders.

As a result of the study, a program change request was created that dictated a two-phase plan. Phase I would realign several active USAF and USAF Reserve AC- and MC-130 units for better utilization. Phase II would pursue the activation of another special operations wing, to be based in the western United States (as per the intent of the earlier Forward Look plan) with a mix of C-130-type aircraft and possibly Pave Lows. The two overseas SOGs would remain in place but possibly lose some force structure to equip the new wing. However, their special operations support squadrons would receive increased manning to provide more dispersed command and control capability. For contingencies, CONUS-based aircrews and maintenance teams could be rotated in to augment the permanent units as needed.

The plan was straightforward and could be completed with internal assets and manpower. However, the development of a CONUS West Coast SOW was problematic at a time when force structure was being reduced. One potential course of action was to be vigilant for a possible base that might become available through the Base Realignment and Closure Commission, which Congress was intermittently conducting.[25]

Haiti

Perhaps in vivid testimony to the need for Commando Vision, in the summer of 1994 AFSOC forces were deployed as part of a much larger multinational task force to Haiti to quell a military takeover of their democratically elected government and the civil unrest that ensued. Thousands of Haitians fled the country in small boats heading for Florida. After initial political efforts failed, Pres. Bill Clinton decided to dispatch military forces for Operation Uphold Democracy to intervene and stabilize the country. A sizeable force of paratroops from the 82d Airborne Division from Fort Bragg was launched. However, the opposition politicians agreed to a negotiated settlement, and the forcible entry was cancelled. Instead, a multinational force of 20,000 US personnel, primarily from the 10th Mountain Division, and 2,000 troops from other Caribbean nations entered the country to stop an outbreak of lawless activity and stabilize the political and social situation. AFSOC had been planning for this contingency for some time and dispatched a task force to Haiti and its environs. Most of it came from the 16th SOW, which sent 1,600 Airmen to fly and support MC- and AC-130s, MH-60s, and Pave Lows throughout September.

At the time, the 20th was well engaged in its yearly training plan and routinely had crews and maintenance personnel deployed across the CONUS to several classified and unclassified training exercises with various special forces units. However, the majority of those were cancelled when the 20th, now led by Lt Col Don Hoover, who had taken command in June from Colonel Rakip, received its deployment order. Hoover had been serving as the operations officer for the squadron, so the transition had been smooth. Like "Pappy" Walters and Tom Aldrich, Hoover was another former Vietnam-experienced US Army warrant officer who had successfully transferred over to Pave Lows, adding to the community his vast flying knowledge and experience. He selected Lt Col Bob Maldonado to be his operations officer.[26]

Within 24 hours of being told to go, he had the 20th airborne to support the operation with 14 MH-53 aircraft, manned and supported with 170 operations and maintenance personnel and augmented by two complete aircrews and 12 maintenance troops from the 58th SOW.

Retracing their activities in the previous December, the helicopters, led by Capt Mitch Petersen, launched out across the Gulf of Mexico in a driving rainstorm and very poor visibility. The passage was challenging, with lots of problems with spacing and lost wingmen. Like the year before, the helicopters flew to Guantanamo Bay and conducted support operations from there. The crews were told to plan for direct-action assault missions that would include an initial large insertion of a Ranger force—another Big Mish type of operation for the 20th crews. Anticipating enemy reaction, Colonel Hoover directed the crews to carry extra barrels for their machine guns and additional loads of ammunition. He also ordered them to carry additional fuel, making the aircraft extremely heavy for assault landings into confined landing zones. Some of the crews were very concerned about the extra weight and addressed the issue with Hoover at a contentious crew meeting. He held fast to his orders. However, the "forced entry" mission was cancelled. Instead, the crews were ordered to prepare to conduct humanitarian missions, SAR alert, and support missions for various ground SOF elements. Their helicopters were the first to land in Port-au-Prince, Haiti, with food and medical supplies. Aircraft maintenance was superb, and Hoover could count on nine aircraft being ready to fly every day. Many of the missions were classified.

On one multiship mission, Capt Jim Slife was the flight lead as the crews inserted and then extracted a special forces team. After recovering their customers, Slife turned the flight toward Guantanamo. Arrangements had been made for an MC-130 to meet the flight halfway for an in-flight refueling to insure that the helicopters had sufficient fuel reserves to safely make the air base. Unfortunately, the MC-130 did not receive the correct refueling point and was much farther away from the helicopters than they had planned for. One of the crews, commanded by Capt Greg Lengyel, was very low on fuel. Slife and Lengyel quickly developed a revised plan, and the rendezvous was accomplished. All aircraft were able to get their needed fuel and proceeded to Guantanamo without further incident. The flight crew debriefing, also attended by Colonel Hoover, was somewhat animated as the crews dissected their mistakes.[27]

Courtesy USSOCOM Public Affairs

20th SOS Pave Lows at Guantanamo Naval Station, Cuba, for Operation Uphold Democracy in Haiti, 1994

The majority of the flying was relatively routine. While deployed for just over one month, the 20th crews logged 716 flight hours on 196 sorties, with a 100 percent launch rate. The high launch rate was indicative of the commendable job the maintenance troops had been doing to sustain unit aircraft. Their efforts were also reflected in the

20th receiving the 1993 Air Force Maintenance Effectiveness Award for best rotary-wing unit prior to its deployment.[28]

Capt Scott Howell also participated in the Haiti operation but in a very different form. A few months prior, he had been assigned to serve as the AFSOC liaison officer to the 75th Ranger Regiment. As the Paves were getting ready to deploy, he traveled to Savannah, Georgia, to join his headquarters unit as it deployed for the Haiti operation. Howell was with his commander on the USS *America* for 28 days, working all manner of joint air-ground operations issues. He also met a number of rising officers and NCOs in the Ranger community with whom he would work in later operations. A few months later, he was able to take over as the squadron chief of plans when his boss, Maj Lance Bodine, departed the squadron.[29]

The Balkans

As 1994 began, AFSOC continued to provide support and augmentation as necessary for the 352d SOG and 21st SOS as they continued to fulfill their CSAR tasking under Operation Deny Flight. They realigned their operations with hard crews as directed by AFSOC. January passed peacefully. The tense quiet was shattered, though, on 5 February, when Serb forces fired artillery into the central marketplace in Sarajevo, Bosnia, killing 68 civilians and wounding 200 more. NATO forces declared a weapons-free zone around the city and announced that they would bomb any weapons found in that zone. As tensions mounted, one of the 352d's more senior Pave Low pilots, Capt J. D. Clem, attended a NATO standardization conference to better coordinate CSAR procedures for all NATO members. Personnel from the 21st SOS subsequently trained with aircrews from the French air force and others on common procedures. At the same time, 16th SOW personnel began to arrive at Brindisi to replace the 352d troops so they could return to Alconbury to prepare for and then conduct an ORI through May. The troops of the two units were used to working together, and the transition was smooth.[30]

Three weeks later, in another provocative move, the Serbs dispatched a flight of six Galeb light-attack aircraft to bomb Bosnian forces near the city of Novi Travnik. They were intercepted by two F-16s from the 526th Fighter Squadron (FS) flying out of Aviano AB, Italy, and piloted by Capt Robert Wright and Capt Scott O'Grady.

20th SOS Pave Lows fly by the USS *America* (CV-66) during Operation Uphold Democracy.

Wright (a.k.a. Wilbur) promptly shot down three of the aircraft, scoring the first-ever air-to-air kills for an F-16. When the remaining Serbian aircraft attempted to flee, another flight of two more F-16s shot down a fourth and watched a fifth crash into a mountain as its pilot tried to evade the USAF fighters.[31]

The next day, a US Navy F-14 went down in the Adriatic Sea, and a 20th SOS MH-53 from Brindisi assisted in the recovery. While politicians from both sides wrestled to work out a cease-fire, it appeared that air action was going to steadily increase. Two weeks later, NATO aircraft began dispatching fighter aircraft to provide direct support for peacekeeping troops and UNPROFOR observers. By early April, NATO aircraft were bombing enemy targets, and the Serbian forces were engaging NATO aircraft with antiaircraft artillery and SAMs.

On 15 April 1994, a French aircraft was damaged by enemy fire. The next day, the 20th SOS scrambled its CSAR task force in response to the downing of Vixen 23, a British AV-8 Harrier shot down by Serbian forces near Goražde, Bosnia. The MH-53s held over the Adriatic Sea for two hours and refueled twice before being directed

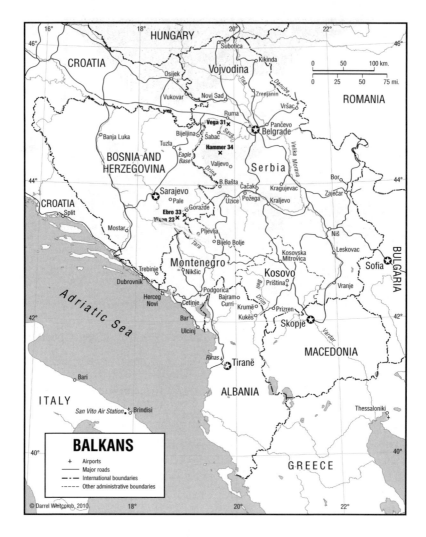

Figure 5. **Balkans area of operations**. (Copyright Darrel Whitcomb, 2010.)

to return to Brindisi. They were, at that point, unaware that the pilot had been recovered by friendly Bosnian Muslims, taken through Serbian lines into Goražde, and turned over to a small British SAS team. A few days later, the pilot and SAS team were able to evade out of the besieged city, avoid Serbian forces, and reach a designated recovery point where a French Puma landed in total darkness and recovered them.[32]

During April and May, the 352d SOG received its ORI. It occurred in two phases and involved deployed operations during Exercise Ellipse Bravo in eastern Europe. As the inspection was being conducted, two MH-53s had to be immediately grounded to conform to a time-compliance technical order modification. Nonetheless, the 21st was able to adjust its operations, and the squadron and the SOG in general passed the ORI with high grades.[33]

In June, the 21st SOS personnel returned to Brindisi to resume their JSOTF2 tasking, and the troops from the 16th SOW returned home, except for two 20th crews that remained as augmentees. On 11 July 1994, Lt Col Jeff Walls replaced Colonel Wurster as the 21st SOS commander. Wurster departed for the Pentagon and staff duty in the OSD.

The wholesale deployment of the 21st SOS aircraft and personnel to Brindisi to support ongoing operations in both Provide Promise and Deny Flight made it impossible for the 21st to participate in any

Courtesy Lt Col Jim Breck, USAF

A well-known landmark, the "Elephant Cage" antenna array at San Vito

other operational exercises occurring in the theater. Additionally, maintaining several aircraft and crews on alert tied up these resources so that flight training while at Brindisi was minimal. To solve this problem, Walls requested that the 20th crews be returned to Hurlburt so that the flying time allocated to them at Brindisi could be used for the 21st crews to accomplish the training that they were receiving at Alconbury. This was approved, and the 21st was able to fulfill its training requirements for the second half of 1994 at Brindisi, including an emphasis on ship landing and boarding operations. However, CSAR alert was still its primary mission, as NATO countries now had almost 170 combat and support aircraft operating in the region.

TSgt Jim Kradel augmented the 21st crews and flew several missions into Bosnia. On one mission he and his crew carried Lt Gen Mike Ryan, the Sixteenth Air Force commander and the Allied Air

Forces Southern Europe (AIRSOUTH) NATO commander, and his aides on a mission to search for mass grave sites. The weather was cloudy, and the Paves had to use their TF/TA radar to navigate in the tight valleys and land at various sites and airfields. It was also cold, and the general did not appreciate the Pave Low crews flying with their windows open. Kradel had to explain to him that the enemy AAA threat required them to have their guns at the ready and gave him a thicker Gortex flight jacket to wear.

On another occasion, a Pave Low crew dropped off General Ryan for a meeting with several Serbian commanders. The Pave Low crew then took off with instructions to return to the same landing zone at a specific time. As Ryan spoke with the Serbians, a thick fog settled over the area and showed no signs of dissipating. As the designated landing time approached, Ryan asked to be taken back to the landing zone. The Serbians questioned the ability of the Pave Low to land in such poor weather. Regardless, they proceeded to the landing zone and watched in amazement as the Pave Low touched down at the designated place and time. The Serbs were greatly impressed as Ryan climbed aboard and the crew lifted off back into the fog.[34]

20th Special Operations Squadron/ 16th Special Operations Wing

After the Haiti mission, Captain Slife volunteered and received orders for a two-year assignment to the 31st SOS. He was most pleased and began organizing his family to go to Korea. However, the USAF decided to institute an intern program for sharp young captains. They would spend two-year tours on the Air Staff in Washington and be exposed to the bigger picture. Hoover directed Slife to submit an application package for the program. General Bailey, the 16th SOW commander, had witnessed Slife's performance in Haiti and wanted to nominate him. Slife submitted the package and was selected for the assignment. He reported to the Air Staff in August 1995.

The assignment was beneficial in two ways. First, he got to see issues from the total USAF perspective and meet and work with a number of individuals of great potential. Second, in a most unexpected way, he received some first-class mentoring. When he arrived there, he contacted Colonel Wurster, whom he had met on a Brindisi tour. Wurster was back in the Pentagon, now working for the ASD/

SOLIC. For several months, he had a series of meetings with the younger officer and gave Slife a trove of information to enhance his staff experience. It was mentoring of the finest kind. Slife would leave the intern tour in May 1997 having amassed a wealth of practical knowledge on the USAF, in general, and officership, in particular, which he would find useful in later assignments.[35]

In the spring of 1995, the 16th SOW held another Commando Look screening. One of the candidates was Capt Vince Becklund. He had been commissioned from the Air Force Academy in 1990 and was currently flying UH-1Ns with the 76th Rescue Flight at Vandenberg AFB, California. Those aircraft had recently been modified with FLIRs, and the pilots routinely used NVGs. Consequently, their UH-1Ns were referred to as "Pave Hueys." Becklund had recently met Maj Bob Leonik, who had come to Vandenberg to observe the squadron's NVG program. Becklund briefed him on how pilots used the NVGs for their range control duties along the coast. Leonik then regaled Becklund with Pave Low stories from Desert Storm and beyond. That sounded like interesting duty, and Becklund mentioned it to his operations officer, who had him sign up for the visit to Hurlburt. While there, he was able to get a Pave Low ride with Captain Lengyel and an interview with Colonel Hoover. Becklund told Hoover that he was interested in Pave Lows but was also considering the MH-60s. Hoover looked directly at him and asked, "Do you want to lead or follow? That's the only question you have to answer." Becklund returned to Vandenberg and requested assignment to Pave Lows and the 20th SOS. He reported to Kirtland AFB in June, where he shared his training flights with Maj Paul Harmon, who had just finished a year at Fort Leavenworth, Kansas, attending the Army Command and General Staff College, and was about to start a tour with the 551st SOS.[36]

Becklund really enjoyed flying with Paul Harmon. He appreciated how easily Harmon dealt with his crews and openly depended upon his enlisted guys. Harmon used the training to make concrete suggestions and observations based upon his vast operational knowledge of the aircraft and mission. Again, Harmon was providing mentoring to the younger officer, a growing staple of the Pave Low community. However, it was mentoring on several levels. Becklund later explained that "you watch how the older guys do it. There are some that you go: 'That's how I want to do it. When I get to be in leadership, that's how I'm going to do it.' Or, 'when I get to be in leadership, that's not how I'm going to do it.' You learn good and bad from watching the guys."[37]

Captain Becklund also noticed something else at Kirtland. Not all of the pilots going to Pave Low had gone through Commando Look. Several of his fellow pilot students were former first-assignment IPs—or FAIPs, as they were labeled—who had flown T-37s or T-38s and were not too happy about being sent to helicopters. Some of them struggled with the aircraft and even the mission. Some also made it clear that if given the opportunity to return to fixed wing or possibly to get a civilian airline job, they would gladly go. Not everybody wanted to be a Pave Low pilot.[38]

Air Force Special Operations Command

As 1995 began, AFSOC was the proud parent of a steadily maturing Pave Low fleet and community. Its three operational squadrons operated 37 MH-53J aircraft and were all almost fully manned. The squadron numbers for officers and Airmen were 60 and 494 for the 20th, 22 and 146 for the 21st, and 22 and 222 for the 31st, respectively. All aircraft had completed the SLEP program before the NADEP at Pensacola was closed. From this point on, long-term maintenance and modifications would be done at the Cherry Point MCAS, where the USMC logistics depot for its H-53s was located.

The closure of the Pensacola NADEP also required another change. Since 1991 Aeronautical Radio, Incorporated (ARINC) had kept a maintenance office at Pensacola that employed several Pave Low retirees, including Tom Aldrich, "Pappy" Walters, and Rick Simmon, to conduct test flights on MH-53s, which received modifications at that facility. However, with the closure of the NADEP, ARINC arranged to move that facility to Hurlburt Field. There the maintenance technicians could provide maintenance flight support directly to the 16th SOW. They would perform functional, operational, and acceptance test flights and ferry flights to and from Cherry Point.[39]

At the same time, the 18th FLTS at Hurlburt was busy testing the IDAS/MATT modification, which appeared capable of significantly improving flight crew situational awareness in challenging environments. Acknowledging the key role that the Pave Low played in the AFSOC, the command historian, Mr. Herb Mason, commented in the 1995 command history that "the importance of the Pave Low cannot be overstated. As the primary long range vertical airlift system, in many critical SOF missions, it provided that last bit of critical airlift so necessary to a successful mission." In that continued role, it directly supported the AFSOC mission. Mason added that "AFSOC is America's specialized air power. It is a step ahead in a changing world, delivering special operations combat power, anytime, anywhere."[40]

In the not-too-distant future, AFSOC would be receiving a new aircraft to further enhance that capability. In January the CSAF, Gen Ron Fogleman, committed to the purchase of 50 CV-22s, beginning in 2000, that were to achieve operational status by 2003. Crew training was slated to be assigned to the 58th SOW at Kirtland, and the first operational squadron would be located at Hurlburt, with follow-on squadrons at the 352d and 353d Groups. With their 230-knot cruising speed, 500-mile combat range, in-flight refueling capacity, and all-weather, day/night precision navigational capabilities, these aircraft were not intended as wholesale replacements for any specific aircraft but as new machines with unique capabilities allowing the air commandos of AFSOC to address mission requirements in different ways. However, AFSOC planners anticipated that some MH-60s, MH-53s, and aging MC-130s would be inactivated as the new aircraft arrived. It was exciting news for the command and portended steady technological advance for the air commandos well into the 21st century.[41]

A Joint Special Operations Aviation Command?

The announced acquisition of the new CV-22 to supplant the Pave Lows and MH-60s was exciting news. However, the AFSOC was not the only service operating helicopters in the special operations arena. The 160th SOAR of the US Army SOC was also an outstanding unit and competed aggressively with AFSOC forces. In fact, the October 1992 crash of the MH-60 suggested that this spirited competition may have contributed to a lack of common operational standards and procedures. Current USSOCOM strategic guidance already called for the establishment of a single proponent for special operations aviation (SOA). To address these issues in a concerted fashion, the USSOCOM commander, Gen Wayne Downing, directed the establishment of a joint special operations aviation study group to develop a plan to establish a single proponent for SOA at Hurlburt, most probably within AFSOC, to standardize all SOA aircrew procedures, safety, training, doctrine, and tactics.

Maj Gen James Hobson had recently taken command of the AFSOC from Maj Gen Bruce Fister. He directed his staff to tackle the problem aggressively and develop a proposal to reorganize the SOA of both services under a single subunified command called the Joint Special Operations Aviation Command (JSOAC). The AFSOC commander would also serve as the JSOAC commander, with an Army brigadier general as his vice-commander.

As the single focal point for SOA issues, the JSOAC would address the standardization challenges. However, the AFSOC staff proposed a larger mission. It recommended that the JSOAC also be the single source for prioritizing SOF air requirements for USSOCOM surface forces; determining requirements for SOA acquisitions and modifications; centralizing SOA doctrine, policy, and planning; managing command, control, communications, and computer systems (C4); and integrating SOF assets into the deep battlefield.

This was a bold proposal that met the commander's intent but suggested much more, including upgrading the AFSOC commander to a lieutenant general position. It gained a great deal of support among the USSOCOM staff. General Downing received the briefing with General Hobson in attendance at a USSOCOM Board of Directors meeting. However, as the briefing commenced, senior Army general officers at or represented at the meeting made it abundantly clear that they vigorously objected to any such overall subunified command, and, as the meeting devolved into fractious acrimony, they voted to scrap the entire project. Instead, a joint air staff division would be set up within the USSOCOM/J3 (operations directorate), with both Army and USAF representatives. The two special operations aviation communities would remain separate and in direct competition with each other. Once more it seemed as if the poison of Initiative 17 had arisen to divide the two communities. While struggling with the JSOAC issue, SOCOM published operational guidance for dissimilar helicopter formation flight procedures and disseminated it to all of the rotary-wing squadrons.[42]

21st Special Operations Squadron

As these fractious debates took place, the 21st SOS was still at Brindisi, working with the JSOTF2 on CSAR alert for the ongoing NATO operations in the Balkans. When possible the crews began flying with other service helicopters to gain experience. Additionally,

Colonel Walls worked with his Airmen to sharpen their skills for possible use as extraction vehicles on noncombatant evacuation operations, a mission for which H-53s had been used since their creation. The crews also stepped up their CSAR training with other coalition forces and A-10s from Spangdahlam AB.

Through the spring of 1995, the 352d SOG was finally able to move all of its scattered units to their permanent location at RAF Mildenhall, the home of the 100th Air Refueling Wing. The 21st sent most of its troops home in March to complete their move from Alconbury to Mildenhall, and personnel from the 16th SOW and 20th SOS, augmented with an MH-53J and crew from the 58th SOW, assumed the alert tasking at Brindisi.[43]

After its move was completed, the 21st SOS returned to Brindisi and resumed duties as part of JSOTF2. NATO aircraft continued to fly in the area, especially reconnaissance and combat air patrol missions in support of Deny Flight. However, conditions remained relatively calm as politicians for both sides tried to broker an agreement to resolve the underlying issues of the conflict. This hiatus ended, though, on 1 May, when ground forces from Croatia attacked Serbian forces still occupying an area near Zagreb. NATO ordered limited air strikes against specific Serbian units that had violated restrictions against the use of heavy weapons. On 2 June, an F-16, call sign Basher 52, from the 555th FS based at Aviano AB, was shot down near the Bosnian city of Banja Luka. The pilot, Capt Scott O'Grady, ejected, and his flight lead—again, coincidentally, Captain Robert Wright—watched him float to the ground. O'Grady did not make initial contact with Wright or anybody else, and his status was unknown. JSOTF2 was immediately alerted for CSAR, and A-10s and other support aircraft were prepared at Aviano and other bases. However, without contact with the survivor, they would not be launched until the status or even existence of the survivor was verified.

A US naval task force was afloat in the Adriatic Sea, led by the helicopter carrier USS *Kearsarge*, and included the 24th MEU, a battalion-sized force with aviation assets, including helicopters. It also had a platoon-sized team trained to conduct tactical recovery of aircraft and personnel (TRAP) operations. The task force was under NATO control. The senior NATO commander in the area was US Navy admiral Leighton Smith. He kept his intelligence sources focused on locating or otherwise determining the status of O'Grady. On the evening of 7 June, reconnaissance assets detected signals that could have been the survivor. Aviano-based F-16s were dispatched to the area, and in the early morning hours of 8 June, one of the pilots made voice contact with O'Grady. JSOTF2 assets were available for the mission but were not given the tasking. Instead Admiral Smith directed the MEU to execute a TRAP recovery of O'Grady. A force of several USMC CH-53s, AH-1s, and AV-8 Harriers launched and, within four hours of initial contact, landed in Bosnia, rescued Capt O'Grady, and returned to safety without loss.[44]

The overall situation in the region became even more chaotic as Serbian forces continued to attack UN forces and protected enclaves throughout the summer. When senior NATO leaders logged vigorous complaints with the UN secretary general, Boutros Boutros-Ghali, he authorized significant offensive air strikes. USAF lieutenant general Michael Ryan, still serving as the Sixteenth Air Force commander and the AIRSOUTH NATO commander, was directed to create a campaign plan for strikes against Serbian forces. He and his staff developed an operational plan called Deliberate Force, which identified almost 550 targets. Political leaders authorized about one-third of them for strike, including several Serbian air defense sites, with an initiation of operations on 30 August. Again, JSOTF2 would provide CSAR support, and it requested assistance from the 20th SOS. It was augmented with three aircraft and crews from the 20th SOS. Lt Col Mike Homan, the CSAR veteran of Desert Storm, had just taken over command of the 20th from Lt Col Don Hoover in late June, when Hoover departed to attend the Naval War College in Rhode Island. Homan scrambled to put together a package of aircraft and personnel and had them on the way to Brindisi within 96 hours.

On the morning of 30 August, dozens of NATO aircraft began pounding the targets. The Serbian defenses put up a spirited array of SAMs and antiaircraft artillery, shooting down a French Mirage 2000K, call sign Ebro 33, 20 miles southeast of Pale, Bosnia-Herzegovina. The two crewmen ejected and were immediately captured by Serbian forces. NATO forces were unaware of that situation, and JSOTF2 was ordered to launch two Pave Lows and an MC-130 to hold off of the Croatian coast pending contact with the crew members. When no contact was established, they were ordered to return to Brindisi.[45]

NATO forces continued to search for the men. Over the next several days, they collected several pieces of intelligence suggesting that the two men were alive and evading in the area. Admiral Smith briefed this information to his NATO superiors, and they authorized him to initiate rescue operations as he saw fit. The US Navy aircraft carrier USS *Roosevelt* was on-station and had SH-60s on board with a detachment of SEALs. He assigned them the mission. JSOTF2 at Brindisi was also monitoring the situation and developing contingency plans.

In the early morning hours of 6 September, as more NATO air strikes pounded the Serbs, two SH-60s and SEALs launched from the *Roosevelt*. Unfortunately, as they crossed the coastline, they encountered a solid line of thunderstorms and fog that covered the mountains and completely blocked their path. When the second aircraft in the flight was struck by ground fire, they turned around and returned to the ship.

Admiral Smith reviewed all available intelligence and decided to launch another effort. This time, the mission was assigned to the JSOTF2. There the mixed 20th and 21st crews were already working the mission. The two lead pilots—Capt Charles (Mark) Harmon from the 21st and Capt Brad Webb, who had recently transferred from the 20th to the 21st SOS—both wanted to lead the mission. A coin toss gave it to Harmon. He and his wingman, Capt Paul Moncrief from the 20th SOS, and crews would fly as Knife 44 and Knife 47, respectively. That night they launched with a support package consisting of two MC-130 Talons, two MC-130 Shadows, an AC-130 gunship, and A-10s and F-18s from Aviano. Additionally, each Pave Low would have a French special forces soldier on board for linguistic purposes. Webb led a second flight of two MH-53s as a backup force, which held over the Adriatic.[46]

Harmon's flight entered Bosnia in the dark of night and at low level, utilizing the Pave enhanced navigation capability and the crews' NVGs. As Knife 44 and 47 entered the Pale Valley, the French soldiers on board began calling to the crew of Ebro 33 on all possible frequencies. The crews were able to search for 45 minutes before thick mountain fog formed and prevented any further visual search. At several points, the crews observed ground fire from 37 mm AAA and machine guns. Sergeant Dinsmore was aboard the second aircraft and called out the ground fire. The two crews turned for home. Knife 47 was hit by one round of small arms fire.

The two crews flew again the next night with a similar support package. This time, though, the weather was perfectly clear. The JSOTF2 intelligence section had determined several probable hiding sites for the two Frenchmen, and the two Pave Low crews and an accompanying AC-130 searched each site in detail. Perhaps anticipating another recovery effort, the Serbian forces in the area brought in an estimated eight antiaircraft guns and put up a stiff fight. The AC-130 and accompanying A-10s and F-18s struck several targets, and even the gunners in the two Pave Lows fired repeatedly, as the French soldiers on board called in vain for their countrymen. Again Dinsmore was aboard the number two aircraft as the left gunner. At one point, he observed ground fire from a farmhouse and fired 200 rounds from his minigun at it. As the aircraft maneuvered, the enemy continued to fire at the Pave Low, and the right gunner, TSgt Billy Breedlove, fired 800 rounds at the same farmhouse. One AK-47 round hit Dinsmore's aircraft but was stopped by a protective Kevlar blanket. In the ensuing melee aboard the lead Pave Low, gunner SSgt Randy Rutledge and flight engineer SSgt Dennis Turner were seriously wounded. Convinced now that the risk to the crews far outweighed the possibility of finding the French crewmen, the two Pave Lows departed for Brindisi as the supporting aircraft continued to bomb enemy guns.[47]

Admiral Smith forbade any further attempts pending the availability of further intelligence that the two Frenchmen were still evading. Three weeks later, updated intelligence indicated conclusively that the men were being held by Serbian forces, and the mission was terminated. Subsequently, Rutledge and Turner were awarded Purple Hearts for the wounds that they received, and Captains Harmon and Moncrief were dually awarded the 1995 USAF Cheney Award for their outstanding leadership of the mission.[48]

Taken aback by the ferocity and intensity of the air campaign, Serbian leaders initially tried to resist the onslaught, which was coordinated with ground attacks by friendly forces in the area. By 14 September, though, they had suffered terrible losses and began to remove their forces as directed. Operation Deliberate Force was terminated. During the 17 days of bombing, 3,535 attack and support sorties had been flown. They had dropped 1,026 bombs, 70 percent of which were precision weapons, and had struck 338 individual targets.[49]

However, small incidents requiring a NATO response continued to occur until 12 October, when both sides were able to agree on a ceasefire. At the urging of the United States, both sides were invited to Wright-Patterson AFB to discuss and craft a Bosnia peace accord. After several days of often fractious discussions, the presidents of Bosnia, Croatia, and Serbia scripted and initialed what came to be known as the Dayton Peace Accord, formally signed in Paris on 14 December.

The accord stipulated that the UN would cease operations in the region and turn all control over to NATO. This was accomplished on 20 December. A multinational organization was formed for Bosnia, with sectors under the overall control of British, French, and US forces. Its mission was to implement the peace accord, and the force was subsequently titled the Implementation Force, or IFOR. The overall operation was labeled Joint Endeavor and detailed the American sector as the northeast section of Bosnia, centered on the city of Tuzla, which included a large military base and airfield. Joint Endeavor was scheduled to last for one year and involve 60,000-plus soldiers, sailors, and marines from several nations.[50]

With the cessation of Deliberate Force, the operations tempo at Brindisi slowed down noticeably. Now more sorties were available for training. Three Pave Lows and crews from the 20th were dispatched to Egypt to participate in a Bright Star training exercise with other teams from the 16th SOW. One of the helicopters developed a leak en route and diverted into Souda Bay, Crete, for repairs. When it was fixed, the aircrew flew on to its assigned base in Egypt. As it entered Egyptian airspace, it unknowingly flew near Egyptian president Hosni Mubarak's private palace and generated a serious international incident that took several days to resolve. Belatedly, the crew also discovered that Egyptian forces guarding the palace had fired at its aircraft. Once all of that was resolved, the exercise was relatively uneventful. One of the crews even got to land in the Qattara Depression in southern Egypt, 500 feet below sea level.[51]

The 21st SOS continued to receive requests to fly various high-ranking officers and leaders into various sites in Bosnia. Like General Ryan earlier, they seemed to prefer the Pave Lows for two reasons. First, the pilots could use the aircraft's enhanced navigations systems to get into just about any location in any weather. Second, the commanders, especially, just seemed to enjoy arriving and departing in big, ugly, "bad-assed" looking helicopters, as the young Pave Low crews could not help but notice. In fact, Pave Lows were used to flying Admiral Smith, the IFOR commander, and Brig Gen Michael Canavan, commander of the Special Operations Command Implementation Force (SOCIFOR), into Sarajevo using the TF/TA radar repeatedly. The crews accomplished flawless landings in zero visibility, delivering these key officers to attend the transfer of authority from the UN to NATO.[52]

The level of activity continued to decrease, and in December, the JSOTF2 was inactivated. In its place, the SOCIFOR was activated with control over the assets of the 20th and 21st SOS. There was still much to do to implement the peace accords in the Balkans.[53]

31st Special Operations Squadron

Throughout 1995 operations were fairly stable for the 31st SOS at Osan, with its parent 353d SOG still at Kadena AB. The 353d staff members were able to review the Commando Vision plan in detail. Assuming that the conceptual West Coast wing would have a Pave Low unit, they realized that it would probably be the 31st SOS. However, they pointed out that to meet their support requirements to SOCPAC for a force of 4 MH-53s permanently assigned in-theater, AFSOC would have to establish a program providing for a steady rotational assignment of varying lengths for aircrews and support personnel. Additionally, war plan contingencies would have to be revised to provide many more aircraft and crews as any developing scenario would dictate.

Like the other units in the group, the 31st was constantly on the go. It dispatched aircraft, crews, and support teams to operational exercises like Balance Mint and and Balance Piston and to joint combined exchange training in Thailand, Australia, the Philippines, Indonesia, and Korea. A team of two MH-53s and support personnel deployed to northeast Thailand to participate in Cobra Gold '95 in May. While there, they operated from several of the same airfields that the crews of the 40th ARRSq and 21st SOS had used 25 years earlier. These deployments allowed the crews to work with other USAF, USN, USMC, and USA elements, allied forces, and special operations forces while performing the full panoply of missions of which the crews and aircraft were capable.[54]

In May TSgt John DeSalle transferred in from the 21st SOS for another tour with the 31st. His wife was also with him, and they both served concurrent overseas one-year tours. Although DeSalle and his wife, Janet, had signed the paperwork for two-year tours, the personnel specialist at Osan would not allow them to do a concurrent two-year tour. Subsequently, he deployed with the unit to the standard set of TDYs in Thailand, Singapore, and Okinawa. She was an electronic warfare specialist and supported the F-16s and A-10s also stationed there at Osan.[55]

Also serving in the 31st at that time was Capt Jonathan Owens. He had been commissioned into the Air Force from Virginia Polytechnic Institute and State University in 1986, where he was a member of the Corps of Cadets. After helicopter pilot training, he served a short tour flying UH-1s at Malmstrom AFB, Montana, before accepting an assignment with the Army like Scott Howell. Owens flew as an OH-58 scout pilot with the 7th ID at Fort Ord, California, and served a short deployment to Panama for Operation Just Cause. He attended MH-53 school in 1991–92 and then flew with the 20th SOS and participated in the Haiti mission before transferring to the 31st in 1995.

On 6 June 1995, Owens was the aircraft commander aboard MH-53J #68-10932, a veteran of the Koh Tang mission in Cambodia, on a tactical sortie to the Koon-Ni Range. Prior to arriving at the range, Owens and his crew—consisting of Capt Carlos Halcomb, flight engineers SSgt Jeff Franco and SrA Erik Fricsons, and gunners SSgt J. P. Herman and SSgt Rick Shore—had performed several practice tactical insertions. While holding for the assigned range time, the crew heard a loud bang and felt a severe engine vibration. Halcomb was flying, and Owens directed him to land at a nearby helipad. Suddenly, the aircraft experienced a complete failure of the right engine that resulted in a hard landing. The engine failure was caused by the malfunction of a shaft coupling that disintegrated and threw pieces of metal through fuel and oil lines, starting a fire in the engine compartment. Luckily the crew was able to escape without any injuries. However, an Air Force Academy cadet along for an orientation ride was slightly hurt. The $27 million aircraft was completely destroyed.[56]

Four weeks later, the unit received a replacement Pave Low for the aircraft lost in June, and within days, the squadron commander, Lt Col Lyle Koenig, and his Airmen were back on the road supporting exercises. In August the west coast of Korea was swept by tropical storm Janis. All aircraft at Osan AB, including the Pave Lows, were forced to evacuate as the torrential rain flooded the base. Returning home a few days later, the Airmen resumed their series of exercise deployments to allied nations in the theater.[57]

58th Special Operations Wing/
551st Special Operations Squadron

Continuing with the force reductions initiated after the end of the Cold War, Congress dictated another round of base closures in 1995 as part of the base realignment and closure (BRAC) process. One of the suggested closures was Kirtland. The 58th SOW was directed to analyze what it would cost to move the wing to Holloman AFB, New Mexico; Beale AFB, California; or Hill AFB, Utah. For two months, wing staff personnel, alongside Air Staff officers and local community leaders, worked the issue. Economic analysis showed that the closure would cost the Albuquerque area almost 12,000 jobs directly or indirectly. Additionally, the cost of moving the wing to Holloman, Beale, and Hill was $231, $150, and $114 million, respectively. Reviewing the results, Air Force Secretary Sheila Widnall and Defense Secretary William Perry reported to the BRAC Commission that the closure of Kirtland and relocation of the 58th SOW would not be cost effective. The commission agreed and removed it from the closure list.[58]

Within the wing, MH-53 training continued unabated at the 551st SOS. All TH-53s had received their air-refueling modifications and were now being used for that training event, saving flight hours on the MH-53Js. The TH-53s were also programmed to receive GPS navigational systems, as was the weapons systems trainer, so that both were more compatible with the operational fleet Paves. Pilot manning was an issue for the 551st SOS, as only 60 percent of its slots were filled. To partly address this shortfall, the 551st commander, Colonel Damron, requested that three contract pilots be hired to do all maintenance FCFs. To keep his crews operationally oriented, he also allowed them to participate in the ongoing Chili Flag exercises held periodically at Kirtland with US Navy SEALs and other special operations forces. His crews also answered calls for local SAR missions as they occurred. On 26 July, he passed command of the 551st SOS to Col Robert Maldonado. Training operations continued apace, and in 1995, the squadron qualified or requalified 30 pilots, 19 flight engineers, and 20 gunners.

The wing staff analyzed training that summer and found that all academic and simulator training needed to be centralized under one unit as it had been with the earlier 542d TCHTS, which had been inactivated as part of the reorganization into the 58th SOW. The wing requested a waiver to the objective wing structure from the Air Staff to activate another squadron for this purpose. In August the waiver was issued, and the 58th Training Support Squadron (TRSS) was activated with Lt Col Edward Reed as its first commander. It was authorized 24 officers, 30 enlisted personnel, and 24 DOD civilians and would directly manage 229 contractors. Its assigned mission was to plan, develop, and evaluate aircrew academics and simulator and flight training in the UH-1, H-53, HH-60, HC-130, and MC-130 aircraft. Additionally, it would manage and operate the sophisticated and constantly upgraded WSTs and all of the ground training systems, including a new Aerial Gunner Scanner Simulator (AGSS), many of which existed because of the funding brilliance of Ed Reed. The 58th TRSS would provide the critical support for ground and simulator training essential to optimize the actual flying training so that the graduates of the various programs could then report to their operational units as highly trained as possible.[59]

Air Force Special Operations Command

As 1996 began, the AFSOC commander, General Hobson, laid out his worldview for his Airmen. Reviewing the "new world order" extant since the demise of the Soviet Union and Warsaw Pact, he saw a rise in regional powers with access to terrible weapons, a surfeit of humanitarian tragedy, and economic and ethnic strains, all of which could lead to conflict. Concerned for the impact these forces were having on the Airmen of his command, he wrote, "The Cold War is over, downsizing is almost complete, turbulence created by external and internal changes is stabilizing—all good news. However, this progress has not occurred without cost: a rise in hot spots around the globe, increased operations requirements, and increasingly scarce resources. The outlook for the future demands on our personnel and equipment remains high."[60]

Doing more with less, while a USAF mantra, was a challenge for AFSOC. As the force of choice in many of the evolving world hot spots, AFSOC personnel were busy. The overall USAF goal for TDY days per calendar year was 120 per Airman. For the various AFSOC aircrews, though, the average was 120–48 days a year. All of the Pave units were busy: the 21st SOS was still directly involved in operations in the Balkans, and its crews were averaging 150 days a year there;

both the 20th SOS and 31st SOS were supporting the 21st while also answering an endless demand for joint and bilateral training all over the world. Stated Colonel Weikel, the AFSOC deputy director for plans, programs, and acquisition management, "We are stretched so thin it's just amazing. . . . It really impacts us because we are on the front lines."[61]

21st and 20th Special Operations Squadrons

As "the" Pave Low unit assigned to Europe, the 21st SOS still had its detachment at Brindisi, Italy, supporting Operation Joint Endeavor. It now worked for the JSOAC of the SOCIFOR, which was relocated to Stuttgart, Germany, and put under the direct control of NATO. Its crews, almost always augmented with additional aircraft, crews, and support equipment and personnel from the 20th SOS—to the point that the two units could almost be considered a consolidated operation—continuously received taskings to move key allied leaders into and out of various locations in Bosnia. They also flew several classified missions with various special operations forces and continued to train for the multitude of missions that they could be assigned. Some missions required the aircrews to fly above 10,000 feet. Since the Pave Lows did not have onboard oxygen systems, AFSOC had to develop specific waiver provisions and procedures for the use of portable systems to safely accomplish missions. Several of their helicopters had problems with their cabin heaters catching fire. For obvious safety reasons, their use was restricted until a NADEP team could evaluate the problem and determine corrective actions. Given the cold winters in Europe, this was a serious crew problem until fixed by late spring.[62]

Any sense of schedule normalcy changed on 3 April 1996, when the JSOAC received a report from the NATO combined air operations center (CAOC) at Vicenza, Italy, that a NATO aircraft had crashed at approximately 3 p.m. while trying to land in bad weather at the airport in Dubrovnik, Croatia. The CAOC told the JSOAC to prepare two MH-53s and an MC-130 for imminent SAR operations. At 5:20 p.m., the CAOC directed them to launch. Ten minutes later, the two Pave Lows—call signs Facet 23, commanded by Capt Steve Kelly, 21st SOS, and Facet 24, commanded by Capt John Conley, 20th SOS—launched and proceeded to Dubrovnik. Both were carrying special tactics squadron (STS) teams.

Courtesy Lt Col Jim Breck, USAF

CT-43 crash site near Dubrovnik, Croatia

Arriving in the area one hour later, the crews found other aircraft searching along the coast. It was not clear what type of aircraft had gone down. With the crash area still shrouded in low clouds and daylight rapidly fading, searching was difficult, especially with the other aircraft now in the area. Regardless, the Pave Low crews persevered, discontinuing their search to land at Dubrovnik to refuel and then returning to the site. While at the airport, the Pave Low crews learned that the downed aircraft was a USAF CT-43 carrying the US secretary of commerce, Mr. Ronald Brown, and possibly as many as 30 personnel on his team. This was a mission of tremendous political importance.

After refueling, Facet 23 and 24 remained at Dubrovnik Airport for updates. They were informed at about 9:30 p.m. that Croatian police had found the crash site on the side of a steep hill, secured it, and discovered one female survivor. Captain Kelly wanted to launch at once to recover the woman. After some discussion with the CAOC about who controlled the crash site, Kelly was cleared to take off singly. A special tactics team and several Croatian policemen were also proceeding to the site to recover the wounded survivor. Kelly launched at 10:30 p.m. and found low clouds still hanging over the crash area. He made three attempts to get through the weather to the crash site but was unable because of the poor visibility, rain, and ruggedness of the terrain. Kelly remembered, "We were all sweating bullets and it was the hardest flying I have ever done in my life." However, they could not get in safely to drop off their troops and returned to the airport.[63]

The Croatian police were notified that the Pave Low could not get in because of the weather. Unfortunately, in the intervening period, the woman died, and the Croatians brought her body down the mountain. The SOCIFOR commander, General Canavan, then took control of the recovery operation and began marshalling a significant SOF force of many components to carry out the mission. As Kelly and his crew were making their attempt, Canavan and a small command and control element flew to Dubrovnik Airport aboard two more Pave Lows, Facet 25 and 26, and set up a small command post in a warehouse. Major Webb, serving as the safety officer for the 352d SOG, was with him to act as mission commander for the Pave Lows supporting the operation.[64]

Departing Dubrovnik Airport after dropping off Canavan and his team, Facet 25, commanded by Capt Mark Harmon, flew over the crash site and, through a small, brief hole in the clouds, spotted it and determined its coordinates. Harmon called those coordinates back to the two crews at the airport. Captain Conley in Facet 24 then launched and headed to the site, just eight miles away. He found a small hole in the weather through which they could work and called for Kelly to also launch. By the time Kelly and his crew arrived, though, fog and low clouds had moved back in, obscuring the site. Nevertheless, they made several attempts to land, also having to take evasive action to avoid unmarked telephone poles. Kelly found a clear area about a mile away, landing there instead to unload his special tactics team. Facet 24 did the same, and both teams were then able to link up with Croatian police and reach the crash site. There they immediately began to mark the locations of all human remains with chemical lights.

Back at the Dubrovnik Airport, General Canavan had a rapidly growing joint and combined special forces team. He personally led them to the crash site, arriving at the base of the hill on which the crash site was located at about 3:30 a.m. After he received permission from the Croatian police to enter the area, accompanying British forces informed him that the area was possibly mined. Canavan decided to wait until sunrise to start up the hill. When they finally made the climb, they found the special tactics team still searching for the bodies. Throughout the day, the four Pave Low helicopters, now staging out of Dubrovnik Airport, flew to the crash site and retrieved 20 bodies using their hoists. One aircraft, Facet 20, flown by Capt Brett Hauenstein and crew from the 20th SOS, flew to Split to pick up the Croatian minister of state. They returned him to Dubrovnik so that he could meet with the senior US leaders there.

Once hoisted out of the crash site, the bodies were taken back to the airport, where a small morgue had been set up. The next day, the weather was appreciably worse, and plans were made to move the remaining 15 bodies down the hill by hand. However, two of the Pave Lows were able to get into the site and hoist out all 15 human remains. By the next day, all bodies had been properly prepared and were now on their way back to the United States. Mission complete. General Canavan then ordered all SOCIFOR forces back to their respective homes or deployed bases.[65]

Operation Assured Response

The Pave Low crews had been back at Brindisi only for a day when they received a warning order for another operation, this time an NEO, to the South African country of Liberia. That nation was experiencing serious civil unrest caused by the disintegration of its government. The US ambassador to Liberia, the Honorable William Milam, reported that the area around the US Embassy in Monrovia had become a focal point for intense fighting and that the Americans in the embassy were essentially hostages, surrounded by as many as 10,000 enraged Liberians. The embassy had only five armed US Marines to guard it, and many in the State Department saw this situation as reminiscent of the 1979 takeover of the American Embassy in Teheran. Milam requested that a military assessment team be sent to determine the danger to American personnel there and estimated that as many as 15,000 individuals—including Americans, some foreigners, and some local citizens—would need evacuation. Additionally, MC-130s and MH-53s from the 352d SOG, as well as aircraft from the 16th SOW, were put on alert for a possible evacuation. It would be conducted by a JTF as Operation Assured Response and commanded by General Canavan, with Col Steve Connelly from the 352d SOG as the JSOAC commander.[66]

At Brindisi three 21st SOS helicopters were broken down and loaded aboard C-5s, which were then airborne within 15 hours of initial notification. The C-5s also carried special equipment such as small cranes to facilitate the reassembly of the helicopters. Other C-5s departed Mildenhall carrying other required support equipment, supplies, and support troops.

Initial plans were to base the helicopters at Freetown, Sierra Leone, 190 nautical miles from Monrovia, and the fixed-wing aircraft at Dakar, Senegal, another 490 miles away. Fortuitously, the C-5s converged on Freetown almost simultaneously on the afternoon of 8 April. Maintenance and support troops began unloading the aircraft and equipment and preparing them to fly. Maj Brad Webb was designated to be the overall flight leader for the Pave Low team. With him were Capt

Steve Kelly and Capt John Conley and their crews from the Brown recovery. They joined a rapidly building task force of US Navy SEALs and US Army paratroops and special forces personnel.[67]

The next morning, one of the arriving Pave Lows received an FCF and was ready for operations. Webb loaded up SEALs, Army special forces, and some USAF special tactics Airmen and departed for the embassy in Monrovia. He flew over water until 10 miles out and then turned directly to the compound. The US Marines at the embassy popped green smoke signaling that it was safe to land. He did so on the very tight landing zone and then instructed the SEALs to remove certain poles, flowerpots, and trees for added safety. As soon as his inbound passengers had cleared the aircraft, Webb had them load him with 26 evacuees. He then lifted out of the embassy and retraced his route from Freetown. Landing there, he disgorged his evacuees into a waiting MC-130 that flew them to Dakar. Webb refueled his aircraft, loaded up with General Canavan and his staff, and flew back to the embassy, where he swapped them for another load of 25 evacuees and repeated the process. When he and his crew were out of crew-duty-day limits, another crew took the aircraft, which ended up operating for 21 straight hours before its engines were shut off.[68]

Courtesy AFSOC History Office

A 21st SOS MH-53J lands at the American Embassy in Monrovia, Liberia, for Operation Assured Response.

On 10 April, two more Pave Lows, crews, and support personnel arrived from the 20th; they and the second 21st aircraft were quickly made ready for operations. The third 21st Pave had a mechanical problem and never flew. Instead, it provided parts for the other aircraft. The crews launched and made steady runs to the embassy throughout the day and night. They also carried supplies, food, and water to the security troops in the embassy. The next day, 11 April, one of the Pave Low crews, commanded by Lt Col Steve Dreyer, observed two rocket-propelled grenades (RPG) fired at their aircraft. Canavan then suspended helicopter operations until the fighting subsided. Believing that the shots were just a fluke as opposed to an enemy attempt to stop the NEO, Dreyer suggested to Canavan that the Paves be allowed to fly a four-ship formation around the city to test for any further response. Canavan consented and the flight was uneventful, leading to a resumption of evacuation flights; however, a larger portion of flights were now flown at night using NVGs.

The next day, four MH-47Ds from the 160th SOAR arrived from Fort Campbell. They were assigned to the JSOAC, were quickly made ready, and entered the helicopter flow. That same day, MC-130s from the 352d SOG and 16th SOW set up a refueling track off the Liberian coast. This obviated the need to refuel back at Freetown, and the flights increased at a rapid rate. Concerned about the crew fatigue that was starting to appear in small ways, Colonel Connelly set up a more formal flying schedule for both the USAF and Army helicopter crews, which was less stressful for them. This also helped the Soldiers in the embassy plan for a smoother flow of evacuees—something almost akin to a bus schedule. Most evacuees did depart from the embassy; however, on two occasions, both Pave Lows and MH-47s flew to other compounds in Monrovia to pick up evacuees. By 17 April, virtually no more personnel in Monrovia desired evacuation, and the AFSOC assets were released to return to their home or deployed bases. As they were preparing to leave, Major Webb said of the evacuees, "They lost everything. When we talked to them, we could sense the mixture of elation at escaping and sadness of leaving their lives behind. It was gratifying, though, to know we helped get people out of a dangerous situation."[69]

An MEU arrived the next day to replace the JTF, but little more needed to be done. By the end of the deployment, 2,126 people from 76 countries had been evacuated by the SOF forces without any significant difficulties or accidents and without having fired a shot. It was a great demonstration of how effective SOF forces could be when they had been able to train together and develop strong intratheater habitual relationships. The Soldiers, Sailors, and Airmen of SOCEUR, as an integrated military force within EUCOM, had successfully executed this vital mission. Delighted with the results, USSOCOM commander Gen Hugh Shelton described the operation as a remarkable "synergy— the right organization, the best equipment and, most important, the finest men and women ever fielded in special operations."[70]

Over the next three days, the Pave Lows departed; this time, they were carried aboard new C-17s—a first for that aircraft. The 20th SOS aircraft returned to Hurlburt. The 21st SOS sent two to Mildenhall and one back to Brindisi for continued duty there. However, all needed some increased maintenance. Each of the four operational Pave Lows flew several missions with weights up to 54,000 pounds. Upon their return to home station, each aircraft was grounded for one week so that engineers could determine whether the aircraft had been damaged by the overuse. Fortunately, such was not the case.[71]

In the 21st SOS, several individuals were specifically cited for their outstanding efforts. Major Webb was noted for his sterling performance in the back-to-back CT-43 recovery and then Assured Response mission where he and his crew flew 13 sorties and evacuated an estimated 350 people. As a result, he was nominated for and received the Cheney Award for 1996 in recognition of his "act of valor or self-sacrifice in a humanitarian interest performed in connection with an aircraft." Likewise, Capt Steve Kelly was awarded the Aviator Valor Award for his work in both operations. Additionally, Maj Mark Harmon and his crew were awarded the Tunner Award as the "best airlift crew of the year" for their efforts in Assured Response.[72]

20th Special Operations Squadron

While the troops were busily engaged at Brindisi, the 16th SOW at Hurlburt faced a more fundamental challenge. From 20 April through 20 May, it received an ORI that was conducted as part of the large CJTF Exercise '96. The wing was directed to mobilize and deploy to Cecil Field, near Jacksonville, Florida. While there, it was given a series of tasks and exercises to fully test its ability to accomplish its assigned real-world missions, including working with British and Australian forces as well as with US special forces at Camp Blanding, Florida.

Overall, the wing received an "excellent" rating. The 20th SOS flew 23 evaluated missions, which required the crews to perform all assigned skill sets on their mission essential task list. The crews were especially lauded for their excellent coordination with their customers to enhance mission accomplishment. Flight planning and threat analysis were very well done. Out of 49 graded events, the average time-on-target deviation was 10 seconds. The inspectors rated the performance of the 20th SOS as excellent and noted that "20th SOS crews demonstrated their ability to react to changing situations, remaining flexible during the most demanding circumstances. Rapid and appropriate responses were observed on missions affected by inclement weather, broken aircraft, and other changing circumstances. . . . Mission accomplishment under adverse conditions reflected an attitude of perseverance and professionalism prevalent throughout the 20th SOS." Perhaps most pleased at the 20th's performance was the commander, Colonel Homan. In his after action report, he specifically cited the squadron mobility section, the planning section, his aircrews, and the maintenance section. He said, "Incredible performance during the ORI. All sorties launched on time. . . . Hard work equaled flawless results." A few months later, he passed command of the unit to Lt Col Thomas Hull, retired from the USAF, and went to work with Bell Helicopter Aircraft Corporation in Fort Worth, Texas.[73]

Settling into the job, Hull decided that he wanted to reorganize the squadron with a formal flight system with majors in charge of essentially deployable packages of crews, and he put his staff to work to make it happen. He also addressed one relatively mundane "personnel" item. He hired retired major John Grove, Pave Low pilot #19, into the squadron as a jack-of-all-trades. His general duties were to serve as an unofficial unit historian and provide general administrative support as needed. As he established himself in the squadron, though, Grove began to spread out into other efforts. He started a project to establish a scholarship fund for children of deceased Pave Low personnel. He took over the administration of the squadron store, in charge of procuring shirts and other memorabilia for sale in the squadron or at squadron parties. His efforts would increase in magnitude over the years as he became a staple of squadron life. Grove was fond of saying, "Once a Green Hornet, always a Green Hornet."[74]

In another personnel move, Hull decided to make MSgt John Sprouse his squadron superintendent. Sprouse was happy to take the job. He had returned from England in 1991, served in both the 20th

SOS and 16th SOG stan/eval sections, and made some deployments to Brindisi. He would serve in the squadron superintendent billet for about a year until it was upgraded to a chief master sergeant position. Then he would move over and serve as the gunner superintendent. Both jobs afforded him the chance to work directly with his Airmen, fly as a crew member and instructor, and go on TDYs with the crews.[75]

With the conclusion of Assured Response, the 20th and 21st SOS troops returned to Brindisi and resumed their mission in support of the SOCIFOR and their multiple taskings there. On 17 July, Lt Col Douglas Salmon replaced Lt Col Jeffrey Walls as the commander of the 21st SOS.

The day after Salmon took over, the 21st dispatched two aircraft, crews, and a maintenance team to Szolnok AB, Hungary, for Partnership for Peace exercise Cooperative Chance. For the next nine days, the Airmen participated in a highly scripted series of humanitarian-relief-type missions, emphasizing the use of "soft" military power like medical and engineering teams for nation-to-nation cooperative ventures. This did not include any night flying. The next month, the crews at Brindisi, when not on CSAR alert, were able to participate in joint and combined training exercises with other US special forces and both French and Italian SOF and rescue units on classic special ops missions, including shipboard operations and CSAR procedures. The Pave Low pilots were able to log some dissimilar formation flight time with Italian HH-3s and French Pumas. In some cases, the CSAR training involved the use of Italian fighter pilots as survivors.[76]

In September, the 21st SOS was directed to support a visit by a US presidential delegation to Bosnia, and two Pave Lows and crews were scheduled for the mission. They rehearsed and then flew a series of flights to transport several high-level dignitaries to several locations within Bosnia and, in particular, the US zone.

The Airmen of the 21st SOS received another excellent chance to participate in coalition training when the operations squadrons of the 352d were invited to participate in Exercise Popex at San Javier AB, Spain, in November. Two Pave Lows and crews deployed along with several MC-130s and spent two weeks performing the classic Pave Low missions with Spanish SOF units. The exercise was shortened somewhat when the 352d SOG received a warning order for a possible deployment of assets to central Africa to provide humanitarian relief for refugees fleeing tribal strife in Zaire and Rwanda. This was labeled Operation Guardian Assistance. Some MC-130s and AC-

130s from Hurlburt were sent. However, the Pave Lows were not deployed and in December were released from the potential tasking.[77]

On 20 December 1996, the mandate for the IFOR and Operation Joint Endeavor terminated. However, it was abundantly clear to all that although the NATO forces had separated the warring factions, allowed for the peaceful transfer of certain territories, and forced the movement of heavy weapons into storage areas, they could not leave. The endemic racial and ethnic hatreds were just too strong and ingrained. Consequently, the NATO leaders agreed to establish a longer-term stabilization force under Operation Joint Guard, which would run for at least 18 months but could be lengthened as necessary. This force would be only one-half the size of the IFOR force. Its missions were to deter hostilities, contribute to a secure environment, and promote the reestablishment of civil authority in Bosnia.

With the change, SOCEUR disbanded SOCIFOR. All SOF forces were consolidated under a combined joint special operations task force (CJSOTF) located in Bosnia. SOCEUR still had responsibility for CSAR and reestablished the JSOTF2 at Brindisi, with a further requirement for MC-130s and MH-53s on location, either from the 21st or 20th. SOCEUR also directed the 352d to man the staff. Reviewing the continued tasking, the 16th SOW commander, Brig Gen Norton Schwartz, requested that the AFSOC commander hold discussions with SOCEUR about moving the CJSOTF2 to consolidate with the CJSOTF staff in Bosnia and to allow the CSAR tasking to be absorbed by the joint and allied 150-plus helicopter force in that country. Additionally, this would eliminate some TDY billet requirements and allow the AFSOF helicopters to become more frequently involved in classic SOF missions. Schwartz did not receive any immediate response to his request.[78]

58th Special Operations Wing/ 551st Special Operations Squadron

The training units of the 58th SOW continued a steady if predictable operational pattern as they entered 1996. The Chili Flag exercises were now a regular occurrence and allowed the 551st SOS instructors and some students to gain initial or continued experience interplaying with all of the customer units with whom the operational Pave Low units worked. Crews continued to answer SAR calls coming in from statewide communities. The TH-53s were especially useful for this since they were lighter and more nimble at the mountain altitudes. The 551st was now conducting 11 different courses for the various Pave Low crew positions. The initial qualification courses for the pilots and flight engineers had been consolidated and were now 30 weeks long; all other courses were shorter. Based upon requests from AFSOC, in March the unit received guidance through AETC to begin training crews on heavyweight handling and dissimilar aircraft formation procedures. Flight engineers and gunners also received additional training on some new infrared aiming devices for the aircraft defensive guns. These items were incorporated into the various training syllabi. The yearly refresher training for all crew members was also reorganized into focused one-week courses. Pilots received 18 hours of academics and 17 hours of simulator training; flight engineers received the same 19 hours of academics and 8.5 hours in the simulator; and gunners received their refresher training on the AGSS.[79]

All of the simulators and training devices were operated and maintained by the 58th TRSS. The 22 different units for all of the aircraft taught at Kirtland ranged from the full-motion, highly sophisticated WSTs (simulators) to other less complex instructional systems such as the AGSS. The MH-53 crews specifically used the H-53 helicopter procedures trainer, TH-53A Operational Flight Trainer, MH-53J Part Task Trainer, and MH-53 Weapon System Trainer and Mission Rehearsal System. The development of the SOF Intersimulator Network (SOFNET) also provided a capability to link the data of different aircraft flight simulators together. This facilitated the interrelated use of different simulators for dissimilar formation work and in-flight refueling training. The 58th was rapidly becoming one of the DOD's most advanced mission training and rehearsal systems. It was all consolidated in one massive building complex costing almost $7.5 million and completed in October 1996. The next month, Colonel Reed passed command of the 58th TRSS to Lt Col Robert Leonik, another Pave Low pilot and veteran of heavy action in Desert Storm. Reed then retired from the USAF and put his extensive knowledge of flight simulators to good use in civil aviation.[80]

Simulator training was well integrated with the flight training done by the 551st. The squadron was still short several instructors, but AETC was working to fix that issue. Its six TH-53As and five MH-53Js were steadily producing trained crew members for the operational squadrons. Included in its small fleet was MH-53J #66-14433, the original Pave Low III, which logged its 10,000th flight hour in November.[81]

One of the pilots who received his initial MH-53 qualification that year was Capt Kent "Lando" Landreth. It was the fulfillment of a desire first spawned in him when, as a young Air Force Academy cadet, he had expressed an interest in special operations. That earned him a visit to Hurlburt, where he observed "those awesome machines" flying in loose formation along the coast. With further investigation, he also determined that they were the ones actually out doing "the" special operations mission and resolved that he wanted to fly them. After receiving his commission in 1991, he reported to Vance AFB, Oklahoma, for pilot training. Upon graduating from flight school the next year, though, his class did not receive any helicopter assignments. Instead, he took an assignment to HC-130Ps with the 67th SOS at RAF Alconbury.

From 1993 to 1995, he flew the HC-130s as they directly supported the Pave Lows in many operations. Landreth truly enjoyed the special operations mission and upgraded to aircraft commander while with the 67th SOS. However, he could clearly see that the HC-130's mission was to support the Pave Lows while they actually conducted the direct action missions. That observation further whetted his desire to transition to the MH-53, especially when he heard that there was a shortage of Pave Low pilots and the USAF was even allowing fixed-wing pilots to volunteer for the program. However, when Lando formally requested a Pave Low assignment, he was closely questioned by his supervisors, who doubted the wisdom of his request. They also pointed out to him that the USAF was offering a bonus to fixed-wing pilots who stayed in the USAF after their initial assignment was complete. But the bonus was not being given to the helicopter pilots, which meant that Landreth would be passing up a sizeable chunk of money to go to Paves. To Landreth, though, that was not an issue. He wanted to get into the mission. His request was approved, and in November 1995, he reported to Fort Rucker, Alabama, for a 12-week helicopter transition and then traveled to Kirtland to qualify in the Pave Low.[82]

Landreth already had over 1,000 hours of flying time and found the transition to helicopters to be exhilarating, recalling that one of his former commanders had told him that "helicopter flying is the best flying I ever did in the Air Force." He especially enjoyed flying the TH-53s. They were "overpowered, agile, and just an absolute ball to fly." Then he switched over to the Pave Lows and engrossed himself in the tactical employment of the aircraft. He remembered,

> That's where you really get an idea of the mission because now you have the FLIR, the TF/TA radar. Flying at night was easy for me because I had already spent all of my previous time flying on goggles. But learning what the airplane could do and how to land in [landing zones] and mountainous terrain at night was a significant challenge. . . . It's stressful, but it's rewarding. That includes the TF/TA part: being up in the caldera up in Albuquerque at 11,000 feet with goggles up, just relying on radar to fly through the mountains. It was awesome . . . everything that I had hoped it would be.

> I really got a great appreciation for how integral the crew is. . . . Everybody was always engaged, and they were all integral to making whatever flight it was a success. There was that bond . . . the MH-53 crews and how they have to work together. [At Kirtland], you really got to see how it's so orchestrated and it's almost like music when a crew really works well.

> The other side is when you don't really click, it can be really painful. You rely on one another. I was a weak link more than I can count. It makes a difference.[83]

Strangely enough, Landreth also discovered that there were times when Pave Low flying involved long periods of just droning along to get to a distant objective. He discovered that crews would find ways to enliven even these moments. He recalls an instance when "the instructor engineer tapped me on the shoulder. I looked back down the cargo compartment, and there was a gunner, on the tail, with a .50-cal, gunner's belt, boots, and helmet—that's all. I don't know where it came from or who initiated it, but, by God, if there was time to kill, there was a gunner." He added that "the personality of each crew position [was] always entertaining because whether it's gunner hugs or an engineer in the seat who decides that he is going to fly in his underwear, there was never a shortage of excitement. There was enough during the mission, but any lull in traffic, and I'll tell you what—someone will be doing something."[84]

Capt Kent Landreth finished up at Kirtland and reported to the 20th SOS at Hurlburt Field in September 1996. Arriving there, he took his wife and children for a quick drive around the base. As he passed by the 20th SOS building, he was staggered to see 22 Pave Lows parked out on the ramp. Then he was exhilarated to realize that he was now a part of a small and unique force that operated the most sophisticated helicopters in the world as part of a command that knew how to use them. He was ready to accomplish their—his—assigned missions "any time, any place."[85]

Notes

1. Weikel and Wurster, interviews. Mr. Peepers was a TV character popular in the 1950s. Played by Wally Cox, he was an iconic representation of a quiet teacher, unruffled by the general give-and-take of daily events but very much aware of unfolding events and skilled at reading people. He possessed the innate ability to stay two steps ahead of others and was quite capable of inserting, at the exact moment, the perfectly pithy—and sometimes wickedly devastating—comment, but always delivered with the utmost courtesy. Wurster accepted the moniker as a compliment.

2. Ibid.

3. History of the 352d Special Operations Group (hereafter referred to as History of 352d SOG), 1 Dec 1992–31 Dec 1993, vol. 1, xvii; Nalty, *Winged Shield*, vol. 2, 1950–1997, 497; and Hilkert, "History of SOCEUR 1954–2004," n.p., USSOCOM/HO.

4. Kradel, interview.

5. Nalty, *Winged Shield*, 499–500; and History of AFSOC, 1 Jan–31 Dec 1993, vol. 1, 110.

6. History of AFSOC, 1 Jan–31 Dec 1993, vol. 1, 162, 185, 189.

7. Rhodes, "Commando Look," 10.

8. Rhodes, "Wild Bill," sidebar to "Commando Look," 10.

9. Rhodes, "Commando Look," 10.

10. History of AFSOC, 1 Jan–31 Dec 1993, vol. 1, 39.

11. History of 353d SOG, 1 Jan–30 June 1993, vol. 1, 48.

12. Ibid., 2, 45, 48–50; and ibid., 1 July–31 Dec 1993, vol. 1, 1–4.

13. "20th SOS History for 1993," unpublished report, 20th SOS historical files, 1st/16th SOW HO; and Howell and Slife, interviews.

14. Lengyel, interview.

15. History of the 16th Special Operations Wing (hereafter referred to as History of 16th SOW), 1 July–31 Dec 1993, vol. 1, 9–11.

16. "20th SOS History for 1993," unpublished report, 20th SOS historical files, 1st/16th SOW HO.

17. Dinsmore, interview.

18. History of ARS, 1 Jan 1991–2 July 1993, 1–6.

19. History of 542d CTW, 1 July–31 Dec 1993, vol. 1, 1–2, 11, 17, 21–23.

20. Ibid., 1 Jan–31 Mar 1994, vol. 1, 1–3.

21. History of the 58th Special Operations Wing (hereafter referred to as History of 58th SOW), 1 Apr–31 Dec 1994, vol. 1, 1–3, 19, 21, 22.

22. Reed to the author, e-mail, 18 Sept 2009.

23. History of AFSOC, 1 Jan–31 Dec 1996, vol. 1, 16.

24. Ibid., 1 Jan–31 Dec 1994, vol. 1, 15, 30, 229–30; and ibid., vol. 5, supplemental doc. 1–66.

25. Ibid., 1 Jan–31 Dec 1996, vol. 1, 23–25, 127–28.

26. Hoover, interview.

27. Hoover, Slife, and Lengyel, interviews.

28. History of AFSOC, 1 Jan–31 Dec 1994, vol. 1, 128, 135; History of 16th SOW, 1 July–31 Dec 1994, vol. 1, 61–63, 65–68; ibid., 1 Jan–30 June 1994, vol. 1, 113; and Hoover and Slife, interviews.

29. Howell, interview.

30. History of 352d SOG, 1 Jan–30 June 1994, vol. 1, 126.

31. Nalty, *Winged Shield*, 501. (Captain Wright was a former Pave Low maintenance officer.)

32. Richardson, *No Escape Zone*, 140, 229; and History of 16th SOW, 1 July–31 Dec 1994, vol. 1, 62.

33. History of 352d SOG, 1 Jan–30 June 1994, vol. 1, xix.

34. Ibid., 1 July–31 Dec 1994, vol. 1, 17, 41, 117; and Kradel and Connelly, interviews.

35. Slife, interview

36. Becklund, interview.

37. Ibid.

38. Ibid.

39. Walters, interview.

40. History of AFSOC, 1 Jan–31 Dec 1995, vol. 1, 2, 100.

41. "AFSOC to Acquire CV–22 Osprey Aircraft," 3.

42. History of AFSOC, 1 Jan–31 Dec 1995, vol. 1, 9–10; and "Just a Good Ole Lynchin'," anonymous, n.d., in ibid., vol. 2, SD1–9.

43. History of 352d SOG, 1 Jan–31 Dec 1995, vol. 1, xvi, 1, 50.

44. Berndt, "Recovery of Basher 52," 41–47.

45. Owen, *Deliberate Force*, 137.

46. Webb, interview.

47. Dinsmore, interview.

48. Whitcomb, "Searching for Ebro 33," 36; and Greeley, "Search for Ebro 33," 6.

49. Owen, *Deliberate Force*, 337; and Nalty, *Winged Shield*, 506–10.

50. Nalty, *Winged Shield*, 510.

51. Strong, interview.

52. Webb, interview.

53. 20th SOS AFSOC Outstanding Squadron Nomination Package 1995, 20th SOS historical files, 1st/16th SOW HO; History of 352d SOG, 1 Jan–31 Dec 1995, vol. 1, xv–xix, 75, 102; and History of AFSOC, 1 Jan–31 Dec 1995, vol. 1, 154–55.

54. History of 353d SOG, 1 Jan–30 June 1995, vol. 1, 11–12, 30–31.

55. DeSalle, interview.

56. Crawford, "Nomads of the Pacific," pamphlet, 16, Heritage File, AFSOC/HO; and Owens to the author, e-mail.

57. History of 353d SOG, 1 July–31 Dec 1995, vol. 1, 21, 47.

58. History of 58th SOW, 1 Jan–30 June 1995, vol. 1, 1–5.

59. Ibid., 1 July–31 Dec 1995, 2–5, 8, 21, 46.

60. History of AFSOC, 1 Jan–31 Dec 1996, vol. 1, 18.

61. Ibid., 24; and History of 352d SOG, 1 July–31 Dec 1996, vol. 1, 9.

62. History of 352d SOG, 1 Jan–30 June 1996, vol. 1, 43, 130.

63. Murphy and Northacker, *Response to Disaster*, 11.

64. Ibid., 1–17; and Webb, interview.

65. Murphy and Northacker, *Response to Disaster*, 17–39.

66. Partin and Rhoden, *Operation Assured Response*, 1–2; and Webb, interview.

67. Partin and Rhoden, *Operation Assured Response*, 13–20; and History of 16th SOW, 1 Jan–31 Dec 1996, vol. 1, 108–11.

68. Thigpen, *Praetorian Starship*, 422; Partin and Rhoden, *Operation Assured Response*, 36; and Webb, interview.

69. Greeley, "They Lost Everything," 7.

70. Thigpen, *Praetorian Starship*, 422; and Partin and Rhoden, *Operation Assured Response*, 37–41, 48–49.

71. History of 352d SOG, 1 Jan–30 June 1996, vol. 1, 132.

72. History of AFSOC, 1 Jan–31 Dec 1997, vol. 1, 55; and data supplied by HQ USAF A3O–ATF (Air Staff).

73. History of 16th SOW, 1 Jan–31 Dec 1996, vol. 1, 149–59.

74. CJTFEX 96/ORI After Action Report, 14 June 1996, 20th SOS, historical files, 1st/16th SOW HO; and Homan and Grove, interviews.

75. Sprouse, interview.

76. History of 352d SOG, 1 July–31 Dec 1996, vol. 1, 28; and History of 16th SOW, 1 Jan–31 Dec 1996, vol. 1, 74.

77. History of 352d SOG, 1 July–31 Dec 1996, vol. 1, 28–29, and Thigpen, *Praetorian Starship*, 424.

78. Hilkert, "History of SOCEUR 1954–2004," n.p., SOCOM/HO; and History of 352d SOG, 1 July–31 Dec 1996, vol. 1, 46.

79. History of 58th SOW, 1 Jan–30 June 1996, vol. 1, 9, 14, 15, 23.

80. Ibid., 1 July 1996–30 June 1997, vol. 1, 54; and Reed, interview.

81. History of 58th SOW, 1 Jan–30 June 1996, vol. 1, 25; and ibid., 1 July 1996–30 June 1997, vol. 1, ix, 23.

82. Landreth, interview.

83. Ibid.

84. Ibid.

85. Ibid.

Chapter 12

Combat Search and Rescue

~1997–98

The CSAR mission area is insufficiently manned and equipped to meet its growing operational demands. . . . It is a broken mission area.

—Gen Richard Hawley

The Pave Low can do CSAR better than any other helicopter.

—Brig Gen Mike Kingsley

Air Force Special Operations Command, Hurlburt Field

As 1997 began, Maj Gen James Hobson was well into his third year as the AFSOC commander. Overall, he was pleased with the evolution of his command to the changing world paradigm. However, he was concerned about a couple of issues directly affecting the Pave Low fleet. The first was the operations tempo for his crews and support personnel. The ongoing commitment in the Balkans was driving the force, especially the 21st SOS, to exceed the USAF individual TDY standard of 120 days per year by a significant amount. As a result, that unit could not accomplish any significant training at home station and could rarely support any other European theater training events. The larger 20th SOS continued to augment with aircraft and personnel; however, the steady commitment also affected them in the same manner.

The second issue was the overall handling of the CSAR mission. Keying upon the request for relief that General Schwartz had sent to him a few months prior, Hobson attempted to address the larger issue of CSAR tasking of AFSOC units. He noted that CSAR requirements were still being maintained for operations in the Balkans and northern and southern Iraq. Rescue units were now fully equipped and trained with HH-60s under ACC control. However, they were not fulfilling the majority of taskings. Instead, AFSOC was still providing aircraft and crews, even though CSAR was still a secondary task for the AFSOC forces. Revising the white paper that his predecessor floated in 1992, Hobson proposed combining all ACC CSAR assets within the AFSOC and formally assigning the mission to that command. This would include the reserve component rescue forces and possibly the assignment of some to the proposed western AFSOC base, if that ever materialized. Such a reassignment would lead to an economy of forces, training and deployment efficiencies, and a better trained and standardized force that "would achieve more synergy and greater effectiveness," the general believed. Hobson also suggested that the addition of the now programmed CV-22 would further enhance his force.

However, Hobson was not able to move his proposal beyond the initial discussion stage before he retired in July, passing the reigns of AFSOC to Maj Gen Charles Holland. Upon taking command, Holland immediately engaged with ACC to have it assume more responsibility for the rescue operations in northern and southern Iraq. He began to explore options for AFSOC to become involved in the ongoing Operation Joint Guard support. However, he could not, at this point, make the CSAR issue his primary focus.[1]

Initially, he needed to deal with more immediate issues within the command. He continued to support the Commando Look program, which had been successful in helping AFSOC find the right personnel to enter the challenging and unique air command career fields. It had already helped to dramatically reduce the number of individuals who had self-eliminated from the training schools because of a lack of character or desire. He directed the staff to increase its efforts to assign promising young officers and NCOs to key joint and service staff assignments to properly season its personnel for increased authority and responsibility, as well as to better expose the larger USAF and other services to the capabilities of AFSOC. To assist this process, he directed his staff to initiate Commando Spotlight to identify the sharpest young operations captains in the seven-to-nine year groups for early assignment to the AFSOC staff for initial seasoning and mentoring. AFSOC officers and NCOs were steadily being promoted at rates ahead of the USAF overall, and General Holland wanted to continue and nurture that trend.[2]

Collaterally, efforts continued to steadily upgrade and improve the Pave Low fleet. In late 1996, the Air Force Operational Test and Evaluation Center (AFOTEC) at Kirtland AFB initiated a field test to investigate the feasibility and applicability of the potential IDAS/MATT upgrade for the MH-53J. Over the next several months, personnel from the AFOTEC detachment at Hurlburt worked with personnel from the 18th FLTS and the 20th SOS to modify and test one of the Pave Lows. The project showed that the IDAS/MATT was operationally effective and had the capability to decrease the overall aircrew workload and enhance situational awareness in a hostile environment. The modification would provide yet another tool to make the Pave Low more effective and useful in an ever-changing and ever more dangerous world as the "prime mover of the rotor-wing force of AFSOC." Later that fall, General Holland approved modifying up to 25 of the Pave Lows with the IDAS/MATT equipment, and a contract was signed with the Crestview Aerospace Corporation, located at Crestview, Florida, to perform the modifications, with the first aircraft to be delivered to Hurlburt in April 1998.[3]

21st and 20th Special Operations Squadrons

Under the auspices of Joint Guard, the political, economic, and domestic situation in Bosnia continued to stabilize. The 21st SOS maintained its presence at Brindisi under JSOTF2. The unit was augmented with two more MH-53s as backup aircraft inventory to provide for more flying and training at home station. Additionally, the 20th SOS still augmented at Brindisi, although the number of aircraft and crews varied from time to time. The missions were relatively routine but did require some crews to deploy to Tuzla or other forward locations for several days to provide shorter response times if any ground force special operations needed help or had detained "persons indicted for war crimes" who needed to be extracted. This gave the crews some experience using the unique Pave Low navigational systems over the challenging Bosnian terrain.[4]

In March the 352d was alerted to prepare several MC-130s and two MH-53s for deployment to the Central African Republic and the Republic of the Congo to conduct another NEO. However, the MH-53 portion of the task force was cancelled. In April combined 20th/21st crews flew support for a visit to Sarajevo by Pope John Paul II to hold a mass for the beleaguered citizens of Bosnia in the city's main soccer stadium.

In-flight refueling with an MC-130

In an attempt to reduce the impact of deployments on his troops, the 352d commander, Col Mike Planert, directed mandatory post-deployment breaks for all personnel to allow them to spend time with their families and restore their domestic lives. As operations steadily slowed at Brindisi, he was able to bring home more of the aircraft and crews. This necessitated an increase in local flying. However, the 21st now had to compete with other units in the UK for ranges and restricted airspace use.

In August 1997, Capt Jim Slife reported to the 21st SOS from MH-53 requalification at Kirtland. A much more experienced and enlightened officer now, he met with Lt Col Doug Salmon and was assigned to work in the plans office. He was glad to have such an interesting and responsible job. However, at the time, the unit was doing rotations only to Brindisi, and little planning was needed to do that. He did notice that the squadron operations officer, Lt Col Paul Harmon, was always extremely busy, and he asked Harmon if he could take over some of the current operations load. Harmon was happy to share the workload and effectively made Slife an assistant DO by broadening his authorities and responsibilities.[5]

In addition to its continued support to JSOTF2, the 352d SOG was notified by AFSOC that in the fall of the year, it would receive an ORI.

Consequently, the group and its subordinate units began a series of readiness exercises designed to prepare them for the inspection. Crews from all units deployed to several different countries and conducted joint and combined training with US and allied special forces elements. They all participated in endless "Warrior Day" drills at Mildenhall to sharpen their skills. The ORI was conducted in October and required the SOG and subordinate squadrons to deploy to an airfield in Norway above the Arctic Circle. There they operated with various allied forces as part of Exercise Nordic Retrieval. Overall, the 352d received an "excellent" rating. MH-53J operations were rated outstanding, with many substantive comments similar to those the 20th SOS received on its recent ORI—all reflecting a standard of excellence across the entire Pave Low community. At the same time, the combined 21st/20th crews at Brindisi averaged 70 sorties a month in support of Joint Guard.[6]

Hurlburt Field

At Hurlburt, the 20th SOS, with its 21 assigned MH-53Js, averaged 165 sorties per month as it continued to participate in an endless schedule of exercises—classified and unclassified, both domestically and internationally. Since reporting to the 20th SOS in 1996, Capt Vince Becklund had had his share of those deployments, especially the Brindisi trips and the continued Southern Watch rotations. At one point, Becklund was dispatched to Kuwait to replace another pilot who had gotten sick. He had just qualified as an IP and was giving a checkout ride to a new copilot. While doing a dust-out landing in an MH-53J, he inadvertently landed in an area of soft sand and snapped off the nose wheel. Fortunately, the aircraft was not further damaged. A safety investigation determined that Becklund had been within proper landing parameters; the unanticipated soft sand was the reason for the crash. Colonel Hull requested that AFSOC allow Becklund to resume his duties, and it did so. Hull told Becklund, "Go forth and do great things. You are still an IP. Get out there and keep doing it." Becklund really appreciated that and finished out his tour in Kuwait as an IP.[7]

The 20th crews still deployed to Asheville, North Carolina, for mountain qualification and proficiency training. Three Pave Lows and crews also deployed to NAS Oceana, Virginia, for two weeks in

April to participate in Exercise Kyrpton Vessel. While there, they worked with elements of the 160th SOAR and naval SOF units. They conducted several sorties involving shipboard operations and small team insertions. The crews reported to a command element located at a base on the West Coast. Now serving as the 20th's plans officer, Captain Becklund reported in the exercise after action report that it was an outstanding deployment and exercise, with much valuable training accomplished by all participants and several valuable tactical lessons learned.

In May 1997, Col Rich Comer took command of the 16th SOW from Brig Gen Norton Schwartz, who departed to command SOCPAC. Comer was the third Pave Low pilot to take wing command.[8] Comer was replaced as the operations group commander by Col James Connors. Three months later, Connors received a short-notice critical assignment to SOCCENT in Bahrain to serve as the vice-commander. Col Donald Wurster was selected to replace Connors. Wurster had just completed the Industrial College of the Armed Forces. He received a quick MH-53J requalification at Kirtland AFB and reported to Hurlburt to take command of the 16th SOG. Shortly thereafter, AFSOC notified the 16th SOW that it would be receiving an ORI in 1998, and Wurster set to work to prepare his group for that challenge.[9]

Settling into his assignment with the 20th SOS, Capt Kent Landreth was initially directed to work in current operations and scheduling. He was also quickly thrust into his share of joint training deployments, which helped him to steadily develop his talents and upgrade to aircraft commander and then IP. Additionally, he was able to work in the weapons and tactics office, which challenged him to develop an even deeper knowledge of the aircraft and its capabilities. This was a fortuitous time because the squadron was just receiving its first two IDAS/MATT-modified aircraft, and he was able to receive one of the earliest qualifications. He especially enjoyed working for Lt Col Tommy Hull, whom he found to be the kind of commander who was able to find that fine balance between dealing with the rules of any ever-growing service bureaucracy and the unique needs of the Pave Low customers with whom the crews routinely worked and had to support operationally, often on short notice. Said Landreth, Hull was definitely a member of the "seek forgiveness, not permission" clan.

Landreth was also given the opportunity to attend the USMC Helicopter Weapons and Tactics Course at the MCAS Yuma in Arizona.

There he developed an intricate knowledge of the larger tactical uses of helicopters. He was somewhat shocked to discover how primitive the majority of USMC helicopters were, lacking precision navigation capabilities and countermeasures equipment. One of the IDAS/ MATT aircraft was sent out for Landreth to use in the course. The Marines were amazed at the capabilities of the aircraft and correspondingly gave Pave Low crews lead responsibilities on all of the big missions. After one large nighttime insertion, one of the Marine commanders thanked Landreth by telling him, "We're just not used to going *exactly* where we are supposed to go."[10]

In November 1997, the Airmen of the 20th SOS were called upon to perform a duty to honor the larger and longer brotherhood of USAF H-53 veterans. Two Pave Low crews, led by Capt Gene Becker and conducting mountain training in North Carolina, flew to northern Virginia and performed a flyby at the Arlington National Cemetery. They were there to honor the crew of Jolly Green 67, which had been shot down and killed in HH-53C #68-10365 near Dong Ha, South Vietnam, on 6 April 1972 while trying to rescue two downed Airmen. In 1996 a recovery crew found the remains of that crew and returned

Courtesy Col Darrel Whitcomb, USAF, Retired

Two MH-53s perform a flyby at Arlington National Cemetery in Virginia for the burial ceremony for the crew of Jolly Green 67, shot down and killed while trying to rescue two American Airmen in South Vietnam in April 1972.

them to the United States. Several hundred family members and friends attended the ceremony, conducted by Capt (Chaplain) Steve Schaick. Looking at the assemblage of highly decorated Airmen there to honor their brothers, he noted, "The price of entry here today is a Silver Star."[11]

Colonel Wurster brought a large contingent of individuals from the 16th SOW, and they paid their respects to the families. Lt Gen Dave Vesely, the assistant vice chief of staff, Headquarters USAF, Washington, DC, and himself a veteran helicopter pilot who served in the 20th SOS in Vietnam, made the official remarks. He stated that "all of us who have flown in harm's way know what a difference it makes to believe that every effort will be made to rescue us if we are down. . . . While we count the high cost, we should also count ourselves fortunate to be the beneficiaries of these, the best of men—who gave their lives so 'that others may live.' " The roar of the two MH-53s passing overhead, trailing green smoke as a salute to their fallen countrymen, perfectly accentuated the general's message.[12]

While serving in the 20th SOS, Colonel Hull had been witness to a dramatic incident of incredible personal and professional courage and determination. Frequently, exchange officers from both the USMC and USN were assigned to the 20th. In 1996 US Navy lieutenant John Alvarez was aboard as a Pave Low pilot. Alvarez was fluent in Spanish and occasionally was tasked with other AFSOC units. In September 1996, he was deployed with a small foreign internal defense team from the 6th SOS to Ecuador. Alvarez was working a mission one day as a passenger on an Ecuadorian Gazelle helicopter when the machine crashed. The pilot was killed. Fortunately, Alvarez and one other American were able to escape. However, Alvarez was seriously wounded with two badly mangled legs and several other grievous injuries. He was medically evacuated to a civilian hospital in Quito, Ecuador, where doctors had to amputate the lower half of his left leg. When his wounds were stabilized, he was transported by a C-141 to the Wilford Hall Medical Center in San Antonio, Texas, where his wife and children could join him.

Lt Col Tommy Hull visited him and told him that he expected to see Alvarez back flying with the Green Hornets. Alvarez did not appreciate Hull's attempt at humor and told him so. Hull then informed him that he had been doing some research and discovered that other amputees had returned to full military service, including a Navy SEAL. From then on, Alvarez determined that he would return to the

Courtesy Col John Alvarez, USAF, Retired

Lt Col Tom Hull and Lt John Alvarez, USN. (At the time, Alvarez was USN. Later, he transferred to the USAF, retiring as a colonel.)

Pave Low cockpit. As soon as he could, he began physical therapy and was walking by November. He was also able to call upon the services of Dr. John Uribe, the team surgeon for the Miami Dolphins, and Mr. Raymond Francis of Tidewater Prosthetics in Norfolk, Virginia, who designed a high-technology prosthetic leg for him. Throughout, the Airmen of the 20th were constantly helping out, building special ramps in his home, generally assisting with whatever chores needed to be done, and always offering companionship and encouragement for strengthening physical activity.

Once he had regained his strength and mobility, he began the arduous process of returning to flight duty. He took and passed simulator evaluations with both the Air Force and Navy and actual fixed-wing flight evaluations with Federal Aviation Administration (FAA) evaluators. He passed both Navy and AFSOC physical fitness tests with outstanding scores. Traveling to Pensacola, he endured a week-long series of tests and a "thorough" flight physical, which he also passed. Then he had to stand before a panel of 15 Navy senior flight surgeons. They determined that he was fit for duty and returned him to flight status. After the formal paperwork flowed up the Navy chain of command and over to the necessary offices in the USAF, he was returned to flight duty as a Pave Low pilot in the 20th SOS and flew again on 4 September. Colonel Hull was very moved by Alvarez's enduring courage and resolve to return to flying. At the time he said, "Lieutenant Alvarez represents the warrior spirit, the special operations spirit in the 20th. He has the right attitude, outstanding motivation and continuous drive—the stuff it takes to be a special operator. The country gets a valuable asset back." Alvarez credited the USAF for his return to flying, stating, "I truly believe that if I were not in Air Force Special Operations Command and not part of the 20th Special Operations Squadron, I wouldn't be flying again. It was amazing to see all these people from the special operations community, many of whom I didn't even know, just come out and help me. What we really have here is a brotherhood, not just a job."[13]

31st Special Operations Squadron

For the Korea-based Pave Low troops, their operations tempo as 1997 began was dictated by a steady schedule of exercises as the unit personnel rotated in and out on their one-year tours. In late January, Capt Jim Cardoso completed his tour with the unit. A 1988 graduate of the Air Force Academy, he had flown for four years as a T-38 instructor pilot before training on the MH-53 and joining the 31st the previous January. He loved flying the Pave Low and during his time in Korea upgraded to aircraft commander while logging several hundred hours of challenging operational flying in this forward theater. He particularly enjoyed the camaraderie of the crews, the focus on tactical flexibility, and the application of the assault mentality. He also quickly discovered that low-level flying presented a unique set of challenges, especially when he realized that the Koreans did not do a thorough job of reporting the construction of flight obstacles such as towers and power lines so that aircrews would be aware of these threats. Completing his tour at Osan, he would now report to the 20th SOS to join the "show" and continue his Pave Low career, having learned lessons that would serve him well in the not-too-distant future.[14]

But not all was routine for the Airmen of the 31st as, occasionally, real-world events would intercede. In July 1997, the 353d SOG was deployed for a humanitarian mission. Civil unrest in Cambodia caused by governmental instability led to the directed evacuation of most Americans from that country. The 353d was ordered to fly MC-130s and MH-53s for possible NEO operations as part of USPACOM joint contingency force Bevel Edge, led by the SOCPAC commander, General Schwartz. Capt Joe DeCaro was the commander of one of the Pave Lows. Commissioned out of the Air Force Academy in 1990, he had followed the then-standard flow for Pave Low pilots: Fort Rucker, a tour in UH-1Ns, and then Pave Lows. After an initial tour with the 20th, he had accepted a remote tour with the 31st and was part of the Pave Low package for this operation. On the ninth, the contingency force arrived at U-Tapao AB, Thailand, and joined waiting AMC C-5s and C-141s. The arrival of the Pave Lows was reminiscent of their predecessors' arrival at this very same air base for the *Mayaguez* rescue 22 years and two months prior. Also similar to the *Mayaguez* mission, US Marines from Okinawa arrived and were organized for load aboard the Pave Lows if they needed to be inserted for evacuation site security. The Airmen and Marines of the contingency force then stood by on short notice for movements to sites in Cambodia. However, the governmental crisis was resolved without endangering any Americans, and the force did not need to conduct an NEO. All elements were released to return to their home bases at the end of the month.[15]

58th Special Operations Wing/ 551st Special Operations Squadron

In February 1997, Col John Folkerts assumed command of the 58th SOW. He was the second Pave Low pilot to achieve wing command. Crew production continued unabated, as did all of the other operational activities of the Pave Low instructors and crews. In May the 551st received a most unusual and disheartening tasking. It was directed to deploy a team of 18 individuals, including a flight surgeon, a chaplain, and PJs, to the crash site of an A-10 that had gone down in the Rocky Mountains near Eagle, Colorado. In an incident that was never fully explained, the pilot flew the armed aircraft from Davis-Monthan AFB, Arizona, where he was undergoing transition training, to Colorado and then committed suicide by crashing the aircraft. The team members deployed on 15 May aboard two Pave Lows. For the next three days, they flew eight sorties to support the recovery operations. The pilots had to hover at elevations as high as 13,000 feet to insert and extract the recovery teams. Fortunately, good weather facilitated an expeditious operation, and the aircraft and personnel returned to Kirtland on 18 May.

Throughout 1997, the 58th SOW also deployed operations and maintenance personnel from the 551st and associated squadrons to several locations in the world to support ongoing operations. In June Lt Col Randy O'Boyle took command of the 551st SOS from Lt Col Robert Maldonado. He had only been in his new job about a month when the USAF announced that at some point, probably no later than 2003, the 551st SOS was a candidate to become the training unit for the CV-22 tilt-rotor aircraft that the service would soon be acquiring, possibly as a replacement for the MH-53s.[16]

One of the pilots who went through Pave Low training under Colonel O'Boyle that summer and fall was Capt Pete Doty. He had graduated from the Air Force Academy in 1992. Ever since his first exposure to the Pave Low supplied by Capt Tom Trask on his visit to the Air Force Academy in 1991, Doty had a strong desire to fly helicopters in general and Pave Low in particular. After flight training, he served a three-year tour with the 76th Rescue Flight at Vandenberg flying the UH-1N "Pave Hueys" with Vince Becklund and several others who would later fly the MH-53s. In fact, it seemed as if the 76th during the 1990s was a pipeline for pilots going to MH-53s, in part because Pave Low veterans like MSgt Eddie Parris also served in the unit and mentored the younger officers.

Like Becklund, Doty enjoyed his assignment at Vandenberg, finding the flying interesting and challenging. And the social life was also good. He was invited out to dinner one evening by Becklund and his wife, who introduced him to a mutual friend, Isabelle. She and Pete were quite taken with each other, and shortly thereafter she became his wife and later an extended member of the Pave Low family.

However, Captain Doty did not have an opportunity to go through the Commando Look program. Sometime after Vince Becklund went through the screening, the program for officers was terminated because of a lack of funding. Enlisted troops were still screened. Doty got his assignment to Pave Low through the standard officer assignment system and some forthright phone calls to Maj Tim Brown, a Pave Low pilot then serving as the pilot assignment officer at AFSOC headquarters. Reporting to the 551st SOS at Kirtland, Doty found the Pave Low training both demanding and rewarding. He requested and received a follow-on assignment to the 20th SOS, arriving at the unit in the spring of 1998.[17]

In May 1997, Greg Lengyel was promoted to major while serving as an instructor with the 551st. He had transferred in from the 20th a year earlier, after having advanced all the way to flight examiner. His last commander there, Lt Col Mike Homan, encouraged him to volunteer for an instructor job, believing that the school needed instructors who were well grounded operationally. After two consecutive tours where he had averaged 200 days a year TDY, Lengyel also wanted to spend a bit more time with his wife and two children.

He found schoolhouse instructor duty quite challenging and rewarding, noting that his NVG skills were dramatically sharpened by developing the ability to teach others to use them. Like most other instructors, he also enjoyed flying the TH-53As, especially with their excess power and maneuverability. During the assignment, beyond his instructor duties, he was able to serve as the 551st assistant DO, as a flight examiner, and as chief of standardization and evaluation for the 58th SOG. He also developed an excellent working relationship with Colonel Folkerts before departing Kirtland in July 1999 for a staff tour with USSOCOM in Tampa, Florida.[18]

In November 1997, SSgt Brian Cessop reported to the 551st SOS for aerial gunner training. He had been in the USAF for 10 years and was a weapons loader, primarily on fighter aircraft. However, he had heard about Pave Low and volunteered to attend Commando Look at Hurlburt earlier in the year. He did well on all of the tests and interviews and liked what he saw. He was accepted into Pave Low as an aerial gunner. He then attended the various survival schools before reporting to Kirtland AFB.

He was a bit surprised at what he found. He expected that his job would be just to fly on the aircraft and fire the guns when ordered to do so. He did well in academics and easily mastered the handling of the .50-caliber machine gun and the minigun and the tactical use of NVGs. However, he did not know that he would also have significant duties as a scanner and be an integral part of the crew, especially as the tail gunner. He remembered, "I was pleasantly surprised. It's awesome to be on an aircraft where the crew is tight. We interacted well together. . . . Shooting the guns is the smallest part of the job. You are more a scanner than you are a gunner. . . . You are calling things that the pilots may not see."[19]

Sergeant Cessop also learned that the gunners had some more informal duties. He explained that

> part of the gunner mission was to keep the crews in good spirits. That was one of our charters. Don't know where that came from. It was always the gunner's responsibility to bring levity to the crew. We were pretty good at it. It was just one of those things that we did . . . 15 hours into a sortie, and everyone wanted to fall asleep. It was the gunner telling stories that kept everyone awake and laughing. . . . Laughter is one of those things that we used a lot in Pave Low. . . . I don't think that . . . any other airframe has the camaraderie that we had among the crew. It worked because it had to work. There was no alternative. It either worked, or people were going to die.[20]

Finishing his training in May 1998, he reported to the 20th SOS. He immediately entered the training program under the supervision of MSgt John Sprouse, a.k.a. the "Big Daddy" gunner, and was soon on the road to exercises with various "customers." Cessop was impressed with the squadron, the size, the operations tempo, and just the general panache exuded by the members. It was all so cool, and he could tell that he had arrived at the "show."

Also attending that iteration of Commando Look was SSgt Bernard "B. J." Jobling. English by birth, he was the son of an RAF veteran and had married an American girl and moved to the United States. There he enlisted in the USAF in 1989 and eventually became a computer technician. However, he sensed that he wanted to be more than that, and when he saw the invitation message for Commando Look, he signed up. His assessment also went well, and he was accepted into the program to train to be a flight engineer. He then went through the same series of schools plus a basic flight engineering course before starting his Pave Low qualification training with the 551st SOS. He found the course to be challenging but also intriguing because it was obvious that what he was training to do was serious and unlike anything he had ever done or really even imagined. He also found that, at times, the course was actually enjoyable, remembering that "it was fun to have a whole bunch of guys who were all going in the same direction. They all [had] different personalities, but to see the personalities merge into a common goal was only a taste of what it was like once you got out in the field. I enjoyed it." Jobling reported to the 20th SOS in May 1999. He also flowed right into the mission readiness training program and was on deployments hither and yon for the next year to become a fully qualified Pave Low flight engineer.[21]

Air Force Special Operations Command

As Sergeants Cessop and Jobling were beginning their respective schools, Gen Michael Ryan was sworn in as the 16th chief of staff of the Air Force. Previously, he had served in Europe and had become intimately involved in the Balkan problems. He was well aware of the changes that had swept the world and the United States since the end of the Cold War and sensed that the USAF had to change further to stay relevant. Starting with the basics, he directed all commands to review their mission essential task lists (METL), which delineated those specific tasks that each command and its subordinate units were required to accomplish as essential parts of their assigned mission.

METLs were integral to both unit organization and operation and defined the metrics against which units were inspected and graded. Receiving the tasking, in early 1998 General Holland directed his staff to form a strategic planning working group to use guidance in volume 2 of the *USAF Strategic Plan* to revise the AFSOC comparable plan as necessary and determine what or how AFSOC METLs needed to be changed to meet General Ryan's tasking. The process would stretch into the fall before it was completed. Aware of the USAF revision, USSOCOM also directed AFSOC to insure that all USAF METLs were in compliance with their published joint METLs to insure proper joint integration and unity of effort. The AFSOC planners worked diligently to insure that all were properly and coherently integrated.[22]

General Ryan also wanted to make fundamental changes to the way the USAF operated. Having participated in the massive relocation of US forces from overseas locations to the CONUS after Desert Storm, and realizing that US military forces would most probably continue to shrink, he believed that the USAF needed to be restructured. He thought the Air Force needed the ability to respond to the more nebulous global threats now extant with a leaner, lighter, and more mobile force, optimized for expeditionary operations. It could be more easily tailored for quicker deployment in support of the requirement of the US global combatant commanders. Accordingly, he directed that the USAF operational forces, both active and reserve components, be reorganized into 10 air expeditionary forces (AEF). Each would consist of geographically separated but operationally linked units that would develop habitual relationships but could be further tailored to the initiating contingency, whether a rapid-response crisis or an ongoing operation. The concept was optimized to smooth out the impact on personnel by providing more predictable work and training schedules and to provide the theater commanders with the forces they needed to meet military objectives and contingency requirements.

AFSOC planners began strategizing how special ops could best integrate into the AEF concept, indicating where and how they could provide their unique contributions to each package of forces. However, the chief of plans, Col John Stephens, pointed out that within the USSOCOM structure, each COCOM already had a theater special operations component, and AFSOC forces with their CONUS wing and two forward deployed SOGs were already well structured to support highly mobile forces for crisis response and contingency operations. All were well versed in forming JSOTFs to support their theater commanders. Additionally, the AFSOC forces possessed specific skills adapted to nonconventional operations across the spectrum of conflict, such as operations other than war, humanitarian operations, and smaller-scale contingencies. Given their operational flexibility, they were considered a deploying "enabling force." Their units would not be assigned to specific numbered AEFs. Instead, they would remain on call as needed for any particular contingency that could best be handled with their unique skill sets. Their mission to deliver special operations combat power "any time, any place" was not altered in the AEF reorganization. The AFSOC units in general and the Pave Low units in particular would continue to do what they were doing.[23]

As noted earlier, General Hobson had tried to start another dialogue about moving the CSAR mission to his command. In early 1998, the ACC commander, Gen Richard Hawley, decided that the issue needed to be addressed directly. The need was obvious. With the inactivation of the Air Rescue Service in July 1993, all rescue squadrons were transferred to ACC, and the command picked up the responsibility for mission area proponency; policy making; and organizing, training, and equipping the rescue forces. Regardless, the AFSOC continued to receive taskings to dispatch its helicopters and M/HC-130s to assume CSAR alert. There were two reasons for this. First, the SOF forces had better equipment, especially the helicopters. All knew that the MH-53s of the 20th, 21st, and 31st SOSs had been initially modified to provide night, all-weather rescue capability based upon lessons learned in Southeast Asia. This had been reinforced by their performance in Desert Storm. They, and the derivative MH-60s of the 55th SOS, were the best aircraft and crews available for the mission. Second, the theater commanders liked having the SOSs in their theaters because they knew that, if necessary, the SOSs could also perform SOF taskings. These factors created a dichotomy. ACC had the mission but the lesser equipment. AFSOC had the better equipment but the mission only as a secondary tasking. The roots of this conundrum ran all the way back to the transfer of the original HH-53H Pave Lows from MAC to TAC in May 1990 to address the debacle at Desert One.[24]

In 1997 General Hobson proposed to square the issue by consolidating all USAF rescue forces in AFSOC. General Hawley would have none of that. Instead, in January 1998 he directed his ACC staff to form a tiger team to examine the issue thoroughly. For the next seven months, the team did its analysis. The findings were sobering and highlighted deficiencies with personnel, training, and equipment, as well as allocation imbalances between active and reserve forces among the helicopter and tanker squadrons and the PJ units. Succinctly, the ACC rescue force could not meet its wartime taskings. General Hawley reviewed the report, stating that "the CSAR mission area is insufficiently manned and equipped to meet its growing operational demands. ACC is taking internal actions to fix CSAR. We will need help from the Air Force. . . . But we can't defer action on CSAR any longer. It is a broken mission area."[25] In his statement, though, Hawley did not indicate any plan to fix the now identified deficiency. For AFSOC, this meant that it could still expect CSAR taskings for the foreseeable future.

Regardless, AFSOC carried on as it sustained its force of 12,500 Airmen to accomplish their assigned deployments and missions. Col Steve Connelly, now serving as the AFSOC director of operations, had several other Pave Low officers and NCOs working for him on the staff as those veterans continued to move up to higher levels of authority and responsibility.

Another longtime Pave Low veteran, Col Gary Weikel, was also serving on the AFSOC staff as the deputy to the director of plans and was specifically charged with heading up the integrated product team working to procure and integrate the new CV-22 into the command. AFSOC officers and NCOs were now being consistently and steadily promoted at rates higher than the USAF at large in almost all grades. The Commando Look program was still operating and screening personnel for the Pave Low program. Throughout 1998, 68 personnel were screened, and 52 were accepted and entered crew training.[26]

However, AFSOC also had a developing problem specifically with Pave Low pilot manning. Many of the first-assignment IPs who had cross-trained into the MH-53 in the mid-1990s were now leaving the service. Commando Look was helping, but it was not covering the losses and anticipated future needs for CV-22 pilots. Noting that the US Army had a surplus of warrant officer pilots, the USAF and AFSOC began scripting a program to recruit Army warrant officers with college degrees to change services and fly Pave Lows.

The lead project officer for this program was Maj Douglas Goodlin. He conceptualized a process that would involve an interservice transfer to the USAF, commissioning through Officer Training School, a direct USAF pilot rating, and conversion to the Pave Low. Before the program was even finalized, potential volunteers began to appear. Two of the very first were warrant officers Mike "Big Daddy" Holder and Frank Lazzara. Both had joined the Army after college in the late 1980s but decided to become warrant officers so that they could fly. Both subsequently served a series of classic US Army aviation assignments. Both also harbored a strong desire to transfer to the USAF as commissioned officers and fly the Pave Low. Each found out about the program through personal initiative and signed up to transfer over. Holder was the first, transferring on 1 March 1998. Lazzara made the switch one month later. Maj Jon Owens had transferred to the 551st after his tour at the 31st and instructed both in the Pave Low qualification course, noting that "both did very well in the program." The USAF used these two to validate and formally establish the process.[27]

The following September, the USAF held a formal board at the USAF Personnel Center at Randolph AFB, Texas, to consider 17 officers and 37 warrant officers for the program. Of those, five officers and eight warrants were selected and offered transfer: CW3 Paul Alexander, CW2 Sean Borland, CW2 Pat Fronk, CW2 Ted Glover, 2d Lt Jay Humphrey, 1st Lt Anthony Kram, CW3 Francis Lankist, 1st Lt Paul Lawrenz, 1st Lt Bryan Martyn, CW2 David Millett, CW3 Martin Schweim, 2d Lt Jeffrey Siino, and CW2 Randal Voas.

Volunteers were also selected for assignment to HH-60Gs and UH-1Ns. For the MH-53 selectees, the average total rotary-wing flying time was 1,619 hours, with an average of 466 hours logged as instructor or evaluator pilots. Three of the selectees had flown CH/MH-47D/E aircraft, and three had flown combat. It was a selective group of aviators who would bring a great deal of experience into the Pave Low program. In reality, the transferees fell in behind a long list of US Army pilots, such as Tom Aldrich and "Pappy" Walters, who had come over in the 1980s and put their wealth of helicopter experience to great use in Pave Low. The USAF would hold several more boards in the next few years.[28] However, the pilot shortage was part of a larger phenomenon across the USAF, and the Air Staff was looking at the issue with the expectation that it might take several years to solve it.[29]

AFSOC was also constantly pursuing ways to upgrade or otherwise improve the Pave Lows. In April 1998, AFSOC took delivery of the first MH-53 fully outfitted with the IDAS/MATT-modified system.

It was assigned to the 16th SOW. There the Airmen of the 20th SOS began developing a training program to convert their crews to the modified machine. They had to quickly learn how to integrate the new capabilities for enhanced situational awareness and threat detection and avoidance into crew operations for maximum effectiveness and safety.

IDAS/MATT was a significant upgrade to the aircraft. Its sophisticated communication and sensor equipment generated a unique logistics trail above and beyond that which was already established for the aircraft. The AFSOC chief of plans, Col John Stephens, recognized this uniqueness and felt that the aircraft needed a new mission design series (MDS) designation instead of MH-53J. Notionally, the next designation for the aircraft would be MH-53K. However, within the USSOCOM, the elements of the 160th SOAR already flew the MH-60K and MH-60L aircraft. To forsake any confusion, Stephens formally requested that the IDAS/MATT-modified Pave Lows be designated the MH-53M. Collaterally, he also requested that the MH-53Js, heretofore informally known as the Pave Low IIIE, be formally given that moniker, while the MH-53M would be officially designated as the Pave Low IV. Two months later, Headquarters USAF approved both requests, and the IDAS/MATT-modified Pave Lows were now officially designated the MH-53M Pave Low IV aircraft.

The intent of the designation changes was to facilitate the logistical support of the modified aircraft as it now required support unique from the Pave Low IIIE. The differences had to be coordinated between the AFMC, several air logistics centers, and all Pave Low–equipped units. To insure that all of the necessary cross-coordination was properly in place as the aircraft became operational, the official redesignation date for the MH-53M Pave Low IV was set for 1 February 1999.

The conversion of the aircraft now occurred at a steady rate. By the end of 1998, 11 IDAS/MATT-modified Pave Lows were on the ramp at Hurlburt Field. They joined the nine MH-53Js of the 20th SOS, eight assigned to the 21st SOS, six assigned to the 31st SOS, and five MH-53Js with the 551st SOS. Regardless of the "official" designation date for the new MDS, tailor shops specializing in the production of stylized nametags for flight suits went to double shifts to produce the now high-demand nametags for the Pave Low IV crews.[30]

20th Special Operations Squadron

As 1998 began, the 20th was busy getting ready for the ORI with the rest of the wing units and averaging 175 sorties per month while supporting classified and unclassified training exercises with other special operations elements all over the CONUS. It had readiness exercises in January and February and actually received the ORI in the second half of March, six months earlier than originally scheduled. The wing was ready. It deployed to Edwards AFB and took the inspection while working with other JSOC units. The inspection terminated with a large direct action exercise that required the wing to launch 24 of 25 available aircraft. Maintenance delivered the necessary sorties, and the crews performed admirably, regardless of moderate to heavy turbulence over the operational area that made inflight refueling a real challenge. All operational aspects of the wing's performance were rated as excellent. At the same time, too, the wing had personnel deployed to Joint Guard in Bosnia and Korea and on short notice in support of operations in Southwest Asia. Colonel Comer was delighted with the wing's ORI performance and rating. In a larger vein, though, he noted that "we had an ORI and didn't even notice. As it turned out, it increased our ops tempo not a whit in this one. . . . We felt the pain of the contingencies that came up, but not the ORI."[31]

At the same time, the 20th also had two aircraft, crews, and support personnel at Brindisi with the Airmen of the 21st in what had effectively become a consolidated operation for the two units. The Pave Low procedures specified by the stan/eval team at AFSOC were so thorough that the units could now operate together almost seamlessly with little or no initial disruption or hesitation. The 20th supported the short-notice deployment to Southwest Asia as part of Desert Thunder. Two MH-53s, crews, and support personnel were part of a JSOAC deployed in support of possible combat operations to enforce the no-fly zone over southern Iraq. Until June, the 20th had personnel in Kuwait to assume CSAR alert and support for special operations forces in the area.

That summer several changes of command involving Pave Low officers occurred at Hurlburt. In early June, Colonel Wurster passed command of the 16th SOG to Col Lyle Koenig. A week later, Wurster took command of the 16th SOW from Colonel Comer and became the fourth Pave Low pilot to assume wing command. As Comer gave up command of the wing, he was notified that he had been selected for promotion to brigadier general, another first for Pave Low. One month after that event, Colonel Hull gave up command of the 20th SOS to Lt Col Jack Hester, one of the earliest Pave Low pilots and the first aircraft commander to fly a combat mission in the Pave Low in Operation Just Cause. Lt Col Tom Trask returned to the squadron after a four-year hiatus of school and staff tours to serve as his operations officer.[32]

As Hester took over, the pace did not slacken. During the summer, the 20th began training programs for its crews to convert to the newly arriving IDAS/MATT-modified aircraft. The systems specifications suggested a dramatic improvement in their combat mission capability, including

> a color, multifunctional, night vision capable digital map screen . . . located on the helicopter's instrument panel [that] gave an MH-53 crew a clear picture of the battlefield. Crews had access to near real time events, including the aircrew's route of flight, man-made hazards such as power lines and even many electronic threats that were "over the horizon."

> Transmissions were beamed from a satellite to the helicopter's computer and then decoded; the data from the screen provided a perspective of potential threats and their lethal threat radius. The heart of the system, advanced software, included an integrated electronic warfare system. Infrared countermeasure controls, including missile warning, radar warning, and jammer inputs as well as chaff and flare countermeasures, were on one display. Crews would receive instant cautions and advisories on threats with immediate communications, including when to disperse countermeasures.[33]

This was quite a dramatic improvement in aircraft combat capabilities, and the crews embraced it wholeheartedly. One exercise, held in the Hurlburt area that summer, allowed the crews to use the system in an operational environment. Additionally, they participated in 13 other CONUS training exercises and then had to evacuate their aircraft with the rest of the wing twice because of hurricane activity. In the fall, they were tasked to deploy several aircraft and crews to the Persian Gulf region for contingency training. This time, they were organized as part of a CJSOTF and focused almost exclusively on special operations events with US Army Green Berets and US Navy SEALs. As the national strategic repository of this unique capability, the 20th was a constantly active unit.[34]

21st Special Operations Squadron

The 21st was still equipped with eight MH-53Js, with conversion to the MH-53Ms scheduled for mid-1999. Three of its aircraft were down at Brindisi supporting the Joint Guard operation, usually with augmentation from the 20th. The addition of the two extra aircraft did allow Capt Jim Slife to develop plans to begin participating again in exercises with other national special forces elements across the theater. However, access to training ranges in Great Britain was a constant struggle because there was so much competition for their use. This was also a problem in Italy, especially after a USMC EA-6B clipped a cable on a ski lift in the Italian Alps and killed several civilians. Regardless, the crews optimized their allocated time on the ranges despite the restrictions to maximize the results of their required training.

In May, the 21st received an unusual tasking. President Clinton was slated to visit Great Britain for two days in May. While there, he would fly in his special USMC H-3 helicopter. The 352d SOG was directed to support the operation, forming a JSOAC to do so. The 21st was assigned to the JSOAC to provide four helicopters and crews to move the presidential support team and provide on-call SAR capability. The package included six US Army UH-60s. Jim Slife was selected to be the chief planner and lead pilot. He met with the White House and USMC planners to organize the mission and then participated with his crews as they flew the routes and practiced landings at all possible landing sites. The actual missions were conducted on 17 and 18 May and occurred as planned. As the president departed for the United States, the JSOAC was dissolved, and the 21st returned to routine operations, taking great pride in a flawless operation. Two months later, Colonel Salmon passed command of the 21st SOS to Lt Col Paul Harmon, another Pave Low veteran of Desert Storm, who was still serving as the squadron director of operations. Maj Mike Kingsley also joined the 21st SOS as an assistant DO. Since leaving the 20th SOS in 1994, he had attended the Army Command and General Staff College at Fort Leavenworth, Kansas, and had done a staff tour at the Pentagon. Additionally, Lt Col Corby Martin arrived to take command of the 352d Operations Support Squadron and lend his expertise to the ongoing operations in the Balkans.[35]

Harmon slid easily into his job and continued to address the various challenges that the 21st faced as it worked to maintain its capabilities to carry out its assigned missions under SOCEUR. The unit was also notified that NEO was now a priority mission, and unit planners had to develop several contingency plans. At Brindisi, Joint Guard duty had become quite routine, as the crews flew about 100 hours a month on mundane support missions. However, because of the USMC EA-6B accident, training flights in Italy were now more restricted than ever. More worrisome was the fact that Serbian forces had become active again, this time in Kosovo, another region of the former Yugoslavia, located just south of Serbia itself. News reports indicated that Serbian forces were committing atrocities against the local population. This was an ominous development with the portent of perhaps more conflict ahead in that region.[36]

31st Special Operations Squadron

Throughout 1998, the 31st SOS, still assigned to Osan AB, continued to maintain a presence within the greater Pacific theater and proficiency in all of its assigned mission sets with its six MH-53J heavy-lift helicopters as its crews and support personnel participated in a full plate of various types of exercises. The unit also participated with the 353d in an AFSOC-administered ORI. That inspection was carried out at Kadena and Osan in late October as the 353d supported the huge annual Exercise Foal Eagle in Korea. Almost lost in the huge event involving 500,000 Korean troops and 30,000 Americans, the 353d was rated as overall excellent, matching the recent performance of its brother units on their ORIs and serving as a true testament to the general level of professionalism of the AFSOC operational and support units.[37]

551st Special Operations Squadron

Life remained relatively stable and quiet at the training unit during 1998 as it continued to offer eight courses of instruction for MH-53 crew members. The 551st graduated 62 flight crew personnel during the year. It also received several more pilot and flight engineer instructors, which helped to even out the training load among the instructors. Four different joint training exercises were conducted through the summer, affording the 551st crews and their students opportunities to work with USMC units, Navy SEALs, and Army Green Beret teams at

Fort Bliss, Texas. In the fall, another Chili Flag exercise was held at Kirtland, where several crews got the opportunity to infil and exfil Army special forces Soldiers. In small increments, 551st personnel were dispatched to overseas ongoing operations as augmentees, although no full crews were sent during this period.[38]

On 22 October 1998, MH-53J #66-14431, assigned to the 58th SOW, was completely destroyed in a tragic accident at the NADEP at MCAS Cherry Point. The aircraft had received long-term maintenance checks and repairs. At the completion of its workup, the aircraft received an acceptance check flight. Because the tail gearbox had not been properly lubricated, the gearbox seized while the aircraft was in a hover, causing it to crash. Fortunately, the USMC check pilots were not killed. The aircraft had a long and distinguished flight career with the 21st SOS, having flown on the *Yarrawonga* rescue in 1989 and the rescue attempt for Corvette 03 in Iraq in January 1991.[39]

Next door to the 551st, the 58th TRSS had its simulators running almost 24/7 to meet the heavy demand of the upgrading students as well as MH-53 crews that now came to the 58th for their simulator refresher training. Crews were increasingly using the MH-53 WST with its global database to practice potential missions anywhere in the world. All combined, it was a powerful consolidated training capability. For 1998 the 58th SOW qualified 31 pilots, seven flight engineers, and 23 gunners for the Pave Low fleet.[40]

Notes

1. History of AFSOC, 1 Jan–31 Dec 1997, vol. 1, 30–35.

2. Ibid., 51–53.

3. Ibid., 70, 376; and ibid., 1 Jan–31 Dec 1998, vol. 1, 123–24.

4. Newman, "Hunting War Criminals," special ops website.

5. Slife, interview.

6. History of 352d SOG, 1 Jan–30 June 1997, vol. 1, 7, 22, 51, 100; and ibid., 1 July–31 Dec 1997, vol. 1, 12, 37, 54, 79–80, 107.

7. Becklund, interview.

8. Col John Folkerts took command of the 58th SOW in February as the second Pave Low officer to command a wing.

9. History of 16th SOW, 1 Jan–31 Dec 1997, vol. 1, 4–5, 99; and Exercise Krypton Vessel After Action Report Inputs, 30 Apr 1997, 1st/16th SOW HO, 20th SOS, historical files.

10. Landreth, interview.

11. History of AFSOC, 1 Jan–31 Dec 1997, vol. 1, 67; and Whitcomb, *Rescue of Bat 21*, 162–64.

12. Ibid.

13. Davenport, "Leg to Stand On," 2–5.

14. Cardoso, interview.

15. History of 353d SOG, 1 Jan–30 June 1997, vol. 1, 14, 19, 21, 24, 66; ibid., 1 July–31 Dec 1997, vol. 1, 31; and DeCaro, interview.

16. History of 58th SOW, 1 July 1996–30 June 1997, vol. 1, 54; and ibid., 1 July–31 Dec 1997, vol. 1, 15.

17. Doty to the author, e-mail.

18. Lengyel, interview.

19. Cessop, interview.

20. Ibid.

21. Jobling, interview.

22. History of AFSOC, 1 Jan–31 Dec 1998, vol. 1, 6–8.

23. Ibid., 13–17.

24. Ibid., 17–18.

25. Ibid., 17–19.

26. Ibid., 35–36, 178.

27. Holder and Lazzara, interviews; and Owens to the author, e-mail.

28. "1998 Helicopter Interservice Transfer Pre-Screening Selection Board," 6 Oct 1998, procured from Maj Sean Borland.

29. History of AFSOC, 1 Jan–31 Dec 1998, vol. 1, 36–37; ibid., 1 Jan–31 Dec 1999, vol. 1, 43; and Holder, interview.

30. History of AFSOC, 1 Jan–31 Dec 1998, vol. 1, 123–26, 277.

31. History of 16th SOW, 1 Jan–30 June 1998, vol. 1, 8–9; and Comer, interview.

32. History of 16th SOW, 1 Jan–30 June 1998, vol. 1, 1, 3, 35–37; and Trask, interview.

33. History of 16th SOW, 1 July–31 Dec 1998, vol. 1, 32–34.

34. Ibid., 31, 34.

35. Kingsley and Martin, interviews.

36. History of 352d SOG, 1 Jan–30 June 1998, vol. 1, 21–25; ibid., 1 July–31 Dec 1998, vol. 1, 18, 102; and Slife, interview.

37. History of 353d SOG, 1 Jan–30 June 1998, vol. 1, 34, 37–39, 59; ibid., 1 July–31 Dec 1998, vol. 1, 16, 22–23; and Crawford, "Nomads of the Pacific," pamphlet, 22, Heritage File, AFSOC/HO.

38. History of 58th SOW, 1 Jan–30 June 1998, vol. 1, 7, 44; and ibid., 1 July–31 Dec 1998, vol. 1, 71, 85.

39. Stringer, interview.

40. History of 58th SOW, 1 Jan–30 June 1998, vol. 1, 2, 7, 32, 40, 78; and ibid., 1 July–31 Dec 1998, vol. 1, 62, 101.

Chapter 13

A Mature Force

~1999–2000

Wires! Climb! Climb!!!

—TSgt Ed Hux

Back to the Balkans

Unfortunately, though, as 1999 began all was not quiet in the fractious Balkans. NATO's benevolent and persistent actions brought relative peace and stability to Bosnia. However, NATO did not completely quash the virulently nationalist enthusiasm of Serbian leader Slobodan Milosevic. He turned his attention to Kosovo, one of the few remaining Yugoslavian provinces. Located just south of Serbia, it had been a historic part of the larger nation, and Serbian roots there ran deep. However, by the 1990s Albanians comprised 90 percent of the population in that province, and they had been given a form of local autonomy. After the loss of Bosnia, Milosevic used his overbearing military to suppress the Albanian Kosovars. In response, they formed a guerilla-type movement, the Kosovo Liberation Army (KLA), and began to retaliate against the Serbs.

The Serbs stepped up their actions and, in one particularly bloody attack, killed 45 Albanian civilians in the Kosovar village of Racak. NATO leaders then invited all involved parties to peace talks in Rambouillet, France, in February 1999.[1]

The talks were futile, as Milosevic refused to accept a NATO peacekeeping force so vital to enabling any cease-fire and maintaining stability in that area. He unleashed his troops to conduct what had clearly been preplanned offensive operations in Kosovo. Heavily armed mechanized troops, special forces, and paramilitary elements ravaged both city and countryside in an orgy of arson, murder, and rape. It was a repeat of the horrible events in Bosnia—ethnic cleansing of the worst sort—all designed to drive out the Albanians and establish Serbian hegemony over the area. The casualties mounted into the thousands, and hundreds of thousands of refugees fled into the mountains or into Albania and Macedonia, threatening to overwhelm those small nations and destabilize the entire area. Allied aircrews flew over 500 missions hauling supplies into Albania, where American engineers quickly built three camps to care for the more than 60,000 refugees.

NATO members resolved to counter the Serbian aggression with strong military actions. However, the supreme allied commander in Europe, US Army general Wesley Clark, ruled out an allied ground campaign. Instead, he directed USAF lieutenant general Michael Short, the commander, Allied Forces Southern Europe, to conduct Operation Allied Force (OAF), an air campaign similar to Deliberate Force. General Short had a massive array of allied airpower under his command, consisting of 650 US combat and support aircraft and 550 comparable allied aircraft from all other NATO partner nations. Short would use this force to achieve three political objectives:

1. Demonstrate the seriousness of NATO's opposition to Belgrade's [Serbia's] aggression in the Balkans.

2. Deter President Milosevic from continuing and escalating his attacks on helpless civilians and create conditions to reverse his ethnic cleansing.

3. Damage Serbia's capacity to wage war against Kosovo in the future or spread the war to neighbors by diminishing or degrading its ability to wage military operations.[2]

All US forces in OAF were organized as JTF Noble Anvil. As expected, SOCEUR would provide supporting special forces. Its commander, now US Army brigadier general Eldon Bargewell, activated JSOTF Noble Anvil to do so. Under it, the JSOTF2 at Brindisi was again assigned to specifically provide recovery capability. The 21st SOS reinforced its element there to four MH-53Js and crews. The 20th SOS was directed to deploy augmenting forces. Capt Jim Cardoso was serving as the B Flight commander and deployed his flight with five MH-53Js, crews, and support personnel for the operations, as requested by the 21st SOS so that it could have a standardized fleet and intermix crews. However, as the Airmen and aircraft were en route, AFSOC ordered them to return the aircraft to Hurlburt for replacement with five MH-53Ms. They were joined by four MH-60s and crews from the 55th SOS as part of the larger Task Force Helo, commanded by Lt Col Paul Harmon.[3]

The 21st SOS weapons and tactics officer at that time was Capt Mark Daley. He had served as an intelligence officer before becoming a pilot and was able to leverage that background to develop an overall squadron CSAR plan that became the basis for the detailed planning done for the rescue forces in OAF. He and his team developed the navigation spider routes for the area and scripted the initial procedures to integrate the operations of the crews from the 21st, 20th, and 55th into a well-functioning task force. They also scripted several courses of action utilizing a mixed package of MH-53s, MH-60s, and STS teams to maximize the inherent strengths of all.[4]

General Bargewell took a proprietary interest in the rescue mission and closely watched the preparation and training. Harmon briefed him on the options that Daley and his team had scripted. Bargewell knew that the Serbians expected the allied force to mount recovery operations for any downed aircrews and wanted his Airmen to have the best possible chance for success and survival. He did not want the Pave Lows operating singly or even in two-ship formations. Instead, he accepted a three-ship mini-task-force option consisting of two MH-53s—one MH-53M and one MH-53J—and an MH-60G. The MH-53s would lead and provide fire support, while the MH-60 would be the designated recovery aircraft. A rescue mission commander (RMC) would be aboard the lead Pave Low. This individual would be someone seasoned—such as Lt Col Steve Laushine, the 55th SOS commander, or Lt Col Tom Trask, the 20th SOS operations officer—who would be in charge and empowered to make whatever tactical decisions needed to execute the recovery. All helicopters would have PJs aboard for the actual pickup. Additionally, Bargewell ordered a US Army special forces ODA unit reinforced with some USAF special tactics personnel to be dispersed on board the helicopters. The ODA element would be available as another tactical option if, for some reason, it made sense to land the team members and have them execute some form of initial overland recovery.

Several of the USAF crew members objected to having the "extra" troops on board, arguing that it forced the helicopters to fly with less fuel and placed more lives at risk. They took their concerns to the 21st SOS commander, Colonel Harmon. He addressed the issue with Bargewell who "in no uncertain terms" made it clear to the helicopter crews that this was the way the missions were going to be organized.

He dictated very specific considerations and criteria for their deployment and use. When that was cleared up, the aircrews assumed alert posture at Brindisi.[5]

Vega 31

Combat operations would begin on 24 March. Colonel Harmon worked with Capt Jim Slife to build five helicopter teams, each led by a very experienced flight lead: from the 20th, Capt Jim Cardoso and Capt Paul Pereira, and from the 21st, Capt Jim Breck, Maj Lou Caporicci, and Capt Jim Slife. Every 24 hours, two teams would be on alert as primary and secondary. They would rotate through on the schedule with secondary, primary, and local duties. The primary would move forward to Tuzla, Bosnia-Herzegovina, reducing reaction time over Serbia, and the secondary would sit alert at Brindisi and primarily respond to calls in Kosovo. Since two models of Pave Lows were on site, whatever type the lead crew flew would lead. The two squadrons did not intermix their personnel. Captain Cardoso agreed with this plan. He had now flown both the MH-53J and M models and knew that the newer M models were more technologically advanced. However, he also believed that the theater experience of the 21st SOS guys was clearly a mitigating factor, later stating that "having theater experience outweighs the machine."[6]

The bombing campaign began as scheduled. That night the primary rescue task force, led by Captain Slife, flew to Tuzla and assumed strip alert there. On the night of 27 March, a 20th SOS crew, including Captain Cardoso as flight lead for the rescue package and copilot Capt John Glass, took off in an MH-53M. Their call sign was Moccasin 60. One wingman, Moccasin 61, was an MH-53J from the 21st SOS, flown by Capt Shawn Cameron with copilot Captain Daley and crew. The other wingman was Gator 07, an MH-60G from the 55th SOS, commanded by Capt Chad Franks with copilot Capt Matt Glover and crew. Colonel Laushine was aboard Moccasin 60 as the RMC. As directed, an ODA package from the 1st Battalion, 10th SFG, as well as USAF special tactics personnel were dispersed among the three aircraft.

As the flight of three helicopters proceeded to Tuzla, the crews checked in with the NATO AWACS on station and overseeing the strikes that evening. The weather over the region was poor, with mixed rain showers and low visibility, and many strikes had been cancelled. Cardoso and his group landed at Tuzla and taxied to the refueling pits to fill their tanks. As they were doing so, the crews aboard Moccasin 61 and Gator 07 heard a Mayday call on the UHF "Guard" (military aircraft emergency) frequency.

Immediately, Laushine and the aircraft commanders went into the Tuzla command center to determine what was going on. There they were told that an F-117 had gone down in Serbia. They quickly began to formulate a recovery plan and tasked intelligence for the most accurate location of the pilot, Lt Col Dale Zelko, call sign Vega 31, from the 49th FW at Holloman. Laushine asked for data on the enemy threats that they would have to deal with to get him out. Cardoso was a bit concerned, thinking, "a Stealth just got shot down and now [they] want us to go in there?" However, he was now a highly experienced Pave Low pilot and knew that, while the immediate plan was not clear, the crews knew what they had to do and would figure out a way to get Zelko out of there.[7]

The requested information promptly flowed into the command center. Intelligence sources indicated that Vega 31 was down near Novi Sad, Serbia, an estimated 90 miles from Tuzla. Those sources also reported that the Serbs realized they had shot down an F-117 and were scrambling to capture the pilot. Several flights of A-10s and other supporting aircraft were being launched to assist in the rescue. With that information, Laushine directed his task force to take off and head north to set up a rendezvous with the A-10s near Osijek in northeast Croatia.

The three helicopters quickly launched and headed north. In this area, at least, the air was clear, and night visibility was good, although the moon was slowly setting. En route, though, they had difficulties establishing communications with the A-10s and other support aircraft as Laushine tried to organize the recovery effort. Meanwhile, Zelko had been able to use his handheld GPS to determine his location and had securely passed it to a C-130 orbiting over Kosovo. The C-130 crew quickly forwarded it through intelligence channels to Laushine. The reported position, validated by the A-10 flight lead, Capt John Cherry, who had established radio communications with and authenticated the survivor, indicated that Vega 31 was on the ground just south of the city of Ruma, 25 miles farther south. This was much closer to Belgrade, the heavily defended Serbian capital, and necessitated a complete rework of the recovery plan as the helicopter crews quickly entered Zelko's reported GPS location into their navigation systems.

To save fuel, Cardoso directed his flight crews to land their helicopters and dismount their PJs and some ODA troops to provide site security. He, copilot Glass, and seat flight engineer SSgt Bill Clemons frantically built a new route to the survivor while the crew of Moccasin 61 coordinated for a MC-130P to refuel the helicopters. Once that was worked out, the helicopters relaunched, quickly rendezvoused with the tanker, just 700 feet above the ground, and took on fuel as ground fog and low clouds were forming in the area. They repositioned to a holding point west of Ruma but still in Bosnian airspace and awaited the arrival of Cherrey's flight, which would escort them in to the survivor and provide top cover against any threats that challenged them.

Enemy forces were now aware of Zelko's presence and were fully mobilizing to capture him. Time was of the essence. As Captain Cherrey was orchestrating his portion of the effort, he received an intelligence report that Zelko had been captured. Cherrey called him on his survival radio and reauthenticated him. The rescue was on.

At the holding point, Cherrey briefed Cardoso and his flight on the escort and recovery plan. He told Cardoso to call him when they were two miles from Zelko so that he could tell Zelko to turn on his signaling device. They all acknowledged the plan, and Cherrey directed them to execute.

Throughout the night, the helicopters had been operating mostly in clear air. As they turned inbound to Zelko, though, they encountered a layer of low-hanging clouds, fog, and rain. Flight engineer TSgt Ed Hux, serving as the right-door gunner and scanner on Cardoso's aircraft, noted, "It was probably in the top five of the darkest nights that I have ever flown in 30 years of flying." As visibility rapidly deteriorated, Cardoso and his crew, already wearing NVGs, began utilizing the FLIR system to proceed. Unfortunately, as they entered the low scud, Cherrey and his flight could no longer see the helicopters to provide direct fire support. They themselves were being engaged by deadly SA-6 missile batteries and were now occupied just avoiding Zelko's fate.[8]

Entering the scud at about 50 feet above the ground, the two other helicopters held tactical formation on Moccasin 60 so that they did not get separated while so dangerously close to the ground. On board all three helicopters, gunners and flight engineers were earnestly scanning for immediate physical threats such as trees, towers, or power lines—anything that could damage or destroy a helicopter—as well as enemy forces. Suddenly, Hux spotted an uncharted power line in the haze, just ahead and level with the helicopters. He quickly shouted, "Wires! Climb! Climb!" as copilot Glass echoed his call. Cardoso immediately reacted and pulled back on the controls, flying his helicopter up and over the threatening wires. The other two crews maintained formation and also avoided the threat. Once clear of the wires, Cardoso descended the flight back down about 100 feet and proceeded toward Zelko.[9]

As the helicopters approached a point two miles from the survivor, Zelko was instructed to turn on his covert signal. He did so, not realizing that it was not working. Without visual contact, the helicopters began to orbit the position. Zelko could hear them. He also could sense that enemy forces were very near. Cardoso could also now see the enemy forces in the area.

Time was now extremely critical; they needed to move in very quickly. Cardoso called to Zelko, "Just give me any signal!" Zelko lit one of his overt signal flares, and everybody in the helicopter task force and probably every Serbian within two miles saw him. Cardoso issued a few last-second directions as Gator 07, the primary actual recovery aircraft, maneuvered to land and pick up the survivor. Captain Franks and crew quickly and expertly landed their MH-60 just a few feet from Zelko as the two MH-53s orbited above, guns at the ready. Franks ordered his two PJs, SSgt Eric Giacchino and SrA John Jordan, to dismount and retrieve Vega 31. As they were doing so, Cardoso, flying above, spotted Serbian vehicles 50 meters away but did not direct his gunners to shoot them since he did not want to unnecessarily highlight his helicopter. Below, the two PJs quickly moved to secure Zelko and put him aboard the MH-60. Gator 07 was on the ground only about 40 seconds before the three men were aboard and Franks lifted off and rejoined the formation.

As the helicopters rejoined into their prebriefed formation, the three aircraft turned west and headed back to Tuzla. When they landed there after their six-hour-and-30-minute adventure, an effusively thankful Dale Zelko was handed over to the flight surgeon and then flown to Aviano AB, Italy, for repatriation. The next day the crews held a debrief and reviewed the operation, identifying lessons learned and issues that needed to be addressed. To Cardoso, the results spoke for themselves. "We went in with 37 [personnel]," he said, adding, "We came back with 38."[10]

The crew of Moccasin 60 the morning after rescuing Vega 31, Lt Col Dale Zelko. *Left to right*: MSgt John Dubuisson, Capt John Glass, TSgt Ed Hux, SSgt Bill Clemons, SrA Chris Bloomfield, and Capt Jim Cardoso.

The members of the task force reconstituted and were put back in the rotation schedule. Later, the rescue mission received the acclaim that it deserved; all participants were recognized for the roles they played, with several receiving Silver Stars, Distinguished Flying Crosses, Bronze Stars, and Air Medals. For his key leadership, Capt Jim Cardoso was presented the 2000 Jabara Award for "superior performance in fields directly involved with aerospace vehicles."[11]

However, this mission had another significance, perhaps unrecognized at this time but profound in its historical implications. In 1967, at a time when the USAF was engaged in an intense theater war and losing aircraft and aircrews on a daily basis, its commanders in SEA forwarded to the Pentagon a requirement, SEA Operational Requirement 114, which called for "an integrated system to enable . . . helicopters to perform the essential elements of search and rescue under conditions of total darkness and/or low visibility."[12] That requirement provided the impetus for the development of the technology that changed HH- and CH-53s into MH-53Js and then MH-53Ms. However, it took the right crews, young air commandos, men of consummate professionalism and intense drive, to operationally bring those helicopters alive, to give them the honor of being Pave Lows. It was the men and machines together that made it all work. The right machines plus the right Airmen together were "Pave Low."

At the heart of the combination was the individual crew, highly trained and formally structured. Each of the two officer pilots and four enlisted flight engineers and gunners had an integrated role to play based on a foundation of fundamental trust. Never was that more graphically on display than when Ed Hux called out those wires. Their presence at that precise moment was an immediate and perhaps mortal threat to those helicopters. However, the Pave Low navigational equipment did not detect them; Ed Hux did, using his "Mark One" eyeballs. His timely verbal warning made the difference. Given the relatively tight formation in which the helicopters were flying, if they had flown into those wires, it is very possible that any or all of the helicopters could have been destroyed, along with their crews. Hux saw them and called them out. His warning to the crew was not questioned; there was no request to repeat or validate or explain. Cardoso and Glass did what needed to be done to protect the flight—instantaneously. Seconds later, the danger was behind them, and they were back on task, a bit wiser nonetheless. Hux rather casually said of that event later, "We had been flying as a group for a little while back at home station, and we could do those things—a simple testament to the idea that you 'train like you fight.' "[13]

Then, the pickup itself was classic Pave Low. Moccasin 60 did not land to recover Vega 31, although it could have done so. Instead, it provided the overall leadership for the mission to facilitate the recovery action by the brave crew of Gator 07. The true meaning of "Pave Low leads" was on display.

Ultimately, the simple truth is that in the early morning hours of 28 March 1999 in the skies over Serbia, a concept germinated 32 years earlier in the frustrations of the long war in Southeast Asia finally came to fruition. Fully 32 years of conceptualizing, planning, modifying, organizing, and training jelled in one seminal moment, and the rescue of Vega 31, Lt Col Dale Zelko, was the final and ultimate fulfillment of that requirement. His freedom was the end result of the right equipment and the right men at the right place at the right time, and for all of the right reasons.

As the air campaign continued, however, some bad blood was developing between the 20th and 21st guys. At the time the secretary of the Air Force had dictated that no personnel could be TDY overseas for more than 179 days in any 365-day period. Slife kept exact counts on all of his personnel. Unfortunately, just after the Vega 31 recovery, most of the 21st SOS personnel ran out of days. Colonel Harmon requested a waiver, but it was denied. Consequently, the squadron, which had been sitting on the Brindisi deployment for several years, would be denied the opportunity to possibly do the Big Mish because of an administrative rule. That did not sit well with the men of the 21st SOS as they were replaced with more 20th crews. This animosity would not soon evaporate.[14]

Some even more serious issues were raised about command and control of SOF forces as they provided combat recovery support for the combined forces air component. General Short felt that there was not enough coordination between the two and had some sharp disagreements with General Bargewell. At one point, the CSAF, General Ryan, visited the theater and spoke with Short. He then visited the JSOAC, where Major Kingsley, serving as the JSOAC J-3, briefed him on the Vega 31 mission. Ryan was not happy with what he was hearing and terminated the briefing by abruptly getting up and leaving the room. It was clear to all that the disagreements between the USSOCOM elements and the USAF about CSAR were fundamental and not easily solved.[15]

The NATO air campaign continued unabated. JSOTF2 maintained the CSAR package forward at Tuzla and also a second backup package at Brindisi. Colonel Trask served as the RMC on several rotations but never had to respond for a recovery. Two weeks after the Vega 31 mission, JSOTF2 was directed to dispatch two MH-53s and two MH-60s to Albania to perform humanitarian-relief missions in support of Operation Shining Hope. Ten days later, the SOCEUR dispatched Task Force Hawk—a 5,000-Soldier, US Army–led force of 24 AH-64s and artillery and ground force elements—to Albania to support the KLA that was forming in Albania. As the KLA tried to initiate significant operations into Kosovo, these aviation elements were designated to provide them direct fire support. Capt Mike Grub and his 20th SOS crew and Captain Daley and his 21st SOS crew flew humanitarian-support missions forward to the small towns of Kukes, Krume, and

Bajram Curri in eastern Albania. JSOTF2 identified another package of two MH-53s and two MH-60s to support TF Hawk out of Brindisi as a backup CSAR force if its internal recovery team was not sufficient. The Brindisi team was led by Capt Kent Landreth, who had just deployed over with crews to replace the initial Cardoso contingent. Landreth and the JSOTF2 crews met with their Army counterparts to develop TTPs, coordinate communications plans, and conduct some mission rehearsals. Captains Shawn Adkins and Pete Doty, also from the 20th SOS, piloted another of the Pave Lows that supported this mission. They flew sorties into Kosovo to perform bomb damage assessments and coordinate actions with US ground forces as they eventually moved into the area. TF Hawk did have two Apaches go down. However, Army aviation assets handled the recoveries, and the services of the Pave Low and Pave Hawk crews were never directly needed. The commitment was terminated at the end of May.[16]

Hammer 34

On 2 May, JSOTF2 was notified that an A-10 had been hit by ground fire over Kosovo. The rescue task force began initial mission planning when it was subsequently notified that the A-10 pilot had safely landed his aircraft at the airport at Skopje, Macedonia. That evening, though, allied forces were not so lucky. An F-16, Hammer 34, from the 555th FS stationed at Aviano was shot down by an SA-3. The pilot, Lt Col David Goldfein, ejected and was on the ground in Serbia, about 40 miles southwest of Belgrade. His position and status had been initially reported by his flight lead, Hammer 33.

The recovery package that night at Tuzla was the same structure as the Vega 31 package. Coincidentally, the RMC was again Colonel Laushine. However, he had different helicopter crews. This time, the Pave Low flight leader was Captain Landreth, the weapons and tactics officer from the 20th SOS. He and his crews were just lounging around near the command center at Tuzla when the alert arrived. The pilots swiftly collected critical mission information and intelligence, while the flight engineers and gunners went out to make sure the aircraft were fully ready to launch quickly. When an initial plan had been developed, Laushine ordered the task force to launch.

Flying with the call sign of Skat 11, Landreth and crew prepared for takeoff. The second MH-53 was Skat 12, flown by Capt Tom Lang,

1st Lt Dan Nielsen, and crew. The MH-60 was Skat 13, flown by Capt Bill Denehan, 1st Lt Tom Kunkel, and crew. It was a humid night, and all of the aircraft windows and NVGs were fogged up. It took a few moments to clear up that problem. Then Landreth led the formation into the crystal clear night air over Serbia with an almost full moon. En route, Laushine checked in with higher controlling agencies, which informed him that it would take two hours to assemble all necessary support aircraft, including A-10s, F-15s, and F-16s. Laushine realized that such a delay would push the entire rescue effort past sunrise. He believed that the cover of night was more valuable than the support package and directed Landreth to execute the recovery operation with just his formation of helicopters and troops on board.

The Serbian border in this area was a river, and Landreth could see that it was covered with a fog bank. His copilot, Capt Tom Palenske, was flying the aircraft, and Landreth directed him to fly right over the mist so that the other two aircraft would maintain visual contact. Suddenly, they observed two explosions a few miles directly ahead of them. Within seconds, they also realized that the explosions were the launches of two SA-6 radar-guided missiles tracking directly toward their aircraft. Palenske performed a hard left turn and initiated onboard countermeasures as the two wingmen followed suit. The missiles passed a few hundred feet above the helicopters. Landreth then used the IDAS/MATT system to determine an escape corridor to avoid the radar sites. As they proceeded into Serbia, though, they observed another missile shot, this time an SA-9 infrared-guided missile. All helicopters dispensed flares, and the missile passed harmlessly overhead. They then set a course directly to the survivor's reported position, taking them over an area of foothills. Several times they observed antiaircraft fire directed at them and actually overflew a 23 mm gun position that did not fire.

Arriving at the reported location, they could not see the survivor's wingman, supposedly orbiting above. Also, they could not make contact with the survivor on the survival radio frequencies. Then they received an updated position on the survivor from a higher controlling agency. Landreth entered it into the aircraft's enhanced navigational system and discovered that it was 19 miles closer to Belgrade. Cross-checking the new position with the IDAS/MATT system, Landreth could see that it was just on the edge of several SA-3 and SA-6 radar missile threat rings. He announced to the crew, "Okay, guys, that is where we are going. It's going to be tough. The crew responded, 'Let's go!' "[17]

As the helicopters turned toward the updated location, the crew members could see the lights of Belgrade ahead. They could also see occasional missile launches, although not at them. However, they did see ever-increasing small arms fire coming up at their aircraft. They were low enough that they could also hear the shooting, even over the roar of the aircraft engines and whirling blades. At one point, Landreth received intelligence data indicating that the Serbian air defenses were aware that his task force was in Serbian airspace and had been ordered to shoot them down. Landreth's response was classic. "No s---!" he responded. "I figured that out at the border!"[18]

As the formation approached the updated location, several Serbians fired at the aircraft from the second story of a building. SSgt Rich Kelley, the flight engineer on the MH-60, returned a six-second volley with his minigun, which suppressed the enemy and partially sawed the building in half. Then crew members heard the ejected pilot talking on his survival radio. Using their precision locator system (PLS), they were able to determine a general direction to him. The survivor, Colonel Goldfein, heard the helicopters and tried to vector them to him. As the pilots were maneuvering the aircraft, the flight engineer in the cockpit, SSgt William "Scooter" Kerwood, was able to get an accurate heading and distance to him with the PLS. They turned directly to his location and could see personnel on the ground with flashlights. Some were randomly firing their weapons. However, the helicopter gunners did not engage them. As the helicopter formation closed within one mile, the crew on Skat 13 saw the survivor's flashing beacon and made an approach to his location, while the two Pave Lows set up overwatching orbits, ready to suppress any credible threat to the operation. Skat 13 landed and within 40 seconds had Goldfein on board. They lifted off, and the two Pave Lows moved in around them to escort them out.[19]

The three helicopters headed west into the rising terrain along the western Serbian border. As they did, they could see the first tinge of early twilight beginning to appear directly behind them. However, they were not yet safely home. Palenske chose a different border crossing point for their leg to Tuzla. Regardless, they drew antiaircraft fire at two different points. As they crossed the border, Skat 11's second flight engineer, SrA Vince DePersio, manning the right door, was hit on his helmet with a piece of shrapnel. Fortunately, he was not hurt, and the rest of the journey was uneventful. The helicopters landed at Tuzla, and crewmen transshipped the survivor to a waiting MC-130 that took him to Aviano.[20]

Courtesy Lt Col Kent Landreth, USAF

The crews of Skat 11 and 12 the morning after rescuing Hammer 34. *Left to right*: (*top*) TSgt Lou Orrie and 1st Lt Tom Lang; (*middle*) SSgt Vince DePersio, SSgt Dan Weimer, SrA Grady Galvin, SrA Erik Fricsons, and 2d Lt Dan Nielson; (*front*) Capt Kent Landreth, SSgt Barry Bergschneider, 1st Lt Tom Palenske, SSgt Dub Scott, and SSgt Bill Kerwood (deceased).

It was another successful rescue operation for the men of the JSOTF2. The IDAS/MATT modification clearly contributed directly to the overall situational awareness of Landreth and his crew. However, all three helicopters were damaged with multiple small arms hits. The lead Pave Low, #67-14995, lost all of the oil out of its accessory gearbox. The maintenance technicians estimated that it would have lasted another 10 minutes before complete failure, which would have caused a full hydraulic failure and possibly severe electrical problems. Regardless, the performance of the crews was superb. Said Landreth of the mission, "There was so much fluidity in everything we did, it seemed that every crew [member] knew what the other was doing. The discipline that was shown is a great credit to everyone involved."[21]

For a total of 78 days, NATO aircraft pummeled Serbian targets within Kosovo and the homeland with over 38,000 sorties. Using primarily precision-guided weapons delivered from higher altitudes to avoid the Serbian air defenses, they destroyed oil refineries and reserves, bridges, command posts, military airfields, and over 100 aircraft on the ground. Ten Serbian fighters were also destroyed in air-to-air combat.

The strategic damage to Serbia was profound, especially when the NATO attacks were focused upon the national electricity grid and the petroleum distribution system. Finally, on 3 June, President Milosevic agreed to withdraw his forces from Kosovo and accede to NATO's demands. He signed a formal treaty with NATO commanders on 9 June. NATO aircraft stopped patrolling over Serbia the next day when it was confirmed that Serbian forces were, in fact, withdrawing. On 20 June, Operation Allied Force was officially terminated. Over the next two weeks, JSOTF2 kept CSAR forces on alert at Brindisi, although the 21st SOS aircraft, crews, and support personnel were released to return to Mildenhall, ending their seven-year stay at that forward base. On 9 July, SOCEUR commander General Bargewell inactivated JSOTF–Noble Anvil and JSOTF2. However, four 20th SOS MH-53Ms, crews, and support personnel remained at Brindisi, while a rescue detachment of four Moody-based 41st RQS HH-60s arrived to also assume CSAR duty.[22]

Lt Col Tim Minish remained to serve as an RMC. He did not believe that the 41st crews were ready to assume their assigned mission and asked Captain Landreth and his crew to stay for a few weeks to help them. Landreth and his Airmen agreed and were shocked to discover that the 41st RQS HH-60s had M-240 machine guns instead of miniguns and did not have infrared flare dispensers. Landreth was concerned about these deficiencies and said so. When the Moody crews explained that they were willing to accept the added risk, Landreth took his concerns to Minish, who requested that the 55th leave four of its fully equipped and armed MH-60s at Brindisi for the 41st crews to fly. This was approved, and the 55th crews went back to Hurlburt to prepare for the inactivation of their unit.[23]

Landreth had other issues with the 41st crews. They sharply questioned the efficacy of carrying the ODA personnel. Landreth explained that it was General Bargewell's firm direction to do so. Landreth himself had initially questioned the purpose of the added Army and Air Force special operations personnel. However, after taking part in the rescue of Colonel Goldfein, he realized that his force would have only one chance to rescue Hammer 34 from the midst of a fully alerted Serbian nation. The ODA team provided one more possible tactical option to be used under specific criteria, and he concluded that such planning constituted very prudent tactical planning and balance of risk and reward.

Landreth was also shocked to discover that the 41st crews preferred to conduct their rescue operations during the day. They questioned Colonel Laushine's decision to push his rescue force into Serbia under the cover of darkness instead of waiting for a large support force to assemble and provide daytime direct firepower support. Landreth was absolutely convinced that the only way he could have rescued Hammer 34 was at night and, having done so, believed that he had the moral authority and responsibility to say so. He subsequently returned to Hurlburt unsure whether his arguments had changed the thinking of the 41st crews. Fortunately, the cessation of hostilities in the region precluded the rescue crews from ever having to put their planned procedures to the test against the lethal air defenses of Serbia.[24]

Return to Mildenhall

It was a cheerful homecoming for the Airmen of the 21st SOS as they finally settled back in at RAF Mildenhall. As SOCEUR's sole heavy-lift helicopter SOF unit, it was again on call for taskings to perform SAR, CSAR, humanitarian relief, NEOs, or the classic SOF missions. With eight Pave Lows available and almost fully manned with experienced troops, the squadron began to expand its participation to exercises in Germany, Denmark, Scotland, and other classified locations. Colonel Harmon received notification that the squadron would soon be swapping six of its eight MH-53Js for the newly modified MH-53Ms by the end of the year, and he directed the squadron to insure that the necessary training capability was in place for both aircrew and support personnel to properly utilize the aircraft. Maj Jim Slife was the first to convert. He was able to get the necessary training from Captain Cardoso at Brindisi and began giving his troops the three days of academics and three required flights up in the mountains and electronic combat ranges in Scotland needed to become proficient on the advanced equipment.

In recognition of the great work Captain Daley did as the chief of the squadron weapons and tactics office, his efforts during Operations Allied Force and Shining Hope, and overall outstanding work throughout the year, Colonel Harmon nominated him for the Sijan Award for 1999. Daley was subsequently selected for the honor and presented with the award in early 2000. Through December, the 21st averaged 70 sorties a month, one-fourth of which were on deployments. Even though the squadron was "home," the Airmen of the 21st still traveled across the expanse of EUCOM as they reengaged with their traditional US and allied customers.[25]

20th Special Operations Squadron

The redeploying Airmen of the 20th SOS also returned to a squadron in full stride. Indeed, while their teams were at Brindisi, the squadron continued to support exercises all over the nation. Unfortunately, on one exercise at Fort Bragg, MH-53J #68-10364, flying with the call sign of Pave 02, was destroyed on 2 June 1999 when the crew landed hard in a dust-out landing at the Camp Mackall Special Operations Training Facility. The aircraft commander was Capt John Glass, who had flown as copilot with Capt Jim Cardoso and crew on the Vega 31 rescue in late March. The tail gunner, SSgt Kurt Upton, was fatally injured. Colonel Hester had to visit Upton's wife to give her the official notification. As the senior squadron gunner, MSgt John Sprouse was directed to accompany him, along with a preacher and a lawyer. Sprouse later recalled that it was "quite the thing I never wanted to have to do again."[26]

The next month, Capt Kent Landreth departed to serve a three-year tour as a liaison officer with the Naval Special Warfare Development Group at Virginia Beach, Virginia. Additionally, Lt Col Jack Hester gave up command of the 20th SOS to Lt Col Tom Trask and departed to attend the Air War College (AWC) at Maxwell AFB. Trask was one of the most experienced Pave Low pilots in the community and was fully capable and ready to assume command of the squadron with which he had already served in two conflicts. He took over, determined to inculcate in his troops the continued drive for quiet professionalism inherent in the Pave Low community. "Train like you fight!" was his mantra, learned indelibly on his first searing combat experience in Panama. He took seriously his charge to mentor the newest generation of Pave Low crews. Two weeks after Trask took command of the 20th, Col Donald Wurster relinquished command of the 16th SOW to Col David Scott and departed for Scott AFB, where he would serve as the AMC inspector general. He was also notified of his selection for promotion to brigadier general.[27]

As Allied Force concluded, Lt Col Mike Kingsley reported to the 20th SOS to serve as Colonel Trask's ops officer. They would be a powerful combination. The unit was still supplying CSAR forces to Kuwait for Operation Southern Watch, and Kingsley went over to serve a short tour as the Pave Low mission commander at the large military airfield at Ali Al Salem, a few miles to the west of Kuwait City. Deployed with him as his senior NCO was MSgt John Sprouse. Sprouse worked diligently to make the living and duty accommodations for his troops as comfortable as was possible in the desert. He coordinated several improvement projects with the civil engineers and held barbeques for his troops. Two crews were always on alert for CSAR taskings. Their alert tent was a bit sparse. To make it somewhat more accommodating, Sprouse ordered a big-screen television for the facility.

A few days later, one of the Pave Lows made a logistics flight down to the Kuwait International Airport. While there, the crew members spotted a crated big-screen television. They called Sprouse, who confirmed that he had, in fact, ordered one for the unit. Sprouse told them to load it, and they put it aboard their aircraft for transport to Ali Al Salem and took off. Unwittingly, they had actually loaded a television that the Kuwaiti government had purchased for its embassy in Egypt. Kuwaiti authorities ordered the Pave Low to return to the airport. When it did, Kuwait police surrounded it and reclaimed the television. Almost simultaneously, Kingsley received a phone call from the American Embassy and instructions to give the television back as soon as possible, as a serious international incident seemed to be brewing. He immediately ordered his troops to do so.

A USAF inspection team was dispatched to Kuwait to investigate. It interviewed Sprouse, who readily admitted his role in the affair and took full responsibility for all of it. This was typical of Sprouse because he would not allow the two enlisted crew members involved in this incident to be punished for regulations infractions when they were following his directions. In response, his troops developed a deep loyalty and respect for him and his counsel.

Based upon the gathered evidence and testimony, the inspection team found Sprouse culpable, and he was ordered home for disciplinary action. However, when he agreed to put in his retirement papers, disciplinary actions were quietly terminated. One other young sergeant was also implicated but was transferred to the 31st SOS in Korea, providing him an opportunity to redeem himself. The incident quietly faded away, but the willingness of Sprouse to stand up for his enlisted crew members was never forgotten by those who served with him—especially Pave Low gunner SSgt John Stricklin, who noted this as an excellent example of NCO leadership. Back at Hurlburt, Sprouse continued his aircrew and instructor duties and oversaw the move of the 20th SOS to a new building on the east side of the field before retiring in 2001 with 26 years of "interesting" Air Force service and *eight* Article 15s.[28]

Throughout the rest of the year, the 20th SOS received more MH-53Ms and by August was able to launch a 10-ship formation of MH-53Ms. The squadron had not had enough personnel at home at one time to mount such a formation in several years. The crews and support troops participated in an endless variety of exercises to be ready to respond to support the operational theaters, as they had for so long at Brindisi, or to support national taskings as a supplier of forces to JSOC. In November Trask took two Pave Lows and crews and several other squadron personnel to Moody AFB to participate in a CSAR exercise with the 41st and 71st RQSs there.[29]

Air Force Special Operations Command

General Holland and his senior leaders at AFSOC were also glad to see the termination of operations in the Balkans. During that period, as much as 10 percent of their force was in some way tied up in that once seemingly interminable operation. As their Airmen returned to their home bases, the overall command TDY rate steadily dropped. The JCS directed a review of all ongoing training and annual theater exercises with the intention of consolidating those as much as possible—consistent with mission and training needs—to reduce TDY requirements. These two events together reduced the AFSOC personnel tempo (PERSTEMPO) from an average of 117 days per Airman per year in 1998 to 67 days in 1999.

Other changes were afoot at AFSOC. Perhaps reflecting the increasing role that AFSOC was playing in worldwide operations, Headquarters USAF, in June 1999, upgraded the AFSOC commander's billet to lieutenant general rank, and General Holland passed command to Lt Gen Maxwell Bailey on 5 August 1999. Holland then departed for Germany to serve as the vice-commander of USAFE and was subsequently himself promoted to lieutenant general.

As Bailey took over, he found a command that was reconstituting and reorganizing to fit into the larger developing USAF AEF structure. The resultant reduction in PERSTEMPO seemed to be boosting the retention rates. He also was pleased to discover that promotion rates for both officers and NCOs were, in almost all categories, above those for the USAF in general.

However, he noticed that his rotary-wing force was about to be reduced. USSOCOM program objective memorandum guidance for FY 2000, approved by the Command Board of Directors in 1998, directed the inactivation of the 55th SOS in fall 1999. Its MH-60Gs would be transferred to ACC for rescue duty. Additionally, the board directed that the 31st SOS at Osan AB, Korea, inactivate in the spring of 2001. The 160th SOAR would then take over the roles formerly assigned to both units. Initiative 17 was slowly, but inexorably, being consummated. However, the twin actions also freed up personnel and funds for the steadily advancing arrival of the AFSOC CV-22s.[30]

The Pave Low fleet continued to improve as the "M" conversions proceeded on schedule. Within a year, both of the remaining operational squadrons would have a full complement of the incredible machines. AFSOC and ACC combined their efforts to develop a weapons instructor course (WIC) for MC-130, AC-130, and MH-53 crews. The courses would be similar to those taught at Nellis for the other combat components. AFSOC selectees would attend the academic block of instruction with the other students at Nellis to learn the overall process of planning and orchestrating airpower in a theater of operations, as well as to teach the conventional force officers about the intricacies of special operations forces. They would also be afforded the opportunity to develop the personal relationships necessary to better facilitate the close integration of USAF special operations forces and conventional airpower. The AFSOC students would then return to Hurlburt for the flying phases of the courses. WIC selectees would be young officers who demonstrated maturity and growth potential. After graduation, they would be directed to assignments in key service, joint, and combined forces headquarters and command centers. It was an ambitious but exciting plan, and the forecast was for the first AFSOC student to attend in 2002.[31]

Pilot manning for the Pave Lows was still a problem, but more US Army warrant officers were transferring. However, the shortage had unintended consequences. Capt Vince Becklund had finished three years at the 20th and was due for a change of assignment. He applied for and was accepted to be an air officer commanding at the Air Force Academy, something he greatly wanted to do. However, he was informed that because of low Pave Low manning, he would not be able to leave the Pave Low cockpit. Becklund was so incensed that he considered leaving active duty and even began working with a recruiting firm for the Fortune 500 companies. However, an uncle who worked for a major corporation advised him to stay in the USAF for a career, pointing out that the experiences he could have in the USAF could not be replicated anywhere else and that after retiring from the service, he could enter the corporate world. Becklund accepted his advice and received an assignment to be an IP at Kirtland with the 551st.[32]

AFSOC also had to deal with one more issue that was a worldwide concern in general. In the 1970s, when computers first came into general use, their internal clocks were programmed to read some dates and years in two digits. As the calendar moved inexorably toward the year 2000, engineers realized that there was a great possibility that on six specific dates, early programming features could cause various computers to lock up or misread dates. Consequently, many key actions had to be completed by 31 March 1999. However, one specific concern was that nobody knew what the computers would do when, at midnight, they would trip over from year 99 to year 00. Would they continue to work as advertised or somehow assume that the year was now 1900 and do things totally unexpected and potentially very damaging? The implications of the possible ensuing confusion were troublesome, and the impact on combat readiness could not be risked. Needless to say, the Year 2000 problem, nicknamed Y2K, occupied everybody's attention. Like all organizations that now relied on computers to run just about everything, AFSOC had to work with USSOCOM, the USAF, and the DOD to insure that it did not lose the capability to fulfill its mission requirements because its computers failed. Many actions had to be taken, right down to the individual aircraft level, to prevent any disruption. This most certainly included all of the Pave Lows. The effort cost AFSOC $4 million

and endless man-hours, but as the computers were steadily repro-
grammed, they did not suffer any significant degradation, and Y2K
turned out to be a footnote to the approach to the millennium.[33]

31st Special Operations Squadron

Throughout 1999, the 31st was still forward deployed at Osan AB,
providing PACOM with its needed special operations precision infil/
exfil and all-weather, heavy-lift capability. Its six Pave Low aircraft,
crews, and support personnel were constantly on the road throughout the theater, engaging in exercises of all types to maintain mission
capability and to constantly hone their ability to work with both US
and allied special operations forces. There were far more requests
than they could possibly honor. During the summer, Lt Col Steve
Otto, the veteran of the Corvette 03 rescue attempt, took command of
the unit. In the second half of the year, he and his squadron planners
worked with Korean and US planners to review and update overall
contingency options for the defense of the peninsula against a series
of potential North Korean attack scenarios. This was the first time
that personnel from the 31st were allowed to participate in such detailed strategizing with their Korean counterparts.[34]

58th Special Operations Wing/
551st Special Operations Squadron

The year 1999 was another relatively quiet one for the training
units at Kirtland AFB. In July Colonel Folkerts finished his tour as the
commander and was selected for promotion to brigadier general. He
passed command to Col Michael Planert, another former Pave Low
pilot, and departed for another staff tour at the Pentagon. In October
the 58th received an ORI from AETC. After spending 11 days with
the wing looking into every aspect of its operations, the inspection
team awarded the 58th an overall rating of excellent, with many laudable unit and individual accomplishments. The wing was especially
recognized for the aggressive actions it was taking to prepare for the
arrival of the CV-22, possibly as early as 2003.[35]

One of those "excellent" unit ratings went to the 551st SOS. The
unit still had its mixed fleet of six TH-53As and five MH-53Js. Both
aircraft were optimally used throughout flying training. Eleven dif-

ferent courses were now being conducted by the 551st to produce the combat crew members needed out in the operational squadrons.

Their use was balanced with the training provided by the 58th TRSS simulators and part-task trainers. That unit continued to develop what had truly become a state-of-the-art system. All of its flight simulators, including the TH-53A operational flight trainer and the MH-53J WST, were integrated into a massive distributed mission training program that linked with other computers into the larger SOFNET system. This network capability allowed aircrews to fly real-time missions against other aircrews in other simulators at other bases. Additionally, the system had access to a global geographical database and satellite-based navigation simulation that allowed crews to literally "fly" a mission anywhere in the world. The practical result of this synergy was obvious—AFSOC now had a simulator system in which combat crews could practice a mission anywhere under any simulated weather conditions. Mistakes heretofore seen only in actual operational situations could now be captured in simulation, studied, and corrected. This was a quantum advance in the operational use of evolving computer flight simulation technology.

On a smaller but no less important scale, the 58th TRSS had built an Aerial Gunner Scanner Simulator (AGSS) to train the Pave Low gunners and flight engineers. The interactive and real-time system allowed these young Airmen to practice crew coordination, target recognition, gunnery procedures, and visual scanning techniques. It simulated the cabin of an MH-53 and was equipped with either a 50-caliber machine gun or 7.62 mm minigun that could be "fired" and scored for maximum safe and dollar-efficient training.[36]

The combined flight and simulator training was further leavened with occasional real-life rescue opportunities that occurred in New Mexico and sometimes other areas in the general southwest region of the United States. In 1999, 551st crews rescued a trapped hiker in the Sandia Mountains and flew several missions in an unsuccessful effort to find a lost Cherokee Piper aircraft and occupants along the New Mexico/Colorado border. The crews and occasionally students also got to participate in the frequent bilateral and Chili Flag training events held in the area, allowing them to work with the classic special operations customers with whom they could possibly work in operational theaters. During the year, the 551st qualified 32 pilots, 22 flight engineers, and 21 aerial gunners for Pave Low crew duty. On 3 June 1999, Lt Col Randy O'Boyle handed over command of the 551st SOS to another career Pave Low pilot, Lt Col Dennis Jones, one of the heroes of the *Yarrawonga* rescue in 1989.[37]

Air Force Special Operations Command

As the last year of the century began, AFSOC was still catching its breath from the Balkans experience. Within the command, General Bailey worked with his staff to make the necessary organizational and personnel changes to support the USAF as it reorganized its forces into AEFs to better support contingency operations. With 10 years of almost constant deployments and contingency operations, the AFSOC was well experienced now at providing its forces to accomplish the classic SOF missions in whatever tailored packages were needed. Additionally, its Pave Low units were still capable of providing first-class rescue capability, even as a collateral mission, as was dramatically illustrated a few months earlier in Serbia. In fact, the CSAF, General Ryan, had received briefings on the CSARs and, while pleased with the results, was concerned that a disconnect existed between service CSAR doctrine and the current allocation of CSAR-capable forces. He was well aware of the recent history of CSAR in the USAF and the AFSOC's several attempts to address shortfalls in the service's ability to provide CSAR forces to the COCOMs. He had also seen the mission from the war-fighting commander's perspective and knew that assigned SOF helicopter and tanker elements could perform CSAR as well as SOF missions, while assigned rescue forces were trained for CSAR duty only. Succinctly, the war fighters felt that they got more value for their dollar with SOF than with the conventional Air Force CSAR units. The math was easy. Ryan directed AFSOC and ACC to sort it out and improve CSAR integration.[38]

In response, the AFSOC director of operations, Col Steve Connelly (followed by Col James Connors, who replaced Connelly in April 2000 when Connelly gave up the position pending his mandatory retirement), directed the 16th SOW and 352d and 353d SOGs to place a priority on participating in exercises that specifically focused on CSAR and utilized their tanker, helicopter, and special tactics squadron assets. Their schedulers also built a sequence of six CONUS exercises and two conferences in which the 16th SOW assets would participate.[39]

However, both AFSOC and ACC planners realized that neither the AFSOC Pave Low units nor the combat air forces rescue units alone could continuously provide CSAR coverage in all the areas where it might be needed. To provide proper coverage for all AEFs, ACC and AFSOC had to work closely and insure that their units utilized common TTPs for uniformity of effort. Additionally, to better address the issue of conventional and SOF force integration, efforts continued toward developing and initiating the WIC, now on track to graduate its first students in 2002. Classrooms were procured in the 20th SOS building, and the initial cadre of instructors began developing course syllabi.[40]

To honor the participants of the Serbian rescue missions, the US-SOCOM commander, Gen Peter Schoomaker, traveled to Hurlburt Field on 4 February 2000 to present three Silver Stars, 15 Distinguished Flying Crosses, and one Bronze Star to 19 Airmen from those missions as squadron mates, families, and local dignitaries looked on.[41]

A few days after the Hurlburt award ceremony, Colonel Trask, crews, and support personnel took two Pave Lows and flew to Moody AFB for another personnel recovery conference and CSAR exercise with the Moody-based 41st and 71st RQSs and several other units and organizations. Arriving, they found a rather frosty atmosphere. The ACC rescue personnel, who were the designated rescue force, openly resented that the Pave Lows were getting most of the operational taskings and, correspondingly, the acclaim inherent in their recent missions in the Balkans. Lt Col Paul Harmon was also there, and he and Trask tried to make the case that they were merely doing what they were ordered to do. Trask pointed out that CSAR was a collateral—but assigned—mission, even remarking in one session that, in his opinion, Pave Low SOF and CSAR missions and TTPs were 80 percent similar. Colonel Connelly, still serving in his last months before retirement, also tried to remind all attendees that even though they wore different command patches, they all still served in the same Air Force. The conventional rescue guys were not in a very receptive mood, and the bitterness remained.

Regardless, as this exercise was going on, two more Pave Lows and Airmen deployed to Fallon NAS, Nevada, to participate with a large joint force in a two-week series of missions utilizing the great tactical ranges in northern Nevada. The 20th also dispatched another rotation of four Pave Lows, crews, and 68 support personnel to Ali Al Salem AB to provide real-world on-call CSAR support for allied aircraft operating over Iraq as part of Southern Watch.[42]

In a somewhat related move, the AFSOC staff took actions to provide more career continuity and stability for the Pave Low gunners by redesigning their career field. Heretofore, all aerial gunners had carried the Air Force specialty code of weapons mechanics. Given the unique role they performed on board several AFSOC aircraft, command staff members worked with their counterparts at USAF personnel to create a 1A7 Air Force specialty code for gunners as their own separate and unique identifier. This change would also allow first-term Airmen, just out of basic training, to go directly into aerial gunner assignments under a process unofficially called the high-school-to-flight-school program. Additionally, all gunners would now receive flight pay as long as they were assigned to flying duty positions. These changes were effective at the end of October 2000.[43]

Operation Atlas Response

While attending the CSAR exercise at Moody, Harmon got a call directing him to return to the 21st SOS as soon as possible. The nation of Mozambique in southeastern Africa had just been inundated with heavy rains and subsequent flooding. USEUCOM was tasked to prepare a humanitarian mission, and the 21st SOS might be directed to deploy Pave Lows and crews to participate in the effort. Already, a humanitarian assistance survey team had been dispatched to the area. As relief supplies began to flow into that beleaguered nation, another tropical cyclone swept ashore and dropped additional torrents of rain, causing widespread destruction and population displacement. On 1 March, Secretary of Defense William Cohen authorized the deployment of US forces to support humanitarian assistance and disaster relief in Mozambique and its neighboring countries. Immediately, USEUCOM issued an execute order to form a JTF for Operation Atlas Response (JTF-AR). In support, the 352d SOG was directed to provide up to six MH-53s, three MC-130Ps, three MC-130Hs, and 100 support personnel to deploy to Maputo, Mozambique, as the joint special operations air component (JSOAC) of a subordinate JSOTF-AR, under SOCEUR control and commanded by Col Mike Russell, the current vice-commander of SOCEUR. He selected Lt Col Corby Martin to deploy with him and act as his director of operations. Their assigned missions would be to provide SAR support as needed and conduct long-range supply and distribution operations over extended distances.

The 352d SOG commander, Col John Zahrt, would act as the JSOAC commander. He decided to dispatch three 21st SOS MH-53s. Initially, he also asked SOCEUR to augment him with three US Army H-60s. However, he changed his request and instead asked that three USAF HH-60Gs from the 41st RQS based at Moody (and augmented with personnel from the 56th RQS based at Keflavik NAS, Iceland, who were just finishing a Northern Watch tour in Turkey) be diverted with their crews and support personnel to assist in this operation. His request was approved, and they were rerouted, arriving at the airport near Hoedspruit, South Africa, on 8 March, where they were under the tactical control of JSOTF-AR.

On 11 March 2000, the first MH-53 arrived by C-5 at a South African air base at Hoedspruit. The next day, the crew launched into Mozambique and began delivering needed supplies. Two days later, the other two MH-53s were in place and also supporting the operation. Their missions were to rescue people, perform medical evacuations as needed, integrate into the growing effort now involving numerous international and nongovernmental or-

Courtesy AFSOC History Office

A 21st SOS Pave Low refuels over Mozambique during Operation Atlas Response.

ganizations, move people and supplies, and conduct photographic reconnaissance to assess damage from the flooding and to locate isolated refugees. With the helicopters now in place, relief operations started in earnest. The HH-60s flew up to the airfield at Beira, Mozambique, and worked primarily over the northern portion of the country. The Pave Lows stayed at Hoedspruit and worked mainly over the southern half of the nation. Both groups of helicopters were supported by the MC-130P tankers, enabling them to work at much longer ranges to deliver supplies to the flooded outlying areas.

This deployment provided a unique experience for the Airmen of the 21st SOS. There was not enough billeting for all of the troops on Hoedspruit, and several were housed in tents on a game preserve. At night they feasted on locally killed game and watched the wild animals prowl about. One evening they were even taken on a driving tour of the area. For many, it was a surreal experience for which some people would pay thousands of dollars.[44]

For the next two weeks, the MH-53s and HH-60s flew missions as required to provide support to the effort. On one occasion, one of the Pave Lows flew a search mission to find a 352d SOG Airman lost on a recreational outing designed to give the hard-working maintenance and support personnel a well-deserved chance to relax. Unfortunately, Amn Jeffrey Costa had fallen into a fast-moving river and was swept over a waterfall. He was killed, and his body was recovered by South African forces. The Pave Low search effort realized a small amount of good fortune when PJs on board spotted two stranded hikers, one of whom was injured, and returned them to safety.

By 26 March, the Mozambique authorities felt that they had the situation firmly under control, and the USAF assets began to leave. At completion, the JSOTF aircraft had flown 319 sorties carrying 203 tons of cargo and 387 passengers. The HH-60s and personnel were the first to leave since this had been an extension of their original deployment. The Paves and their crews left via C-5 on 30 March, with the Airmen feeling satisfied that they had made a tremendous contribution to the overall relief effort.[45]

Returning to Mildenhall, the 21st SOS resumed its standard training schedule as aircraft and crews were dispatched to work and train with both US and allied special forces elements in Scotland, Norway, and throughout the theater. In June Colonel Harmon relinquished command of the 21st SOS to Colonel Minish, his fellow Desert Storm rescue veteran, to whom he had seemingly been joined at the hip almost ever since, and departed to attend AWC. Major Slife departed to attend the Air Command and Staff College (ACSC) and ultimately also the School of Advanced Airpower Studies (SAAS) at Maxwell AFB.

Lt Col Joe Becker joined the squadron to serve as the operations officer. Since leaving the 551st FTS in 1994, he had served in a series of nonflying assignments, primarily in the special operations world. His last assignment had been at SOCEUR headquarters. When his assignment to the 21st SOS and requirement to requalify in the

MH-53 arrived, he happily packed up his wife, Susan, and three daughters, Emily, Ellen, and Elise, and moved to England.[46]

Becker was joined there by MSgt John DeSalle. He had served four years with the 20th as the NCO in charge of scheduling and for a short period as the squadron first sergeant, while also doing his share of Brindisi rotations. Now serving at the 21st as the squadron operations superintendent with Becker, he was also flying and going on TDYs to get crews ship-landing qualified and to work with the various allied special forces elements throughout the theater. He helped train the gunners, although the 21st did not have as many as the 20th, before moving up to the 352d SOG to serve in the standardization and evaluation office. Regardless, he was right where he wanted to be, and his wife, now a technical sergeant, was with him on a concurrent tour.[47]

In November Minish led the squadron in a somber duty. It gathered in the base chapel to hold a remembrance ceremony for a unit predecessor, long gone. Twenty-five years earlier, 2d Lt Richard Vandegeer, a copilot flying a CH-53 with the 21st SOS, then assigned to Nakhon Phanom AB, Thailand, had been killed when his CH-53 was shot down and destroyed near Koh Tang Island, Cambodia. He was officially declared the last US casualty of that long and long-ago-divisive war. His body had been recovered in 1995 and positively identified in 2000. On 1 November 2000, his remains were buried at Arlington National Cemetery. Minish gathered his Airmen to remember that young lieutenant and his sacrifices as a precursor to what would later become the community of Pave Low.

One month later, in early December, the 21st SOS was once again tasked to support a presidential visit as President Clinton decided to travel to Dublin and Belfast in Ireland and to London. The entourage would include 100 people requiring transportation. Colonel Becker was the 21st SOS operations officer and did the planning. Looking at the projected travel itinerary, he realized that the 21st would not be able to move such a group on its own and requested support through SOCEUR. It assigned him six US Army CH-47s and three UH-60s to assist with the mission. Becker had to arrange to support operating locations in Dublin and at RAF Brize Norton in the UK. Given the visit schedule, the operation would require flying with NVGs and into some tricky landing zones in all three cities. Regardless, the almost ad hoc "task force" that Becker had to build performed well and had only a few minor glitches. In all, the teams flew 12 sorties, logging almost 70 hours in the support effort—really a short-notice, high-profile, no-fail mission that brought out the best attributes of SOF forces. For the second half of 2000, the squadron averaged about 115 sorties a month, half of which were at deployed locations, quite a testament to the Pave Low maintainers at RAF Mildenhall.[48]

The 21st SOS provides support to President Clinton's trip to the United Kingdom.

20th Special Operations Squadron

Back at Hurlburt, the 20th assisted in the preparations for the WIC by preparing rooms for the classes while also participating in the endless flow of exercises and training deployments that were the unit's regimen. The squadron was flying about 170 sorties a month with its 19 assigned MH-53s. In September, the 20th coordinated with its supporting 16th Helicopter Generation Squadron (HGS) to mass launch 13 MH-53s at one time. The crews then replicated a series of tactical missions until thunderstorms sweeping through the area forced a cancellation of the flights. The aircraft were regenerated and made ready for a second mass launch after dark. Continued inclement weather forced cancellation of that launch. Regardless, it was quite an accomplishment for the maintenance teams to generate so many sorties at once and spoke well of their expertise and dedication to supporting the mission.

The next week, five of the aircraft were flown to Fort Campbell with support teams to work with US Army ground and aviation units there. They focused on direct-action-type assaults into urban areas and simulated terrorist-fortified areas. The next month, the 20th dispatched its helicopters and Airmen to Norfolk to work with US Navy SEAL Team 2 and conduct deck qualification training on the USS *Shreveport*. At almost the same time, Colonel Trask led a task force of three Pave Lows and an MC-130 to Pope AFB to work with the 75th FS, an A-10 unit based there, on combat rescue missions. For three days and nights the two groups worked through a variety of scenarios to provide excellent training for both groups. Wrote Trask in his after action report, "Execution was not flawless but the lessons learned were extensive and operations improved over the three days. This type of bilateral exercise should remain one of our regular options as we try to do at least a quarterly CSAR exercise."[49]

Similar to the rescue units at Kirtland, the 20th SOS responded to rescue calls from the southeastern region of the United States. Such was the case when on 13 December 2000, the unit diverted a Pave Low on a training mission to recover an F-16 pilot who had bailed out into the Gulf of Mexico. Working with a US Coast Guard HU-25 Falcon, the Pave Low crew dropped down below a 400-foot ceiling to find the pilot floating about 20 miles off the coast south of Apalachicola, Florida. The two flight engineers, TSgt T. J. Carmichael and SSgt Gary Mishey, pulled him out of the water and provided first aid as the pilots delivered him to the hospital at Tyndall AFB, Florida. It certainly was not as dramatic as the rescue of Vega 31; however, it was another of the many missions that the crews could and did do with the world's finest and most capable heavy-lift helicopters on an almost routine basis.[50]

At the same time, the AFSOC staffers located just down the flight line from the 20th SOS were still struggling with the CSAR issue. In reviewing the results from the now almost steady CSAR exercises so far in 2000 and recent CJCS concerns expressed by combatant commanders about CSAR coverage, Colonel Connors—replacing Colonel Connelly as the AFSOC DO—provided guidance to all units to participate in a minimum of three major CSAR exercises a year. Connors further proposed to ACC that the AFSOC would commit to provide a CSAR task force of four MH-53Ms, two MC-130s, and an STS team each spring for a 90-day deployment to Southern Watch. This would allow that command to reduce the operating tempo of its rescue units to an acceptable level while still meeting the theater commander's needs. For AFSOC, the CSAR issue was not going away. Even though it was doctrinally a collateral mission, the immutable reality was that the USAF did not have enough conventional air rescue force structure to cover all contingencies. It still needed augmentation. It was widely understood, too, that the MH-53M was far and away the best CSAR aircraft for the mission and was being operated by a community of crew members who were now highly experienced as a result of an almost continuous decade of contingency and combat operations.[51]

31st Special Operations Squadron

The last year of the century found the "nomads of the Pacific" still based at Osan with their six assigned MH-53Js. True to their moniker, they were constantly on the move. They availed themselves of the rich training opportunities extant with all of the customers available to them in the theater. Accordingly, their aircrews also became adept at long-range, overwater flights and air-to-air refuelings under any conditions. However, being the only AFSOC Pave Low unit assigned to a remote location, and geographically separate from its mother unit, the squadron was constantly challenged to maintain a stable 248-person maintenance and support workforce, especially its highly specialized Pave Low technicians. Regardless, the unit possessed one of the best maintenance records in the USAF. On 30 June, Colonel Otto handed over command of the unit to the operations officer, Lt Col Brendan Clare, and departed to attend AWC. Within a week of assuming command, Clare and the 31st deployed with other 353d elements to Taegu AB, Korea, to participate in another exercise as a workup for an ORI expected in the fall. As planned, the 353d SOG returned to Taegu in mid-October with 492 personnel to participate in the huge annual Exercise Foal Eagle. As part of the exercise, the 353d formed a headquarters and functioned as a combined joint special operations air component (CJSOAC) for US and Korean forces. The 31st was tasked to support the exercise and inspection with four aircraft, which were then assigned classic SOF missions. The 353d received an overall "excellent" rating for the operational readiness portion of the inspection. Since Korean elements were involved in the operations, the detailed ORI report was classified. The rest of the year was relatively mundane as the 31st then began to prepare for its planned inactivation in 2001.[52]

Overwater training with the 31st SOS

551st Special Operations Squadron

As the end of the century approached, life remained stable and predictable at the training unit. The basic qualification course for pilots and flight engineers remained at 160 days and still utilized the TH-53As and MH-53Js. Scheduling was a bit tight, though, because the unit was manned with only 80 percent of its authorized pilot and aerial gunner instructors and 90 percent of flight engineer instructors. In October the 551st SOS was notified that it would be receiving the MH-53Js from the inactivating 31st SOS sometime the next year to replace the TH-53As that would then be retired. The unit also learned that none of the Kirtland MH-53Js would be modified to the "M" configuration.

The part-task trainers and simulators maintained and operated by the 58th TRSS continued to directly supplement the procedures and flight training, although course syllabi were constantly analyzed and adjusted for efficiencies. The simulators were also used for the three-day recurrent training for the Pave Low crew members who came to Kirtland for the training.

Reflecting the establishment of a specific Air Force specialty code for aerial gunners, AETC established a basic aerial gunner's course at Kirtland. The course was slated to last 25 days, and graduates would receive an Air Force specialty code of 1A731, preparing them for follow-on specific gunner's training for their assigned aircraft. This training track opened up the gunner's career field to initial-tour USAF enlistees. The first class started in October. This change would have a direct, if initially indeterminate, impact on Pave Low. Heretofore, all gunners coming to the aircraft were at least second-tour enlistees, generally holding at least the rank of sergeant. This meant also that they were a bit more mature and settled in their lives. Now the Pave Low units could expect to begin receiving first-term Airmen, young men who not only needed to be trained as gunners but also would probably need a bit of help to mature. Fortunately, the Pave Low squadrons had a plethora of senior NCOs like MSgt John DeSalle to help them do just that.[53]

Throughout the year, crews from the 551st participated in several training exercises, affording them the opportunity to stay exposed to the various customer elements they would work with in the operational squadrons. Additionally, the 551st provided crews for newly developed virtual exercises being conducted with the MH-53 WST and integrated through the SOFNET system with flight simulators in other locations. This creative use of the WSTs provided an excellent opportunity for various command and control centers to accomplish some valuable decision-making training at much lower cost. In December 551st crews were called out to do another local SAR, this time to find and recover two missing teenagers lost while skiing near Santa Fe, New Mexico. A TH-53A with PJs aboard launched to the site and found the two skiers. Because of the rugged terrain, the two had to be hoisted out. Suffering from hypothermia, they were given first aid by the PJs and then flown to Kirtland AFB and transported to a local hospital.

For the year, the 551st qualified 32 pilots, 17 flight engineers, and nine aerial gunners for the operational Pave Low squadrons. Additionally, the 58th TRSS provided simulator refresher training for 118 MH-53 pilots, 102 flight engineers, and 93 aerial gunners.[54]

It was an eventful decade for Pave Low. At its beginning, the 20th and 21st SOSs saw heavy duty in Operations Desert Storm and Provide

Comfort, where their aircraft and crews flew CSAR, classic SOF support missions, and humanitarian operations. At the same time, the 31st SOS was coming to fruition as the third Pave Low operational unit when the squadron was swept up in the debacle of the Mount Pinatubo eruption, completely disrupting the unit's operations and necessitating its relocation to Korea.

A customer's view of Pave Low

Next, the Pave Low force was dispatched to the seemingly endless imbroglio in the Balkans, again performing a variety of missions, fully exercising the aircraft and crews across the broad spectrum of its capabilities. It also answered several taskings to deploy to various parts of Africa either for NEO or humanitarian missions. At the same time, AFSOC was constantly upgrading the aircraft and searching for those Airmen best fitted for Pave Low duty, while producing promising young officers and NCOs who showed potential for service at higher ranks and positions of authority.

As the year 2000 was coming to a conclusion, the MH-53 fleet was healthy, although constantly going through some form of update—

this time with the addition of Kevlar blankets in the cabin area, a Block 10 upgrade to the IDAS/MATT, and improved self-defense systems. The aircraft inventory consisted of two MH-53Js and 17 MH-53Ms in the 20th SOS, eight MH-53Ms in the 21st SOS, six MH-53Js in the 31st SOS, and five MH-53Js and six TH-53As in the 551st SOS.[55] However, when considering that these MH-53s derived from a fleet that originally consisted of 52 HH-53s and 20 CH-53s, the staggering loss rate indicated that the missions assigned to them were inherently challenging and fraught with danger.

The operational units were fully manned and functioning as designed, with the 21st and 31st as forward-based units specifically focused on the two most important theaters and the 20th SOS as the national reserve. Concurrently, the 551st SOS continued to produce qualified aircrews for all. Pilots who had flown Pave Low now numbered almost 400. Of those, 37 had risen to command these units, five had matriculated to wing command, and three had been selected for general officer. There is no way to count all of the great enlisted Airmen who either flew, maintained, or supported this fleet of aircraft. However, the performance of all the officers and enlisted troops together in Desert Shield/Storm, the various Balkans operations, the numerous NEOs, and all the myriad operations and rescues—classified and unclassified—in between speaks to their dedication and professionalism. This fact was validated in the series of ORIs that took place during the decade. It was clear that the cadre of individuals who had grown up with the MH-53 fleet in the 20th SOS during the 1980s had now become a full-fledged and matured community of like-minded, highly skilled, and professional Airmen who, when crewed on those marvelous aircraft, became Pave Low. It is most heartening, too, to note that as busy as the units were, they could still take time to remember their predecessors from the Jolly Green and Knives days in Southeast Asia by gathering as they did for the funeral of the six downed crew members of Jolly Green 67 and Lieutenant Vandegeer.

At the end of this challenging decade, the entire Pave Low community seemed to have become a "unit of confidence," harking back to the phrase coined by Joe Guilmartin to describe the 40th ARRSq and 21st SOS after their Koh Tang mission fully 25 years earlier. Like their earliest predecessors, the operational Pave Low units in existence had developed that "will and ability of their members to perform under stress" and create "the cohesive mechanism that holds units and crews together in combat . . . a group phenomenon, not an individual one."[56]

However, there were still challenges. Initiative 17 appeared to be alive as a looming threat and seemingly a contributor to the inactivation of the 31st SOS. The whole issue of CSAR still festered as the USAF struggled to solve the mismatch of mission capability and mission requirement. The aircraft were aging and steadily dwindling in numbers. More ominously, though, Saddam Hussein was still there, as were a growing number of terrorist groups intent on directly challenging the Western world in general and the United States in particular. They presaged dramatic challenges in the new millennium.

Such realities simmered in the background as Col Steve Connolly met his mandatory retirement in June 2000 after 30 solid years of service. His entire career was interlaced with the development and utilization of Pave Low, from the very first test aircraft, to three unit commands, to serving as the DO of the only organization in the world that operated the aircraft. It was a career long in distinction and too quickly ending. Lt Gen Clay Bailey officiated at his retirement ceremony, reminding all that Connelly was an "inspirational and irreplaceable leader" and highlighting Connelly's incredible record of achievement before yielding the podium to the honoree himself. To the crowd of over 400 of his fellow air commandos, he said,

> AFSOC is right where things are happening in the world. People come here because they are looking to put their lives into something meaningful. . . . Whether it be rescuing a downed fighter pilot, or providing food to some war-torn piece of Africa, or rescuing hostages or evacuees from who knows what little country in some little crowded embassy some place in a corner of the world—they want to be here.
>
> It's a great mission . . . the protection of freedom. . . . It's the mission that pulls it all together.

Speaking directly to his Pave Low brethren, he conveyed, "The MH-53s are going to be retired here in the next 10 years or so. I am glad that I left before they stuck one on a [pedestal] in the airpark somewhere. . . . But we're not done with the MH-53s. They'll be called again. And there'll be no time to get ready. They'll be packed up for a C-5 or C-17 and moved out of Hurlburt, and within 24–48 hours, they'll fly into combat."[57]

Nobody standing there that day could—in their wildest imagination—divine how quickly those words would come true.

Courtesy Col Steve Connelly, USAF, Retired

Col Steve Connelly, who retired in 2000, foresaw a busy future for Pave Low.

Notes

1. Stewart, *American Military History*, vol. 2, 446.
2. *Air War over Serbia*, 1.
3. History of AFSOC, 1 Jan–31 Dec 1999, vol. 1, xviii, 283.
4. Daley to the author, e-mail, 10 Sept 2010.
5. Whitcomb, "Night They Saved Vega 31," 70–75; and Harmon and Trask, interviews.
6. Slife and Cardoso, interviews.
7. Cardoso, interview.
8. Whitcomb, "Night They Saved Vega 31," 70–75; and Hux, interview.
9. Hux, interview.
10. Whitcomb, "Night They Saved Vega 31," 70–75; After Action Report for CSAR for Vega 31, 5 April 1999, OAF file, 1st/16th SOW HO; and Cardoso and Hux, interviews.
11. Data supplied by Lt Col Steve Simon, USAF, retired, and Ms. Jean Bickford, Association of Graduates, Air Force Academy, CO.
12. History of ARRS, 1 July 1970–30 June 1971, vol. 1, 191.
13. Hux, interview; and Cardoso to the author, e-mail, review comments.
14. Slife, interview.
15. Kingsley, interview.
16. Stewart, *American Military History*, vol. 2, 446; Trask and Landreth, interviews; and Doty to the author, e-mail.
17. Landreth, interview.

18. Ibid.

19. Ibid.

20. Ibid.

21. Hewson, "Operation Allied Force, Part 2," 100; Wright and McKenna, "To the Rescue," 17–19; and Landreth, interview.

22. Brown, "AFSOC in the Balkans," 52–53, AFSOC/HO; History of AFSOC, 1 Jan–31 Dec 1999, vol. 1, 120–21; and History of 352d SOG, 1 July–31 Dec 1999, vol. 1, vi.

23. Landreth and DePersio, interviews.

24. Landreth, interview.

25. History of 352d SOG, 1 July–31 Dec 1999, vol. 1, 1, 40, 48, 51; Slife, interview; and Daley to the author, e-mail, 10 Sept 2010.

26. History of AFSOC, 1 Jan–31 Dec 1999, vol. 1, 137, 344; and Sprouse, interview.

27. Landreth and Trask, interviews; and History of 16th SOW, 1 July–31 Dec 1999, vol. 1, 1–2.

28. Trask, Kingsley, and Sprouse, interviews; and Stricklin to the author, e-mail, 22 Jan 2011.

29. History of 16th SOW, 1 July–31 Dec 1999, vol. 1, 23–24.

30. History of AFSOC, 1 Jan–31 Dec 1999, vol. 1, 21, 38, 44; History of 353d SOG, 1 Jan–30 June 2001, vol. 2, supplemental doc. 1–9, AFSOC Programming Plan (PPlan) 99–04: Inactivation of 31st Special Operations Squadron, 30 Sept 1999, 1.

31. History of AFSOC, 1 Jan–31 Dec 1999, vol. 1, 25–26.

32. Becklund, interview.

33. History of AFSOC, 1 Jan–31 Dec 1999, vol. 1, 66, 168–70.

34. History of 353d SOG, 1 Jan–31 Dec 1999, vol. 1, 4, 29–31.

35. History of 58th SOW, 1 Jan–31 Dec 1999, vol. 1, 1, 31–34.

36. Ibid., 2–4.

37. Ibid., 3, 14, 36, 51, 64, 139.

38. History of AFSOC, 1 Jan–31 Dec 2000, vol. 1, 93.

39. Ibid., 1, 70, 93–95.

40. Ibid., 27, 33.

41. Ibid., 26.

42. History of 16th SOW, 1 Jan–30 June 2000, vol. 1, 4, 22–23; History of AFSOC, 1 Jan–31 Dec 2000, vol. 1, 94; and author's personal notes, Moody conference.

43. History of AFSOC, 1 Jan–31 Dec 2000, vol. 1, 48.

44. Slife, interview.

45. History of AFSOC, 1 Jan–31 Dec 2000, vol. 1, 72–81; Partin, Herlocker, and Murphy, *Special Operation Forces in Operation Atlas Response*, 23–39, 74–75; and Slife, interview.

46. Joe Becker, interview.

47. DeSalle, interview.

48. History of 352d SOG, 1 July–31 Dec 2000, vol. 1, xiii, 52–61, 77.

49. Pope AFB, Combat Search and Rescue Exercise After Action Report, 20 Nov 2000, 20th SOS, historical files, 1st/16th SOW HO.

50. History of 16th SOW, 1 July–31 Dec 2000, vol. 1, 30–31, 63.

51. History of AFSOC, 1 Jan–31 Dec 2000, vol. 1, 97.

52. History of 353d SOG, 1 July–31 Dec 2000, vol. 1, vii, 3–4, 8–10, 26; and History of AFSOC, 1 Jan–31 Dec 2000, vol. 1, 105–6.

53. DeSalle, interview.

54. History of 58th SOW, 1 Jan–30 June 2000, vol. 1, 17–18, 45, 47; and ibid., 1 July–31 Dec 2000, vol. 1, 4, 9, 15, 20, 27, 39, 41.

55. History of AFSOC, 1 Jan–31 Dec 2000, vol. 1, 233.

56. Guilmartin, *Very Short War*, 41–42.

57. MSgt Cathy Landroche, "A True Special Operator Says Goodbye," *Commando*, 9 June 2000, 12.

PART IV

Into the Millennium

Chapter 14

9/11

Everybody in America wanted to do something. Instead of just sitting around . . . we were busy and involved. . . . This was an event on par with Pearl Harbor.

—Col Brad Webb

Hurlburt Field

With Lt Gen Maxwell Bailey still in command, the AFSOC entered the twenty-first century now fully established as the air arm of the USSOCOM. AFSOC's 11,700 military and civilian personnel were active in all theaters and living by the command motto Air Commandos—Quiet Professionals. It was now routinely providing unit packages for participation in the USAF AEF program. The CSAR issue was still not resolved, and AFSOC and ACC started a staff initiative to explore the possibility of moving the mission in toto to AFSOC. Although slowly shrinking, its Pave Low force had proven that it could accomplish all of its assigned tasks and was a key component of AFSOC's ability to operate "any time, any place."[1]

Collocated at Hurlburt Field, the 20th SOS was back into its training cycle. For most of January, the unit had three MH-53Ms, crews, and support personnel in San Diego, California, training with SEAL Teams 1 and 3 and focusing on those specific actions necessary to support the SEALs and their unique mission capabilities. These crews returned to Hurlburt to watch Lt Col Tom Trask pass command of the squadron to his Desert Storm 20th SOS co-veteran, Lt Col Mike Kingsley, on 1 February. Lt Col Brad Webb was selected to serve as the squadron operations officer. Trask then departed to attend the NATO Defense College in Rome, Italy.

Kingsley inherited a full plate. Over the next several months, his troops supported the growing SOF MH-53 WIC being conducted at Hurlburt. Captains Mike McKinney, Lance Tilghman, and Paul Mullis had already been working with the weapons center at Nellis AFB to develop a Pave Low curriculum, and they and Capt Mark Daley had

Courtesy Brig Gen Mike Kingsley, USAF

Lt Col Mike Kingsley commanding the 20th SOS as the new century began

been chosen as the initial cadre of instructors to stand up the course. Their initial training lasted through December, when they were awarded the coveted weapons instructor patch, and they then began to work to expand the course so that more of their brethren could attend and spread their tactical expertise into the operational units.[2]

Additionally, the 20th provided CSAR support for a Red Flag rotation at Nellis AFB and direct support for the USAF Weapons School there. All three initiatives highlighted the ongoing issues about integrating AFSOC elements into larger conventional air forces. However, many in the AFSOC community did not support the initiation of the weapons course at Hurlburt, believing that it was too much of a drain on limited AFSOC resources. As one of the first AFSOC graduates, though, Captain Daley believed that the WIC was an unqualified gain for the command, remembering that the WIC was very, very controversial. It was a resource drain on an already overcommitted force. We didn't have the aircraft or the pilots to do it properly, and there was always a fight over use of aircraft and personnel. . . . It all came down to making a near-term sacrifice for a long-term gain—building tactical experts who could take SOF into the future. . . .

The weapons officers we graduated had a huge, lasting impact on moving SOF from an organization that did not integrate well with the larger conventional force to one that better understood the "Big Air Force" capabilities and better integrated them into SOF air operations.[3]

In the not-too-distant future, these skills would be put to good use in dealing with challenges unimaginable in the near future.

That winter and spring, the 20th SOS also deployed another package of aircraft, crews, and support personnel for Operation Southern Watch at Al Jaber AB, Kuwait. Capt Pete Doty and 1st Lt Greg Peterson were crewed together for the rotation. On 12 March, they supported recovery operations for five American troops and one New Zealand soldier killed and seven others (five Americans and two Kuwaitis) injured on the Udairi bombing range when a US Navy F-18 misidentified a training target and dropped three Mk-82 500-pound bombs on an observation point. Doty was also directed to act as the initial investigating officer and had to secure and preserve all of the "evidence," pending the formal investigation.[4]

At the same time, Kingsley had to get his squadron prepared for a two-phase ORI that the 16th SOW would be receiving in April and June. As scheduled, the wing took its inspection. Overall, the wing was rated excellent, with the tactical aspect ratings all classified.

Several "outstanding" ratings were also awarded, one to the 16th HGS that provided the direct maintenance for the Pave Lows. In the overall ORI report, the squadron received specific kudos:

During the launch, technicians displayed a strong sense of urgency as they transferred the crew and equipment from one helicopter, which had developed a first stage hydraulic system malfunction, to a spare aircraft. Aggressive maintainers quickly replaced the faulty hydraulic pump and the aircraft departed with minimum delay, allowing the eight MH-53s to accomplish the takeoff within the required timelines. The squadron's remarkable maintenance at the ORI location produced an astonishing 354.2 hours from 67 sorties with a 94 percent MRE [mission effectiveness rate].[5]

Also of note is that for the preceding 24 months, the 16th HGS had kept the 20th SOS Pave Low fleet above a 75 percent overall mission-capable rate. That certainly made Kingsley's job much easier. A few

days after the ORI concluded, the Pave Low community received another honor of sorts, when a sixth Pave Low veteran, Col Lyle Koenig,
achieved wing command as he took over the 16th SOW from Col
David Scott.[6]

31st Special Operations Squadron

As directed by USSOCOM, the 31st SOS at Osan AB prepared for
its inactivation. The ceremony took place on 31 March 2001, when
Brig Gen Rich Comer, now serving as the AFSOC vice-commander,
traveled to the unit to officiate. He was joined by former commanders
Col Lee Massey and Col Gene Correll, both now retired, as the last
31st SOS commander, Lt Col Brendan Clare, furled the squadron
flag. Squadron personnel were then released for other assignments,
and four of the aircraft prepared for shipment to training duty with
the 58th SOW at Kirtland AFB to replace the TH-53As.

However, the six-ship MH-47E unit designated to take the 31st
SOS's place, Echo Company of the 160th SOAR, was not fully combat
capable. Consequently, two MH-53s were held at Osan as a residual
fleet until the MH-47Es and support element were ready to assume
the mission. AFSOC coordinated with the 16th SOW to provide necessary personnel. The 20th SOS sent a small detachment over to attend
Exercise Tandem Thrust in Australia, which allowed the crew to work
with the Australian Special Air Service Regiment. One of the pilots
on that deployment was 2d Lt Sean Borland, among the recent Army
warrant officers who had come over to the USAF to fly the Pave Low.
Typical of that selective group, he brought with him a wealth of helicopter and NVG experience as an AH-1 and AH-64 pilot. He flew
quite a bit on the 45-day TDY and, upon return to Hurlburt, began
his upgrade to first pilot and then mission pilot. Clearly, the Army
exchange program was already benefiting the Pave Low force.

The 21st SOS also provided several aircrew members and mainte-
nance troops to help uphold residual Pave Low capability at Osan.
This augmentation force remained at Osan until late June, when Colonel
Clare and Col Doug Salmon flew the last Pave Low sortie and Echo
Company fully accepted the mission. The Pave Low no longer had
any permanent presence in the Pacific theater, and the replacement of
USAF special operations helicopter assets by US Army special opera-
tions assets proceeded apace as per Initiative 17. During its almost 12

years in existence as the sole Pave Low unit in the huge theater, the 31st SOS "nomads of the Pacific" had been commanded by 11 officers and had provided an excellent training venue for a whole generation of air commando officers and Airmen.[7]

21st Special Operations Squadron

During the first six months of the new year, the 21st SOS also maintained its normal peacetime routine. However, its flight activities were severely restricted over the UK when that nation suffered a terrible outbreak of hoof-and-mouth disease that devastated its cattle herds. The unit received its full complement of eight MH-53Ms. The aircraft and crews were dispatched to joint and combined exercises with various elements throughout the SOCEUR area. However, one of the aircraft required more attention than the rest. The previous year, MH-53M #69-5784 had been seriously damaged in a crash on one of the training ranges. Extensive repairs were made, and the aircraft was returned to flight status. However, as if assuming the role of a Jonah,

Courtesy Lt Col Pete Doty, USAF

21st SOS Scottish dining-in

the aircraft suffered several more incidents, all of which required significant maintenance repair. Fortunately, by the summer it was again fully mission capable. Also during this period, 21st SOS crews flew several support sorties to locate two F-15 pilots who had gone down in a midair collision. In another incident, Capt Steve Plumhoff diverted his crew off of a training sortie to successfully rescue two seamen adrift in a small boat that had lost power.

Courtesy Air Force Historical Research Agency

A 21st SOS crew practices ship landings aboard the USS *Kalamazoo*

On 26 June, Lt Col Tim Minish gave up command of the 21st SOS to Lt Col Joe Becker and departed to attend AWC. The next month, Lt Col Greg Lengyel joined the squadron to serve as the operations officer. On the flight over, he and his family traveled with Capt Pete Doty and his family, also proceeding to the 21st where Doty would serve as the squadron chief of standardization and evaluation. Arriving, they encountered Steve Plumhoff. He was just completing his tour in England and preparing to move his family back to the United States. He and his wife, Yvete, convinced Pete and Isabelle that they should move into the rustic country "guesthouse" on a traditional family estate named Kilverstone, not far from the base where the Plumhoffs had enjoyed living while there on their tour.[8]

Four weeks later MSgt Jim Kradel followed Colonel Lengyel and Captain Doty. Upon completing his previous tour with the 352d in June 1997, Sergeant Kradel had returned to Hurlburt Field but was assigned as a gunner to the 55th SOS. He served with the unit until he was reassigned to the AFSOC stan/eval team as a gunner evaluator. His assignment back to the 21st SOS coincided with his selection for promotion to senior master sergeant, and he would serve as the squadron superintendent. However, just prior to moving to England, Kradel had broken a wrist and would not be able to fly until it healed.[9]

September 11

The terrible and tragic events on that beautiful late-summer day are well documented. Like all Americans and freedom-loving individuals, the Airmen of Pave Low were shocked and appalled as they watched the television screens. Most realized, too, that in all probability, many of them would soon be in some form of action, most likely somewhere in the Middle East.

Colonel Kingsley, along with several other 16th SOW squadron commanders, was engaging in a paintball contest with the wing senior NCOs at the newly installed facility at the south end of Hurlburt when all of their beepers began to erupt. One individual then shouted that the news stations were reporting that an aircraft had just hit one of the Trade Towers in New York City. That ended the paintball contest, as they all headed back to their units.[10]

AB Eric Ezell was on a work detail at Lackland when he heard about the events in New York and Washington, DC. Just two weeks into his Airman basic training, he and several of his cohorts were doing some general cleaning when their supervisor sat them down in a snack bar and told them to watch the TV as the stark events unfolded. Simultaneously, the noise and energy level in the building rapidly increased as everybody else became aware of the news. Ezell and his team were then moved on to several other tasks as the base responded to the security alerts being sent out to all bases. Ezell was a bit concerned. He had joined the Air Force expecting to spend four or maybe more years training and traveling and taking advantage of educational opportunities. The possibility of combat duty was distant at best. As he watched the events unfold on the TV, though, he began to sense that they would involve him personally. He had enlisted under the high-school-to-flight-school program to be an aircraft gunner, and it slowly dawned on him that aircraft that carried gunners would probably soon be very busy.[11]

As Kingsley drove back to the squadron, he could see that base security was being dramatically increased. He ran into the squadron building to find his Airmen in a somber mood, gathered around the televisions as the horrifying events of the day unfolded. TSgt Brian Cessop, the duty superintendent, could not keep up with the ringing phones. He ended up working a 16-hour day as all squadron personnel were recalled and speculation ran rampant with rumors sweeping through the building.[12]

Colonel Kingsley received a phone call from the 16th Operations Group commander, Col Frank Kisner, telling him to get helicopters and crew ready to provide immediate disaster-relief support to both New York City and the Pentagon. Across the base, all units were moving quickly to dramatically increase base security. The wing commander, Colonel Koenig, was at the head of the effort. He told his troops, "We'll continue to do whatever is necessary to help . . . keep our people safe and our base secure."[13]

Just a few days earlier, Kingsley had dispatched Colonel Webb with three Pave Lows, crews, and support personnel to Fort Bragg for joint training and Capt Paul Pereira with four Pave Lows and crews to Asheville, North Carolina, for mountain training. On 11 September, one of Webb's crews, with Capt Dave Tabor and Capt Joe Michalek and their engineers and gunners, had taken off at 4 a.m. to work with JSOC elements. Webb and his other crews were sleeping late in preparation for several days of night flying. When Webb arose and turned on his television, he learned of the ongoing events. Tabor's crew had already been instructed to land at nearby Pope AFB, where they kept their aircraft. Webb immediately called the 16th SOW command post at Hurlburt and was instructed to get all of his troops into the JSOC compound as soon as possible. Arriving there, he talked with Kingsley, who instructed him to get his aircraft airborne as soon as possible and fly to McGuire AFB, New Jersey, and report to the Twenty-First Air Force commander for tasking as needed. Kingsley also called

Pereira and told him to send two aircraft and support personnel to join Webb at McGuire and to dispatch the other two back to Hurlburt.

These actions were taken strictly on verbal orders from Lt Gen Robert Fogelsong, the DCS for air and space operations, Headquarters USAF, who directed all USAF units to "go help Americans." The crews quickly got the helicopters ready to go. However, Webb and Kingsley took several hours to work out airspace coordination with the FAA. Regardless, while en route, the helicopters were intercepted and visually inspected by fighter aircraft now on patrol above several major cities, especially in the northeast. Webb and his crews stopped at Andrews AFB to get gas. They also procured maps of the local Washington flying area from the 1st HS just in case they were instructed to return. Taking off from Andrews, they proceeded directly to McGuire, arriving there at about 11:00 p.m., followed shortly by the aircraft and crews from Asheville. Webb then contacted the McGuire command post and was directed to report for the 6:00 a.m. battle-staff update. He put his aircrews into crew rest as his maintenance team made sure that the aircraft were ready for possible heavy action the next day.[14]

That evening as the Pave Low crews were proceeding to McGuire AFB, Pres. George W. Bush addressed the nation regarding those horrific events:

> Today, our fellow citizens, our way of life, our very freedom came under attack in a series of deliberate and deadly terrorist acts. . . . Thousands of lives were suddenly ended by evil, despicable acts of terror.
>
> The pictures of airplanes flying into buildings, fires burning, huge structures collapsing, have filled us with disbelief, terrible sadness, and a quiet, unyielding anger. These acts of mass murder were intended to frighten our nation into chaos and retreat. But they have failed; our country is strong.
>
> A great people has been moved to defend a great nation. Terrorist attacks can shake the foundations of our biggest buildings, but they cannot touch the foundation of America. . . .
>
> America and our friends and allies join with all those who want peace and security in the world, and we stand together to win the war against terrorism.[15]

The next morning Webb reported as ordered, only to find staff members more concerned with supporting Operation Noble Eagle, the now ongoing air defense shield of fighters and tankers that had been initiated immediately after the twin strikes in New York. They had no idea what to do with the Pave Lows and directed him to contact Federal Emergency Management Agency (FEMA) representatives for tasking. He spoke with them, and they linked him with liaison personnel for several urban SAR task forces also working for FEMA.

Captains Tabor and Michalek were instructed to fly a FEMA crew to the Pentagon. Michalek had flown in the 1st HS and knew the local route structure by heart. They flew as instructed in MH-53M #68-10357 and then returned to McGuire AFB. Webb was also requested to send two aircraft up over New York City. Led by Capt Steve Gregg and copilot Capt Casey Ward, they were able to procure permission to land on the USS *Intrepid*, a retired aircraft carrier docked on the Hudson River now serving as a floating museum. There they were able to link up with elements from the New York City Fire and Police Departments, Federal Bureau of Investigation, and whoever else needed their support. Initially, the demand for flights was high. The assigned police helicopters could not fly over the area because of residual dust and smoke and lingering concrete particulates in the air. FEMA requested that the Pave Low crews move medical teams around the city and take aerial photography of the downtown area.

On 15 September, Tabor, Michalek, and crew flew a mission using their FLIR system to attempt to identify residual hot spots or areas where humans might still be trapped. The 16th SOW augmented Webb's team with additional maintenance personnel who kept the aircraft mission capable throughout.[16] Captain Tabor was interviewed several days after his experiences that day. Clearly understanding the

Courtesy Brig Gen Brad Webb, USAF

A Pave Low over the Pentagon

Courtesy Brig Gen Brad Webb, USAF

A Pave Low over New York City

Courtesy Brig Gen Brad Webb, USAF

MH-53M #68-10369 aboard the USS *Intrepid* on the Hudson River

role that the Pave Lows could and would play in this unfolding tragedy, he conveyed:

> We're here to help in any way possible. . . . The crews are motivated and the morale is high. . . . The Pave Low's high-lift capability and "long-legs" make it an ideal platform for these types of operations. Combine that with the . . . crews' training and experience with night flying, [and] the Pave Low is an amazing asset in such operations. The Pave Low is the largest and most powerful helicopter in the Air Force inventory, and the most technologically advanced helicopter in the world. . . . What we can do here are the things we've trained for and done in places such as Mozambique and Kosovo.[17]

As the 20th SOS crews were flying over the still smoldering wreckage, Defense Secretary Rumsfeld began to issue initial guidance to the men and women of the armed forces by stating that "the task of vanquishing these terrible enemies and protecting the American people and the cause of human freedom will fall to you—the men and women of the Department of Defense. I know we are ready, I know America can continue to count on your selflessness, courage, and dedication to duty."[18]

Intelligence reports quickly linked the 9/11 attacks to elements of an extremist organization called al-Qaeda (meaning literally "the base") led by a shadowy Saudi named Osama bin Laden. As calls mounted for retaliation, the United States and its allies began intense diplomatic efforts to isolate his influence, find him and his organization, and hold them to account. Anticipating the president's actions, on 14 September the US Congress passed a joint resolution authorizing "the use of United States armed forces against those responsible for the recent attacks launched against the United States." Secretary

Courtesy Air Force Historical Research Agency

MSgt Nelson Neal checks his GAU-2B minigun prior to flight.

Rumsfeld immediately signed orders calling thousands of guardsmen and reservists to active duty. Bin Laden and a subordinate bevy of his group leaders were reported to be in Afghanistan as "guests" of the brutal and demonic Taliban regime in power there. All signs pointed to a winter combat campaign in the high terrain of that distant and little-understood nation. After reviewing options, President Bush directed the launch of a joint air-ground effort relying primarily on airpower and, initially at least, special forces elements. That would, most certainly, include Pave Lows as the United States engaged in the global war on terror, or GWOT, as it was quickly termed by the press.[19]

The pace was almost frantic at Hurlburt as the 16th SOW prepared elements from all of its operational and support squadrons for deployment. Colonel Kingsley rapidly identified four crews and a small support package for deployment as the aircraft were also prepared. On 18 September, he directed Colonel Webb to return his team to Hurlburt to join the process. The team, which had swelled to almost 90 personnel, complied and was home by the next day. Webb had a lot of catching up to do. He knew that the Pave Lows would be some of the first to deploy. He also knew that Kingsley would want to go with the initial detachment, meaning that he would remain at Hurlburt and serve as the acting squadron commander. There was so much that needed to be accomplished quickly.[20]

21st Special Operations Squadron

Colonel Becker learned about the attack while deployed to Tazar AB, Hungary, for EUCOM exercise Jackal Cave. He was there with five Pave Lows, most of the squadron, and a large support team, including Colonel Lengyel, Lt Col R. K. Williams, who was serving as the exercise operations officer, and SMSgt Jim Kradel, who was still nursing his broken wrist but was there to provide planning and operations supervision. The crews were in the flight planning section getting ready for some night sorties when the 352d SOG commander, Col Jeff Walls, walked in and said, "We have to find a TV. I just got a message that something is happening in New York City." Some of the Airmen thought that he was making an input for the exercise and chided him for the unreality of such a suggestion. Walls assured them that he was serious and repeated his request. That was a problem because Tazar was an austere location, and any unsecured means of communication was problematic. However, they were able to find one, and the unit communications technicians were able to link it to a satellite feed. As the troops watched the dizzying events, Colonel Walls received a message that the exercise was cancelled and he and his Airmen were to return to Mildenhall as soon as possible. They departed early the next morning, spent that night at an air base in Germany, and arrived at home station on the 13th. Colonel Lengyel could not help but notice how courteous and supportive the usually irascible European air traffic controllers were as the Pave Lows flew through their almost empty airspace.[21]

Courtesy Col Paul Harmon, USAF, Retired

The 21st SOS flight line at RAF Mildenhall

There at RAF Mildenhall, the rest of the 21st SOS had worked with the host 100th Air Refueling Wing to also dramatically increase base security. This was a real challenge because the town of Mildenhall had grown up intertwined with the base. Several main roads literally criss-crossed the military areas, and security gates had to be installed on several main roads. Colonel Becker lived in the town, one mile from his office. Pre-9/11 transit time was about 10 minutes. With the new security, though, it now took him about 40 minutes to get to work.[22]

The 352d SOG was also directed to launch, ultimately, 27 sorties to reposition key SOCEUR personnel. Immediate intelligence indicated that al-Qaeda elements in the eastern Mediterranean area were transporting weapons and money aboard several ships transiting that area.

Anticipating some form of tasking, Lengyel put together a series of "Purple Flex" train-ups and local exercises working with various elements from Naval Forces, Europe; the US Sixth Fleet; and SEAL Teams Two and Ten to sharpen the shipboarding and assault skills of the 21st SOS crews.[23]

The Path to War

On 20 September, President Bush addressed a joint session of Congress, where he made his views clear about what the American people could expect in terms of the country's response to the 9/11 attack and its policy toward terrorism in general.

> On September the 11th, enemies of freedom committed an act of war against our country. . . . All of this was brought upon us in a single day—and night fell on a different world, a world where freedom itself is under attack. . . .
>
> Americans have many questions tonight. Americans are asking: Who attacked our country? The evidence we have gathered all points to a collection of loosely affiliated terrorist organizations known as al Qaeda. . . .
>
> Our war on terror begins with al Qaeda, but it does not end there. It will not end until every terrorist group of global reach has been found, stopped and defeated. . . .
>
> These terrorists kill not merely to end lives, but to disrupt and end a way of life. With every atrocity, they hope that America grows fearful, retreating from the world and forsaking our friends. They stand against us, because we stand in their way. . . .
>
> Americans are asking: How will we fight and win this war? We will direct every resource at our command—every means of diplomacy, every tool of intelligence, every instrument of law enforcement, every financial influence, and every necessary weapon of war—to the disruption and to the defeat of the global terror network.
>
> This war will not be like the war against Iraq a decade ago, with a decisive liberation of territory and a swift conclusion. It will not look like the air war above Kosovo two years ago, where no ground troops were used and not a single American was lost in combat.
>
> Our response involves far more than instant retaliation and isolated strikes. Americans should not expect one battle, but a lengthy campaign, unlike any other we have ever seen. It may include dramatic strikes, visible on TV, and covert operations, secret even in success. We will starve terrorists of funding, turn them one against another, drive them from place to place, until there is no refuge or no rest. And we will pursue nations that provide aid or safe haven

to terrorism. Every nation, in every region, now has a decision to make. Either you are with us, or you are with the terrorists. From this day forward, any nation that continues to harbor or support terrorism will be regarded by the United States as a hostile regime.[24]

The president's declarations quickly came to be labeled the "Bush Doctrine." They were incorporated into the next iteration of the US *National Military Strategy* and fundamentally changed the way the United States would ensure its national security. Preemptive action would now be a strategic cornerstone of security and would require a fully expeditionary force capable of rapidly imposing America's will on hostile foreign soil and then maintaining a robust presence to ensure lasting change. It was the kind of challenge for which the USSOCOM was created. Planners at its headquarters in Tampa were hard at work divining force packages for deployment as directed by the president. Afghanistan was rapidly becoming the initial destination. However, there were real challenges to operating there, and already debates were taking place within the headquarters about which helicopter force would be most appropriate for the mission.[25]

Notes

1. History of AFSOC, 1 Jan–31 Dec 2001, vol. 1, 2, 18.
2. Daley to the author, e-mail, 16 Sept 2010.
3. Ibid.; and follow-up e-mail, 19 Sept 2010.
4. Doty to the author, e-mail; and Paul Richter, "Warning Came Too Late in Kuwait Bomb Run," *Los Angeles Times.com*, 14 Mar 2001.
5. History of 16th SOW, 1 Jan–30 June 2001, vol. 1, 36.
6. Ibid., 1, 25–28, 36–37.
7. Borland, interview; History of 353d SOG, 1 Jan–30 June 2001, vol. 1, 3; and History of 352d SOG, 1 July–31 Dec 2001, vol. 1, 40.
8. Doty to the author, e-mail.
9. History of 352d SOG, 1 Jan–30 June 2001, vol. 1, 4, 32, 54, 56; and Lengyel and Kradel, interviews.
10. Kingsley, interview.
11. Ezell, interview.
12. Cessop, interview.
13. Kingsley, interview; and "Mission Continues despite Attacks," *Commando*, 14 Sept 2001, 1.
14. History of AFSOC, 1 Jan–31 Dec 2001, vol. 1, 12; Webb, interview; and Stricklin to the author, review remarks, 23 Jan 2011.
15. Fontenot, Degen, and Tohn, *On Point*, 22.
16. Webb, interview; and Michalek to the author, e-mail. Note: In June 2003, FEMA presented a special award to the 20th SOS for its direct support of that agency

in the initial recovery efforts in both New York City and at the Pentagon. Michalek, personal notes, provided to the author; and "Pave Low Squadron Honored by FEMA," *Commando*, 27 June 2003, 1.

17. "Pave Lows Support Relief Efforts," *Commando*, 21 Sept 2001, 1, 5.

18. Garamone, "Rumsfeld Charges DoD to Vanquish Terror Enemies."

19. Briscoe et al., *Weapon of Choice*, 33.

20. Kingsley and Webb, interviews.

21. History of 352d SOG, 1 July–31 Dec 2001, vol. 1, xvi, 33–34; and Williams and Lengyel, interviews.

22. Joe Becker, interview.

23. Lengyel and Williams, interviews.

24. Fontenot, Degen, and Tohn, *On Point*, 23.

25. History of AFSOC, 1 Jan–31 Dec 2001, vol. 1, 133–34.

Chapter 15

Operation Enduring Freedom

~2001–2

You guys are the CSAR force . . . in Enduring Freedom!
—Col Paul Harmon

Hurlburt Field

As President Bush was making the case for offensive operations in Afghanistan, operational deployment orders were streaming to US military units around the world for what had initially been labeled Operation Infinite Justice but had subsequently been changed to Operation Enduring Freedom (OEF). Initial planning directed that elements from the CIA and various special forces units would be inserted into that country from both the north and south. They would work closely with an armada of fighter and bomber aircraft to destroy al-Qaeda and its supporting Taliban allies throughout the country. The air campaign was being rapidly developed. A key component would be the inclusion of aviation elements capable of providing CSAR support from both the north and the south. Defense Secretary Rumsfeld and the CJCS, Gen Hugh Shelton, were in agreement that the air campaign would not be initiated until CSAR forces were in place and capable of responding. Both feared that the initial capture of an American aircrew member could negatively impact support for the operation.[1]

At the 20th SOS, Colonel Kingsley was ordered to prepare his initial six aircraft, six crews, and a support package for deployment to an unspecified destination. He handed control of the squadron and remnants at Hurlburt to Colonel Webb, and on 21 September, he and his Airmen and an element from the 8th SOS departed Hurlburt on C-17s. Several hours later in the middle of the night, they landed at the British air base on Masirah Island, off the coast of Oman—the same airfield from which the ill-fated mission to Desert One had been launched over 21 years prior. Kingsley knew the history of that event and the impact that it had had on special operations forces in general and Pave Low in particular.

He and his Airmen were greeted by the British troops who were conducting an exercise, the Omani base commander, and a representative from the American Embassy, who informed Kingsley that he had no place to billet them. Kingsley spotted an empty warehouse and received permission to bed down his troops there in the sleeping bags they had brought with them. The next day, he met a retired USAF chief master sergeant who was working for a local contract support company and had access to a large repository of equipment specifically pre-positioned for such operations. He allowed Kingsley and his small task force to draw tents and equipment that they used to set up as a separate camp. The facility steadily grew in size as more and more elements from the 16th SOW and other USAF units continuously arrived. De facto, Kingsley was the commander of a growing expeditionary force.[2]

The US Navy also operated a small detachment of P-3s on the airfield, and Kingsley was able to work with them to establish a secure communications link. He utilized that link to contact Col Paul Harmon, who was serving as the head of the special operations liaison element within the CAOC for the combined forces air component commander (CFACC), CENTCOM—Lt Gen Chuck Wald (USAF), located at Prince Sultan Air Base (PSAB) in Saudi Arabia. That headquarters would be responsible for conducting the air campaign in Afghanistan and its surrounding countries. Harmon gave Kingsley his operational tasking. "You guys are the CSAR force to start this mission in Enduring Freedom," Harmon explained to Kingsley through the secure telephone unit, STU-III. He added that Colonel Kisner, the 16th SOG commander, would be deploying to an airfield in Uzbekistan to serve as the overall air component commander for special operations aviation forces deploying to the theater. Kisner would be receiving elements from the 160th SOAR and would directly support a large task force from the US Army 5th SFG, which was deploying to insert its ODAs into Afghanistan. Kisner would be Kingsley's direct, if distant, operational supervisor.[3]

With that mission guidance, Kingsley put his aircrews to work to develop a CSAR plan for Afghanistan from Masirah Island. The maintenance crews built up the Pave Lows, and the flight crews flew some local sorties and practiced higher altitude refuelings with the

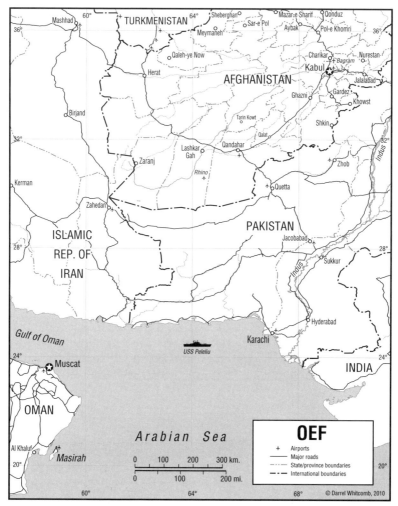

Figure 6. Operation Enduring Freedom area of operations. (Copyright Darrel Whitcomb, 2010.)

8th SOS MC-130Es required over the high mountains of Afghanistan. At the same time, as the senior USAF officer present, Kingsley had to deal with the multitude of problems inherent with the arrival of the ever-expanding USAF contingent at this remote base. His incessant requests for support from the British and Omanis quickly began to strain relations between him and his local counterparts. Fortunately, he had within his task force a cadre of excellent senior NCOs who effectively took over the running of what was literally growing into "Camp Kingsley." In one of his many STU-III telephone calls to Colonel Harmon, Kingsley implored him to work with the CFACC staff to get a USAF colonel to come to Masirah and take over as the de facto base commander so he could focus on his mission.

Kingsley had reason to be concerned about the operational tasking. Masirah was just too far from Afghanistan. Even with in-flight refueling, his crews would take several hours to reach those areas where aircrews might be shot down. He needed to get his forces closer to the action. At one point, General Wald visited Masirah and gave Kingsley a direct and stern admonition. "You've got CSAR in your hands. Don't screw this up."

"Got it," Kingsley responded, and then he directly asked Wald for a USAF O-6 to take over as the Masirah base commander so he and his Airmen could concentrate on their operational assignment.[4]

One of the options that Kingsley and Harmon considered was the possibility of placing at least two Pave Lows aboard a US Navy ship that could then move much closer to the Pakistani coast. An entire amphibious ready group with a USMC contingent was already operating in the Arabian Sea, and plans were developed to put the Pave Lows aboard the USS *Peleliu* (LHA 5).[5] Kingsley was notified that the Pakistani government had given permission for him to move his entire contingent to a combined civil/military airfield near Jacobabad in

Courtesy Maj Mike Holder, USAF

Pave Lows aboard the USS *Peleliu* before flying into Pakistan

central Pakistan, just 200 nautical miles from the Afghan border. Kingsley ordered Maj Tom Dermody, serving as the 20th SOS deployed operations officer, to lead the Pave Lows aboard the ship. While aboard, he was to be prepared to perform CSAR and figure out how to get the aircraft and crews to Jacobabad. Dermody complied and led four Pave Lows aboard the *Peleliu*. The remaining two Pave Lows at Masirah would proceed later to Jacobabad.

On 7 October, Kingsley loaded the rest of his task force aboard C-130s for the flight to Jacobabad. He had also been assigned Lt Col Steve Hadley, a USAF pilot-rated ophthalmologist, as his deputy. As they were leaving, Kingsley happily passed responsibility for the growing USAF complex at Masirah to a newly arrived USAF colonel and then turned his attention to what lay ahead.[6]

Pakistan—and Points Beyond

The task force arrived at the airport at Jacobabad and parked its C-130s on a ramp at midfield in front of an old hangar. The Pakistani officer greeting the task force members said that they could use the hangar as a mass billet. That made sense from a security perspective. However, the hangar was old, dirty, and long unoccupied. In fact, it was infested with birds and various critters—including a colony of bats up in the rafters—all of which had deposited sizeable droppings throughout the hangar. Additionally, the building had just one primitive latrine with four Arab-style toilets—literally just holes in the ground—for what was going to be a troop component of several hundred individuals. Kingsley had to put his troops to work to make the facility fit for habitation. SSgt Brian Cessop was on one of the first crews to arrive. As bad as it was, though, he knew that really tired troops could sleep anywhere. He also knew that the Airmen arriving could handle such arrangements because they already knew how to respect one another's privacy.[7]

Again, Kingsley was the senior USAF officer present. He met with the Pakistani base commander to facilitate the beddown of the American forces and discuss overall base security, which was provided by a sizeable Pakistani army force. Additionally, Kingsley received a 250-person contingent of US Marines for an internal security perimeter directly around their immediate area.

Also on 7 October, 1st Lt Mike Holder led the four Pave Lows off the USS *Peleliu* to fly to Jacobabad. They were supposed to be joined by two MC-130s from Masirah for in-flight refueling. Unfortunately, the MC-130 crews received the wrong rendezvous coordinates and time. Consequently, the second two Pave Lows, commanded by Major Dermody and Captain Pereira, had to return to the ship. They and the two remaining aircraft would be flown to Jacobabad the next day.

Pave Low on the fantail of the USS *Peleliu*

To save fuel, Holder and the second aircraft commanded by 1st Lt Frank Lazzara had to land at a remote site in Pakistan until the MC-130s could join them. They then relaunched with only 700 pounds of fuel remaining and were able to take on the fuel they needed to fly directly to Jacobabad.

Just a few hours after Colonel Kingsley had arrived, Holder and Lazzara landed. As they shut down their engines, Kingsley was there to meet them. He knew that they had done their initial CSAR flight planning into Afghanistan. When he determined that the aircraft were mission ready, he directed the two crews to assume CSAR alert. He then called Col Paul Harmon at the CFACC CAOC and reported, "I have my crews here. We are ready to go." Harmon dutifully reported that status up the chain of command, and President Bush directed the air campaign to begin that night. Within hours B-1s,

B-2s, and B-52s were joined by swarms of carrier-based F-14s and F-18s and cruise missiles launched from US and British ships as they struck al-Qaeda and Taliban positions and forces across Afghanistan.[8]

As at Masirah, a steady stream of cargo aircraft began to arrive at Jacobabad and disgorge more equipment and troops. Kingsley had to billet them all in the hangar, with small operations areas for each specialty group. The steady growth in personnel quickly overwhelmed the primitive toilet facilities. Kingsley had his troops dig slit trenches. However, the water table was very high in the area, and the trenches quickly filled with putrid water. He had to direct them to burn the feces. After being apprised of the problems at Jacobabad, General Wald dispatched a civil engineer team that built a tented toilet facility with drainable waste tanks. However, even this was not sufficient for the rapidly growing troop population. Consequently, the engineers worked with the Pakistanis to develop a large leach field to handle the waste problems. The contingent of Airmen also included a number of females. The only amenity Kingsley could grant them was the designation of one toilet for women only.[9]

With the initiation of air operations, Kingsley relied on his aircrews to handle flight operations. Once again, he had been thrust into

Courtesy Maj Mike Holder, USAF

Living in the hangar at Jacobabad

the role of an air base commander as more US military elements arrived at the airfield. The hangar also lacked any adequate shower or bathing facilities. Within days Kingsley began to receive reports that the lack of cleanliness was beginning to cause medical problems, with the development of hacking coughs, skin rashes, and folliculitis. One of the problems was that the hangar was surrounded by areas with standing water—perfect breeding areas for mosquitoes, another major irritant and health concern. One of the collateral arriving units was a small medical team. It supported the troop population as best it could; however, the team commander recommended to Kingsley that he shut down his operation for health reasons. Kingsley could not do that. He had to maintain his CSAR capability in place and operational. Kingsley worked with the civil engineers and was able to arrange the delivery of some portable shower facilities for his Airmen.

After a couple of weeks, Kingsley began to disperse some of his personnel because, collectively, they were just too much of a target. He was able to use some revetted areas on the base and had the helicopters moved there with their crews nearby. Pave Low flight engineer MSgt Rob Colannino recalls that

> for security purposes, we decided to disperse the crews because if we were to get hit with a mortar in that one building, it would wipe out a bunch of us. So we lived in F-16 revetments, right next to where our bird was parked. . . . All you had was a cot and some mosquito netting; showers were a bottle of water. We had to pull security duty, so we would leave one guy up at night with goggles on to scan to make sure no bad guys were getting in. The aircraft was literally 50 yards from where we slept, so when the horn went off, in 10 minutes we were airborne.[10]

Kingsley relied on his cadre of solid NCOs who ran the facilities and worked constantly to improve them for their troops and the new arrivals. During this extremely busy period, he had zero discipline problems, remembering that "if there is a lesson in leadership, it's 'keep your people busy, and they will surprise you with how well they do.'" He was also called upon to escort several distinguished visitors to the facility such as the US ambassador to Pakistan, the Honorable Wendy Chamberlain, and Senators John Warner and Carl Levin. As a lieutenant colonel and squadron commander, Kingsley was being called upon to perform duties well beyond his position or rank.[11]

On 19 October, AFSOC MC-130s airdropped 200 US Army Rangers and USAF STS personnel onto a remote desert landing strip and small compound 90 miles southwest of Kandahar, Afghanistan, code-named Objective Rhino, to seize it as a base for future operations. AC-130s provided direct support for the mission, and 160th SOAR helicopters shuttled in and out to support the operation. One MH-60K crashed at the site and was destroyed. The crew escaped, but two Soldiers were wounded and pinned in the wreckage. Two Pave Lows led by Major Dermody were launched to provide medevac. He landed his aircraft near the crash site and ordered one of his gunners, TSgt John Stricklin, to dismount and help the Soldiers recover the wounded from the wreckage. As he ran over to them, Stricklin could see that the Rangers were using their knives and other accoutrements to disentangle the two men. Once free, they were quickly loaded aboard the Pave Lows for return to Jacobabad. Unfortunately, both died en route. Stricklin could not help noticing that one Soldier still wore his wedding ring. He quietly reminded himself that "these Soldiers are the reason we put ourselves in harm's way on every mission."[12]

Overall, though, the operation was a solid success. US and Australian special forces immediately occupied the compound. In the not-too-distant future, it would become an even more crowded place.[13]

Courtesy SSgt Glen Fleming, USAF

A tail gunner's view of Afghanistan

Within days Pave Lows were flying classified missions into and out of Rhino. Other special forces and CIA elements began to arrive at Jacobabad. Colonel Kingsley was designated as the commander of a JSOAC, and some of these elements were assigned to his command. Major Dermody and the other Pave Low pilots began meeting with the other elements to consider further possible missions into Afghanistan. Crews flew night surveillance missions in the local area and inserted weather observation teams. They also developed an evacuation plan for the base in the unlikely, but still possible, event that the base was overrun by al-Qaeda sympathizers. In late October, Kingsley received a possible tasking for two Pave Lows to insert some personnel into Afghanistan north of Kabul. He assigned the mission to First Lieutenants Mike Holder and Frank Lazzara and their crews. They were deep into planning the mission when it was cancelled due to unacceptable risk of flight over the extreme elevations along the flight route.[14]

In later October, a combined CIA and US Navy SEAL team infiltrated southern Afghanistan and brought back an Afghan politician named Hamid Karzai and seven supporters. They were kept in a highly secure location so that the Pakistanis would not know of their presence. Colonel Hadley met with them and tended to their medical needs. Kingsley and his crews then began to work with a 5th SFG team, ODA 574, to develop a plan to return Karzai and his cohorts back into southern Afghanistan to incite the tribes in that area to rise against al-Qaeda and the Taliban, as were their brethren in the northern portion of the country.[15]

Knife 03

On 2 November, the 20th SOS was assigned a mission up into northern Afghanistan. A member of 5th Group ODA team 555, located in a valley about 10 miles northeast of Kabul, was suffering from altitude sickness, and his brain was swelling. A 160th SOAR MH-47 launched to recover him but was unable to penetrate the severe weather hanging over the northern mountains. Colonel Kisner called Kingsley and gave him the mission. Kingsley had two Pave Lows on CSAR alert that night, one flown by Capt Bill Rowell with 1st Lt Sean Borland and the other by Capt Mark Newell with 2d Lt Steve Cherrington. However, since Lieutenants Lazzara and Holder had recently planned a mission into that area, he pulled them out of crew rest and assigned them the mission. They would fly as Knife 03, commanded by Lazzara, and Knife 04, commanded by Holder. Both had formed crews including PJs and a combat controller. Additionally, specifically for the CSAR tasking, Knife 03 had a rescue mission commander, Maj Pete Lehew, and direct support operator, TSgt Navid Garshasb, also on board. This crew configuration was similar to that used for CSAR operations in Serbia, with a USAF STS element but lacking the additional ODA detachment.[16]

The two aircraft took off at sunset and headed north. The weather was clear, with a temperature above 90 degrees and an almost full moon. Near the Afghanistan border, they rendezvoused with an MC-130E and refueled. As they continued now more northeast, crew members on Knife 03 noticed that their TF/TA radar had failed. They switched over to the FLIR system and continued with the flight. As the flight passed 30 miles west of Gharzi, they encountered an area of solid clouds. Lieutenant Lazzara determined that the visibility was too poor to continue safely and did a 180-degree turn to hold in a clear area. Lazzara then cleared Holder in Knife 04 to see if he and his crew could proceed with their TF/TA radar.

Knife 04 had a fully functioning TF/TA radar and took the lead. Its crew estimated that visibility was about one mile with snow showers and instructed Knife 03 to rejoin it. It did so, and the formation turned to head up the valley. Almost immediately, though, the crew in Knife 03 lost sight of Knife 04 and made an immediate separation turn to the left while notifying Knife 04. In doing so, Lazzara could see that the weather was also closing in behind them and elected to abort the mission. He called for Knife 04 to return to Knife 03's position so that it could rejoin and follow Knife 04 back to Jacobabad. But the two aircraft were not able to rendezvous and rejoin. Lazzara and crew noticed that their FLIR was now losing its effectiveness in the steadily deteriorating weather. They called for Knife 04 to return for them and attempted to pass their coordinates. Lieutenant Lazzara realized that they were rapidly approaching steeply rising terrain and attempted to make a high bank turn. As he did, his airspeed bled off; the aircraft, MH-53M #69-5791, descended, impacted the ground, and broke up. Fortunately, there was no fire.[17]

As the aircraft came to a rest on the ground, the crew shut off the engines and scrambled to exit the machine. Lazzara took out his survival radio and made contact with US Navy F-18s that had been attempting to escort the two Pave Lows. One of the combat controllers from the USAF STS element on board also made emergency radio calls. However, he used his assigned tactical radio call sign of Jaguar 03. This caused some confusion for the various agencies trying to coordinate a rescue response until the different call signs were rectified.

Crew members on Knife 04 heard some of the radio calls and several also made by an orbiting AWACS aircraft indicating that the helicopter was down. They attempted to return to the estimated position of Knife 03 but were blocked by rapidly rising high terrain and deteriorating weather. Instead, Holder held over a dry lake bed for about 30 minutes as they discussed options and hoped for the weather to improve before turning south to rendezvous with an MC-130 to refuel. While receiving their gas, they observed what appeared to be an RPG shot at them as they traversed the ridges. When the aircraft was full of fuel, the Knife 04 crew again turned north to proceed to the crash site. The crew received updated coordinates for Knife 03's location from one of the F-18s and proceeded back to attempt a recovery.

At the crash site, all 11 members of the crew were together, although several had injuries, and had established a perimeter. The tail gunner, Sergeant Cessop, had suffered a broken bone in his back and another in one foot. Some local tribesmen attempted to render aid to the crew, but their approach unnerved several of the Airmen. TSgt Navid Garshasb, the direct support operator, talked to them and warned them to keep their distance.[18]

Monitoring all of this at Jacobabad, Colonel Kingsley ordered two more Pave Lows—Knife 01 and Knife 02—to take off and join the effort. Those were the aircraft commanded by Rowell and Newell. The crews were already communicating with Maj Martha McSally, the SAR duty officer at the JSAR at PSAB, and were aware of the overall situation. McSally was also coordinating with Maj Jon Owens, who was working as a night duty officer in the special operations liaison element at the JFACC CAOC at PSAB and scrambling to deconflict the mission with other operations ongoing in the theater. Unfortunately, the aircraft were over two hours away from the crash site. They launched and rendezvoused with an MC-130 along the border and held there, pending developments at the crash site. While refueling, though, they received ground fire.[19]

Any quick recovery would have to be accomplished by Knife 04. As Holder approached the crash site, the orbiting F-18s indicated that the weather was noticeably clearing. Additionally, the Knife 04 crew was able to establish the elevation of the survivors as 10,400 feet. Holder's flight engineer, SSgt Chad Ackman, quickly determined that to take off from that elevation with all 11 survivors, Knife 04 would have to dump its current fuel down to 1,000 pounds. That meant that as soon as it lifted off from the crash site, a tanker needed to be available.

Knife 04 flew over the survivors' location, and its crew visually sighted the wreckage, crew, and CCT on the ground. Kingsley then arranged for an MC-130 to be right over the helicopter as it lifted off. When that was confirmed, the crew activated the fuel dump system until Ackman indicated that the necessary fuel had been dumped. Holder then maneuvered to land the Pave Low next to the survivors. As he hovered down through 10 feet, blowing snow obscured the pilot's view. Immediately, the scanners talked him to the ground. When the helicopter settled, Knife 04's PJs dismounted, collected all 11 survivors, and loaded them aboard. Holder lifted the aircraft off of the ground as the engines strained at full power. Luckily, he had a slight river gully to fly down, which allowed him to build up just enough airspeed to achieve effective translational lift. With a great deal of assistance from his copilot, Capt Jay Humphrey, and Sergeant Ackman, he was able to finesse the aircraft so that they could climb to altitude to safely rendezvous with the MC-130E at 11,000 feet and receive some fuel. The high-altitude training at Masirah had paid off.

Courtesy Maj Mike Holder, USAF

The crews of Knife 03 and 04

Lieutenant Holder passed control of the aircraft to Humphrey, who flew the refueling. However, Knife 04 was not able to receive a full load because as it gained the weight of the transferring fuel, it could not maintain position behind the MC-130, forcing Humphrey to disconnect. Thirty minutes later, the crew initiated another refueling and then repeated this procedure several more times as the aircraft steadily descended over the lower terrain of Pakistan until it was able to reach Zhob. Knife 01 and 02 had been diverted there and, using onboard security teams, would establish a secure transload site so that the casualties from Knife 03 could be transferred to an MC-130 for direct movement to Masirah.[20]

Only Sergeant Garshasb and Major Lehew required evacuation. The rest of the Knife 03 crew remained aboard Knife 04 as it flew back to Jacobabad, where it had to land in low-visibility conditions. After the numerous debriefings, Cessop was able to relax and take off his boot. His foot was black and blue. Medical personnel noticed his foot and confirmed the broken bone in his foot and then his back with X-rays. He was immediately medevaced all the way back to Hurlburt.[21]

The flight back to Jacobabad was a bit more interesting for Knife 01 and 02. They received AAA several times, and their gunners returned fire. One small arms round hit the cockpit of Knife 01, slightly wounding the flight engineer on the side of his head. Fortunately, Colonel Hadley was on the aircraft and quickly determined that the Airman was only superficially scratched. They proceeded on to Jacobabad and also had to make the difficult and challenging approach through the combination of smoke, haze, and fog.[22]

The Knife 04 crew members logged 10.4 hours on the mission, exhausted but very proud of their efforts. The actions of all the crew members had directly led to the successful recovery of their squadron mates. It was a stunning display of outstanding crew coordination, for which the Airmen of Knife 04 were awarded the Mackay Trophy for 2001.[23]

Colonel Kingsley was there to meet the crews as they landed. He had already directed that the two Knife 03 crewmen who had gone to Masirah could go home from there. The others went back into the rotation schedule. They needed to be ready to support the steadily increasing activities of the various special forces elements streaming into Jacobabad to conduct highly classified missions in the region.

Unfortunately, the wreckage of Knife 03 was in an area that could not be secured. Consequently, US Navy fighters bombed it to prevent the use of any of its components. However, insurgent forces did recover pieces of it, which then appeared in video clips shown worldwide. The next day, with much better weather conditions, a civilian contract helicopter was able to finally retrieve the ailing Soldier from ODA 555. He fully recovered from what turned out to be a case of meningitis. Reviewing the recovery mission for Knife 03, though, the CFACC, General Wald, was not satisfied with the command and control arrangements in place for the Pave Lows while they were on theater CSAR alert. He decided to ask the USAF to deploy a conventional rescue squadron that would be under his operational control. Within two weeks, the 66th RQS based at Nellis was deployed with its HH-60s and supporting PJs and maintenance team to the theater to perform this mission. The 20th retained its requirement to perform recovery missions for SOF elements, but the removal of the larger theater requirement allowed the Pave Low crews to now focus on classic SOF missions.[24]

Heavy Combat

On 14 November, two Pave Lows launched to carry ODA 574 and Karzai and his seven supporters to a remote site near the Afghanistan border. There they landed and transferred the group to waiting MH-60s from the 160th SOAR, which then flew them into tight landing zones 20 miles west of the mountain village of Tarin Kowt. Karzai and the team were being inserted to attempt to rally the tribes of southern Afghanistan to join the efforts of the northern tribes to destroy the Taliban and their al-Qaeda allies. Over the next three weeks, several more Pave Low sorties were flown to support the team and Karzai in their efforts. They delivered necessary supplies and reinforcements and evacuated wounded personnel.[25]

The number of Americans in Afghanistan increased dramatically on 25 November, when 1,000-plus US Marines from the 15th MEU were helilifted from ships in the Arabian Sea to Objective Rhino. The force included four CH-53s and six CH-46s. After a few days, they seized the airport at Kandahar and began building it into a major joint and combined stronghold, signifying sustained US and coalition presence in that area. Pave Lows flew several missions into both locations.[26]

Later in the month, Colonel Kingsley put himself on the schedule to fly a mission to insert some special forces troops in Afghanistan. En route to the site, though, his aircraft experienced an engine failure. He aborted the mission and decided to recover in Pakistan. The closest airfield was at Quetta, about 150 miles northwest of Jacobabad. He did not have enough time to notify the American Embassy by satcom prior to landing, and as he and his wingmen arrived at the airfield unannounced and touched down on the runway, Pakistani troops surrounded them. Luckily, Kingsley had previously met the Pakistani base commander. He arrived and calmed the situation so that Kingsley could do what needed to be done to protect his crews and passengers and arrange to have the aircraft flown on its single good engine back to Jacobabad.[27]

In early December, two more Pave Lows and relief crews arrived at Jacobabad. This group, led by Lt Col Brad Webb, included a crew with pilots Capt Jim Peterson and Capt Joe Michalek, flight engineers TSgt Wayne Lively and SSgt Brian Fahey, and gunners TSgt Ryan Crowley and TSgt Michael Ferguson. In Afghanistan ODA 574 and Hamid Karzai had been somewhat successful in rallying tribal leaders in the south to join forces against the Taliban. Their team requested some resupply and reinforcements, and in the early morning hours of the fifth, four Pave Lows, flown by a mix of original and relief crews, arrived at a small landing zone near the mountain village of Shawali Kowt to deliver the requested goods and personnel. The aircraft were quickly unloaded and departed to return to Jacobabad. The resupply mission was much appreciated by the members of ODA 574 because they and their growing allies were engaged in a running battle with Taliban forces. Shortly after sunrise, the ODA requested air support, and a B-52 arrived overhead to deliver GPS-guided bombs to support the team. The ODA passed very precise coordinates for a suspected enemy position to the circling bomber and cleared it to deliver a 2,000-pound bomb. The bomber crew programmed the coordinates into its weapons delivery computer, followed the resulting aiming guidance, and dropped the bomb. After a 35-second fall, the bomb landed precisely on the designated coordinates and detonated with a horrendous blast.

Through a series of human errors, the coordinates passed to the bomber crew were not for an enemy position but for a fighting position occupied by friendly troops. The team and its supporting local tribesmen suffered massive casualties, and the team leader called in an emergency medical evacuation request as he tried to assess the damage, account for all of his troops, and determine the number of killed and wounded. Even Hamid Karzai was wounded, although only slightly. The evacuation request was forwarded to the special operations liaison team with MEU 15 at Rhino and to Jacobabad for the 20th SOS. The initial report did not indicate that the injuries were caused by fratricide.

Rhino was much closer than Jacobabad, and the special forces liaison personnel went to see the 15th MEU commander, Brig Gen James Mattis. He listened to their request but refused to dispatch his helicopters until he knew what the tactical situation and enemy threat were at Shawali Kowt.[28]

Colonels Kingsley and Hadley were both asleep when the Jacobabad command center got the message because they had stayed up until their resupply aircraft had returned from the position of that very team. When they were awakened, they directed that all crews be summoned to the operations center ASAP because they had no idea of how many casualties they would have to extract. However, as they gathered, Hadley could see that they were all exhausted and illegal to fly per the stringent rules for mandatory crew rest. Hadley pointed out the obvious to Kingsley, who was considering sending the crews regardless. However, Maj Shawn Silverman pointed out to him that just a few hours earlier, two more Pave Low crews had arrived to swap out with crews that had been there since the initial deployment to Masirah. Kingsley directed him to summon them for flight duty and also directed that two PJ CSAR teams be selected for the mission. Then he called the maintenance section and ordered it to prepare two aircraft for immediate launch.

The pilots were the first crew personnel to reach the operations center. The flight lead would be Capt Steve Gregg with 2d Lt Marty Schweim as his copilot, and the wingman would be 1st Lt Pat Fronk with 1st Lt Paul Alexander. Except for Gregg, all had recently come from the Army under the warrant officer transfer program. The crews would again use the call signs of Knife 03 and 04, respectively. Kingsley introduced them to Colonel Hadley, who had developed a close relationship with the Soldiers of ODA and Hamid Karzai and would be aboard the lead aircraft as the mission commander. He would also perform as a doctor as the patients required. This was going to be an unusual and rare daytime mission. Kingsley's briefing to the crews was direct and to the point. He told them,

Welcome to the war, gentlemen. Americans are requesting emergency MEDEVAC north of Kandahar, at the same location our squadron flew last night. We've got the routes, we know where they are, but that's about it. I know you haven't been briefed on intel, routes, or procedures, and I wouldn't be asking you to fly if you weren't our only option. Lt Col Hadley has been in on every intel brief since we got here, and he has flown dozens of missions into Afghanistan. He will brief you en route. Flight time is just shy of three hours. From the moment you cross the border, you will be flying in bad-guy country all the way. . . . As I learn more, I'll relay it to Lt Col Hadley. Ground crews are turning around two of the -53s that flew last night; they're already refueled. CSAR teams are getting their gear and will meet you at the aircraft. Godspeed.[29]

As the pilots quickly put together a tactical plan and began arrangements to coordinate tanker support, Colonel Hadley turned to medical issues. He had no idea yet of how many casualties awaited their arrival or what exactly had caused their wounds. He went to the small medical detachment on base and requested the services of its most qualified doctor. "Doc Frank," a family practice physician, stepped forward and shook hands with Hadley. They grabbed several bags of medical supplies and packets of whole blood, and Hadley led Doc Frank to the helicopters and assigned him to the second aircraft while Hadley would fly in the lead. The crews were already strapping in. Kingsley met Hadley there and told him, "It's daylight, and this is a no-shit very dangerous mission. Get the job done and bring everybody in my squadron home alive."[30]

The two helicopters lifted off from Jacobabad, and Captain Gregg leveled off at about 300 feet above the ground. Lieutenant Fronk reminded him that shooting at helicopters was a national sport in Pakistan, and Gregg dropped the formation down to about 50 feet. On Knife 03, Hadley made radio contact with the team members at Shawali Kowt and told them that the helicopter would be there in two hours and 45 minutes. The Soldier replied, "Sir, Americans are dying. Please hurry. Please." Hadley leaned forward and said to Gregg, "Fly the most direct route we can avoiding any towns." Gregg pushed the aircraft to the maximum airspeed possible and replied, "I think we can make it in two hours." As they crossed into Afghanistan, Gregg dropped the aircraft down to 25 feet, the best altitude for evading any heat-seeking missiles. Hadley knew that by flying over enemy-controlled terrain in broad daylight, they were at great risk. He tried to make light of it by saying, "This is something that I never thought I would see, Afghanistan in the daylight." Captain Gregg certainly felt the urgency of the situation. In-theater for less than 24 hours and already flying combat, he was reminded of the sense of urgency that he had also felt as he flew over the smoldering wreckage in New York City, fewer than 90 days earlier.[31]

About an hour out of ODA 574's location, the Pave Lows were joined by a flight of F-18s that provided escort protection. The team medic contacted Hadley and provided a casualty update. Two Americans were dead, another was dying, and eight more were critically wounded. Thirty minutes later, the medic called again and asked how many wounded the helicopters could evacuate over to Camp Rhino. Hadley checked with the flight engineers on both aircraft and responded "32." The medic replied, "Roger, you are going to need all the room you've got." Hadley notified Doc Frank and the PJs.

Arriving over the team's location, the two crews spotted a pre-arranged signal and landed their helicopters in clouds of dust. Hadley told Gregg, "You are now the mission commander. I am going to shift to doctor," as he took off his headset and left the helicopter to organize the loading. The flight engineers brought the engine throttles to idle but did not shut them down. Aboard Knife 03, the copilot, Lieutenant Schweim, noticed right after takeoff that their aircraft GPS was not updating correctly. Fortunately, he had brought along a handheld GPS. He turned it on, and when it was accurately locked onto available satellites and giving good positional data, he used its coordinates to update the INS portion of the navigational system. Schweim also had a map of the area and was fully prepared to use that as the ultimate backup navigational "system." As they sat there, though, they felt extremely vulnerable. The gunners aboard both aircraft had not received any detailed briefings on the security situation at the site and remained suspicious of any personnel that they could not identify as American.[32]

Hadley was joined by Doc Frank, and they met several trucks carrying the American wounded and deceased. Quickly, they triaged each of the casualties and divided them up between the two helicopters. The most critical would go in Knife 04 so that it could take off first. However, there were 17 American wounded vice the nine that he had earlier been told to expect. As they were working, Hadley noticed that a large contingent of Afghan troops was approaching the aircraft. Hadley asked and was assured that they were friendlies, bringing in their wounded. Hadley was stunned. He had not been told that he would also be evacuating Afghan wounded and had made no allowances for them. He had to quickly change his game plan.

When Knife 04 had a full load, Lieutenant Fronk called Captain Gregg and reported that he was ready to depart for Rhino. Neither pilot was happy with the thought of separating. However, medical necessity dictated it; several of their wounded were very near death. Gregg asked if Fronk could wait for a few more wounded, but Doc Frank told him that they needed to depart ASAP. Fronk lifted off and turned on a direct course for Rhino.[33]

The trucks with the Afghan wounded began to converge at the tail of Knife 03. The tail gunner, SSgt Scott Diekman, watched apprehensively as heavily armed men got out of the vehicles and began to bring their wounded toward the back ramp. Determined to protect his aircraft and crew, he quickly got permission from Gregg to depart the aircraft and try to sort this out. As he did, the left side gunner came back and manned his .50-caliber machine gun as Diekman walked toward the trucks. There he met one of the PJs who was tending to the wounded. The PJ assured him that the men were friendly, and Diekman directed the loading of the wounded aboard Knife 03, insuring that the most severely wounded were by the tail ramp for quickest offload at Rhino. They also loaded the body of one American Soldier. It was in a sleeping bag, covered with an American flag.

When Knife 03 was fully loaded and Hadley and the PJs were back aboard, Captain Gregg prepared for liftoff. Their plan was to proceed directly to Rhino, with Schweim tracking their progress on his map. But they had another problem. To carry more wounded, Gregg had dumped some fuel prior to landing. Also, they had remained on the ground for 45 minutes vice the 15 minutes planned. They needed gas ASAP! Gregg made a "Texaco" call, meaning that he was fuel critical and needed a tanker to come to him on an improvised refueling track instead of both trying to make it to a predesignated track. Gregg made radio contact with Ditka 04, an MC-130, for the impromptu refueling. When Hadley asked how critical they were, Gregg told him that they would flame out in 15 minutes at cruise power settings. Hadley made sure that the 18 casualties on board, stretching all the way to the aft end of the back ramp, were properly tied down and secure as Gregg took off and turned southwest.

As Knife 03 climbed away from the landing zone, Gregg called Ditka 04 for the rendezvous. Unfortunately, at that very moment, Ditka 04 was refueling Knife 04. When Fronk heard Gregg's call, he told Ditka 04 that he had the fuel he needed to get to Rhino and ended his refueling. Ditka 04 then turned back to the north to pick up

Knife 03. The MC-130 crew spotted the helicopter at 100 feet above the ground crossing over the suburbs of Kandahar. This was one of the most dangerous areas in Afghanistan, especially in midday. Regardless, it had to be done, and the pilots aboard Ditka 04 maneuvered the lumbering aircraft so that they were directly in front of the helicopter and about 100 feet higher. Gregg climbed the helicopter up into refueling position. "We are seven minutes to flameout," Schweim said as Gregg then slipped the MH-53 refueling probe into the receptacle trailing from the right wingtip of Ditka 04. "Got it, we're on," Gregg announced as the fuel began to transfer into the Pave Low's tanks. The relief among the crew was palpable, especially the gunners, who had been anxiously scanning for a place to land the helicopter if necessary.[34]

While Knife 03 was receiving its fuel, Knife 04 landed at Rhino. Fronk taxied his aircraft over next to two MC-130s, specially equipped with medical equipment, doctors, and technicians for such contingencies. To help with the transfer of the wounded, several SEALs from SEAL Team 3 arrived and carried the litters from the Pave Low to the MC-130s.

With the necessary fuel now on board Knife 03, Ditka 04 departed, and Gregg set a direct course for Rhino, now 20 minutes away. Back in the cabin, Hadley and the PJs continued to tend to the wounded. At one point, one of the PJs determined that he needed to amputate the severely damaged arm of an Afghan soldier. He had to call upon Sergeant Diekman to hold the patient still while he performed the procedure, not something that the gunner was trained to do. In spite of the best efforts of Colonel Hadley and the PJs, one American and one Afghan died on the flight. The rest were awash in an almost continuous pool of American and Afghan blood that covered the cabin's floor. The blood found its way to the back of the aircraft, and the rivulets escaped into the wind stream, forming a thin vapor trail of pink all the way to Camp Rhino.[35]

Two days later, Lt Col Mike Kingsley handed over command of the detachment to Lt Col Brad Webb, and Kingsley and several of his crew members and maintenance personnel departed for home. He was concerned that some of his returning troops were suffering from the stress of the intense operations and arranged to stop for a few days at Masirah for some relaxation. Since their initial visit in September, the base had been dramatically improved with facilities that would allow the Airmen to relax in a stress-free environment prior to returning to their homes and families. As they arrived on the island, his only instructions were, "Don't get in trouble." Simple enough. Then he took his troops back to Hurlburt. Kingsley took some leave to spend with his family, even stealing away for a week to a resort with his wife.

On 12 December, captains Peterson and Michalek and crew launched as the second Pave Low on a mission to recover Hamid Karzai and entourage from a secured compound. They would then deliver Karzai to Rhino so that he could be transported to Kabul to act as the head of a forming Afghan government. Friendly ground elements in the area reported that the helicopters received quite a bit of ground fire; however, the crews did not observe it, and their gunners did not return fire. The flight was essentially uneventful. However, Karzai did present the recovery team with his battle flag.[36]

Courtesy Lt Col Mike Grub, USAF

The 20th SOS detachment at Jacobabad, Pakistan, in December 2001 surrounding the Afghan flag given to them by Hamid Karzai.

The next night, Capt Mike Grub was scheduled to lead a four-ship of Pave Lows to resupply an ODA team that had occupied a compound north of Kandahar that belonged to Mullah Omar, a key al-Qaeda leader. His number two aircraft would carry in some civil engineering gear to a repair team at the Kandahar main airport so that the primary runway could be repaired for use by larger aircraft. The second two aircraft would also be carrying gear to Kandahar. He briefed his formation to proceed to the designated landing areas as two two-ship formations with 90 miles of spacing to facilitate rendez-vous and refueling from the assisting MC-130. Grub and his wing-man proceeded to the compound, skirting around Kandahar City for obvious reasons. A fog layer developed as they proceeded, further complicating their approach to the compound located in a tight valley and with numerous objects sticking up around the landing zone. The crew of Grub's number two aircraft lost sight of Grub's aircraft and climbed above the fog. Grub and his crew had to use their TF radar to get into the area of the compound. As they were trying to work their way in, Grub's wingman asked him how the visibility was down below the fog. It was an incredibly dark night. Grub notes that "there was not a single photon of light present in that part of Afghanistan" that night, as he gave a stark and blasphemous report to his wingman, basically explaining "how f---ing dark" it was.

Unfortunately, he broadcast his report over the satcom radio in-stead of his FM radio. This definitely insured that his wingman heard him—as well as anybody in the world who was monitoring that sat-com radio frequency that night. Grub's number two aircraft was eventually able to get below the fog and rejoin with the lead aircraft. Grub flew the approach to the compound down through the narrow valley. At 50 feet above the ground, he encountered terrible dust and aborted the approach. He and the crew maneuvered for another at-tempt and this time were able to get the aircraft safely on the ground. They then flew to Kandahar so that their number two aircraft could deliver its equipment. When that delivery was complete, they flew back to Jacobabad. The next day, Grub heard about his errant visibility report from everybody but took the ribbing in a good-natured way. To him, it was a minor item compared to the sheer difficulty and dan-ger of flying in Afghanistan. Remembered Grub, "Every mission we ever flew in Afghanistan was the most dangerous mission we would ever fly."[37]

When Kingsley returned to Hurlburt, he reengaged with the myriad issues inherent in being a squadron commander: reviewing the long-range rotational plans for OEF or whatever else came up and the on-going squadron training program and exercise schedule. Responding to deficiencies he observed in Pakistan and Afghanistan, he engaged with the 551st SOS to improve high-altitude mountain training and brownout landing procedures. He also made sure that the unit re-mained prepared to answer any JSOC taskings that might arise on short notice.[38]

In mid-January 2002, Colonel Kingsley attended the change-of-command ceremony at AFSOC as Lt Gen Maxwell Bailey passed command to Lt Gen Paul Hester and retired after 31 and a half years of service. A career fighter pilot, Hester threw himself into the job. Taking his cue from President Bush's comments that "Americans should not expect one battle, but a lengthy campaign . . . includ[ing] dramatic strikes, visible on TV, and covert operations, secret even in success," Hester quickly grasped the essence of air commando operations as a key part of the larger USSOCOM effort ongoing now in several parts of the world. Hester highlighted that performance by pointing out that "Americans . . . heard, saw, and read about the team of 'Quiet Professionals' in special operations. They learned that the Air Force was an integral part and full partner on that team."[39]

At Jacobabad, Colonel Webb continued in the same modus as Kingsley as the JSOAC commander. However, within a few weeks the JSOAC headquarters was transferred to Masirah Island, and Col Tommy Hull, the former 20th SOS commander from four years earlier, was dispatched from Hurlburt to command it. Webb activated an Air Force special operations detachment (AFSOD) to command the eight Pave Lows, four MC-130s, their crews, four CSAR (PJ/CCT) teams, and support personnel at Jacobabad.

His Airmen were flying a steadily increasing schedule of classified missions supporting a variety of customers vice just standing by for CSAR. Almost exclusively, his crews were now flying up to Kandahar and supporting Combined Joint Special Operations Task Force–South, called Task Force K-Bar. It was led by Navy SEAL captain Robert Harward, the same SEAL who had assisted the 31st SOS at Cubi Point in the Philippines when it had evacuated Clark AB because of Mount Pinatubo. K-Bar included other special forces elements from the United States and coalition nations. They had moved up to Kandahar from Camp Rhino and were going after al-Qaeda and the Taliban with aggressive direct action missions. These actions were being co-ordinated with Hamid Karzai as he was working to form a coalition of the various ethnic groups in the south against al-Qaeda and the Taliban. Nightly, the Pave Lows would fly the teams and their specialized "nonstandard" vehicles into their designated landing zones.

TSgt B. J. Jobling was over there then on a 90-day rotation and flew many of the missions with the vehicles. Some of them were very heavy and required a great deal of special handling. He and his crew flew mostly logistical support missions with a few direct action missions interspersed. Since he had arrived at the 20th, he had done his share of deployments. However, it was here in the high mountains and valleys of Afghanistan where he felt that his training had fully matured, and he realized the key role the flight engineer played aboard the Pave Low. He explains that

> everyone in the crew is tasked, depending on how busy the mission is going to be. . . . We had six radios on that thing. Pilot and copilot—really it's a pilot and commander and mission commander. Your one pilot is going to be flying everything; the other pilot is basically the safety pilot but also running the entire mission, so he is talking to the ground teams, the other aircraft in the formation, other aircraft that are up there also, command and control elements, and following the pace of the mission.

> The flight engineer is pretty much backing him up, keeping everybody up to speed on what's going on in the airplane. . . . On the Pave, we were responsible for defensive systems; the navigation system because it was a center map, which was a great tool, but not being right in front of the pilots, we had to feed them a lot of information. We were radio operators in addition to monitoring the systems and fuel. . . . We are also trained as aero-gunners and loadmasters.

> The gunners are doing their things [and] also scanning. You got a taste of it going through the schoolhouse here, but the more you do it, the more you realize that. . . . Do you watch ballroom dancing on TV? It's watching six guys being able to dance together and knowing what each one will be doing next. You are thinking as a group.

> My thing about being a flight engineer: you're the world's best caddy. That's what I try to teach the guys. "The pilots are the ones who fly; the pilots are the ones who take the shots. Your job is to make sure before they even think about it, you've already got the right club in their hand."[40]

Nightly, Jobling and his fellow 20th SOS crew members were "playing through" on what had to be the most challenging "golf course" for helicopters and crews in the world. Flying as they were on the "edge of the envelope," they constantly modified their procedures and use of the unique Pave Low navigational systems to make their operations safer, even developing a procedure to use oxygen on board at the higher elevations at which they flew. As Jobling recalled, the Pave Low mentality was "give us a task. We'll figure out how to do it."[41]

Settling into his job at Jacobabad, Colonel Webb was somewhat taken aback at what he found. He was used to a certain modicum of form and structure inherent in Air Force operations. He had been at FOLs before under combat or potential combat conditions, such as in Saudi Arabia and Bosnia. But Jacobabad was the "wild, wild West," where approval procedures and processes were not mature. Webb recounts,

I was in a position where I was making the calls for execution of direct action missions and what have you. It was thrilling: we had the highest of highs, and we had the lowest of lows. . . . We did the first direct action missions with coalition forces and . . . multiship helicopters that were landing at altitudes of 7,000 feet and above to targets that were opposed. Guys were landing automatic flight control systems off. They failed but we continued the missions. The heroism during that time was unbelievable. It was, by my estimation, the accomplishment of what the early pioneers of Pave Low set out to do because we were employing TF/TA; we had an assault mentality assaulting directly on al-Qaeda strongholds and Taliban strongholds.[42]

The operations did not come without cost. In two accidents occurring on classified missions, the Pave Lows were seriously damaged, although no personnel were severely injured. It was obvious that the Pave Lows needed updates to their hover symbology systems, and the necessary data was sent back to AFSOC for analysis and corrective action. The combination of high elevations and brownout conditions was a serious operational challenge to the Pave Low crews. Webb found it to be "the single most demanding environment that you could ever ask of a helicopter pilot. It's the high altitude, mountains, blacker than black, and dust-outs starting at 150 or 200 feet down." Stalwart performers during that period were Captains Joe Michalek, Dave Tabor, Lee Anderson, and Shawn Cameron.[43]

On one notable night mission in January 2002, a flight of seven Pave Lows lifted a US and Canadian force to landing zones at 7,500 feet elevation. Captain Anderson was flying in the fourth aircraft as leader for the last four in the force. All helicopters were heavily loaded with troops and equipment and operating above 50,000 pounds gross weight. After the teams were inserted, the helicopters took off and rendezvoused with an MC-130 and refueled. They then held at an orbit point while the ground force executed its mission and as AC-130s orbited overhead and provided on-call direct fire support for the ground teams.

When the assault elements had finished collecting weapons and intelligence and seizing several al-Qaeda personnel, they radioed for pickup. Anderson made another landing in brownout conditions to collect his element. He then took off and held above as the other three aircraft attempted to land and recover their loads. The number five aircraft was able to land and recover a team. However, aircraft six and seven were not able to land after several attempts and proceeded back to the MC-130 for more fuel, as did the covering AC-130. As the tactical situation rapidly deteriorated, Anderson did not want to leave

Courtesy SSgt Glen Fleming, USAF

The ever-dangerous brownout landing

the ground elements with no top cover. He and his crew unanimously decided to bring out all remaining allied soldiers and landed to recover them. The mission narrative describes the challenges that Anderson and his crew faced as they attempted to take off:

> With over triple the planned exfiltration load and barely enough power to break ground (less than 10 foot hover power available), the crew began their most dangerous maneuver of the night. With a high stone wall on one side, more compounds off of the nose and right side and rising terrain, the aircraft strained off the ground and slowly started forward as Capt Anderson carefully increased rotor thrust and watched the rotor speed decrease as the engines reached maximum available power. Drifting several feet off the ground in zero visibility, he maintained control using only the hover symbols as the aircraft accelerated slowly. Eventually, they gained flying airspeed and accelerated away from the ground and clear of the dust and immediately realized the narrow margin by which the main rotor blades had missed hitting the stone wall on the left.[44]

Anderson and his crew were not yet out of danger. They had less than 30 minutes of fuel available and needed to get to a tanker fast. Additionally, their aircraft was beset with intercom and radio communications problems, and they had a difficult time contacting tankers in the area. When they finally did, they discovered that they were already busy refueling the other aircraft from the formation. After a quick realignment of refueling priority among the helicopters, an MC-130 was able to pull into position for Anderson to refuel. When the aircraft had sufficient fuel, the crew proceeded back to base and landed at sunrise, closing out a 14-hour duty period.

Courtesy Maj Mike Holder, USAF

Refueling over the barren stretches of Afghanistan

Of the seven Pave Lows used on that mission, there were a total of 10 blown tires and two airframes with significant structural damage sustained during the assault landings. However, the trove of intelligence collected and prisoners taken were well worth the effort. For his role in this intense and rewarding mission, Capt Lee Anderson was nominated for and was a corecipient of the Jabara Award for 2003.[45]

On another mission on 12 January, Captains Peterson and Michalek and crews flew a night direct action mission against a Taliban/al-Qaeda compound in Shkin, Afghanistan. The site was a suspected transit compound that senior Taliban leaders had used in the past and where they might be on 14 January. The crew flew as the second aircraft as Knife 12 and inserted an ODA from Fifth Group. The execution was perfect, as the assault team was in and out in 60 minutes. No senior leaders were found; however, the team detonated a cache of 105 mm

Courtesy Lt Col Lee Anderson, USAF

Capt Lee Anderson and his crew. *Left to right*: (*top*) SSgt Christian Mackenzie, SSgt Andre Bell, SSgt Dan Weimer, TSgt Brad Martens, Capt Lee Anderson, and Capt Chuck Augustin, USMC.

and 81 mm howitzer and mortar rounds. It also confiscated bags of Pakistani and Afghan money; AK-47s and ammo; RPGs; and crew-served weapons, passports, and propaganda posters, as well as photos of senior leaders at the compound, two bags of heroin, and hypodermic needles. The assault team detained seven terrorists who were transported out of the compound. The Pave Lows received small arms fire during the flight (not aimed) and had a bit of an emergency situation to deal with when a light illuminated behind the instrument panel and made NVG flight almost impossible. One of the flight engineers came up with a workable solution, and the crew completed the flight.[46]

Not all of the 20th crew members were so stalwart. Some were not up to the demands and presented Webb a huge leadership challenge. As if replicating the movie *Top Gun*, two pilots came to him and placed their pilot wings on his desk. He reminded them, "Look, this isn't the movies. You don't get to choose whether you're going to do this mission. You're doing the mission. I am expecting you to do your duty, and this is your duty!" As a result of the Knife 03 crash in November and several incidents since, Webb watched guys come off of landing zones so shaken that they could not find their tanker or did not have a backup plan. He remembers that "they were scared to death" and watched several struggle through some very difficult days and nights. But none actually refused to fly. He had to give constant attention to the crew combinations to ensure that each crew had the right mix of individuals who could work together and bring out the best in one another so that they could be as operationally effective and as safe as possible when flying. There was no shortage of challenges.

In one instance, Webb took an entire crew off of the flight schedule, placing it in the plans office to give it a break. It had been flying steadily on very challenging missions, and the pilots in particular seemed a bit rattled. After a few days, though, the gunners and engineers on the crew wanted to get back in the action. One of the gunners, TSgt Aaron Bettison, went to his pilots and said, "Look, we're going to do this. We'll help you do this. . . . We're going to get back on the horse and ride." And the crew did. Webb was extremely proud of that, pointing out that it was an excellent example of NCO leadership where and when it was most needed.

Regrettably, Webb had to rotate home in late February 2002 because of a family emergency. Colonel Kingsley came back over to replace him as the AFSOD commander at Jacobabad, amid the increasing operations at Kandahar.[47]

21st Special Operations Squadron

In late September 2001, as the wreckage in New York City and the Pentagon was still smoldering, the 352d SOG at RAF Mildenhall received an updated mission statement directing that it add counterterrorism and personnel recovery to the assigned missions for its operational units. In response the 21st SOS commander, Lt Col Joe Becker, deployed five aircraft, crews, and support packages to Stuttgart for a large multimission combined training exercise in November. Two weeks later, he deployed three of his aircraft and crews to NAS Sigonella, Italy, to conduct shipboard training aboard the USS *La Salle.* However, the 21st SOS was not initially called to support the growing operation in Afghanistan.[48]

These deployments continued into 2002 as the 21st SOS returned to Sigonella with five MH-53s, crews, and support personnel for two weeks in January and again in May. The USS *La Salle* remained a constant companion as the crews honed their skills for shipboard operations. On the January deployment, one of the Pave Lows struck an antenna aboard the USNS *Kanawha* as it maneuvered to deliver exercise personnel. While damage to the ship was minimal, the helicopter's rotor system was extensively damaged, grounding it for several months until repairs were completed. Throughout the period, 21st SOS personnel also participated in numerous bilateral exercises with several other NATO member nations.

In May, the 21st SOS was once again called upon to perform a distant sea rescue from home station when a 65-foot yacht in rough seas had two severely injured personnel on board who needed to be evacuated. Lt Col Greg Lengyel served as mission commander for a task force of two MC-130s, two MH-53Ms, and several PJs. The two aircraft commanders were Capt Sean LeRoy and Maj Kevin Churchill. They commanded the crews that planned the mission and then flew to the boat located almost 700 nautical miles southwest of RAF Mildenhall, recovering the two injured personnel while fighting a 40-knot wind and 15-to-25-foot sea swells. Combined, the crews logged 46.8 flight hours, accomplishing what was confirmed to be the longest distance air-sea rescue ever launched from the British Isles. In recognition of their leadership of this humanitarian mission, LeRoy and Churchill were nominated for and received the Cheney Award for 2002.[49]

Two months later, Colonel Becker passed command of the 21st SOS to Colonel Lengyel and departed for AWC. Lengyel easily slid into his new job as the squadron continued its training cycle and participated with the group as it passed an AFSOC-directed ORI with an overall "excellent" rating. In September the unit deployed a small contingent of operations and support personnel to a classified location in Afghanistan to support the 20th SOS.[50]

Jacobabad

When Lt Col Mike Kingsley returned to Jacobabad in late February, he found a base that had finally received the necessary infrastructure to make it generally inhabitable. He jumped right back into the operation as his crews were engaged in a plethora of classified operations throughout the theater. On 18 March, the 20th SOS lost another Pave Low, MH-53M #68-8286, while supporting allied forces on a mission in Afghanistan. As the crew approached the flare for landing in brownout conditions, one of the engines experienced a compressor stall that precipitated a hard landing and catastrophic damage to the aircraft. Injuries to the crew and passengers were not serious, but the aircraft—a veteran of the Son Tay mission in 1970—was destroyed. Two weeks later, two Pave Lows were launched out of Jacobabad to recover a Joint Direct Attack Munition (JDAM), a GPS-guided bomb, which had been inadvertently dropped in Pakistan. Its expeditious recovery precluded an international incident and also prevented its use by al-Qaeda forces.[51]

In May 2002, Lieutenants Holder and Borland returned to Jacobabad for second tours with several other crew members. As they stepped off of the C-130 into the already oppressive heat, Holder thought, "Man, I can't believe I am back here again." Apprised of the detachment now up at Kandahar, he immediately volunteered to go up-country. Two weeks later, Holder conducted a logistics mission up to Tarin Kowt where coalition forces were maintaining a medical facility for Afghans. As his helicopter and another commanded by Capt Paul Pereira landed at Kandahar and were being hot refueled, the pilots received a call from the command center asking if they could re-launch and fly to northeastern Afghanistan to perform an emergency extraction of a special forces team. The location was five hours away, north of Asadabad. Holder and Pereira accepted the mission and lifted off into the darkening sky.

The illumination was almost 100 percent as they flew through the crisp night air. Arriving in the recovery area, they were able to make radio contact with the team, divided into two elements almost half a mile apart in the rugged mountainside. The pilots decided that each would pick up one element of the separated team. They were in an area with hard lava rock and little dust. As Holder was landing to recover his team, he heard Pereira call "Mayday, Mayday" on the radio. Holder quickly got his Soldiers on board and then pulled pitch. As he gained altitude, he could see Pereira's aircraft perched on a sandbar in the river below. On his attempted exfil of the team, Pereira had followed the directions of a team member and had landed on an upslope in a nose-high attitude. As his helicopter began to slide backwards, he applied forward cyclic in an attempt to stop the roll. When he did so, the main blades came down and hit the refueling probe and the leading edges of both engines and knocked off all of the forward pitot-static probes. As this happened, Pereira believed that the main blades had also hit one of the team members. He shut down his engines and discovered that his main rotor blades were seriously damaged.

The crew of Ninja 12. *Left to right*: SSgt Eric Weidanz, 1st Lt Mike Holder, Capt Steve Cherrington, TSgt Shawn Hammond, TSgt J. B. Lackey (killed in Afghanistan in 2010), and SSgt P. J. Wright.

Flying overhead, Holder quickly contacted the second team on the radio and discovered that none of its members had been injured in the accident. Holder then landed his aircraft on the tight and narrow ridge, placing the second element of the team with the first for additional security at the downed aircraft. He had to leave Pereira's crew and the entire team there as he flew his aircraft to the airfield at Bagram. The command center at Kandahar had been monitoring the mission and instructed him to shut down there and go into crew rest. As Holder was landing, his crew was contacted by an Army CH-47 crew with a quick reaction force (QRF) that wanted Holder to lead it to the team. Holder got permission to do so, refueled his aircraft, and led the CH-47 back to the team. The CH-47 offloaded a fresh team of Soldiers to secure the site and then loaded up the exfiling team. Holder and crew picked up the Pave Low crew members and brought them out.

Courtesy Maj Mike Holder, USAF

Refueling at night

The next day, a recovery team with Lieutenant Borland as lead, copilot 2d Lt Geoffrey Petyak, and crew flew up from Kandahar with a 10-man maintenance element led by MSgt Fred Bishop to repair the damaged aircraft so that they could fly it back. Sergeant Colannino was on that team and describes the effort:

> We worked on the bird; we changed three main rotor blades, one tail rotor blade. We had to use speed tape to tape up the top of the aircraft so it wasn't exposed. We had to take some parts of the aircraft off that were too damaged. As soon as the sun started to come up, we were getting in the seats. We fired it up, did a quick hover check, made sure nothing was going to fall off the aircraft or that it was going to rattle itself to death, and we took off back to the base. All we had for instruments was static stuff because everything else was out. It was a challenge getting back. We got it back though and landed. They fixed it up, and that aircraft lived on.[52]

Borland and his team were protected by a security element from the 10th Mountain Division. Regardless, they received harassing small arms fire as they worked. When the maintenance team indicated that the aircraft was ready to fly, Borland discussed the aircraft status with Petyak, who had been a helicopter maintenance supervisor in the Army. Petyak believed that the aircraft was "good to go." Additionally, the entire maintenance team volunteered to fly on it as a sign of confidence in its work. Borland was impressed. However, as a precaution, he called Bagram and requested that it dispatch another helicopter to come out and recover the maintenance team and security force. When it arrived, Borland made sure that everybody was aboard one of the two helicopters and then took off for Bagram.

Landing there, Borland anticipated that the Pave Low would be loaded aboard a C-17 for return to the CONUS. However, because of runway repairs, a C-17 could not land there, and Borland was instructed to fly the aircraft to Kandahar. To minimize the threat, Borland and crew took off at sunset. They were escorted by another Pave Low. Most of the aircraft systems were operating normally, except for the pitot-static system and related indications. Flying southwest, they had to divert around a thunderstorm and then encountered a dust storm. Borland remembered,

> The only thing I can equate it to is the movie, *The Mummy*. We hit a haboob; it was a wall of dirt that went up to . . . about 8,000 feet. We were at about 300 feet on radar at the time. We still didn't have any pitot-static indication, . . . but I've got ground speed, which is what really saved our lives that night. . . . We went from about 130 knots ground to 70 knots ground nearly instantaneously. It was so disorienting in the FLIR because when we hit that wall of dirt, it spun our gyros pretty quick.[53]

The haboob also caused problems for the left engine because the engine air particle separator had been damaged and removed, and the engine was ingesting great quantities of dirt, making the engine run much hotter than the right one and produce smoke. At the same time, the crew in the second aircraft was having a difficult time maintaining visual contact with Borland's machine. Borland had his seat engineer, Sergeant Colannino, turn on all of the aircraft lights so that they were easier to see. Additionally, Borland started a climb to clear the haboob, while he and Petyak had to trade off control of the aircraft about every five minutes because of the heavy turbulence—an occurrence very similar to the crews that dispatched to rendezvous with the USS *Forrestal* in the southern Caribbean on Operation Pokeweed 12 years earlier. Once clear of the dust cloud, they were able to proceed directly to Kandahar. En route, they were directed to go to Jacobabad. Borland refused, citing his low fuel state and the fact that the two crews were just worn out. They would fly the aircraft down to Jacobabad the next day. The repairs to the aircraft cost over two million dollars.[54]

At about that same time, Kingsley determined that he needed to move his Pave Low force completely out of Jacobabad into Afghanistan because the flow of the fighting had concentrated in the eastern and southeastern portions of the country as allied forces pursued Osama bin Laden and his remnant minions. Initially, he tried to find room at the Bagram air base about 25 miles north of Kabul. However, that base was already overcrowded. Instead, he decided to consolidate his Pave Lows at Kandahar while awaiting space at Bagram. As the unit was beginning this move, though, he received an operational order to move four of his Pave Lows, crews, and support personnel and two MC-130Ps to Camp Lemonier, Djibouti, to support operations in that region. They moved as ordered, only to find another austere location that required a great deal of improvement to make it habitable. Regardless, they were part of an initial deployment of a CENTCOM crisis response element that included US Navy SEALs and other US special forces elements. They began operations with French, Spanish, German, and other coalition special forces units so that they could get used to one another and develop standard TTPs. Within a few months, they would be joined by a USMC task force to become JTF-Horn of Africa. This was another evolving front in the efforts against al-Qaeda.[55]

In June, with the dispatch of the last of his personnel from Jacobabad, Kingsley returned to Hurlburt to pass command of the 20th SOS to Colonel Webb and then attend the US Naval Postgraduate School in Monterey, California. Webb was assigned Lt Col Jim Slife to serve as his operations officer. At almost the same time, Brig Gen Lyle Koenig gave up command of the 16th SOW to Col Frank Kisner, an MC-130 pilot, and longtime Pave Low pilot Col Randy O'Boyle took command of the 16th SOG.[56]

After assuming command, Colonel Webb joined his unit detachment at Djibouti for a six-week tour to develop a feel for that operation before returning to the United States with the 20th SOS contingent still in Afghanistan to prepare for other operations being contemplated in other parts of the world. Colonel Slife replaced him at Djibouti to command the small Pave Low detachment of four aircraft and six crews.[57]

Jim Slife shared many of the same experiences as Kingsley and Webb as he served there and in Afghanistan. He came to believe that in the longer nights of Afghanistan, the Pave Low community reached the pinnacle of its capability. He recalled how the "old heads" had inculcated in the younger troops the expectation that in going into any conflict, they would be there to do the prime hit, or takedown, or rescue—and then head back home to acclaim. The Big Mish, they called it, kind of like Honey Badger or the Noriega grab in Panama. However, the reality was that plans changed, and campaigns dragged out. Instead of using the magic technology to go out and do the one big event, the truer norm was a longer and involved period of deployment such as Desert Storm or Bosnia, which stressed the units over time and called to the fore their full "bag of air commando tricks." Like Webb, Slife remembers this intense period in Afghanistan:

> We found ourselves in an environment—particularly in the early days in Afghanistan—where we were flying missions every night that at any other point in the history of Pave Low would be the Big Mish. . . . You don't have time to even write down who was on the crew two nights ago because you're worried about tonight. We were flying seven-ship opposed assaults to compounds at 7,000-feet density altitude in talcum powder dust. Bullets are hitting the helicopter and you're shooting back. That's what we're doing *every night*.

> [A long campaign] is a different proposition, and none of us had ever experienced it. As captains, as lieutenants . . . we didn't know how to do this. We just knew how to get ready for a single mission. So this idea of conducting sustained operations and the relentless pace that we were operating at took some getting used to, frankly. You know, we adapted pretty well.[58]

Watching the dramatic actions in Afghanistan from afar, Brig Gen Rich Comer, still serving at AFSOC, was very concerned about the brownout landing problem and initiated quick actions to modify the Pave Low's Hover Symbology Queuing System to provide the pilots critical visual inputs in the landing phase of flight to preclude the drifting issues inherent in the brownout conditions. Like Colonel Slife, though, he was impressed with the performance of the young Pave Low crews and their commanders, some of whom had served with him back in his days as the commander of the 20th SOS. He also believed that "it was in Afghanistan that Pave Low finally came to full fruition of its capabilities." Just a few months later Comer would be promoted to major general, the first Pave Low pilot to reach that rank.[59]

Kirtland AFB

Given the turbulent events occurring in the world, the pace of life and operations was a bit more staid at the schoolhouse at Kirtland. The 551st SOS was steadily training Pave Low pilots, engineers, and

Courtesy Maj Gen Rich Comer, USAF, Retired

Brig Gen Rich Comer serving as the AFSOC vice-commander

gunners, although there were scheduling challenges because of a chronic shortage of instructors. The course syllabus was modified a bit to include increased classroom and flight instruction on CSAR, and the simulators assigned to the 58th TRSS were upgraded with the IDAS-MATT system in March, enabling the students to become familiar with the systems while still at Kirtland. However, the 551st was not slated to receive any MH-53Ms, so the actual flight training would have to occur either at the 20th or 21st. In June 2001, Lt Col Dennis Jones relinquished command of the 551st SOS to fellow Pave Low pilot and combat veteran Lt Col Tim Leahy and proceeded to Maxwell AFB to attend the AWC.[60]

During June and July, the 551st SOS received the MH-53Js from the inactivated 31st SOS. They were immediately put into the training program to replace the TH-53s. On 3 August, all of the TH-53s were flown to the Aerospace Maintenance and Regeneration Center (AMARC) at Davis-Monthan AFB, Arizona, for long-term storage. Henceforth, all Pave Low qualification training would take place in MH-53J aircraft. Four weeks later, the personnel of the 58th SOW were as devastated as their countrymen at the horrific scenes on their TVs. Kirtland AFB was also placed under maximum security, and all flights were cancelled for several days except for those specifically directed under Operation

Noble Eagle. As training resumed, all 58th SOW personnel were in-fused with an increased sense of urgency concerning the training they were imparting to their students. All expected that soon the wing would be tasked to provide augmentation personnel for deployment with the operational squadrons. Many, too, knew that at some point in the future, they would also be assigned PCS to those same units.

Courtesy 58th SOW History Office

In August 2001, the six TH-53As assigned to the 58th SOW depart Kirtland AFB, escorted by three MH-53Js, for their final flight to Davis-Monthan AFB.

As Colonel Kingsley and his Airmen were beginning operations at Jacobabad, Capt Derrick Stamos was beginning his Pave Low qualifi-cation at Kirtland. He had been commissioned in 1992 through USAF ROTC at the University of South Florida with a slot for pilot training. Post–Desert Storm, USAF pilot training was severely re-duced, and Stamos was given a nonflying job as a contracting officer at Moody AFB until receiving orders for flight school at Columbus AFB, Mississippi, in June 1996. After his initial T-37 training, he selected the helicopter track and proceeded to Fort Rucker for rotary-wing training. Graduating from that course with his pilot wings, he went to Vandenberg AFB to fly the UH-1N with the 76th Helicopter

Flight, as had so many previous Pave Low pilots. It was an assignment that he dearly enjoyed. The UH-1Ns there were modified with FLIRs, upgraded radios, and GPS navigation. Additionally, the crews flew with NVGs so that they could spot intruders into the restricted areas around the base at night. It was very good training for prospective Pave Low pilots; in fact, the pilots there still referred to their aircraft as the "Pave Hueys." While there, Stamos logged over 1,000 hours of rotary-wing time on his four-year assignment.

All of that was the precursor for the Pave Low. Stamos was well aware of the role that the Pave Lows were already playing in Afghanistan and had no misconceptions about where he was going or what he would be doing. He wanted to get all that he could out of the course and immersed himself in it. The TH-53As were gone, so all of his flights were in the MH-53Js, and he learned as much as possible about the various aircraft systems. He quickly discovered that unlike the UH-1N, he could not fly the Pave Low by himself. He found that the real challenge was on the human side and that the most important skill he needed to learn was "how to deal with, manage, utilize, and then go to war with a full up crew." He further explained, "If you were going to put a Pave Low into a tight spot, you need the inputs of all six of those crew members to get you down safely. You can't see your own landing gear; you don't have the option of leaning out through an open window to look down and see the ground. So working with that crew—it was huge."[61]

He had to learn the functions of each of the six crew members and to delegate duties as necessary to facilitate the operation of the aircraft to perform the mission. He also learned the now almost timeless "tricks" that had been passed down through the generations to fly the Paves. One of these was the use of the crew cadence. Stamos described the technique:

> Learning to integrate all of those inputs and all of those voices is one of the biggest challenges in the entire program. They have something they call the "cadence." You would say that you are on the approach; each crew member in turn would say his own piece all throughout the approach until it came back to you, and then you would give an update of what you were doing. So basically you would say that you are on the approach.
>
> The engineer would call the ground speed and altitude; the right door would look out and say, "I've got the LZ in sight; come left/come right." Tail would say, "Clear on the tail." The left gunner would say, "Clear on the left." The non-

flying pilot usually had nothing to say; he would give a navigation update if he needed to say something that he saw on the nav or FLIR. . . .

That skill, which was primarily honed in the tactical phase—which was the second half of the schoolhouse, done day and night, on goggles and radar—was probably the single greatest skill that we mastered. The helicopter itself is a helicopter. . . . But using the systems and integrating that crew is where it really becomes something special. It enhances the capability beyond the machine. It's the men in the machine who give it the capability.[62]

This was what the great instructors at Kirtland taught. It took persistent instruction sortie after sortie and was ingrained in the Pave Low community year after year. Stamos also discovered that some of the mission debriefings could be quite harsh, with the enlisted instructors and crew members not hesitating to make sometimes stingingly critical comments concerning the performance of one another or the pilots. Comments were focused on the professional vice personal level; however, Stamos could quickly see that Pave Low duty was not for those with thin skins. The community had developed a fine-tuned ability to self-police because everyone knew that the price for poor performance could be measured in lives lost. He clearly remembers that "it was the case with the senior guys setting the example for the young guys and letting them know, in no uncertain terms, when they didn't meet standards. It was understood that you had to rise to a certain level, particularly in combat, to execute the mission." After Kirtland, Stamos was scheduled to report to the 21st SOS at RAF Mildenhall, where he would most assuredly put all of his newly acquired Pave Low training to good use.[63]

The new year of 2002 did not start well for the Pave Low community at Kirtland. On 9 January, a Cessna 172 with three persons on board crashed in the southern Colorado mountains near Durango. The pilot was able to walk out and make contact with emergency services on his cell phone. That evening the 58th SOW was contacted and requested to help. Two Pave Lows and an MC-130 were launched to assist in the search and possible rescue, made all the more urgent by the subzero temperatures in the mountains.

Arriving in the area, the lead aircraft landed and picked up the pilot, who then helped the crew find the crash site. While hovering over the wreckage, the helicopter, MH-53J #68-10363, struck some trees with its main rotor blades and crashed. No one was seriously hurt. A ground rescue unit then found the site and picked up the Cessna pilot and passengers and the Pave Low crew. Maintenance technicians determined that the aircraft was salvageable. However, the crash site elevation of 9,700 feet made the Pave Low unrecoverable by helicopter lift; instead, it had to be hauled out. However, the site was quite remote with no road immediately available. Consequently, the recovery crew, led by CMSgt Mark Self, brought in a modified flatbed trailer to serve as a sled. Two large tractors were then driven up the mountain to push and pull the sled out through 14 miles of wilderness. The entire operation took almost a month and added to the eventual $5 million total cost of repairing the Pave Low. The aircraft maintenance team was led by MSgt Jackie Powell, who said of his 10-person recovery team, "Each one of these guys worked unselfishly and with tremendous dedication to accomplish this recovery."

Based upon feedback coming in from the 20th and 21st Squadrons, the 551st continuously updated its course curriculum to graduate crew members as technically and tactically proficient as possible. However, the 551st would not receive MH-53Ms. Those aircraft were needed in the operational fleet. For the year, the instructors of the 551st SOS and 58th TRSS qualified or requalified 26 pilots, 15 flight engineers, and 17 aerial gunners and provided simulator refresher training for 259 crew members. The training provided by the professionals at Kirtland AFB was vital to the standardization and professionalism of the Pave Low fleet operation. Given the challenges now faced by the Pave Low community in the GWOT and its indeterminate duration, those two attributes were more important than ever.[64]

Notes

1. Woodward, *Bush at War*, 152, 178.
2. Kingsley, interview.
3. Ibid.
4. Ibid.; and Holder, interview.
5. *LHA* is the Navy designator for an amphibious assault ship.
6. Kingsley, interview.
7. Cessop, interview.
8. Kingsley and Holder, interviews.
9. Kingsley, interview; and Blehm, *Only Thing Worth Dying For*, 67–69.
10. Colannino, interview.
11. Blehm, *Only Thing Worth Dying For*, 67–69; and Kingsley, interview.
12. Stricklin to the author, e-mail, review remarks, 23 Jan 2011.
13. Briscoe et al., *Weapon of Choice*, 109–11, 113; and Stricklin to the author, e-mail, review remarks, 23 Jan 2011.
14. Holder and Schweim, interviews.

15. Blehm, *Only Thing Worth Dying For*, 67–69.

16. Kingsley, interview; and Knife 03 Incident Report, n.d., procured from Lieutenant Holder.

17. Knife 03 Incident Report, n.d., procured from Lieutenant Holder.

18. 1st Lt Brandon Lingle, "Pave Low Hero Earns 2002 Pitsenbarger Award," *Commando*, 26 July 2002, 11; and Cessop, interview.

19. Borland, interview.

20. Ibid.

21. Cessop, interview.

22. Borland, interview.

23. 1st Lt James Holder, memorandum for record, subject: Knife 04 CSAR Report, 4 Nov 2001, provided to the author by Holder.

24. Robinson, *Masters of Chaos*, 157; and "66th Rescue Squadron," fact sheet.

25. Blehm, *Only Thing Worth Dying For*, 88, 175, 260; and Briscoe et al., *Weapon of Choice*, 106.

26. Blehm, *Only Thing Worth Dying For*, 299.

27. Kingsley, interview.

28. Michalek, personal notes; and Blehm, *Only Thing Worth Dying For*, 260, 274–301.

29. Blehm, *Only Thing Worth Dying For*, 292–304.

30. Ibid., 304–7.

31. Ibid., 312.

32. Schweim, interview.

33. Blehm, *Only Thing Worth Dying For*, 324–28.

34. Ibid., 333–35; and Schweim, interview.

35. Blehm, *Only Thing Worth Dying For*, 335–39; and Schweim, interview.

36. Michalek, personal notes.

37. Lt Col Mike Grub, personal mission narrative, n.d., provided to the author; and Grub to the author, e-mail.

38. Kingsley, interview.

39. Fontenot, Degen, and Tohn, *On Point*, 23; and History of AFSOC, 1 Jan–31 Dec 2002, vol. 1, 1.

40. Jobling, interview.

41. Bahmanyar and Osman, *SEALs*, 107–9; USSOCOM, *History of the United States Special Operations Command*, 107, USSOCOM/HO; and Jobling, interview.

42. Webb, interview.

43. Ibid.; and History of AFSOC, 1 Jan–31 Dec 2002, vol. 1, 168–69.

44. Lt Col Leighton Anderson, personal mission narrative, n.d., provided to the author.

45. Ibid.; and Webb, interview.

46. Michalek, personal notes.

47. Webb, interview.

48. History of 352d SOG, 1 July–31 Dec 2001, vol. 1, 10, 18, 57; and Lengyel, interview.

49. http://www.rotorheadsrus/documents/514.html, accessed 13 July 2009; and 21 SOS/DO to Lt Col Gregory Lengyel, memorandum, subject: Mission Commander AAA for 21–22 May 02 Rescue Mission, provided to the author by TSgt John Hickman.

50. History of 352d SOG, 1 Jan–30 June 2002, vol. 1, 20, 39; ibid., 1 July–31 Dec 2002, vol. 1, xi, xvii; and Lengyel, interview.

51. History of 16th SOW, 1 Jan–30 June 2002, vol. 1, 20.

52. Colannino, interview.

53. Borland, interview.

54. History of AFSOC, 1 Jan–31 Dec 2002, vol. 1, xxiv; and Borland and Holder, interviews.

55. Kingsley and Webb, interviews; and Sean Naylor, "Hunting Down Terrorists," *Navy Times*, 7 Nov 2011, 24.

56. Ibid.; and History of 16th SOW, 1 Jan–30 June 2002, vol. 1, 1–2.

57. Webb, interview; and Slife to the author, e-mail, review comments, 13 Sept 2010.

58. Slife, interview.

59. Comer, interview.

60. History of 58th SOW, 1 Jan–30 June 2001, vol. 1, 46; and Jones, interview.

61. Stamos, interview.

62. Ibid.

63. Ibid.

64. History of 58th SOW, 1 Jan–30 June 2001, vol. 1, 4, 12, 21; ibid., 1 July–31 Dec 2001, vol. 1, 8–10; ibid., 1 Jan–31 Dec 2002, vol. 1, 12–16, 50–51, 68; and "Teams Led Helo out of Rockies," *Commando*, 8 Mar 2002, 4.

Chapter 16

Operation Iraqi Freedom

2003

If you start a rumor and repeat it enough times, it will catch on and can become the truth.

—Brig Gen Greg Lengyel

Washington, DC

Afghanistan was not the only area of concern. When the United States led the effort to free Kuwait in 1991, numerous pundits and governmental leaders felt that it was just a matter of time before Saddam Hussein would be overthrown by disparate, disaffected elements within Iraq. Indeed, expecting direct American and allied support almost immediately, primarily Shia groups revolted in the southern portions of the country. Very quickly after their victory, however, US and coalition forces pulled back into Kuwait and only watched as Saddam unleashed his remaining forces on the rebels, brutally suppressing them with both conventional weapons and chemical WMDs. These actions and similar ones taken in the north led to the death of tens of thousands of Shiites and Kurds and resolidified Saddam's grip over the nation.

Encouraged by the rapid departure of the allied forces from his country and the success of his suppression of the rebels, Saddam reassumed a defiant pose toward the Western powers. Once again, he began subtle but aggressive actions against Kuwait and was allegedly involved in an assassination plot against Pres. George H. W. Bush when he visited the Gulf region. Saddam ordered his air force to fly in violation of a United Nations–imposed no-fly edict, triggering coalition air forces to continuously patrol the two formalized no-fly zones in northern and southern Iraq. In response, he ordered his antiaircraft gunners to fire upon allied aircraft patrolling the sectors. For many years, Pave Low crews sat CSAR alert in Turkey and Kuwait supporting these operations. Fortunately, they never had to mount a CSAR effort.[1]

After assuming office in January 2001, Pres. George W. Bush directed his administration to review these long-ongoing operations. In doing so, it determined that Saddam's hostile actions and intent and stated determination to develop and use more WMDs or pass them to international terrorists presented a serious danger to the United States and its interests in the Gulf region. President Bush addressed this threat in a speech at the United States Military Academy on 1 June 2002. To the gathered cadets, their families, faculty, and friends, he said,

> The gravest danger to freedom lies at the perilous crossroads of radicalism and technology. When the spread of chemical and biological and nuclear weapons, along with ballistic missile technology—when that occurs, even weak states and small groups could attain a catastrophic power to strike great nations. Our enemies have declared this very intention, and have been caught seeking these terrible weapons. They want the capability to blackmail us, or to harm us, or to harm our friends—and we will oppose them with all our power.
>
> For much of the last century, America's defense relied on the Cold War doctrines of deterrence and containment. In some cases, those strategies still apply. But new threats also require new thinking. Deterrence—the promise of massive retaliation against nations—means nothing against shadowy terrorist networks with no nation or citizens to defend. Containment is not possible when unbalanced dictators with weapons of mass destruction can deliver those weapons on missiles or secretly provide them to terrorist allies.
>
> We cannot defend America and our friends by hoping for the best. We cannot put our faith in the word of tyrants, who solemnly sign non-proliferation treaties, and then systemically break them. If we wait for threats to fully materialize, we will have waited too long.[2]

Laid out in such stark terms, the president's speech was immediately labeled a doctrine of preventive or preemptive war. The service chiefs realized that it most probably meant renewed hostilities with Iraq in addition to Afghanistan and stepped up preparations.

Weighing Iraq's belligerence, its interest in producing and using WMDs, and potential connections to international terrorist groups, President Bush decided to remove Saddam Hussein and his Baathist regime from power. Bush was heartened in that decision by the realization that the American people also saw Saddam's governance as a threat and, in the face of the dramatic events of 9/11, were more supportive of his planned actions.[3]

While President Bush was making his case for war and Secretary of State Colin Powell was appealing to the United Nations for diplomatic support, the commander of USCENTCOM, Gen Tommy Franks, was driving his staff to develop the detailed plans necessary to execute an attack. However, the political dynamics within the Middle East region had changed greatly since 1991. As opposed to its unlimited support in Desert Storm, Saudi Arabia now put strict limits on its backing for any proposed campaign against Iraq. While Air Force and some ground units could be based there, any significant ground campaign with substantial conventional ground forces would have to be mounted from Kuwait.

General Franks's campaign plan, titled 1003V, directed that a main attack would be mounted from Kuwait with three-plus divisions and numerous auxiliary elements. A supporting attack would be launched from Turkey into northern Iraq. It would consist of Task Force Horse, formed around the 4th ID and its associated units, and a large number of special forces units. These two operations would be bolstered by a third effort in western Iraq. There a strong coalition special operations force would be inserted and reinforced to tie down Iraqi units and prevent the launching of surface-to-surface rockets from the region against Israel and Saudi Arabia, as had been done in Desert Storm. At the same time, a ceaseless air campaign would detect and destroy strategic Iraqi targets and directly assist the coalition ground forces as the three task forces converged on Baghdad and destroyed the regime. The timing of the campaign was not yet set. However, Franks wanted to initiate it as soon as possible, preferably in the cool weather of the winter months instead of the blinding heat of late spring and summer. February or March of 2003 seemed to be the most propitious time.

As forces continued to build up in Kuwait for the southern portion of the attack, the government of Turkey debated and then voted not to allow the passage of Task Force Horse through its territory to mount the northern attack. Some of the Soldiers and most of the equipment of the 4th ID and support units were aboard ships in the eastern Mediterranean Sea, and General Franks ordered that they be diverted to ports in Kuwait and Saudi Arabia. They would be fed into the campaign as they arrived. The northern effort would be centered around a special forces task force with ad hoc conventional force augmentation.[4]

US V Corps would conduct the southern attack from Kuwait with three divisions—the 3d ID (Mechanized), the 101st Airborne Division (Air Assault), and the 82d Airborne Division—with numerous supporting units. Joining V Corps would be the US I Marine Expeditionary Force (MEF) with its 1st Marine Division, the British 1st Armored Division, and supporting units to attack generally northwest to destroy Iraqi forces, clear the main roads and adjoining towns and cities, and capture Baghdad. Subsequent operations would send forces farther north to seize Tikrit and Mosul. To partially replace the cancelled attack of Task Force Horse from Turkey, coalition special forces units would conduct supporting operations in northern Iraq in conjunction with the 173d Airborne Brigade and Kurdish forces in the region.

Springing forth from Kuwait, the V Corps would attack on an axis—taking it generally through the cities of Jalibah, As Samawah, An Najaf, and Karbala—and then close in on Baghdad from the south and west. To its right, the I MEF would use British forces to clear the city of Al Basrah. Then it would sweep generally northwest to close in on Baghdad from the east and be prepared to continue operations to the north as needed.

AFSOC elements would deploy to support all three operations, and warning orders went out to the 16th SOW and the 352d SOG. Arriving in-theater, their forces would be under the operational control of SOCCENT. They would be organized by task into a JSOAC commanded by the 16th SOW commander, Col Frank Kisner. To optimally command and control his assets, he organized them into several detachments: AFSOD-A at Camp Lemonier, Djibouti, which would support the ongoing operations there and included a small 20th SOS detachment; Joint Special Operations Air Detachment–North (JSOAD-N), to be located in Turkey, which would support northern Iraq operations; JSOAD-W, at Al Jafr AB, Jordan, which would support western Iraq operations; and AFSOD-S, to be located at Ali Al Salem AB, Kuwait, which would support southern Iraq operations.

The 20th SOS was alerted for duty with the AFSOD-S, and the 21st SOS was alerted for deployment to support the JSOAD-N.[5] Deploying to support the offensive were over 1,800 US and allied fighter, bomber, and support aircraft. Arrayed at airfields across the region and aboard aircraft carriers in the Gulf, these forces were led by officers who fought in the first Gulf War and largely consisted of personnel who had been in action against Iraq while flying missions in the no-fly zones over Iraq. They would be supported by a significant CSAR force. Rescue task forces, each consisting of an HH-60 squadron, an HC-130 squadron, and a PJ squadron, would be assigned to support operations in the south, west, and north, although the northern task force was facing the same restrictions as Task Force Horse. All would be under the operational control of the new CFACC, Lt Gen Michael "Buzz" Moseley, who would use them to conduct his theater rescue plan. However, the Pave Lows were not completely free of personnel recovery responsibilities. They still had to maintain two aircraft available to carry a QRF to recover any special operations forces in extremis.[6]

20th Special Operations Squadron

The squadron used the latter part of 2002 to absorb new personnel and prepare its aircraft and Airmen for the anticipated taskings. Colonels Webb and Slife did a complete review of the personnel structure of the squadron and made several changes to the flight system. Anticipating that the war against Iraq could be a long struggle, they wanted the talent of the unit to be spread out—no "A" or "B" team but balanced so that overall performance would be at a predictable standard. Webb formed hard crews, believing that they would be better for the challenges ahead. The two colonels were also deeply involved with the planning for the squadron's anticipated deployment to Kuwait; they intended to take 10 aircraft and 15 crews with them. Counting the four aircraft and six crews in Djibouti, fully 80 percent of the squadron would be deployed for the war. Webb departed Hurlburt in December 2002 to travel to Djibouti, where Lt Col Mitch Petersen was now in charge. Capt Mark Newell and Capt Joe Michalek were also in Djibouti with their own crews. Webb directed them to begin working with US Navy SEAL elements in-theater to plan a series of missions into the Al Faw region of southern Iraq to seize and protect oil platforms and pumping sites there as part of a larger campaign into Iraq. In early January 2003, Colonel Webb traveled on to Kuwait to prepare for the arrival of his squadron team. He took Newell, Michalek, and their crews with him.[7]

While at Djibouti, Colonel Petersen was joined by SrA Eric Ezell. After basic training at Lackland AFB, he had gone through his airmanship and survival schools before attending the basic aerial gunner's course and then MH-53 qualification at Kirtland. In October 2002, he reported to the 20th SOS, where he received his final mission qualification training and was immediately scheduled for deployment. He arrived at Camp Lemonier as a 19-year-old MH-53 gunner, still a bit in shock over the dramatic changes that had occurred in his life over the previous 16 months. There he was assigned to TSgt John Stricklin for his final training and mission qualification. Stricklin had total empathy for the young Airman, remembering his initiation to true operational flying under the supervision of SMSgt "Large Sarge" Hunter back in Desert Shield. He resolved to insure that the young troop learned everything he needed to know to do this job as safely and professionally as possible. Ezell remembers, "I went from being an 18-year-old kid with no responsibilities in the world to . . . my first deployment . . . held to the same standard as that of any NCO . . . in the flying world. [It] would be . . . a great personal experience."[8]

Over the next two months, the 20th deployed aircraft and personnel to Ali Al Salem AB in Kuwait. Slife oversaw the deployment of his aircraft and people from Hurlburt through February and then led the last group over in early March. He arrived after Colonel Webb and discovered that the Green Hornets were tasked with three war-opening missions: two insertions of several ODA teams from the 5th SFG and a US Navy SEAL insertion on several oil platforms in the Al Faw region. Slife would lead the first ODA insertion, possibly prior to the beginning of declared hostilities, and Webb would act as the airborne mission commander on the SEAL mission, led by Capt Mark Newell. The third mission would be led by Maj Bill Rowell.[9]

Courtesy SSgt Glen Fleming, USAF

The Ali Al Salem flight line through NVGs

The 20th SOS lost the services of another aircraft, MH-53M #68-10930, on 13 February 2003, when a crew led by Capt "Woody" Woodworth made a hard landing in brownout conditions at night in the Kuwaiti fine dust. The nose gear collapsed on impact, allowing the main blades to strike the ground and severely damaging the tail structure. Captain Michalek was his flight leader and landed to recover the crew and passengers, none of whom was seriously injured. However, the aircraft was extensively damaged and had to be returned to the United States for significant and time-consuming repair. This was the same problem that the young crews of the 20th SOS had encountered in Saudi Arabia 12 years earlier and in Afghanistan just the previous year. This very aircraft had been part of that earlier Iraq deployment. It was flown by Capt Tom Trask and crew on the recovery of Slate 46A in January 1991. Needless to say, the Pave Low crew was quite shaken by this event. Slife flew with the crew in an attempt to sharpen its skill and reestablish its confidence.[10]

However, he and Webb and most of the Pave Low crew members had learned a great deal since Afghanistan. Slife came to the conclusion that because of individual personalities, some of the crews did not work well as assigned. Slife finally had to go to Webb and work out a plan to realign some personnel, a dramatic move surely, but one made necessary by the exigencies of impending combat. However, the changes were selective. Most crews had jelled as cohesive units, each developing its own distinct DNA, or identity and capacity for handling the steadily increasing stress as combat approached. Said Slife of this phenomenon, "There is some really intense bonding that takes place; guys develop their own personalities as crews."

Webb and Slife had another problem. The AFSOD-S commander, Col Randy O'Boyle, was collocated with them at Ali Al Salem. After the accident, he also turned a close eye to the 20th. He was hesitant to intrude into the actions of the squadron; however, he asked Webb pointedly if Webb needed to make any changes. It was ultimately Webb's call, and he did make several more crew realignments. Slife also manipulated the flying schedule, making sure that key supervisors flew with certain crews on certain missions. It was all part of combat aviation.[11]

Desert Combat

Intelligence sources indicated that the Iraqi people wanted to be rid of Saddam and would welcome an invasion by coalition troops to depose him and his Baathist regime. Skeptics believed that these reports were overinflated and that a large portion of the Iraqi response to any invasion would be the initiation of guerilla-type operations against allied forces.

Saddam, believing that any substantial allied attack against Iraq would mirror the Desert Storm campaign, expected an extensive air campaign to precede any ground attack. Sensing an opportunity to achieve at least operational surprise, General Franks decided to initiate the ground campaign with the forces in Kuwait prior to the air campaign. He would do it in March, before the heat had built up.[12]

On 17 March, President Bush addressed the nation. He gave Saddam and his sons, Uday and Qusay, 48 hours to leave Iraq, explaining that "their refusal to do so will result in military conflict, commenced at a time of our choosing." Saddam immediately responded with his own appearance on television saying, "This will be Iraq's last great battle with the malicious tyrant in our time, and America's last great war of aggression, too."[13]

Saddam and his sons did not withdraw as directed, and 48 hours later, General Franks was ordered to begin his campaign. The first mission to launch was a seven-ship of Pave Lows led by Lt Col Jim Slife. They proceeded into south-central Iraq to deliver several ODA teams from the 5th SFG, along with special "nonstandard vehicles" to perform strategic reconnaissance along US V Corps and I MEF advance routes. Slife was crewed with 1st Lt Tom Lessner, flight engineers TSgt John Tharp and TSgt Todd Buice, and gunners TSgt Aaron Bettison and Amn Eric Ezell.[14]

All of the helicopters were at their absolute maximum wartime-waivered takeoff weights. As they taxied out for takeoff, the maintenance crew members lined up to salute them, waving a large American flag illuminated by flashlights. The ground crew's gesture touched the aircrews, especially when they considered how hard the maintenance crews had worked to get those almost 40-year-old aircraft ready to go to war one more time.

Slife and his flight of three Pave Lows lifted off into a terrible sandstorm with low ceilings and poor visibility. Captain Michalek led the second element of four. At the first landing zone near the key city of

Courtesy Brig Gen Brad Webb, USAF

The 20th SOS commander, Lt Col Brad Webb, addresses his Airmen before the initiation of OIF.

Nasiriyah, one of the crews in the first element, carrying ODA 553, crashed in the brownout conditions. The helicopter, MH-53M#67-14493, flipped on its side and was destroyed. The crew and passengers escaped, although several were injured. Michalek landed his helicopters around the crash site; a security team he was carrying secured the site so that the helicopter crew could be recovered. The men of ODA 553 retrieved enough of their equipment to continue their mission, initially to overwatch a key bridge near the city and, eventually, to infiltrate into Nasiriyah and begin working with anti-Saddam forces.[15]

When Slife and his six remaining helicopters returned to Ali Al Salem, though, all was in chaos. The crews had another insertion mission to fly and were now behind schedule to get all teams in safely before sunrise. As they refueled and reloaded and the ODA troops began coming aboard, Slife could see that he had a serious morale problem. Colonel O'Boyle met him at the aircraft. He was very direct. "What do you think?" he asked of Slife. "We've got to go," Slife responded firmly. "We cannot cancel at this point. We've got to go and do this second mission." O'Boyle swallowed hard. "Okay," he said and walked away. Webb and Slife then talked with the other crews. Some were brimming with confidence; some, less so. One crew was obviously too shaken to continue. Webb replaced it with a spare crew, and the six aircraft lifted off with their teams.

Needing another aircraft, Slife and Webb grabbed the one spare that was available with its crew. The pilots were 1st Lt Jim Peterson and 1st Lt Matt Berry. Peterson was another of the highly skilled and experienced US Army warrant officers who had crossed over to Pave Low. Berry was in awe of Peterson's flying ability and felt fortunate to be paired with him, in particular. Sergeant Jobling was the lead flight engineer. In preparing the aircraft for departure, the crew discovered several issues with its countermeasures, fuel, and hydraulic systems. Regardless, the crew members pressed on, receiving a quick mission brief as the US Army team with its equipment and vehicle were quickly loaded. The initial landing zone had been compromised, and they were handed another set of coordinates as their destination. The weather was still very poor with low clouds and limited visibility. Jobling had his hands full as his pilots battled vertigo in the dark, featureless night. He recounts, "I pulled such stuff out of my a-- that night. That is when I realized that I really knew how to do my job." At the time, Jobling had a broken bone in one of his feet. The break had occurred in Afghanistan a year earlier, but he had deferred surgery on it twice to make deployments to Djibouti and then to Kuwait. He later admitted that "it was just uncomfortable."[16]

Slife and his flight inserted ODA 555 near Samawah; however, they had to divert to an alternate landing site when intelligence sources informed them in-flight that enemy forces occupied the primary location. Unlike the first sortie, though, Slife and his flight were able to uneventfully insert all of the teams as planned. But the mission was not without excitement.

Returning from their insertions, Slife and his crews had a difficult time linking up with their designated tanker and almost ran out of gas while deep in Iraq. In the world of combat aviation, there are many stressors; concern for fuel is a primary one. Slife's crews were flying so far into Iraq with such heavy loads that they could not do the missions without tanker support. A flight of MC-130s was scheduled to support them but was delayed when it encountered some active Roland SAM batteries. The batteries were most probably on high

Courtesy SSgt Glen Fleming, USAF

Loading special forces elements for insertion into Iraq during the initial actions of OIF

alert because as Slife's flight was delivering its loads in south-central Iraq, USAF F-117s and 39 cruise missiles were sweeping into Iraq in an attempt to kill Saddam Hussein. Slife's flight was instructed to immediately climb to 1,500 feet as the cruise missiles transited their approximate location.

Under General Franks's war plan, the air campaign was not scheduled to begin until 22 March, after the conventional ground forces in Kuwait and the coalition special forces from Saudi Arabia and Jordan had initiated their attacks. However, when solid CIA sources reported Saddam's location, General Moseley received permission from the president to attack it. The strikes went in as targeted; however, Saddam was not there. Intelligence had been faulty, and the element of surprise was lost. Apparently, the strategic impact of that development was minor, for the surface attack occurred as scheduled. However, for the MC-130s and six Pave Lows over southern Iraq, the unintended consequences could have been dramatic. For Slife and his crews, it was an eventful night.[17]

The actions of Slife and his crew that night had quite an impact on their junior member. Reflects Amn Eric Ezell, who flew as his left gunner,

> I was the left scanner, Chalk Lead [the mission command helicopter]. I would say that I would consider at the time that it was the most important thing that I

had done. . . . There was so much going on. . . . We sit in the brief, hear the plan, talk to the teams. We go and preflight the aircraft. We load up vehicles and get ready to go. We launch; we take off. Here's a [flight] of helicopters flying across to basically start a war. It was exhilarating, though it had some scary moments. . . . There were times where I was nervous or anxious, but I was with a really great crew. All the backenders were great . . . my being, at the time, a 19-year-old kid. They brought me in; we had probably been crewed together for not even a month, but they knew what was going on; they showed me all the ropes for training and whatnot. I think we meshed well as a crew.

We had a problem with one of the tie-down straps on the truck. The vehicle had shifted a bit; it was pulled taut so you weren't able to release the strap. What should have taken a matter of seconds to get the ramp down, pop the straps, and get the vehicle out was taking longer. You could hear the hesitation in the pilot's voice. I [can't] remember if it was [Slife] or Lessner who was asking, "What's going on? What's going on?" We said, "We're working it!" "Okay, work it," he replied. So it was one of those things where he trusted his people.[18]

During the day, maintenance crews worked diligently to prepare the aircraft for the next night's big missions. The flight crews tried to sleep; however, with all of the local activity and missile alerts, sleep was in short supply. Crews kept having to move into the bunkers and several times had to don their protective chemical suits. For this mission, Colonel Webb flew with Capt Mark Newell as they led a flight of seven Pave Lows on a direct action mission to deliver several teams of US Navy SEALs and British Royal Marines. They were to seize oil platforms and facilities in the Al Faw area—preventing their destruction by Saddam's forces as in the first Gulf War—or their use as ecological weapons. This was one of the highest priority missions of the campaign. Newell's number two aircraft was commanded by 1st Lt Sean Borland.

Again, Capt Joe Michalek led the second flight of helicopters. He was extremely concerned about the threat of Iranian antiaircraft guns and the multiple SAM batteries in place just along the Iranian-Iraqi border. Maj Gene Becker flew as Capt Bill Rowell's copilot on this mission as they landed the SEALs and their specially modified vehicles at several land sites, many located within oil fields or production facilities and platforms.

Lieutenant Borland and his crew encountered an unusual problem. As they landed at their assigned spot, Borland's SEAL team attempted to drive its vehicle off of the aircraft. But they had touched down in a field of soft, oil-soaked mud. As soon as the front wheels of the SEAL vehicle dropped into the mud, it was stuck fast in the muck

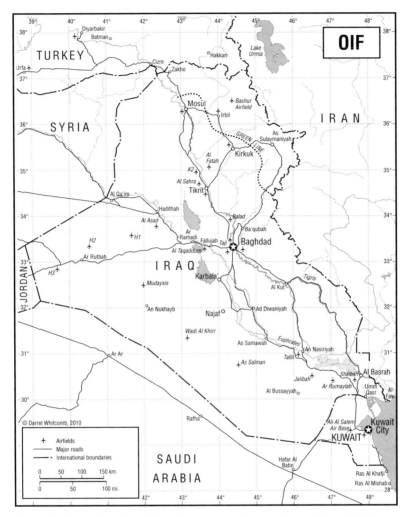

Figure 7. Operation Iraqi Freedom area of operations. (Copyright Darrel Whitcomb, 2010.)

with its rear half still in the Pave Low. When notified by his rear gunner, MSgt Flo England, Borland had no choice but to hold his position as his troops worked the problem. He did call Colonel O'Boyle above to apprise him of the situation and to request some on-call fire support from AC-130s and A-10s, if necessary. After a few minutes, Borland spotted an enemy vehicle trying to approach his location. He reported the target to a flight of A-10s, and the flight lead destroyed the vehicle with a Maverick missile. Working feverishly, Borland's "back-end" team was finally able to get the vehicle clear of the aircraft. Borland then had to use all of the power that the aircraft could generate to break clear of the clinging mud—after having spent 20 minutes in enemy territory. The crew then flew to a forward arming and refueling point to pick up a team of British Royal Marines for another insertion. However, because of the delay, another crew had taken their load, and Borland's crew assumed alert for rescue or medevac.[19]

Another SEAL team landed on the top of a bunker that had not been so identified by intelligence. The quickness of the assault so stunned the Iraqi soldiers that they just raised their hands in surrender. At another site, SEALs captured several Fedayeen fighters who had just executed seven Iraqi officers intending to surrender their position and units.

The flying was very dangerous because the crews were landing their heavily laden helicopters in tight landing zones or on platforms with many obstructions around them. Before the initiation of hostilities, the crews rehearsed the mission several times with the SEALs on the Udairi Range complex. However, nothing could match the reality of the actual missions, especially when the Iraqis reacted to the attacks by firing missiles at coalition sites in Kuwait. Several times the crews, along with everybody else, had to don their bulky and uncomfortable chemical protection suits when the warning sirens announced that missiles were inbound.

Another danger existed in the operation that night. They were not the only helicopters in the air in that area. British helicopters were also airborne, as were untold numbers of aircraft from the large US Army, Marine, and allied maneuver forces queuing up to move into Iraq. Maj Gene Becker was there when his crew observed a large aerial explosion. They assumed that it was an exploding missile. The helicopters then loaded their assignment of British Royal Marines and delivered them to several more targets. A few days later, though, they discovered that the explosion they had witnessed was actually a midair collision between two British helicopters that killed six British troops and one American. For several more nights, the crews of the 20th supported the SEALs and also British Royal Marine forces as they operated in the Al Faw-Basrah area on a variety of follow-up missions.[20]

During the assault on Al Faw, Colonel O'Boyle orbited above in an AC-130 as the air mission commander and worked diligently to coordinate the actions on the ground with the movement of all the helicopters shuttling in and out to support the 1,000-plus main assault force, the fighter aircraft available above to provide immediate close air support, and the AC-130 gunships ready to provide the same. All of that had to be deconflicted from the other helicopter forces, the orbiting remotely piloted vehicles (RPV), and US Navy P-3s providing real-time intelligence and video link to the various commanders. The entire operation lasted over six hours.

Captain Michalek remembers that mission clearly, stating, "This was one of the most exciting missions that I've ever done in my career. There was a massive air armada, where the gunships prepped the LZs and took care of the enemy, but this was definitely a Pave Low mission and a good one. . . . For us, this was months of intensive planning that was capped with a hugely successful mission." Reviewing the performance of his crew in just the first two nights of the war, he also recalls that "these two [missions] were the biggest of OIF [Operation Iraqi Freedom] for my crew and, arguably, anybody in the war. We kicked off the war as the first crews to cross into Iraq and secured the #2 strategic priority, second only to the capture of Saddam Hussein."[21]

Colonel Slife monitored the Al Faw missions from the joint operations center as they were carried out uneventfully—quite a relief from the semiterror of the first night. Approaching sunrise, he directed the crews to return to Ali Al Salem to terminate. As they arrived, Slife met the crews and congratulated them all for a great night's work.[22]

The morning after the SEAL insertions, the strong forces of the US V Corps and the I MEF swept forward on their drive to Baghdad. Over the next several nights, Pave Low crews joined with other special operations assets to infiltrate and exfiltrate ODAs and other teams ahead of the advancing forces, to provide critical reconnaissance around major Iraqi cities and towns, and to team up with anti-Saddam elements. They developed plans to place several teams into the Karbala Gap, a narrow passageway between Lake Razzaza and the city of Karbala, through which the V Corps would have to pass to attack Baghdad. This mission was threatened with cancellation when a retired-military television talking head in the United States, while providing commentary on how the war would probably unfold, explained this very concept to anybody in the world who cared to pay attention. SOCCENT planners watched anxiously for any Iraqi response to the gaffe. When there was none, they executed the preplanned Karbala Gap missions. A flight of five Pave Lows, led by Maj Bill Rowell, inserted forces with more nonstandard vehicles and reinforced with USAF special tactics teams to seize an old Iraqi airfield at

Wadi al Khirr, near Najaf. It was to be used by MC-130s to bring forward even larger special forces elements to establish a base of operations for more ODAs operating ahead of the steadily advancing forces of the V Corps forces. Borland and his crew also flew on this mission, once again assuming the rescue role. Colonel Webb was on board and gave Borland the good news that he had been selected to attend the Weapons School starting in June 2003.[23]

After the turbulent events of the first few days, however, once the ground campaign started, the Pave Lows were steadily called upon to support the 5th SFG in particular and other special forces elements in general as they operated in front and on the flanks of the V Corps and the I MEF as they steadily advanced on Baghdad.

Colonels Webb and Slife watched their crews and support troops closely as the grind of steady and dangerous operations slowly took its toll. Slife began to see manifestations of fear developing. He had crew members who were obviously shying away from flight duty, using medical excuses to be removed from the flight schedule. Some of it, he felt, was cowardice, and he addressed the issue with the flight surgeons, only to discover that if a crew member reported certain maladies, the flight surgeons were obligated to declare them DNIF (duty not

Courtesy Wayne Mutza

Preparing to carry special forces teams into Iraq

including flight). Raised and inculcated with the idea that the Pave Low community was made up exclusively of heroic fire-eaters, he realized that this community, too, had its share of malingerers, individuals not so enamored with the mission or image, or those who did not have the true depth of courage which certainly *was* generally present among the group as a whole. He also realized that there was a difference between physical fear and cowardice as he watched crew members who developed nervous ticks or vomited before getting in the aircraft to fly successful missions. He accepted that as a leadership challenge and realized that he had to focus on the missions at hand, learning to recognize the externalization of fear that he now saw among a number of his troops. He had to help them deal with those challenges and also to isolate those nonperformers so that they did not detract from mission accomplishment or infect the others. Those were lessons hard learned earlier in the mountains of Afghanistan and now reinforced in the heat of Iraq. He and Webb did not hesitate to change the crews around as necessary to insure the best utilization of their personnel to accomplish the missions. It affected morale and upset many. But it had to be done.[24]

By early April, the V Corp had swept through the Karbala Gap and was attacking into Baghdad from the south, while the I MEF was attacking the capital city from the east and dispatching smaller task forces to sweep northward along the main north-south road to attack enemy units near Balad, Samarra, and Tikrit. The 20th continued to support the main effort with direct support to special forces elements continuing to screen the heavier forces. By mid-April, though, the V Corp divisions and I MEF units had fought into Baghdad and effectively terminated the Iraqi government. Saddam Hussein and his two sons were in hiding. On 14 April, the DOD issued a terse statement that all major combat operations had been concluded and began planning to rapidly reduce US presence to 30,000 troops for stabilization duty.

During the main attacks on Baghdad, the 20th was assigned another SEAL mission. This time, it flew a mixed force of SEALs and Polish commandoes to the Mukarayin Dam, 57 miles northeast of the capital city. Intelligence sources indicated that Fedayeen or other former Iraqi soldiers intended to destroy the dam and flood the local area. As the Pave Lows hovered over the structure, the Soldiers and Sailors fast-roped down and took the guards by surprise. Some of the attackers took up their own guard duties as others searched the facility for explosives. Fortunately, no explosives were found, and enemy elements never attacked the structure.[25]

The Pave Low crews of the 20th continued to support their special operations customers as they attempted to sweep up remnants of resistance. The demand for sorties steadily declined. But disturbing reports of scattered resistance began to arrive at the various headquarters. In a last desperate attempt to foment social chaos to frustrate the allied forces, Saddam opened his prisons and armories, spreading armed fighters, weapons, and explosives across the country. At the same time, coalition leaders ordered the dissolution of the Iraqi armed forces. The rapid release of so many trained men from active and organized military service provided a recruiting pool for anti-coalition forces, which were soon active along the road and within the villages and cities of Iraq. This became glaringly obvious when, on 24 April, an infantry battalion from the 82d Airborne Division entered the city of Fallujah, 25 miles west of Baghdad, and was met by a lawless, well-armed mob carrying signs saying, "US killers, we'll kick you out." Somebody fired a weapon, and the resulting "battle" led to the death of 17 Iraqis, with 60 more wounded. The action also signaled that perhaps this war was not yet over. Regardless, on 1 May, Pres. George W. Bush announced to the nation that "major combat operations in Iraq have ended. . . . Now our coalition is engaged in securing and reconstructing that country."[26]

As did most other units, the men of the 20th SOS began packing up to go home. One of the first to leave was Sergeant Jobling, who went home and had surgery on his foot. Initial plans called for one-half of the detachment to return to Hurlburt within the next several weeks, leaving five of its aircraft at Ali Al Salem and the four still at Djibouti. Lieutenant Borland and crew went over to Djibouti for several weeks. He had qualified as an IP just a few months prior to OIF and was dispatched to train new crew members in the relatively benign environment of the Horn of Africa for a few weeks prior to returning home to attend the Weapons School.

During the major combat operations of OIF, the crews of the 20th had inserted 322 SOF teams and logged 966 combat flight hours on 276 missions. Arriving back at Hurlburt, Lt Col Brad Webb passed command of the 20th SOS to Lt Col R. K. Williams on 30 June. Lt Col Jim Slife remained with the 20th as the operations officer.[27]

Courtesy Col Darrel Whitcomb, USAF, Retired

Col R. K. Williams, USAF

21st Special Operations Squadron

As early as the summer of 2002, the 352d SOG began to receive indications that it would be involved in any reengagement with Iraq, as both EUCOM and SOCEUR began to look at possible contingencies. During October, though, it had to focus on another ORI conducted by an AFSOC inspection team. The group deployed to RAF Fairford for over three weeks and performed well, receiving an overall excellent rating. The 21st SOS and one other squadron received "outstanding" ratings. Colonel Lengyel was extremely proud of his officers and Airmen for their accomplishments, especially their performance on the tactical missions. His squadron troops were also closely watching the operations of the 20th SOS in Afghanistan and learning from its experiences. Lengyel appointed Capt Matt Smith to serve as his primary planner for any Iraq contingencies as they began to consider what was apparently on the horizon for the unit. In that capacity, he would work closely with Maj Pete Doty, who had been transferred from the 21st SOS to the plans office in the 352d SOG and was working on the larger scheme for the entire group.[28]

As 2003 began, the 352d was now getting fairly clear guidance from SOCEUR that it would be deploying with the US Army 10th SFG and some other special forces elements to Turkey to support operations in northern Iraq as part of the overall 1003V plan. However, the Turkish government had not granted the United States entry rights for its forces, pending the outcome of a vigorous debate within the government concerning its support for the war. Regardless, the 352d SOG commander, Col Otis Mannon, wanted to act proactively. He had the authority to move his units anywhere within the EUCOM area of responsibility. As his Airmen scrambled at Mildenhall to take care of last-minute items such as required shots and inoculations, he decided to deploy his operational forces forward to a military airfield at Constanta, Romania, on the Black Sea coast, only 200 miles from Turkish airspace. In mid-February, a 30-person advance element departed for Constanta to arrange for the arrival of the main body. One week later, the 21st SOS launched six Pave Lows for the long flight. Using a series of in-flight refuelings and quick "gas-and-goes" at airfields in Germany and Hungary, the crews made it to Constanta after a 17-hour duty day with all six aircraft mission ready. The crews were met by the advanced element and bedded down in an unused portion of the airport terminal. They joined an overall 352d contingent of 1,000-plus Airmen that also included AC-130 gunships from the 16th SOW. That contingent was also a component of a larger JSOTF named Task Force Viking, led by the commander of the US Army 10th SFG, Col Charles Cleveland. Maj Pete Doty was dispatched to serve with Colonel Cleveland as his joint air operations officer.[29]

Courtesy Col Darrel Whitcomb, USAF, Retired

Col Greg Lengyel, USAF

Under operational plans extant at that time, the 21st SOS was instructed to be prepared to perform rescue for forces in the north and
also serve as a potential recovery element as part of the overall theater
rescue plan. It would also conduct its classic SOF missions in support
of the 10th SFG and Kurdish forces deployed along the "Green Line,"
a 350-kilometer front that divided them from 13 Iraqi army divisions
arrayed along that line. Two Pave Low pilots, Maj Max Sears and Maj
Ed Vanzandt, were attached to the 10th SFG to serve with two of their
battalions as air liaison officers.[30]

The 21st's ultimate mission was to work with the ground forces to
keep those Iraqi forces tied up and incapable of reinforcing their
units being engaged by the heavy coalition forces attacking out of
Kuwait and the other special forces task forces attacking in the western
part of Iraq.[31] In Iraq the squadron would be under the operational
control of the JSOAD-N, commanded by Colonel Mannon. He dispatched a small team including SMSgt John DeSalle to Qatar to act as
a liaison element with the theater CJSOAC.

The weather was predicted to be cold and snowy. The crews were
told to prepare for their follow-on flight to the airfield at Batman,
Turkey, the same airfield used by the 21st SOS helicopters in Desert
Storm. Again, living conditions there would be austere. They were
also told to begin tactical planning for several contingency missions
in the region with various special forces and coalition elements.
However, Turkey still had not approved the missions, and Lengyel
was instructed to develop a CSAR contingency plan for providing
coverage of forces in northern Iraq from Constanta. His planners did
as directed, pointing out that current seasonal weather conditions,
the topography of Turkey, and the distances involved made such a
contingency minimally acceptable at best. Unsure as to how long they
would be at Constanta, Lengyel also had Williams begin local flying
so that his aircrews could maintain some level of flight currency. On
one occasion, two aircraft were launched on local training sorties.
However, heavy fog moved in over the airfield before they could recover. The crews put the aircraft safely down in fields one-and-a-half
miles away. Security forces from the 352d dispatched to the site and
worked with Romanian police to secure the aircraft until they could
be flown onto the airfield the next day. However, the flight crews were
assessed heavy beer penalties for violating squadron protocol dictating
that such landings within two miles of the intended airfield were not
looked upon as "manly." Such penalties, though, could only be assessed

back at Mildenhall since CENTCOM General Order Number 1 specified no alcohol in its theater.

Lengyel and Williams realized that combat operations originating in Constanta were just not realistic. They grabbed aerial charts of the region and began to conceive a new plan. They were aware that the British had a large base at Akrotiri, Cyprus, and that other USAF elements were moving in there. Quick calculations indicated that the flying time from there into northern Iraq was just five hours for the Pave Lows. So Lengyel and Williams, believing that "if you start a rumor and repeat it enough times, it will catch on and can become the truth," started the rumor that "the Paves are moving to Cyprus." Lengyel let it germinate for a few days and then approached Colonel Mannon with a well-thought-out plan. He approved it and got the concept accepted by headquarters.

On 5 March, Colonel Williams and a small support team flew to Akrotiri and met with British and American commanders. They were amenable to the move but made it very clear that they could provide little beyond ramp space. Williams encountered some British personnel that he knew from their Special Boat Squadron. Using relationships that the squadron had established back in Great Britain, he was able to procure the use of some very fine tents and even four "chefs" to prepare meals for the 21st SOS Airmen. Williams put his small detachment to work setting up their small camp, quickly named "Camp Mohawk" in honor of several of the Pave Low flight engineers and gunners who had begun to cut their hair in the style of Mohawk Indians. He then called back to Colonel Lengyel and told him that they were ready for the aircraft and crews. Lengyel moved quickly, and all were in place at Akrotiri by 10 March.

A few days later, another 21st SOS Pave Low with extra crew members flew down from Mildenhall and joined the unit. Initially left behind at Mildenhall to handle "rear area" items, the squadron superintendent, SMSgt Jim Kradel, was also able to join the unit there and even joined a formed crew. In fact, 10 full crews were now available for combat duty. Crew number 10 was led by Capt Steve Edwards; his copilot was Capt Derrick Stamos. Morale was high, and everybody felt that he was as prepared as possible. They were subsequently joined by a company of Soldiers from the 10th SFG and some special tactics teams from the 321st STS, also from the 352d SOG, and the 123d STS from the Kentucky ANG. Two Pave Lows and crews were placed on alert for CSAR. In place and ready to go, all now awaited the decision of the Turkish government.[32]

Unfortunately, permission for US and coalition forces to enter Iraq through Turkey was not forthcoming. The Turkish government debated the issue, and its parliament took a vote. While the yeas outnumbered the nays, the significant number of abstentions precluded a clear majority for approval. Accordingly, Task Force Horse was diverted to Kuwait, and CENTCOM began exploring other options to get its designated special forces into northern Iraq. The troops of the 21st SOS monitored the efforts of the 20th SOS crews as they initiated operations on 19 March. Some crews even sat in their helicopters and used their SATCOMs to listen to the 20th crews conduct their missions. They also watched as the ground units in the south attacked on 21 March. At the same time, behind-the-scenes efforts were ongoing to convince the Turkish government to authorize limited overflight privileges to US and coalition flights. Consideration was also given to diverting the 21st SOS to the coalition special forces task forces working in western Iraq.[33]

Finally, the Turks granted overflight permission on 25 March. In the early afternoon, two Pave Lows took off for the Bashur Airfield in northern Iraq. The lead aircraft was flown by Capt Randy Voas and Capt Craig Prather; Colonel Lengyel was aboard as the overall mission commander. Since the weather over Turkey was extremely bad, the flight had to return to Akrotiri. As the helicopters landed, Voas knew that other crews would want to take their place the next day. Before reentering the squadron area, he asked Lengyel, "Same crews, just rolling 24 hours. Right, sir?" Voas and Prather held their breath. Lengyel smiled and said, "Okay, we will do that." Predictably, the other crews were not happy.

The two crews relaunched the next day. The weather was better en route, with clouds in the arrival area. Both aircraft were at their absolute maximum wartime weights for takeoff. Rendezvousing with an MC-130, they proceeded east along the Turkey-Syria border, refueling several times. As the two aircraft approached the Iraqi border, Lengyel replaced Prather in the right seat, explaining, "I'm the squadron commander. It is my prerogative to lead my squadron into combat." Each helicopter had a partial ODA and an STS team aboard. Approaching Bashur Airfield, the crews had to use the full TF/TA, FLIR, and precision navigation capabilities of the Pave Lows to get down through the low clouds and darkness to land. Prather was a bit surprised at what he saw. He had expected Iraq to be desert. These mountains, with their accompanying grungy weather, looked a great deal like Scotland, where the 21st did its Pave Low mountain training.[34]

As the engines were shut down, Colonel Lengyel immediately disembarked and went to find whoever was in charge. He was soon accosted by a very excited senior officer who told him that his helicopters were sitting in the drop zone for a mass night parachute assault by two battalions of the 173d Airborne Brigade, expected in a few hours. Lengyel had the two crews start up and then flew about three miles farther south in the valley, where they landed, shut down their engines, and relaxed to watch the paratroopers. As scheduled, the lumbering C-17s entered the valley and began disgorging their heavy equipment first and then strings of paratroopers. The successive C-17s dropped their sticks of jumpers farther and farther to the south until Lengyel realized that some of the paratroops were in danger of landing on their machines. He shouted to the crews to turn on their position lights so that the falling Soldiers could see them. Regardless, several landed all around the helicopters, one with his parachute canopy draped over one of the stationary main rotor blades. The fields were wet and soggy from recent rain and snow, and several of the troops needed assistance from the Pave Low crews to dig themselves out of the mud. The crews enjoyed watching the "combat" jump as the troops of the 173d "seized" the airfield. Numerous troops were injured in the jump, and the 21st SOS troops transported 34 of them down to the first-aid station set up at the airfield. The crews then flew around the valley helping to locate and direct isolated "LGOPPs"— little groups of pissed-off paratroopers. Quickly, though, the Soldiers of the 173d formed into ever-larger groups and within two hours were functioning as coherent units and occupying their initial designated positions. Above them the Pave Lows remained within the confines of the valley and under the weather; they rendezvoused one more time with an MC-130 to fill their fuel tanks before finally landing and terminating their mission. The crews slept in their helicopters.

As their engines slowly wound down, Lengyel had a chance to reflect on the incredible events of that day. His crews had planned and launched out of a forward base into an austere airfield high in dangerous snow-capped and cloud-shrouded mountains of a nation torn by war. After arriving, they were engaged in a series of events that 24 hours before were hardly imaginable. His crews had shown great courage and imaginative skill in handling it all, logging 13 hours of flight time

Courtesy Maj Craig Prather, USAF

The lead 21st SOS crew into northern Iraq. *Left to right*: (*standing*) MSgt Doug Darner, 1st Lt Craig Prather, A1C Brandon Midthun, MSgt Paul Bratcher, and TSgt Shane Genis; (*kneeling*) 1st Lt Randy Voas and Lt Col Greg Lengyel.

during the mission. He was especially proud of his lead pilots, Captains Voas and Prather, and nominated them for the Cheney Trophy. They were subsequently selected to receive that prestigious award for 2003.[35]

Over the next several days, the rest of the Pave Lows, crews, and support personnel of the 21st SOS were moved into Bashur, many aboard MC-130s. Sergeant Kradel was part of that contingent. Upon arrival, he became decisively engaged with procuring the equipment and supplies that his Airmen needed to operate. He was also able to participate in several flights with his assigned crew, although he never had a requirement to fire his weapon in anger. Clearly, though, his focus was on providing for his troops, saying later of this time, "That was probably one of my proudest accomplishments of my career— what we did in the initial stages of [the operation]."[36]

Two aircraft and crews were placed on CSAR alert. The rest began working directly with the Soldiers of the 10th SFG, many of whom they had worked with as far back as Bosnia and even Provide Comfort. All three battalions were now in place, with 51 individual ODAs performing a variety of missions. The Pave Low crews began to work with them as they teamed with Kurdish units to neutralize a terrorist element in that area known as Ansar al-Islam and led by Abu Musab al-Zarqawi. This estimated 700-man force was operating along the Iranian border and needed to be neutralized before any significant operations could be launched against Iraqi main force units along the Green Line. For several days, the five ODAs involved in the effort orchestrated an effective campaign with their Kurd allies to attack and neutralize the element. Pave Lows, staging out of a small airfield near As Sulaymaniyah, 70 miles southeast of Bashur, flew many support missions, providing reconnaissance, logistic support, and casualty evacuation for the allied forces. The Airmen of the 21st SOS were performing the same kind of air commando missions in Iraq that their predecessors in Laos had performed 33 years earlier—and with just as much professionalism and gusto. The Pave Lows also supported the ODAs and various Kurdish forces as they attacked and drove back Iraqi main force units to seize and hold the key cities of Kirkuk and Mosul. Their efforts prevented the units from being moved south to engage the allied forces converging on Baghdad.[37]

As the 21st SOS Airmen settled in at Bashur, Colonel Williams worked with Sergeant Kradel to provide for the care and feeding of his men and women. He had to set up strict rules and conditions for crew rest because his crews were clearly being worn out by the pace of operations. His maintenance teams were absolutely superb, sustaining a 98 percent launch rate in the most austere of conditions. All troops were billeted in 20-person tents with little privacy, except for one private toilet for the females. He had to insist on the highest decorum from all of his troops but rediscovered the timeless maxim that the best way to keep troops out of trouble is to keep them so busy that they have to use any off-duty time for sleep. Williams remembered telling them, "I don't want to hear about any issues. You figure out what level of human dignity and respect is required, and the first issue—you're on the next plane home. Whoever it is."[38]

In early April, Williams received a personal phone call from Colonel O'Boyle, who had to address a personnel issue from the perspective of his "real" job as the commander of the 16th SOG at Hurlburt. One of his subordinate units, the 20th SOS, would be losing its commander, Lt Col Brad Webb, in a few months because he had been selected to attend the National War College. O'Boyle was going to need a new commander for the unit and offered the job to Williams, who really didn't need to answer the question.

On 21 April, Colonel Lengyel moved his unit west to an airfield seized near the large city of Irbil. There Williams was able to find more permanent billeting for his troops, including some showers. Additionally, he rotated some of his troops home, replacing them with newly qualified Pave Low crew members and support personnel so that as many 21st Airmen as possible could gain combat experience. While at Irbil, Sergeant DeSalle was able to join the squadron and even fly a few sorties as a crew gunner.

Likewise, Colonel Williams himself took an operational mission. When the JSOAD-S could not accept a mission because of poor weather conditions in the south, the 21st SOS received the tasking. Williams led a flight of three Pave Lows on a day mission to recover a SEAL element off of a dam they had seized and were guarding in central Iraq. They landed at Baghdad International Airport (BIAP) to drop off the Sailors just as the sun was setting. Lifting off in the dark, they turned north for Irbil. Just a few minutes north of the city, they were engaged with ground fire from several positions. The gunners on all three aircraft returned fire and also observed an RPG directed at one of the aircraft. One helicopter did receive some small arms hits. A month later, Williams turned over his operations officer duties to Lt Col Mark Harmon and departed for Mildenhall so that he could move his family to Hurlburt.[39]

Most missions flown in support of the ODAs were flown during the day. Except right along the Green Line, most areas were low threat—many Pave Low crews never observed any ground fire and never had to fire their guns. Occasionally, A-10s flew into the area and provided escort for the Pave Lows whenever they flew into an area where there might be a threat. Captains Edwards and Stamos flew missions into several areas where heavy fighting with conventional Iraqi forces had taken place. They saw the death and destruction rained down upon Saddam's forces. They also noticed great stockpiles of weapons and explosives scattered over the terrain and military bases completely unguarded. Ominously, they watched "civilians" as they looted the bases and stockpiles and carried off truckloads of those implements of death: bombs, grenades, RPGs, and machine guns. Those actions did not suggest peaceful times ahead.[40]

However, as relative calm began to return to Iraq, USAF and other coalition units were allowed to begin returning to their home bases. In

June 2003, Colonel Lengyel was directed to return four of his aircraft and one-half of his personnel to Mildenhall. They flew their aircraft back to their home base. Craig Prather had upgraded to aircraft commander in combat. He commanded one of the aircraft on the flight home as they returned over Turkey, Greece, Italy, and France. Sergeant DeSalle flew out as a gunner on one of the last aircraft to return home. Arriving back at Mildenhall, he was selected to take over as the superintendent of the 352d SOG Weapons and Tactics Office.[41]

They had been home only a few days when the 21st SOS was called upon to deploy two Pave Lows, crews, and support personnel to assist with another NEO in Liberia, as once again that country was ravaged by political unrest and indications of possible civil war. The deployment was of only short duration as a USMC MEU replaced the 352d team. However, it highlighted the fact that NEO was still a key mission for the Pave Lows. The rest of the 21st SOS returned to RAF Mildenhall in July, and the JSOAD-N was inactivated. Responsibility for any residual SOF aviation activity in Iraq passed to the JSOAD-S.[42]

For the rest of the year, the 21st SOS returned to its cycle of training exercises and deployments as experienced personnel left the squadron and new ones arrived. There were deployments to Scotland, Belgium, Spain, and Germany. In September Lt Col Mark Harmon led a three-ship Pave Low deployment back to Albania to participate in a combined exercise with British elements. Major Doty was one of his aircraft commanders and enjoyed the flying over Albania, Macedonia, and Bulgaria. Sadly, though, those were his last flights in the Pave Low. Shortly after returning to England, he and his family were transferred back to the United States to a nonflying assignment.[43]

In November 2003, the 21st SOS was again called upon to support a US presidential visit to Great Britain when President Bush and the First Lady arrived for a three-day sojourn. Three Pave Lows were utilized as part of a larger fleet of helicopters to shuttle the president and entourage from London's Heathrow Airport to Buckingham Palace and several other locations, all without incident, and in the best traditions of a now long history of such support by the 21st SOS. It was an anticlimactic end to a very climactic year.[44]

20th Special Operations Squadron

Standing in front of his troops as he assumed command of the 20th SOS on 30 June, Lt Col R. K. Williams could not help but notice that very few of his troops were present. In fact, about a third of the squadron was still in Djibouti and Kuwait. After a short three weeks learning to find his office in the squadron building, he was off to Kuwait to observe the unit operations there. The unit was still at Ali Al Salem AB. What he found was an operation that had dramatically wound down. Expectations were heavy that the Pave Lows would be ordered home very soon, possibly at the end of July. Williams made plans to travel on to Djibouti to visit his unit element there. He was anxious to do so because its operations seemed to be picking up in support of the larger GWOT. One of the crews there was led by Maj Casey Ward and 1st Lt Matt Berry. Even though it was extremely hot, they felt that the deployment was relatively benign and provided an opportunity to gain some very good and low-stress training compared to the recent events in Kuwait and Iraq.[45]

However, disturbing events continued to occur across Iraq, especially the use of car bombs and improvised explosive devices (IED) placed along roads. Indications seemed to point to the beginning of an organized resistance or even a guerilla-type effort by nascent pro-Saddamists. Williams began to realize that these events portended a longer mission for the Pave Lows. Within a week, Williams's orders were changed; he was not going to Djibouti. Instead, he would remain in Kuwait and take command of the remaining JSOAD-S, with a residual force of four Pave Lows and other AFSOC assets and responsibility for SOF aviation throughout Iraq. Williams would report to the JSOAC under SOCCENT and work closely with the now consolidated CJSOTF-AP (Arabian Peninsula), which absorbed all of the residual units from the earlier multiple CJSOTFs and commanded the 5th SFG and a small detachment of US Navy SEALs. Williams flew up to Baghdad to coordinate with the 5th Group commander, Col Hector Pagan, as his Soldiers began to orient upon and attack these growing rebel groups. Pagan's first request was that Williams bring his Pave Lows to Baghdad. Williams so moved his aircraft and personnel, dramatically reducing his unit's response times for missions. He also began to coordinate with a US Navy Reserve helicopter unit that was supporting 5th Group so that the aviation elements of CJSOTF-AP could conduct joint operations.

Williams returned to Hurlburt in October, just in time to congratulate Col Otis Mannon as he arrived to take command of the 16th SOW from Col Frank Kisner. Before leaving Mildenhall, Mannon had given command of the 352d SOG to Col Dennis Jones, another career Pave Low pilot. Shortly thereafter, the 20th SOS received an operational order to deploy a Pave Low element back into Afghanistan to participate in Operation Mountain Resolve. Working quickly, Williams was able to convince USSOCOM to move his remaining element in Djibouti to Bagram. Lt Col Jim Slife went over to command that detachment. He understood that the environment in Afghanistan would be much more challenging than what his Djibouti crews were used to encountering, and he augmented it with more experienced Airmen from the 20th SOS as they moved to Afghanistan for the highly classified operation against al-Qaeda and Taliban elements established along the Afghanistan/Pakistan border. Several Pave Low crew members from the 551st SOS also deployed with the detachment.

Tragically, that operation suffered a terrible loss on 23 November when MH-53M #70-1625, originally a CH-53 that had flown hard combat with the 21st SOS at NKP, Thailand, from 1971 to 1975, crashed nine miles east of the Bagram Airfield. The aircraft was the wingman in a two-ship formation flying an infiltration mission at dusk. The aircraft was heavy and experienced a stall and failure of the number two engine. The aircraft commander, Maj Steve Plumhoff from the 551st SOS, attempted to return to Bagram. He tried to jettison his external tanks, but they did not release. The aircraft could not maintain level flight at its current weight. While dumping fuel, Plumhoff next tried to land the aircraft on a small sandbar along a river. However, during the approach, the second engine failed, and the aircraft landed on a rocky riverbank. As it did, the tail boom separated; the helicopter rolled to the left, came to rest inverted, and burst into flames. Capt Mark Newell was the aircraft commander on the lead aircraft and landed nearby to attempt to rescue the crew and passengers. He and his crew braved the fire and exploding .50-caliber rounds to pull survivors from the wreckage. They were only partly successful. Major Plumhoff was killed, as were MSgt William Kerwood, TSgt Howard Walters, and SSgt Thomas Walkup Jr., all three from the 20th SOS. Additionally, one Soldier on board was killed. The fire burned for several days, making remains recovery and identification challenging for Slife, who had to handle the attendant issues in Afghanistan, and for Williams back at Hurlburt, who had to work in a straightforward fashion with the families of those lost.[46]

Courtesy 58th SOW History Office

Maj Steve Plumhoff, USAF

The accident was a terrible shock to the 20th SOS. Over the years, it had flown so much combat in so many theaters. It had lost numerous aircraft in both accidents and combat. However, in terms of troops lost, the numbers were small. Consequently, the loss of three of its guys and a fellow Pave Low pilot from Kirtland hit the unit hard, and it rallied around the families and surviving members. The 20th SOS held a moving memorial service to honor those lost, and Colonel Williams eulogized his Airmen, saying,

> Bill, Howie, and Tom were pillars of esprit de corps, and added infinite strength to our unit cohesion. They were professional and moral leaders of our "Greatest Generation." To them, everything was for the team . . . for the greater good . . . for all of us. . . . Through courage, honor, and character, and by their heroic actions, our brothers have shown us that our American freedom has been given to us on a golden platter . . . made by the hand of God . . . and paid for by the blood of our brothers.

Subsequently, three streets on the east side of Hurlburt Field were redesignated with the names of the Airmen as a form of permanent remembrance.[47]

Then they went back to work. The unit still had its detachment of four aircraft and personnel in Iraq, now firmly ensconced in Baghdad. Operation Mountain Resolve was terminated, and Colonel Slife and three aircraft, crews, and support troops moved to Baghdad to rejoin the 20th element there. In mid-December, Pave Low crews played a role in the mission that led to the capture of Saddam Hussein. All in all, 2003 had been as eventful a year for the 20th as it had been for the 21st.[48]

After his foot healed, Sergeant Jobling made another rotation over to the unit at BIAP. He returned to Hurlburt just before Christmas and went to work in the squadron tactics office. The unit still had responsibilities and obligations in other parts of the world. However, for the last two years, the unit had been operating exclusively in the Middle East. Jobling could see that its tactics training was being steadily modified to focus on the conditions in that region. He was concerned that no training was now being done for contingencies in the Pacific or South America. Questions were being asked, "Can we do this? Are we prepared to operate there?" In many cases, the answer now was no. Most ominously, though, he could sense that the unit as a whole was tired. Regardless, the rotations to Iraq continued. Jobling met the rotation schedule as his turn arrived.[49]

The Pave Lows would not be used again in Afghanistan. The reason was practical. When the aircraft were modified with foldable blades for storage aboard ships, the ensuing aircraft weight increase was about 3,000 pounds, which correspondingly reduced the useful load capability of the aircraft by the same amount. At the higher elevations of Afghanistan, this meant that the Pave Lows could not provide as much lift capability as the MH-47s, which did not have the blade-folding capability and limitation. However, Pave capabilities were perfect for the special forces units working in Iraq to attack and destroy the insurgent forces.[50]

Back at Hurlburt, Colonel Williams welcomed home his detachment returning from its classified deployment in Afghanistan and began to address several larger items. The unit appeared to be committed to Iraq for an indeterminate length. To help even out the personnel tempo of deployments for his troops, he and Colonel Slife worked out a flight rotation plan whereby troops would deploy for 90 days and then be home for 180 days, in general, as integral flights.

The 20th also needed additional aircraft. The losses in Afghanistan and Iraq over the last two years had left the squadron with only 17 aircraft. Williams requested two machines from the 551st at Kirtland. These would be MH-53Js, since that was all Kirtland had. They would not be available for deployment. However, he could use them for local training and exercises.

Williams further began an initiative to have the 21st SOS replace the 20th SOS in Iraq for a long duration so that the 20th could reconstitute. Such a move would require detailed coordination among USSOCOM, CENTCOM, and EUCOM and would eventually have to be decided at the OSD level. Regardless, Williams pushed the effort forward.[51]

Air Force Special Operations Command

As the USAF became increasingly involved in combat operations in OEF and now OIF, senior service leadership finally decided to address the long-festering problem of what to do with CSAR. After a series of extensive reviews that had been ongoing since the Bosnia operations and some of the difficulties identified by Lt Gen Chuck Wald in Afghanistan, the CSAF, Gen John Jumper, signed out a directive transferring all USAF CONUS CSAR-designated units from the ACC to AFSOC effective 1 October 2003. The intent was to enhance the mission training and efficiencies by combining similar missions, skills, and personnel within a single command. This would capitalize on synergies inherent in combined personnel and organizational structures. From a historical perspective, the reorganization harkened back to the Forward Look concept created when Twenty-Third Air Force was activated with rescue and SOF components. The ACC commander, Gen Hal Hornburg, concurred with the change, believing that it was a positive move for the rescue community overall. The directive also pointed out that these forces would not be USSOCOM assets. They were designated as USAF rescue forces and, when deployed into any operational theater, would be under the operational control of the C/JFACC, while the SOF forces would be assigned to SOF commands. Organizational efficiencies would be realized by unit realignments, and career opportunities for both officers and enlisted would be broadened. The realignment would also allow each community to cross-train with the other on a steady basis so that TTPs could be better shared.[52]

AFSOC would take control of Moody AFB, Georgia. It would also take administrative control of the Moody-based 347th Rescue Wing, its subordinate 563d Rescue Group at Davis-Monthan, and the 66th RQS at Nellis. It would gain 45 HH-60s, 14 HC-130s, five C-130s, and 122 new manpower authorizations, plus 3,993 officers and Airmen. Another 15 HH-60s, five HC-130s, and four MC-130s were also available from aligned AFR units, and another 12 HH-60s and five HC-130s from aligned ANG units, along with 1,140 AFR and 1,779 ANG assigned personnel. It was a significant development for AFSOC. However, the two mission areas—special operations and CSAR—would be handled separately. The move seemed to indicate that the USAF had finally decided to acknowledge that the HH-60 community was its de facto rescue force of choice, finally releasing the Pave Lows for complete focus on their special operations tasks. Only time would tell. General Hester set the vector for the change, though, when he stated that "the introduction of CSAR to AFSOC should mean little change to rescue organizations or individuals within these units. This realignment will be transparent, outside of the patch change on uniforms. There will be no change on how forces are presented to combatant commanders."[53]

58th Special Operations Wing

By design and intent, operations at the training unit were much more staid than they were at the operational units. Throughout 2003 the 551st SOS and 58th TRSS trained and graduated 11 pilots, eight flight engineers, and eight aerial gunners for the fleet. Additionally, another 286 individuals received recurrent training in the MH-53 simulator, which had now been upgraded with MH-53M modifications. The unit had 10 MH-53Js available for training; none was scheduled for the MH-53M modification. All actual MH-53M flying had to be done in the operational squadrons. On average, 5.8 aircraft were available daily for missions, a lower than normal rate due to a shortage of spare parts caused by the increased demand for the 20th and 21st Squadrons.

Responding to the experiences of Colonel Kingsley and the 20th SOS in Afghanistan, the flying curriculum was modified to include much more training on brownout landings. Instructor crews also made the training available to operational unit personnel prior to deployment. Overseeing these changes in the 551st SOS, Lt Col Tim Leahy handed over command of the unit to Lt Col Lance Bodine on 20 June. Similarly, just two months later, Col Paul Harmon assumed command of the 551st's parent unit, the 58th SOG.[54]

The 58th Wing and the 551st SOS also directly supported the units in combat by augmenting personnel. Unit Airmen went to Afghanistan with the 20th SOS and flew in the classified direct action missions in support of Task Force Dagger and Task Force K-Bar. They also augmented the 20th detachment at Djibouti, where on a mission in June 2003, one crew recovered the injured personnel from two USMC CH-53Es seriously damaged by bombs errantly dropped by B-52s on a bombing range in Djibouti. As the deployment of the 20th was extended in Iraq in the summer of 2003, the 551st sent six instructor crew members to help out. When the 20th sent the Djibouti detachment to Afghanistan in the fall, one of the 551st pilots, Maj Steve Plumhoff, was killed in the tragic crash in November along with the three enlisted Airmen from the 20th SOS while participating in Operation Mountain Resolve. To honor him, the entryway into the 58th SOW area was named Plumhoff Way, a permanent reminder that even the training units had to bear the cost of war.[55]

Notes

1. Stewart, *American Military History*, vol. 2, 476.
2. White House, "President Bush Delivers Graduation Speech at West Point," press release, White House website.
3. Stewart, *American Military History*, vol. 2, 477.
4. Ibid., 477.
5. History of 352d SOG, 1 Jan–31 Dec 2003, vol. 1, 1.
6. Whitcomb, "Rescue Operations in the Second Gulf War," 95–102; and Webb, interview.
7. Webb and Slife, interviews; and Michalek, personal notes, provided to the author.
8. Ezell, interview; and Stricklin to the author, e-mail, 23 Jan 2011.
9. Webb and Slife, interviews.
10. Slife, interview; and Michalek, personal notes, provided to the author.
11. AF Safety Report: Executive Summary, Aircraft Accident Investigation MH-53M #68-10930, n.d., AFSOC Judge Advocate's Office (JAO), Hurlburt Field, FL; and Webb and Slife, interviews.

12. Fontenot, Degen, and Tohn, *On Point*, 478–79.

13. Atkinson, *In the Company of Soldiers*, 93.

14. Ezell, interview.

15. H-53 Major Aircraft Accident List, n.d., AFSOC Safety (SE) Office; Robinson, *Masters of Chaos*, 277; and Michalek, personal notes, provided to the author.

16. Berry and Jobling, interviews.

17. Berry and Slife, interviews; Gordon and Trainor, *Cobra II*, 169–77; and Michalek, personal notes, provided to the author.

18. Ezell, interview.

19. Borland, interview.

20. Berry and Gene Becker, interviews; and Whitcomb, "Rescue Operations in the Second Gulf War," n.p.

21. Michalek, personal notes, provided to the author.

22. Boyne, *Operation Iraqi Freedom*, 281–85; Bahmanyar and Osman, *SEALs*, 148–54; and Borland, interview.

23. Slife, interview; Robinson, *Masters of Chaos*, 248, 254; Briscoe et al., *All Roads Lead to Baghdad*, 134–39; and Rowell to the author, e-mail.

24. Slife, interview.

25. Bahmanyar and Osman, *SEALs*, 155–57.

26. Atkinson, *In the Company of Soldiers*, 462; Stewart, *American Military History*, vol. 2, 486–90; History of 16th SOW, 1 Jan–31 Dec 2003, vol. 1, xx; and Gordon and Trainor, *Cobra II*, 463.

27. History of 16th SOW, 1 Jan–31 Dec 2003, vol. 1, xx; and Borland, interview.

28. Williams and Lengyel, interviews; and Doty to the author, e-mail.

29. Robinson, *Masters of Chaos*, 296; and Williams, interview.

30. Doty to the author, e-mail.

31. Williams and Lengyel, interviews.

32. Lengyel, Williams, and Kradel, interviews; and History of 352d SOG, 1 Jan–31 Dec 2003, vol. 1, n.p., original doc. n42.

33. Robinson, *Masters of Chaos*, 297–99.

34. Prather, interview.

35. Gordon and Trainor, *Cobra II*, 340–41; Fontenot, Degen, and Tohn, *On Point*, 227–29; and Lengyel and Prather, interviews.

36. Kradel, interview.

37. History of 352d SOG, 1 Jan–31 Dec 2003, vol. 1, n.p., original doc. n452; Robinson, *Masters of Chaos*, 324–35; and Williams, interview.

38. Williams, interview.

39. Ibid.

40. Stamos, interview.

41. DeSalle, interview.

42. History of 352d SOG, 1 Jan–31 Dec 2003, vol. 1, n.p.; and Prather and Williams, interviews.

43. Doty to the author, e-mail.

44. History of 352d SOG, 1 Jan–31 Dec 2003, vol. 1, n.p.

45. Berry, interview.

46. Todd Lopez, "Local Airmen Laid to Rest," *Commando*, 23 Jan 2004; Williams and Slife, interviews; and Executive Summary: Helicopter Accident Investigation MH-53M #70-1625, n.d., AFSOC/JAO, Hurlburt Field, FL.

47. Williams and Becklund, interviews; and Williams to the author, e-mail, 9 Aug 2010.

48. Slife, interview.

49. Jobling, interview.

50. Becklund, interview.

51. Williams, interview.

52. History of AFSOC, 1 Jan–31 Dec 2003, vol. 1, 1, 27–33.

53. Ibid.; and Hebert, "CSAR, Under New Management," 84.

54. History of 58th SOW, 1 Jan–31 Dec 2003, vol. 1, 44–45, 56.

55. Ibid., 16–19.

Chapter 17

The Terminal Years

~2004–8

I didn't care about heroics. What I cared about was guys not getting killed because we hadn't given them the right flight equipment or tactics. I wanted them to do the mission and come home.

—Col Jim Slife

Iraq

Unfortunately, things were not settling down in Iraq quite as planned. More attacks were occurring across the country, and anticoalition forces consisting of former Saddam supporters and violent Islamist groups appeared to be growing and consolidating. In several instances, their forces set off huge truck bombs in public places, killing dozens of Westerners and Iraqis. In another incident, terrorists used a heat-seeking missile to shoot down a US Army CH-47, killing 16 US troops and wounding 20 more. Redeployment orders for many US and coalition units were rescinded. The V Corps returned home, and overall command of forces was consolidated under CJTF-7. It would command multinational divisions throughout the country as they carried out stabilization efforts so that the Iraqis could form a functioning government. Additionally, the CJTF-7 forces began conducting operations against these groups and organizing and training a new Iraqi military to take over. The CJSOTF–Arabian Peninsula (AP) remained in Iraq in direct support of this effort. The US Army 5th SFG was still its core unit, although slated to be replaced by the 10th SFG in January 2004. Collocated with them was a small detachment of US Navy SEALs from another task force. Increasingly, they were carrying out reconnaissance missions and psychological operations and hunting for high-value targets. The 20th SOS detachment of four Pave Lows and troops, located now at BIAP, provided them with an "any time, any place" capability.

20th Special Operations Squadron/ Expeditionary Special Operations Squadron

Lt Col Jim Slife was on-site as the commander. He also had control of a small detachment of US Navy SH-60s from HCS-4 and HCS-5 and worked closely with a detachment still in Iraq from the 160th SOAR. One of his aircraft commanders there was Capt Joe Michalek, now a flight commander. He worked diligently to help enable the movement up to BIAP. Michalek and his flight helped plan for and fly numerous missions in support of CJSOTF-AP forces and subordinate task forces as they nightly attacked al-Qaeda and insurgent elements across Iraq. For his combined and consistent outstanding efforts during OIF, he was nominated for and received the 2004 Lance P. Sijan Leadership Award.[1]

As 2004 began, Lt Col Jim Slife was not happy having his helicopters based at BIAP because the airfield was about to be given back to the Iraqis. Just south of there, SOCCENT was building a large complex at the Radwaniyah Palace that included helipads. However, Slife felt that if he put his detachment there, it would have a difficult time getting the logistical support it needed to operate. Consequently, he made a quick trip up to the largely unoccupied air base at Balad, 40 miles north of Baghdad, which was being slowly developed into a major military aerial port. A short discussion with the base commander indicated that it would be possible to lodge the Pave Lows and detachment in a compound in the northwest corner of the base. In February Colonel Williams arrived to take over the detachment, and he supervised the move. Shortly thereafter, other service aviation detachments joined them at Balad.[2]

At the same time, CJSOTF-AP was receiving an increasing number of taskings for direct action missions against the disparate elements aligned against the new Iraqi state. Actions and battles of varying size and intensity took place across the nation. In late March, insurgents kidnapped and brutally killed four American contractors working on a security detail near Fallujah, mutilated their bodies, and then hung them up for all to see. Shocked by the actions, the CJTF-7 commander, Lt Gen Ricardo Sanchez, ordered the I MEF to attack into the city and clear it of insurgents. I MEF launched Operation Vigilant Resolve on 4 April with two infantry battalions. When enemy resistance stiffened, two more USMC battalions were committed, and an Iraqi battalion was brought in to support the effort. Unfortunately, the battle wreaked havoc on the infrastructure and people of Fallujah. When the Iraqi battalion refused to fight against its "countrymen," General Sanchez ordered the I MEF to desist and withdraw its forces.[3]

In support of this operation, the CJSOTF-AP performed several collateral missions. AC-130 gunships and the 20th SOS flew direct support for several of them. As the fighting raged, on 12 April, two Pave Lows commanded by Capt Steve Edwards and Capt Marshall Groves and crews—call signs Mongoose 33 and 34—departed BIAP in the late evening to fly a series of support missions to deliver supplies and personnel to special forces elements around Fallujah. Edwards and his crew were flying MH-53M #69-5797. Lifting off into the dark but clear evening sky, they proceeded to their first landing zone. As they arrived, though, they discovered that it was occupied by other helicopters and discontinued their approach. As Edwards and Groves were discussing whether or not to proceed on to the second planned landing zone, Edwards observed the firing of an RPG toward his helicopter from the 11 o'clock position. Before he had a chance to react, the RPG struck the aircraft on the front left side just below the center windscreen. When the missile hit, the copilot, Capt Thomas Lessner, was flying the aircraft straight and level at 200 feet above the ground and maintaining 100 knots. The resultant blast devastated the instrument panels, the center instrument cluster, and most of the windscreen. The entire overhead throttle quadrant and emergency panel were completely destroyed. Captain Edwards was seriously injured in the face and on both arms and legs from flying glass particles. The flight engineer, TSgt Christian Mackenzie, suffered injuries to his eyes, face, and upper torso and was no longer capable of functioning in his job. Lessner sustained injuries to his left eye and side of his face, his left shoulder, and both legs. None of the cabin crew was injured, although the intercom system was intermittent. Momentarily stunned, Edwards quickly regained his composure, grabbed the cyclic and collective, and announced over the intercom that he had control of the aircraft. Lessner did not realize that he had done so and initially tried to fight him for the controls until he realized that Edwards was flying the aircraft.

Edwards then realized that he had lost all aircraft instrumentation and he needed to put the aircraft on the ground as soon and as safely as possible, hopefully on a landing site that would not produce a brownout. He called his intentions to the crew over the intercom, and the left scanner, MSgt Randy Kensey, began immediately giving him guidance to a grassy field off of their left front quarter—the only area that Edwards could see through his undamaged left chin bubble. At the same time, the tail scanner, SSgt Jesse Lee, came forward in the aircraft to gain some protection from a possible hard landing.

It all happened abruptly as Edwards brought the aircraft to a full and safe stop on the grassy field. As he did so, he called to Mackenzie to shut down the engines. The flight engineer replied that because of his injuries, he was not able to do so. Edwards then called to Kensey and the right scanner, MSgt Robert Colannino, to get Mackenzie out of the seat so that Colannino could shut down the engines. They quickly complied, placing the seriously injured Airman on the cabin floor. Colannino climbed up into what was left of the cockpit to shut down the engines. He remembers,

> I hopped in the pilot seat, and luckily I had a little headlight. I turned the head-light on and looked around the cockpit, and all the controls are gone. We couldn't shut the aircraft down like we normally would with the throttles. The electronic switches were all gone. . . . I hopped back out, and there are cables that run in the roof of the aircraft for the throttles and for the fuel levers, and of course I'm an engineer, so I know where they are. I looked up, pulled all four of them, and the engine shut down. We got the hell out of there.[4]

At the same time, the rest of the crew was attempting to move to the rear of the aircraft for egress. Captain Lessner needed a great deal of help because he could not see out of either eye. Sergeant Lee grabbed his PRC-112B survival radio and stepped off of the aircraft so that he could call Mongoose 34 for an immediate pickup.

Sergeant Lee did not need to make any radio calls because the crew members of Mongoose 34 had already acted. They had witnessed the firing of the RPG and, after taking immediate evasive action them-selves, had watched Mongoose 33 thrash through its wild gyrations as it reacted to the devastating blow and then respond to Captain Edwards's immediate inputs to put the aircraft safely on the ground. Captain Groves was flying his aircraft and quickly began to maneuver to land next to his Chalk Lead. In the middle of the turn, the flight engineer, SSgt Brian Bowling, observed what appeared to be another RPG off of the nose of their aircraft. The three scanners all dispensed flares that illuminated behind the aircraft and revealed to the tail gunner, TSgt Byron Allen, a group of about 12 enemy personnel. He fired 20 rounds at them with his .50-caliber machine gun. At the same time, Groves made an evasive right turn and descended. When enemy forces fired another projectile at the aircraft, he then made a hard left turn as the missile passed by. Groves continued to maneuver the aircraft to avoid the incessant enemy fire and locate Mongoose 33. Simultaneously, his copilot, Capt Matt Berry, made a Mayday call on the Guard frequency, asking for any immediately available help. Two AC-130s operating over Fallujah promptly responded, and one aircraft, Slayer 74, turned to head to their location.[5]

Unfortunately, in all of the evasive maneuvering, the crew of Mongoose 34 lost sight of Mongoose 33. The crew frantically searched until the tail scanner, Sergeant Allen, spotted the downed helicopter and called its relative position to his pilots. Groves immediately started a landing approach as all of the scanners provided him critical inputs for his landing. He put their helicopter down in the grassy field, just two rotor widths away from what was left of Mongoose 33. Groves had his gunners remain at the ready as he cleared two special forces Soldiers on board to dismount, proceed over to Mongoose 33, and render assistance. Overhead, Slayer 74 arrived and quickly oriented to the situation on the ground, guns at the ready and sensor systems rapidly scanning the immediate area for any individuals with apparent hostile intent.

Aboard Mongoose 33, Captain Edwards and Sergeant Colannino picked up Sergeant Mackenzie to carry him over to the other aircraft. They met the two special forces Soldiers who assisted them aboard Mongoose 34. As the left and right scanners of Mongoose 34, A1C Casey Mabry and SSgt Chris Dalton, helped the crew members of Mongoose 33 get settled on their helicopter, the tail scanner, Sergeant Allen, assured that all personnel were on board and notified Captain Groves, who then lifted off. His scanners maintained an earnest watch for any further enemy action as they talked Groves around known or suspected enemy positions. Their efforts were warranted because Sergeant Allen spotted another rising projectile directed at the tail of the aircraft. "Break right, descend," he called as Groves responded, the missile passing over the aircraft. Mabry then called out ground fire from the left side of the aircraft. Allen opened up on the site with his .50-caliber machine gun, later claiming that he fired only "10 or 15 rounds." With the AC-130 still watching from above, Mongoose 34 then set a course for BIAP. Twenty minutes later, the crews touched down and were immediately met by ambulances and a trauma physician. Groves kept the engines running in case the physician determined

Courtesy MSgt Byron Allen, USAF, Retired

MSgt Byron Allen receiving the Combat Action Medal from the CSAF, Gen Michael Moseley, for his actions to help rescue the crew of Mongoose 33

that the wounded needed to be directly medevaced to the larger hospital at Balad AB. When the physician assured them that the wounded members could get the care they needed at the BIAP hospital, Groves told his crew to shut them down. They had only flown for about an hour and 15 minutes, but it had been a very eventful and, for all, unforgettable experience.[6]

As Mongoose 34 was conducting its recovery mission, the orbiting AC-130 above, Slayer 74, contacted local USMC forces below for a force to try to secure the wreckage. The commander of the 1st Battalion of the 5th Marine Regiment deployed a QRF commanded by 1st Lt Josh Glover consisting of 55 Marines in nine Humvees. With guidance and top cover from Slayer 74, the Marines quickly drove the 10 kilometers to the location and arrived just a few minutes after Mongoose 34 lifted off. They quickly set up a perimeter and recovered sensitive items from the helicopter. The next morning enemy mortar rounds began to land in their perimeter, and Lieutenant Glover ordered his force to return to base. As it was leaving though, enemy forces closed in around it, and the QRF had to literally fight a running gun battle as teams of terrorists salvoed RPGs at its vehicles and con-

Courtesy AFSOC Public Affairs

MSgt Robert Colannino receives the Bronze Star for his actions on the Mongoose 33 mission.

stantly raked it with machine gun and small arms fire. Of the 55 Marines who went to the Mongoose 33 crash site, 21 came back wounded, and one was killed. Fallujah was a very dangerous place.[7]

The men aboard Mongoose 33 and 34 were well recognized for their efforts. All played their individual role in the chaotic events that night in the skies over Fallujah. Capt Steve Edwards was presented the Aviator Valor Award for 2004; Capt Marshall Groves received the Cheney Award for 2004; and MSgt Robert Colannino was given the Pitsenbarger Award for 2004, designed to recognize "an Air Force enlisted member who has performed a heroic act . . . that resulted in the saving of life or the prevention of serious injury."[8]

Fallujah remained an extremely dangerous place, but the crews were not cowed by it. R. K. Williams remembered the experiences of another flight of two Pave Lows shortly after the Mongoose 33 mission:

> A two-ship of helicopters was out flying a resupply mission. . . . It was a relatively routine mission, at night of course . . . south of Fallujah and west of Baghdad. . . . [The enemy] had figured out generally the routing of helicopters. They dispersed themselves into a cross-fire scenario with three [guns].
>
> This two-ship took several bullet holes in the machines. . . . The crews executed perfectly; no one was injured; the helicopters were both damaged. So they aborted the mission and flew back to Balad. They landed and came off the aircraft. They said, "Maintenance, we need the two spare aircraft. . . . They had just taken significant fire with significant battle damage and all they wanted to do was to get into a fresh helicopter and go back and finish the mission. We started being a little bit concerned that the crews were a little too callous to the danger, but after several discussions and talks at crew commander level, that wasn't the case. They weren't calloused at all; they just had it in their minds that the mission was the mission and as long as they weren't hurt or injured, equipment was equipment, humans were more important than hardware, and they were just going to get the other helicopters and go finish the mission.[9]

Taking advantage of the chaos sweeping over the land, local religious and political leaders such as Muqtada al-Sadr fomented opposition to the forming Iraqi government. They incited armed opposition in Najaf and other cities and towns. The Soldiers and Sailors of the CJSOTF-AP were very busy, as were the men of Pave Low who were carrying them on their highly classified missions during that fiery spring of 2004.

Multi-National Force–Iraq

At about the same time, the overall coalition structure within Iraq was being changed. Gen John Abizaid had replaced Gen Tommy Franks as the CENTCOM commander a few months earlier and wanted to begin integrating the Iraqi military into the overall coalition structure in the country. Accordingly, he received approval to restructure his commands. The CJTF-7 would be inactivated; in its place two commands would be stood up. The new headquarters for US and coalition military operations in Iraq would be called Headquarters, Multi-National Force–Iraq (MNF-I). It would provide theater strategic- and operational-level command and control of all coalition forces in Iraq. It would also directly deal with the various overarching governmental agencies and the emerging Iraqi government and synchronize security, diplomatic, economic, and information operations with the US Embassy and Iraqi government. In turn, the MNF-I would command the Multi-National Corps–Iraq (MNC-I), which would control tactical-level military operations of the several multinational divisions in place throughout the country. It would also oversee the operations of the CJSOTF-AP. The changes took place through the spring and summer of 2005. To the men serving with the Pave Low detachment at Balad, all of this was almost irrelevant. They received their tasking and flew their missions in support of the special forces units engaging the enemy every night.[10]

21st Special Operations Squadron

In June 2004, Lt Col Jim Slife handed over his position as the 20th SOS operations officer to Lt Col Scott Howell and moved to RAF Mildenhall, UK, to assume command of the 21st SOS from Lt Col Greg Lengyel. The ceremony took place on 21 June, and Lengyel moved to Virginia to serve as a military assistant to Secretary of Defense Donald Rumsfeld. Lt Col Mark Harmon had been serving as the 21st SOS operations officer and remained in that position.

Settling into his job, Slife determined that the 21st was a well-run unit that had been fully vetted by its experiences in northern Iraq and, since returning, had reengaged in the full spate of activities inherent with being the only heavy-lift, all-weather helicopter unit in EUCOM. In fact, 21st SOS crews had supported Vice Pres. Dick Cheney's visit to Switzerland in January and had participated in a series of exercises with US and allied special forces units in Scotland, Spain, Germany, and even Tunisia.[11]

However, Slife wanted to engage with one personnel issue at the squadron. He wanted to strengthen his cadre of NCOs, feeling that they saw themselves as engineers or gunners who were NCOs vice NCOs who held a particular job. He began moving to reorganize the unit so that NCOs were truly in charge of sections and programs and had to rate their troops and answer for specific actions. In this, he received a goodly amount of push-back, sensing that many intended to bide their time until he left so that they could settle back into their older habits. He would not allow that and gradually began to find that most rose to the occasion and performed very well. He tried to dispel the gunners-as-comic-relief paradigm and found that when he went beyond that and treated them as individuals with position and responsibility, they, in most cases, responded in kind. One gunner of whom Slife was most proud was TSgt John Stott, a charismatic and natural leader. Slife loaded him up with responsibility, and he rose to the task. There were others, too. Slife was humbled by the fact that of all the NCOs he sent through the NCO Academy, 78 percent of them were distinguished graduates.[12]

About a month after Slife took command, the unit was ordered to deploy to Balad Air Base, Iraq, to relieve the 20th SOS. This was only a personnel swap-out because the 20th left its aircraft. However, the 21st SOS did ship two Pave Lows to Hurlburt to support the 20th there.

Arriving at Balad, Slife was appointed to the position of JSOAD commander. The JSOAD also included MC-130 and Army and Navy detachments. Lt Col Mark Harmon commanded the MH-53 detachment. Slife designated senior individuals from the other groups to be in charge of their elements so that he could concentrate on the larger issues inherent in his position. Mission taskings were coming down nightly from the CJSOTF-AP and the MNC-I for direct action missions as well as standard logistics runs and occasional VIP support, and the Pave Low crews remained busy.

Back at Mildenhall, Slife had decided to directly engage with the Pave Low crews on one particular issue that had been concerning him since his time at Hurlburt. He was a great believer in operational risk management, or ORM as it was called, and had come to the conclusion that low-level flying was no longer necessary, especially after the Mongoose 33 incident. His analysis indicated that there were six things that threatened helicopters: terrain, wires, towers, other helicopters, small arms and RPGs, and heat-seeking missiles. Of the six, five could be mitigated by flying above 3,000 feet. The heat-seeking missiles could be handled with the warning and flare dispenser systems on the aircraft, designed exactly for this threat. However, when he presented his ideas to the young pilots, they always rebutted by saying that the danger from the heat-seeking missiles was just too high in Afghanistan and Iraq. He steadfastly counterargued that flying even higher at 8,000 to 10,000 feet insured that the aircraft could also have enough flight energy and room to be maneuvered against approaching missiles. Many of the young pilots still resisted. Slife did not want to use "I said so" leadership and had the 18th Flight Test Squadron do a classified test, which showed that the helicopters *were* far more survivable at altitude than down at 100 feet.

At Balad, Slife decided to change flight procedures. Using the report as his bludgeon, he gave firm guidance to his crews to do the en route portion of their flights at 8,000 to 10,000 feet or above. The grumbling was predictable and steady for a bit. But the crews began to appreciate that the flying was less stressful and less dangerous. They also noticed that they were returning from missions with fewer holes in their aircraft, and the carping began to dissipate. There were, however, the ever-present individuals who used any excuse to return to low level, and Slife had to reinforce his decision constantly and insist that his midlevel supervisors do the same. He was also heartened by the fact that R. K. Williams fully supported his actions as the 21st crews utilized the higher-altitude tactics in their direct support of the CJSOTF-AP operations. This included several classified support missions when US and Iraqi forces reengaged enemy forces in Fallujah in November 2004 in Operation Phantom Fury. During this two-week operation, the forces surrounded the city and worked through it block by block, rooting out the terrorists, killing over 2,000 enemy personnel, and capturing 1,200 more. However, the cost was high; 70 American and seven Iraqi troops were killed, with over 600 more wounded. Such battles indicated that there was still much hard fighting to do.[13]

551st Special Operations Squadron

Throughout 2004 the training squadron and its fellow unit the 58th TRSS worked steadily to produce more Pave Low crews. There were constant challenges as the unit received steady levies to send personnel TDY to the operational theaters. Spare parts continued to be a problem because the needs of the 20th and 21st were higher priority. In response to Colonel Williams's request, the 551st was also ordered to send two of its MH-53J aircraft to Hurlburt to help that unit with home-base training. In July all wing training was curtailed for two weeks as the entire unit received an ORI. Overall, the wing did well, with a few problems noted. The 551st was one of only two units to be highlighted for superlative work.

Regardless of the interruptions, the Pave Low training programs ran at a steady pace. The aircraft qualification courses were adjusted somewhat for various identified needs. However, they were still some of the longest courses in the USAF, with the pilot course running 171 days and the flight engineer course taking 173 days. For the year, 12 pilots, 12 flight engineers, and 12 aerial gunners were trained for the fleet; 197 other crew members received refresher training in the flight simulator.[14]

In March 2004, Capt Mike Holder reported to the 58th SOW for duty as a Pave Low IP. After his exploits in OEF, he had completed a rotation with the detachment at Djibouti. Then he attended the Weapons Instructor Course at Hurlburt and Nellis AFBs. At Kirtland, as the first MH-53 weapons instructor in AETC, he was directed to create a weapons and tactics office for the 551st SOS.[15]

Air Force Special Operations Command

As the campaigns in Iraq and Afghanistan continued unabated, the command remained decisively engaged in both arenas. Indeed, as the efforts of the antigovernment forces in Iraq continued to expand and become ever more violent, the 12,900 men and women of AFSOC were directly involved in the combined and joint efforts mounted to staunch and then defeat the enemy forces. Squadrons and detachments from its two wings and two groups were constantly present in Iraq, and it appeared that the Pave Low detachment, now ensconced at the Balad AB, was at least a semipermanent presence. Additionally, in support of the aerospace expeditionary forces concept, AFSOC began to designate detachments such as this as "expeditionary" units, and the 20th SOS detachment at Balad became the 20th Expeditionary Special Operations Squadron (ESOS). Henceforth, officers deployed for 90 days or more as commanders could now receive "G" Series orders officially designating them as such, which clarified their roles both administratively and operationally.[16]

The harsh conditions of Afghanistan, Djibouti, and Iraq were hard on equipment, especially the Pave Lows, and the AFSOC logisticians were monitoring the condition of the 32 remaining aircraft closely. The MH-53s were experiencing rising failure rates with small gearboxes, including the nose gearbox, intermediate gearbox, tail gearbox, and accessory gearbox. The machines also had continuing troubles with their engine air particle separator (EAPS) systems and main rotor swashplate and servo assemblies. The fine grit sand found in all of these areas was also eroding the main rotor blades. The stress of sustained combat operations further aged the already 35-plus-year-old aircraft. In fact, the aircraft most probably were older than the men who now flew them.[17]

On 1 July 2004, Lt Gen Paul Hester gave up command of the AFSOC and proceeded to Hawaii to take command of the Pacific Air Forces (PACAF), with a promotion to general. Replacing him at AFSOC was Maj Gen Michael Wooley, who was promoted to lieutenant general the next month. An airlift pilot by background, he had already served a tour as the AFSOC vice-commander and came to Hurlburt from command of the Third Air Force at RAF Mildenhall. Upon taking command, he laid out his priorities for the organization, focusing on his Airmen, their families, and their obligations as ambassadors for the nation in its many endeavors. And he reminded them that they were a part of the "tip of the spear," as America's military forces conducted operations in nearly two dozen nations, "seen and unseen," in the ongoing GWOT.[18]

21st Special Operations Squadron

Lt Col Jim Slife brought his squadron home from Iraq in early February 2005, when another detachment from the 20th arrived to replace it and maintain the Pave Low force (20th ESOS) at Balad. After a well-deserved period of time off, the squadron reengaged in its standard exercises within EUCOM. Crews flew up into the hills and mountains of Scotland to accomplish classic Pave Low TF/TA training; they deployed to Spain and the eastern Mediterranean for deck landing qualifications; and they did combined training with coalition special forces units in Spain, Italy, and Albania. As the Pave Lows were traveling across the breadth and depth of Europe, Col Brad Webb arrived to take command of the 352d SOG from fellow Pave Low veteran Col Dennis Jones on 23 June 2005. Webb had served with the unit for three years during the long Bosnia experience and was most pleased that he had received this assignment. He arrived to the thrilling news that the unit would be receiving an ORI in the fall.

In September Colonel Slife received an operational order directing the 21st SOS to deploy several crews and support personnel to augment the 20th ESOS at Balad. In October the AFSOC IG team arrived and submitted the 352d SOG to its ORI, and the 21st was operating with only a partial manning roster. Operational details of the exercise were classified, but the unit deployed to RAF Machrihanish, Scotland, for three weeks to display its capabilities. Overall, the group was rated satisfactory, with the 21st receiving an overall "outstanding" rating.[19]

20th Special Operations Squadron

Lt Col R. K. Williams used the respite from Balad duty to rebuild his squadron. Right after arriving and taking over as the operations officer, Lt Col Scott Howell had departed for Kirtland for his Pave Low requalification. He had been back to the squadron only a few weeks and was well into creating several training plans when Hurlburt was hit by Hurricane Ivan, and the entire 16th SOW had to evacuate. Howell and Williams dispatched all of the flyable helicopters and then remained behind with their families to watch over the rest of the squadron as best they could. Once the storm passed, they had to grant their troops liberal time off to deal with the damage and flooding. The time had to be taken out of their training plan as they were trying to prepare the unit for a return to Balad rotations in early 2005. However, the squadron was able to resume, even sending some aircraft and crews to Asheville for mountain training and other locations to work with special forces units from the other services.[20]

Working closely with Williams and Howell was SMSgt John DeSalle, now serving as the 20th SOS superintendent. He had returned from the 21st SOS in the summer of 2004 and initially served as a flight superintendent before moving up to the squadron position. Additionally, he maintained his gunner and evaluator qualification and flew when he could. However, watching out over the entire unit, especially the 175 enlisted troops, was a staggering responsibility. In particular, though, he placed a lot of emphasis on the development of his NCOs, making sure that they had specific responsibilities and opportunities to develop and grow professionally. He insured that they, too, were rotating overseas and serving in billets which required key NCO leadership. He rotated to the theater and flew missions as much as he could.

He was concerned, though, that in focusing exclusively on Iraq, the squadron was using its time at Hurlburt solely to prepare crews for those tours at the expense of developing them for other possible national missions. Training opportunities with other services and "customers" had been dramatically reduced. He observes, "I think we lost when we started doing OIF because we didn't get those TDYs, especially when we started drawing down the Paves. The guys didn't get to [go] to Fort Bragg or go to Fort Benning . . . we were always in Iraq. So the guys who became gunners and engineers, even pilots, after 9/11 really got cheated out of that, [which] gave them a deeper appreciation and the camaraderie with the teams."[21]

DeSalle also put a great deal of emphasis on crew building, believing that, "The one thing about Pave Low is that it is truly a crew aircraft." Unlike other squadrons with enlisted crew members, he would not allow separate sections for flight engineers and aerial gunners. Instead, he encouraged his Airmen to learn as much as possible about each other's job. On TDYs, he encouraged the crews to billet together, do things together, and ask lots of questions about every facet of the aircraft and mission. He always stressed proper aircrew decorum but emphasized especially to the new pilots that "you have to listen to your backenders because that is where a lot of the experience is, and that's where the knowledge of the systems is." He reinforced that with a simple amplification. "There are too . . . many realms of flight that we could die in." To all, he offered sage advice based upon his 15-plus years in Pave Low: "If you have thin skin, it will be hard for you to hang around. . . . If you don't suck it up, then you are going to have issues. . . . That is how we weed out the weak."[22]

In February Colonel Williams led his detachment to Balad for another tour with six crews and four aircraft. Like Colonel Slife, he was also ordered to serve as the JSOAD commander and did get to work somewhat with attached US Navy SH-60s. Two months later, Colonel Howell came over and replaced him for a 90-day tour in that role. After spending so much time away from operational assignments, Howell enjoyed being in the center of the action, directing joint and combined operations, and having to deal with real-time problems. Capt Matt Berry, now an aircraft commander, was back over for another tour. Carrying Iraqi special forces and

Courtesy AFSOC Public Affairs

Capt Matthew Berry receives the Distinguished Flying Cross for his actions on the Mongoose 33 recovery.

police elements aboard, he flew several direct action missions right into Baghdad. He recounts one mission in particular, though, that remains foremost in his mind:

> It was my first deployment as an aircraft commander, probably my third or fourth mission. I led a 12-ship of helicopters and there were 18 air assets overall in the formation into As Sutarai, Iraq. It was coordinated a little more extensively; we knew that it was coming about a week in advance because we had a lot of air assets getting play. Here I am, a dude with less than 1,000 hours, leading in an armada to take down this town that was just filled with insurgents. We pulled out 15 targets from that objective, everything from taking the town al-Qaeda leader down to the guy who was throwing IEDs out.[23]

Howell believed that his crews performed well. A goodly number of the missions were detailed and involved quite a bit of planning and precoordination. However, the majority were standard infiltration/ exfiltration or resupply of special forces elements. He utilized his senior officers, NCOs, and flight commanders to oversee various parts of the overall operation as a way to train and test them. He described how "guys like . . . Shawn Cameron, Joe Michalek, Steve Edwards, John Conmy, and Manny Fiterre . . . were combat flight commanders. When they deployed with their flight, they were a deployed squadron commander. . . . They commanded and they led."[24]

In April the 16th SOW commander, Col Otis Mannon, visited Balad to observe his troops. He had another purpose to fulfill. While there, he cornered Howell and informed him that he would take command of the 20th SOS—now officially recognized as the second busiest squadron in the USAF—from Colonel Williams that summer. Howell came back to Hurlburt for the ceremony held on 1 June 2005. Lt Col R. K. Williams passed him the unit guidon and subsequently departed for duty at the Air Force Academy.

Lt Col Vince Becklund then became the squadron operations officer. After his tour with the 551st SOS, he had spent two years at JSOC and then one year each at ACSC and SAAS and needed to requalify in the Pave Low. Replicating Howell's experience, he immediately departed for Kirtland AFB to requalify on the Pave Low. Howell was on his own.[25]

Also joining Howell in the 20th was CMSgt Jim Kradel. He had returned to Hurlburt in June 2004 from his tour at the 21st SOS and was assigned to the 16th SOG standardization and evaluation team as the rotary-wing chief; he also served as the group operations superintendent. Now he would work directly with Howell as his squadron superintendent, a job he greatly relished. Very quickly, he was immersed with issues and problems to be addressed and solved.[26]

The personnel requirement for the 20th ESOS at Balad was such that one squadron flight could fulfill the need, and Williams and Howell had set up a very effective system to rotate the flights in and out. However, shortly after taking command, the 20th was ordered to dispatch two more aircraft and four more crews to provide a CSAR capability for a special operations task force in Iraq. Howell was still at Hurlburt, attending the squadron commander's course, and had to develop a modified personnel flow to meet the added tasking. As he was working through that and trying to absorb what he was being taught in the course, he was notified that one of his helicopters had been damaged on a mission in western Iraq.

Capt Scott Minas and Capt Tim Matlock were the pilots. They made a brownout approach onto a plowed field. As the aircraft settled on the soft ground, the nose wheels snagged on a dust-covered concrete drainage berm and collapsed the gear braces. The nose gear folded back up in the wheel well and damaged some control tubes, rendering the aircraft unflyable. The crew and passengers were unharmed. The second aircraft, flown by Captains Paul Lawrenz and Jonathan Graham and crew, brought Minas and his crew back to Balad.

One of the 20th SOS flight commanders, Capt Steve Edwards, was at Balad, and Howell ordered him to handle the issue. Edwards and his replacement, USMC exchange officer Maj Nicholas "Buzz" Morris, did so, working with USMC forces in the area to secure the site and then procure a USMC CH-53E to lift the Pave Low back to Balad for repair.[27]

Finishing his course, Colonel Howell flew back to Balad for another rotation with the 20th ESOS. While there, he worked out a flow to extend his flights out for 120-day vice 90-day rotations. Additionally, he worked with the AFSOC DO, Col Eric Fiel, to request crew augmentation from the 21st SOS. When Slife got the request, he quickly obliged. With the augmentation, Howell now had a long-term sustainable plan to keep the necessary crews at Balad to meet operational requirements. The operational tempo for the units was steady and relentless. Through 2004 and 2005, they transported 216 detainees, delivered/extracted 9,162 special operations forces personnel, and carried 731,800 pounds of cargo in support of the special forces elements.[28]

Integral to the operations of the 20th was the absolutely great support it received from the 16th Helicopter Maintenance Squadron (HMXS). Practically speaking, the two squadrons were literally joined at the hip because the 20th simply could not function without the efforts of the Airmen and officers of the 16th HMXS. Since the initiation of OEF, its personnel had deployed 23 times to four different areas in the Middle East with the 20th. The 16th HMXS had generated over 3,000 local flying hours and 1,500 deployed flying hours. Its personnel had recovered and repaired unit aircraft in several remote and dangerous locations. The squadron also made great strides in improving the safety and reliability of the aging and irascible fleet of MH-53s. Additionally, it had accomplished every major modification program for the aircraft while supporting the local flying and steady CONUS and overseas deployments. In recognition of its superior performance, in April 2005 the unit was awarded the 2004 USAF Maintenance Effectiveness Award in the rotary-wing aircraft category. This was the third year in a row that the unit had been so honored. Said Lt Col Stuart Lum of his unit, "This is the kind of unit that each of us joined the military to be part of, where people are committed to their values, achieve squadron goals, and show real teamwork. We're a family of winners. . . . Here's to us and those like us."[29]

The next challenge for the 20th SOS came from a most unexpected quarter. In late August, a tropical storm formed southeast of the Bahamas and started tracking to the northwest. As it gained strength, it was declared a hurricane and named Katrina. The storm crossed Florida and entered the Gulf of Mexico, where it dramatically strengthened. It then turned north and slammed into New Orleans, doing great damage to the city, its suburbs, and most of southeast Louisiana and southern Mississippi. The next day, levees around New Orleans ruptured, allowing floodwaters to inundate the city and environs, adding to the destruction and misery. The USAF and AFSOC reacted swiftly. The 347th Rescue Wing, recently gained by AFSOC, prepared a task force of HH-60s and HC-130s that deployed to Jackson Airport, Mississippi, and began rescue and recovery operations as part of a huge national effort to help the people of the region. 20th SOS crews flew three aircraft on local sorties from Hurlburt, and they worked during the daytime with MC-130s to remain over the city and environs. Since Colonel Howell was still in Iraq and Colonel Becklund was at Kirtland for his Pave Low requalification, the 20th effort was commanded by one of the squadron assistant DOs, Lt Col

"Rusty" Kaskel. Throughout, the Pave Low crews operated under the tactical control of the 347th. The Paves flew 17 sorties in the effort; the 347th Wing was credited with saving 1,395 people from the flood-waters and ferrying 272 more to safe areas and emergency support centers. Howell had family in New Orleans and watched the cable news channels as the recovery progressed. He was most heartened to see scenes of the Pave Lows flying over the city and assisting in the huge recovery effort. He later remarked, "We were tasked to send Pave Lows over to New Orleans and help rescue the folks there and do what needed to be done . . . not what we were used to doing, . . . but we had the capability and we had the right experience. So we stepped into the breech and did a great job with that." It was another classic use of heavy-lift helicopters and very much in keeping with the broad type of missions that the Pave Lows and their HH and CH predecessors had performed from their very inception.[30]

Courtesy Lt Col Fred Koegler, USAF

A Pave Low over New Orleans after Hurricane Katrina

Lt Col Vince Becklund finally arrived at the 20th SOS in October 2005. He found a squadron very different from what he remembered from the 1990s. Then, it was the "show," the place to be, lots of specialty missions working with all manner of special operations elements on endless "really cool" exercises all over the CONUS and globe, with

Courtesy Lt Col Fred Koegler, USAF

Flooded New Orleans from the back ramp

lots of TDY funds, nice hotels, and rental cars. All crew members had considerable experience and practically nobody was below the rank of captain or staff sergeant. It generated a great sense of trust. Now, the unit was filling with younger pilots right out of flight school and the 551st, arriving without the benefit of seasoning time in UH-1s or anything else. Additionally, the majority of the enlisted force was similar, with senior Airmen and staff sergeants abounding. Becklund had to scramble to get up to speed with the current training programs, continued rotation of his crews to Balad, and a wing ORI now looming on the horizon.[31]

Air Force Special Operations Command

The year 2005, the fourth year of AFSOC in the GWOT, was another year of change and challenge. On average, at any moment fully 25 percent of its force structure was engaged in operations somewhere in the world, giving AFSOC the highest operations tempo of any MAJCOM in the USAF. The new USAF chief of staff, General Moseley, directed that the Air Staff and all MAJCOM staffs be reorganized as "A-staffs" to parallel the joint staff structure of numbered vice named directorates. As an example, the director of personnel would now become the A1, the director of operations would now become the A3, and so on. AFSOC complied and was directed to form a war-fighting headquarters, which it did by creating the Air Force Special Operations Forces, with its own A-staff and the capability to function as an operational headquarters.

The new staff would be useful in allowing the AFSOC to better command its assets as it steadily expanded. The CV-22 program was part of that phenomenon. On 20 May, the 71st SOS was reactivated at Kirtland AFB as the training squadron for the new aircraft. Its new commander was Lt Col Jim Cardoso. After his time at the 20th SOS, he had attended staff college at the Western Hemisphere Institute for Security Cooperation and then served 23 months as an aide to the USSOCOM commander, Gen Charles Holland. That tour allowed the young officer to see the big picture of the ongoing conflicts and world situation. Additionally, Cardoso could see that Pave Low's days were waning. In December 2003, he transferred to Kirtland AFB to serve as the operations officer of the 551st SOS until he was designated to take command of the 71st SOS.[32]

Additionally, AFSOC was developing plans to deploy operational CV-22 squadrons with the first unit at Hurlburt Field, possibly in 2007. At the same time, the command was forthrightly expanding its use of RPVs, activating squadrons equipped with them. Personnel in the Pave Low community were now beginning to realize that they would have to reorient their careers, possibly into one of these two areas, as the command itself was evolving and changing. With this expansion, it was obvious, too, that AFSOC needed another base, especially one that was not as exposed to the vagaries of extreme weather such as the hurricanes which had so disrupted operations and life at Hurlburt over the last two years.

Senior members on the AFSOC staff recalled that 11 years earlier, Maj Gen James Hobson had proposed a western AFSOC base as part of his "Commando Vision" plan. Now, another congressional base realignment committee was looking at bases to close. It had initially identified Cannon AFB in eastern New Mexico as a closure candidate. Cannon was spared, but its resident fighter wing was identified for inactivation, leaving Cannon available as possibly the elusive western AFSOC base. Throughout the year, AFSOC site survey teams traveled to Cannon and other West Coast bases to look for possible candidates. Their carefully considered recommendation was Cannon AFB. However, any decisions would not come before 2006.[33]

At the same time, changes were being programmed for the Pave Low fleet. USSOCOM program planning documents as early as 2000 had indicated that the Pave Lows would be inactivated by 2012, and AFSOC plans reflected that eventuality. Consequently, some deep repair maintenance and supply contracts had been allowed to expire. This was already having an impact on the fleet. Plainly, the aircraft were wearing out; the gearbox failures were occurring more frequently. However, that supplier had been eliminated. Consequently, the AFSOC A-4 (logistics) developed a program with the US Navy to redesign the gearbox so that Navy parts could be used until a new supplier could be contracted. Additionally, USSOCOM, in its 2000 program planning, had indicated that the 21st SOS at RAF Mildenhall, UK, would inactivate in 2007 and its mission would be assumed by US Army Special Operations Command MH-47s slated to be assigned to the theater.[34]

In conjunction with the planned drawdown, AFSOC considered requesting that the 551st SOS at Kirtland AFB be closed and the entire MH-53 training program be moved to Hurlburt by October 2006. This would include the transfer of the remaining seven MH-53Js, all training personnel, and a significant number of maintenance technicians. At Hurlburt, the 19th SOS would assume the training role. A site survey team conducted a study at Hurlburt and determined that a severe shortage of ramp and facility space would make any such move problematic and that any construction required to provide the needed facilities would take far too long. Accordingly, the initiative was tabled. However, as Colonel Cardoso had seen at USSOCOM, to anyone else who cared to ponder these developments, it was clear that Pave Low was in its terminal years.[35]

58th Special Operations Wing

On 4 February 2005, Lt Col Charles "Pat" Nussman, another career Pave Low pilot with over 3,300 hours in helicopters, assumed command of the 551st SOS. His assumption of command was a bit unexpected and unusual. Lt Col Lance Bodine had passed command of the unit to another officer three weeks earlier. However, that individual had allowed a breach of rules among his Airmen while overseas and was relieved of command of the 551st. Nussman took command of the unit under a bit of a cloud and had some personnel challenges to deal with. He also had some operational headaches. With the transfer of two aircraft to Hurlburt in 2004, throughout 2005 the 551st struggled to meet its training goals. Since the 551st had only MH-53Js and the operational squadrons had mostly MH-53Ms, the training squadron could not swap out its aircraft with other units so that they all wore out at the same rate. Consequently, its aircraft showed much higher maintenance abort and discrepancy rates than the other squadrons. Spare parts were still a problem, and for the year, the squadron qualified only nine pilots, 11 flight engineers, and 10 gunners. Another 134 Pave Low crew members passed through for simulator refresher training.

Even though the CSAR units had been transferred to AFSOC, MH-53s could still be called out to do civil SARs if they were the best aircraft to handle the mission. Such was the case on 16 July 2005, when the 551st was asked to launch a Pave Low to rescue an injured climber near Pagosa Springs, Colorado, because of the high elevation. The mission was approved; however, severe thunderstorms in the Albuquerque area precluded launch until the next morning. The aircraft commander was Capt Mike Holder. His copilot was his fellow Afghanistan veteran, Capt Pat Fronk, both selected by Colonel Nussman because of their extensive high-altitude flying experiences in Afghanistan. In addition to their engineers and scanners, they had two PJs and a survival, evasion, resistance, and escape specialist on board. The crew launched and proceeded to Pagosa Springs to meet with the local sheriff and coordinate a recovery plan. They were then able to locate the climber and his party up at an elevation of 10,100 feet. The aircraft was too heavy to safely land at that elevation. Holder consulted with his flight engineers and determined that they could dump fuel to 2,000 pounds and accomplish the rescue. This would give them enough fuel to make it back safely to Pagosa Springs. Holder landed the aircraft, and the PJs recovered the climber. When he and all of the recovery team members were safely on board, Holder lifted off and proceeded to the airfield at Pagosa Springs. Arriving there, they transferred the patient to local medical control, refueled their aircraft, and flew back to Kirtland AFB, having logged a save for the 58th SOW.[36]

Looking to the future, the Airmen of the 551st realized that the life of Pave Low was finite. The USSOCOM program plan was now common knowledge. It and supporting AFSOC plans called for a slow reduction of the 551st Pave Low fleet starting in 2006. This would begin to eliminate personnel positions across the board. Since the 551st reduction would be part of a larger elimination of the entire Pave Low force, these individuals faced some amount of cross-training into new positions. The AFSOC RPV fleet seemed as if it might be a destination for some of the pilots.

At the same time, the CV-22 fleet was growing. As it expanded, many new slots would be opening up, and many Pave Low troops—from aircrew to specialist mechanics—would likely be switching over to the new aircraft. Colonel Cardoso at the 71st SOS was working hard to grab as many of them as he could. One of the pilots interested in switching over was the current 551st weapons and tactics officer, Capt Mike Holder. He put in a request for assignment and within a year was selected to be a member of the initial cadre of Pave Low pilots to convert to the CV-22 Osprey.

At Kirtland AFB in 2005, another longtime Pave Low pilot received an additional opportunity to command a flying unit. Col Tom Trask took over the 58th SOW from Col Eric Fiel on 23 May 2005. It

Courtesy 58th SOW History Office

MH-53J #68-10367 being filmed in its role as a Decepticon for the movie *The Transformers* in April 2006

would afford him the opportunity to once again qualify on the MH-53. He did not know at the time, though, that he would end up being a key participant in the steady inactivation of the Pave Low fleet.[37]

Colonel Trask could not have anticipated the very sad crisis that he would have to deal with on 12 February 2006. On that date, he was notified that the 551st SOS squadron commander, Colonel Nussman, had died in his sleep. The squadron operations officer, Lt Col Todd "Burt" Lancaster, was given command of the unit. He worked to rally the squadron and get it refocused on the mission because there were still Pave Low crew members to train, many of whom were going into combat in the not-too-distant future. After a moving memorial ceremony for Nussman, his body was cremated and his ashes were flown aboard a Pave Low and dispersed over the Gulf of Mexico.

Two months later, the squadron was able to assume a lighter duty when it was tasked to provide two Pave Lows to star in a movie. The aircraft, commanded by Capt Brian Reece and Maj Kevin Churchill, launched on 30 May and flew to Holloman. There they were filmed in several different settings and scenes for the movie *The Transformers*, where they replicated "Decepticons," creatures that could portray themselves as Pave Low helicopters and then transform into hideous and overpowering "bad guys." The filming lasted for several days, and Captain Reece was also filmed in several other settings. It was reminiscent of the filming of the movie *Airport 1975*, featuring an HH-53 then assigned to the 551st's predecessor, the 1551st FTS.[38]

Air Force Special Operations Command

As 2006 arrived at AFSOC, the rate of change steadily increased. In fact, sometimes it seemed that the only constant was change. On 25 February, General Moseley decided to reverse the decision that Gen John Jumper had made three years earlier to move the CONUS CSAR force structure to AFSOC by ordering it moved back to ACC. Moseley directed ACC and AFSOC to expedite the move and have it done by 1 October. His action was not because of any dissatisfaction with AFSOC's administration of the rescue force. He simply believed that CSAR was an inherently USAF mission and that ACC was best organized to properly administer and control it. He also felt that the USAF did a better job of advocating for the mission and its need for a new rescue helicopter than did USSOCOM. The ACC and AFSOC staffs immediately began drafting plans for the transfer.

Two days later, Maj Gen Donald Wurster replaced Maj Gen John Folkerts as the vice-commander of AFSOC. It fell to Wurster to fully explain the transfer, which he did in a subsequent speech, saying,

> The mission of rescue is closely tied to the combat air forces it supports. Rescue of an Airman from deep in enemy territory is inherently an air function. The [JFACC] owns the aircraft that was lost. He owns the aircraft that will support the search and rescue task force, and he owns the airpower that will enable our daring rescue crews to get to the area, find the survivor, and recover him or her to friendly control. Combat rescue is a deep air operation and a core task for our airpower responsibilities.[39]

This was essentially how General Moseley conducted his theater CSAR plan when he served in OIF as the CENTCOM JFACC. Wurster further explained that as AFSOC moved into the future, the command was divesting itself of its helicopter force. The MH-60s were gone, and the MH-53s had a pending end date. Beyond the fleet of C-130 variants, the command's future was now tied to the CV-22 and increased utilization of RPVs and possibly other "specialty" fixed-wing aircraft that were beginning to appear. The USAF rescue force belonged in ACC. He could also have added that in moving the consolidated CSAR force into ACC, the USAF was finally meeting its almost forgotten obligations laid out as Issue 16 of the controversial 31 Initiatives signed between the USAF and US Army chiefs in 1984 specifying that "the Air Force will remain the proponent for Air Force Search and Rescue . . . with Special Operations Forces . . . providing a back-up capability in special situations."[40]

As the transfer of the rescue forces was taking place, the AFSOC staff was consolidating all of the site survey data concerning the possible AFSOC acquisition of Cannon AFB. All of the studies showed that the move was not only feasible but desirable. On 20 June 2006, the entire transfer plan was briefed to Secretary of Defense Donald Rumsfeld. He approved it with a transfer date of 1 October 2007. The AFSOC staff began detailed planning for the move. The base was projected to receive AC- and MC-130s, possibly CV-22s, RPVs as they continued to develop, and various other unspecified "low signature" aircraft. It was done—AFSOC would finally get its western base. Conspicuously absent, though, was any mention of MH-53s.[41]

There was a very good reason why the Pave Lows were not in the Cannon plan—they were going away, sooner rather than later. In

June 2006, the USSOCOM board of directors reviewed the current Pave Low structure and operational costs through the FY 2008–13 POM. They decided to accelerate the inactivation of the remaining 31 aircraft. All MH-53s would be decommissioned by the end of FY 2008. This recommendation was forwarded to the USSOCOM commander, US Army general Doug Brown, for his approval. General Wooley then sent a memorandum to his staff directing them to program the inactivation of the remaining MH-53s at Kirtland by the end of March 2007, at the 21st SOS by the end of September 2007, and at the 20th SOS by the end of September 2008. He also notified them to begin terminating all vendor support contracts and initiate requisite personnel reassignments. He stated unequivocally that "aircraft sustainment concerns, coupled with operations and maintenance personnel issues, will make extending the MH-53 fleet past FY 08 impractical."[42]

There was another element to the Cannon AFB selection. Since the currently based 27th FW would be inactivating, General Wooley decided to transfer the 16th SOW flag there, hopefully allowing the Hurlburt wing to reclaim its designation as the 1st SOW. However, such a change was not a done deal. When General Hester was at AFSOC, he tried to generate some interest among the senior USAF leadership to reverse the decision General McPeak had made when he was the chief of staff to change the 1st SOW to the 16th SOW. As AFSOC was acquiring Cannon, Wooley seized the moment and was able to engage General Moseley on this issue and gain his concurrence. On 16 November 2006, the 16th SOW was officially redesignated the 1st SOW, and every subordinate unit went through the same process. Patch makers across the nation were inundated with orders for new patches.[43]

However, the 16th SOW flag did not transfer to Cannon AFB. Because of heritage regulations, since the 1st SOW was reestablished at Hurlburt Field, it reclaimed its original heritage and honors. This meant that the 16th SOW designation would have gone to Cannon with no recent heritage. The 27th FW, with its long and distinguished heritage, had been located at Cannon since 1959 and had existed since 1947. Additionally, the designation had strong local support. Therefore, General Wooley decided to retain the 27th Wing, now converted to a SOW.[44]

58th Special Operations Wing

Notice of the acceleration of deactivating the Pave Lows came as a rude shock to the Pave Low troops at Kirtland AFB. Based upon the earlier guidance, the wing staff had already developed an overall plan for a slow phaseout of aircraft through the end of 2010. Now it was being told that all aircraft would be gone in nine months. Accordingly, all training plans for crew members and maintenance personnel had to terminate by the end of March 2007. The planners quickly adjusted all training schedules. An aircraft disposition plan was developed with the departure of the first two aircraft in December. One aircraft, MH-53 #66-14433, the original Black Knight flown through all of the initial testing at Wright-Patterson AFB and at Kirtland by Frank Pehr and Steve Connelly, would be retained at Kirtland as a static display.

Colonel Lancaster went to work to find assignments for all of his Airmen and officers. However, he had to keep them focused on training; students were still going through the courses. All would be going to either the 20th or 21st SOSs and faced the real possibility that they would still see combat in the Pave Low. By the end of the year, the 551st had fully qualified 15 pilots, five flight engineers, and 11 gunners and only had eight student pilots to finish up in 2007.[45]

21st Special Operations Squadron

On 10 February 2006, Lt Col Jim Slife passed command of the squadron to Lt Col Kirk Smith. For the last 44 months Slife had served as the operations officer and then commander with the two remaining operational Pave Low squadrons and had flown in Afghanistan, Djibouti, and Iraq. He would now serve a short tour working again with Col Brad Webb as his deputy commander of the 352d SOG before departing in the summer to move to Washington, DC, to serve a one-year tour as a Secretary of Defense Fellow with Microsoft Corporation.

Colonel Smith picked up the reigns and had his aircraft and crews on the road across the theater, training with other US and coalition special forces units. In June he dispatched two aircraft and crews to support President Bush's visit to Hungary. The 21st continued to provide three Pave Low crews and several support personnel at Balad with the 20th.[46]

In July the 352d SOG received a real-world mission from SO-CEUR. When Israel initiated combat operations against Hezbollah forces in Lebanon, the US ambassador to that country, the Honorable Jeffrey Feltman, requested military support to evacuate American citizens who wanted to leave, estimated to be about 5,000 of the approximately 80,000 Americans believed to be in the country. Similar to the evacuation conducted from Lebanon in 1976, the US military was directed to assist, with USMC forces afloat in the eastern Mediterranean the first forces to respond. The 352d SOG was ordered to augment the effort, and on 16 July, an initial element of air commandos flew into the RAF base at Akrotiri, Cyprus, the same base that supported the evacuation operation in 1976 and that the 352d had used to launch into northern Iraq in 2003. Capt Derrick Stamos, now a fully qualified Pave Low aircraft commander, was dispatched as the Pave Low liaison officer. He quickly made arrangements for the arrival of helicopter crews and support personnel. Two days later, three MH-53s, two MC-130s, and the support team arrived at the base and became part of CTF-59, which included a US Army helicopter detachment, a USMC detachment, several US Navy ships, and coalition forces of various types. A fourth MH-53 joined the group a week later. Because of the large number of potential evacuees, several contract ships were dispatched to the Port of Beirut and began bringing out the larger portion of evacuees. Additionally, an air bridge was established between the American Embassy in Beirut and Akrotiri.

For the next 78 days, the Pave Lows joined with US Army and USMC helicopters and a detachment of British CH-47s to extract evacuees from that war-torn country. The 21st SOS flew 100 percent of its requested sorties, hauling 117,000 pounds of cargo and supplies to the embassy and carrying out 520 Americans and 413 foreigners. The air bridge was terminated on 30 September, and US and British troops at Akrotiri staged a large party to celebrate their success. The elements from the 352d SOG remained at Akrotiri for two more weeks while the situation in Lebanon stabilized. Captain Stamos notes of the deployment, "We did some really good work there. We worked with ships [and] Marine Corps aircraft . . . , we flew the secretary of state in, [and] some of our birds went to Israel to bring the State Department folks to negotiate a cease-fire."[47]

The various parts of the 352d SOG returned to Mildenhall. A few weeks later, Colonel Webb held a commander's call for his troops to thank them for their great effort and also explain to them all of the things that were now happening in AFSOC, especially the now pending inactivation of the Pave Lows and 21st SOS. Colonel Smith was already seeing the impact of the pending changes. His personnel were beginning to get orders to CV-22 conversion, the 20th SOS, or other aircraft. He had to keep the squadron functioning as long as possible while still meeting its commitments to the detachment at Balad and dealing with an ever-dwindling number of Airmen and officers. To the last days though, the squadron was still the on-call, heavy-lift helicopter force for SOCEUR and EUCOM until replaced by the US Army MH-47s. It is interesting to note, too, that the unit's last significant tasking prior to inactivation had been an evacuation, somewhat analogous to the mission to evacuate the crew of the SS *Mayaguez,* which had been the last major event for the 21st SOS at NKP, Thailand, prior to its inactivation there in September 1975.[48]

20th Special Operations Squadron/ Expeditionary Special Operations Squadron

During 2006 the 20th SOS maintained a continuous presence at Balad, Iraq, as part of OIF. Generally, one-third of the unit was there. They were now deep into counterinsurgency operations, and the pace was steady throughout the year as they provided direct support to the "shooters." They continued to work with every special forces component in the country, both US and coalition. In February Colonel Howell was notified that Lt Col Vince Becklund was going to be deployed over to serve as the J3 with the CJSOAC at Balad. Howell appealed the selection, pointing out that Becklund was still new to the 20th SOS and was just flat needed in the unit as it covered the Balad deployment and now the approaching ORI. His appeal was not honored, and in April Colonel Becklund reported to Balad as ordered to work with the CJSOAC, commanded by Col Norm Brozenick, the 1st SOW commander. The CJSOAC had operational control of numerous assets from both the 1st SOW and other service components, including the 160th SOAR. As the J3, Becklund directed joint and combined operations on a nightly basis. His forces worked at the highest operational tempo of the war to date, running direct action missions against insurgent forces that were trying to inflame a Shia-Sunni civil war. As part of that effort, the 20th ESOS—commanded by USMC major Buzz Morris—made a significant contribution, flying 558 direct action sorties and logging 2,891 combat hours during the year. The squadron hauled over 325,000 pounds of supplies and equipment to isolated units and returned with 304 captured insurgents and 70 seized weapons. For eight months, the unit also maintained aircraft and crews on alert to provide specific CSAR and casualty evacuation support for a special operations task force operating in western Iraq.

In June the 20th ESOS at Balad was directed to fly to the Baghdad Airport to provide support for President Bush and his entourage's visit to Iraq. Four Pave Lows, as part of a group of 12 helicopters, picked up the visiting group members as they arrived on Air Force One and flew them into the Green Zone in the middle of Baghdad for meetings with key US military and Iraqi governmental leaders. When they were complete, the helicopters safely returned them to the airport. Both movements took place in daytime.[49]

While the Pave Low crews were supporting the president, their squadron mates back at Hurlburt were also busy preparing for the ORI. This was a real dilemma for Colonel Howell, who was at Hurlburt at the time. He fully understood how important such inspections were. However, he would not interfere with the squadron crew rotation schedule to stack the deck for the inspection at the risk of possibly weakening his operations at Balad. Consequently, the squadron flew with the personnel who were available on the flight rotation schedule. He trusted his flight commanders and NCOs, crews, and support personnel to do what was needed. His overall approach was simple: he focused on personal responsibility as the linchpin of their operations, admonishing his troops to "be ready" in every sense of the word to do those things that the nation was relying upon the 20th SOS and its Airmen to do, especially meeting assigned times on target, so critical for precision special forces operations. To his commanders and senior NCOs, he was also forthright, admonishing them to "take care of our Airmen. Develop our Airmen. We're all developing leaders—it's the most important thing we can do, and we have to have that next generation to follow us. Make sure we are picking the right guys, mentoring them, developing them." Similar to the experiences of Colonels Webb and Slife, Howell also had some malingerers. With them, he was just as direct, saying,

There were people in the squadron, some who had lingering injuries. I said, "I can't have you in the squadron. This squadron is a deploying squadron. We are in the fight all the time. When you are sitting here with a hurt back or whatever your issue may be, the other guys notice that because they are rucking up, and they keep going. It's not that I don't love you, but I can't have you in the squadron if you're not deploying for me." So I made a conscious effort to peel off some of these guys and find other jobs for them so they are not there in the middle of these guys who were fighting. . . . The message was getting through.[50]

During the ORI operations phase, four Pave Lows were deployed up to McChord AFB, Washington. There they flew numerous missions with US Army Rangers and were evaluated in multiple mission events. Right in the middle of the inspection, Howell received the notification of the USSOCOM decision to inactivate the Pave Lows. He quickly briefed his troops as best he could and told them to worry about it later. Then they returned to Hurlburt and participated in the drills designed to test their ability to survive and operate under wartime conditions and conventional, chemical, and biological threats. The 20th SOS as well as the 16th SOW received "excellent" ratings.[51]

Colonel Howell was extremely proud of his troops. He used one of his young pilots, Capt Matt Doberman, as an example of the caliber of troops he had in the 20th. When Doberman arrived at the squadron, he made it clear that he wanted to go over to Iraq to be in the action. A few weeks later, though, Howell found out that Doberman's wife was pregnant. Howell's policy was to have fathers home when their children were born, if at all possible. He told Doberman, who saw this as some form of personal failure. Howell assigned him to a flight that was training up for a deployment after the birth. A week prior to that deployment, Doberman suffered a burst appendix but fully intended to tough it out and deploy. However, when told of Doberman's condition, his flight commander took him off of the deployment. Howell was tremendously impressed with Doberman's determination and sense of mission and felt that it was indicative of the Pave Low spirit, or as he said, "It was a great tribute to the whole red scarf community."[52]

Howell deployed back over to Balad in August for another 90-day rotation as the JSOAD commander. His crews began working steadily with Iraqi special forces elements to give them the training that they needed to be able to take over the fight. While there, the 1st Ops Group commander, Col Mark Alsid, now serving at Balad as the CJSOAC commander, called Howell and notified him that he had been selected for promotion to colonel. He also told Howell that he wanted him to pass command of the 20th to Colonel Becklund to give him a full tour as the commander before the squadron's inactivation. The change of command was set for January 2007. Howell flew his share of missions and decided to have a final flight. He was assigned a direct action mission and selected Captain Doberman as his copilot. Doberman flew the assault approach to a confined compound. It was a dust-out approach, but Doberman handled it perfectly, and the mission was totally successful. Howell came home in December and prepared to hand over the squadron to his operations officer, Colonel Becklund.

Howell took some family leave over the holidays and was home in Kentucky. On 29 December, Lt Col Joe DeCaro, the deployed commander, called Howell to tell him that one of his gunners had been accidentally shot in the right eye. SSgt Eric Ezell, serving on his fifth combat tour, was injured when an Iraqi interpreter improperly charged his rifle as Ezell's Pave Low approached a landing zone for a troop insertion. Becklund was flying a local night sortie and was recalled to begin working the myriad details. Howell called him to get all of the information that he could about the incident and then called Ezell's parents and informed them of the accident.

Fortunately for Ezell, combat medics were on the helicopter during the mishap, and they were able to start treatment immediately as the pilots aborted the mission and headed for Baghdad. There the physicians directed that he be flown to the big hospital at Balad; doctors were able to stabilize him and determine that while he had lost his right eye, there was no further serious damage to his brain or head.

Ezell was then medevaced to Landstuhl, Germany, and on to the Walter Reed Army Medical Center in Washington, DC. Colonel Howell and his squadron superintendent, CMSgt John DeSalle, traveled up to see him and insure that he was getting the care and handling that he needed and deserved. They stayed with him for a week and then had another squadron NCO come up to remain with him until he could return to Hurlburt. A week later, Howell gave up command of the 20th SOS to Lt Col Vince Becklund.

Becklund inherited a full plate of issues that required his immediate attention. However, he spared no effort to work with Ezell to insure that he could stay in the USAF, remembering of the young Airman, "There's a success story. Here's a guy who is still in the Air Force, still contributing, without an eye. . . . We take care of guys like that. I think many other places would have said, 'We're sorry it happened to you. You're out.' . . . We did everything we could to keep him in the Air Force."[53]

Surge in Iraq

As Becklund was settling into his command, dramatic changes were talking place in OIF. In 2005 the Iraqi government conducted a series of open and fair elections. Throughout 2006, as Iraq's newly elected leaders struggled to implement their new government, al-Qaeda terrorists and Sunni insurgents unleashed a reign of terror that threatened the very stability of the government and nation. After meeting with his military leaders and members of Congress, President Bush decided to increase US military forces in that country by utilizing a surge strategy. On 10 January 2007, he announced that he was ordering an additional 20,000 troops—primarily conventional US Army forces—to deploy to Iraq. Forces already there would be extended by as much as six months. The CJSOTF-AP would also be reinforced. However, with the drawdown of the Pave Low fleet, no more aircraft could be deployed. As much as they could be tasked, the aircraft and crews of the 20th ESOS would be involved in the operations. The additional conventional troops would help stabilize and secure the Iraqi population, but it was the combined special forces elements that nightly went out and dealt with the hard-core al-Qaeda and insurgent forces.[54]

Maj Mark Daley witnessed the beginning of that surge effort. He deployed over to Balad in March 2007 to serve as the commander of the 20th ESOS for a 60-day period. While he was there, his young crews flew almost 400 hours, mounted 46 direct action missions, and captured 106 enemy combatants. Daley personally led his last sortie, an 11-aircraft joint and combined assault mission. For over seven hours, the strike force attacked four targets, coordinating its efforts with orbiting RPVs, F-16s, and AC-130 gunships. Daley had the ground force commander aboard his aircraft, which provided excellent coordination between the ground and air elements as the force brought back 27 detainees. Returning home to Hurlburt a few days later, Daley remembered this as his "most favorite" Pave Low mission.[55]

Air Force Special Operations Command

As the surge commenced, the logistics directorate of AFSOC was building a firm schedule for the inactivation of the Pave Low aircraft and transfer of all of their type-specific support equipment based upon the termination of Pave Low flying in September 2008. However, the 20th ESOS was still utilizing the aircraft very effectively in Iraq. Consequently, the aircraft were still getting upgrades, such as improvements to the ALE-40 chaff/flare dispenser system, strengthening of the flight engineer's seat, and the new altitude hold and hover stabilization (AHHS) system, specifically designed to deal with the brownout problem. Some of the 20th crews tested the system at Hurlburt and found it to work well.

The projected schedule called for all aircraft at Kirtland AFB and all except one at RAF Mildenhall to be inactivated in 2007. One aircraft from the 21st would be sent to Hurlburt for continued use. This would leave 13 aircraft still in commission for combat operations into 2008. Additionally, several aircraft were being programmed for permanent static display. Projected plans called for Pave Lows at Kirtland AFB; Hurlburt Field; the Air Force Armament Museum, Eglin AFB; Hill AFB; the Air Force Museum, Wright-Patterson AFB; Robins AFB; the Pima Air Museum, Tucson, Arizona; RAF Cosford, England; and possibly Maxwell AFB. However, the details for all of that would be worked out over time. The more important item to stay focused on was the continued combat operations of the 20th SOS in Iraq.[56]

58th Special Operations Wing/ 551st Special Operations Squadron Inactivation

As per the drawdown plan, activities at the Pave Low schoolhouse steadily waned. On 4 January, Col Tom Trask and Col John Maubach, the 58th SOG deputy commander, piloted MH-53J #66-4428, the first H-53 procured by the USAF 41 years earlier, on its last flight from Kirtland AFB down to the AMARC near Tucson. This mission was also Colonel Trask's official "*fini* flight" as a USAF pilot because he relinquished command of the 58th SOW to Col Eugene Haase four weeks later and moved to Maxwell AFB to serve as the commandant of the Squadron Officer's College and receive a promotion to brigadier general.

The 551st continued to train aircrew members until 31 March, by which time the last 11 pilots, 14 flight engineers, and four aerial gunners had been aircraft qualified and sent on to the 20th and 21st SOSs. The last listed qualified pilot was 1st Lt William Thompson—Pave Low pilot number 453. He was also very lucky because he was then held over at Kirtland and put into the CV-22 qualification course. The squadron cadre slowly began transferring out, with several pilot and flight engineer instructors going to the 71st SOS for CV-22 conversion, the gunners to HH-60s, others to nonflying jobs, and many into retirement. A small group of squadron personnel remained in place to accomplish the myriad details that were necessary to inactivate a training squadron, disperse its property and equipment, and attend to the endless administrative details that it all entailed.

On 27 April, the official inactivation ceremony took place, and Lt Col Todd Lancaster returned the squadron colors to 58th SOG commander Col Leonard Smales. In addressing the crowd, Smales stated the obvious by saying, "For those of us who have flown the -53, it's a sad day. . . . The guys who have flown the -53s will keep on the same

The last Pave Low from the 551st SOS was flown to Davis-Monthan AFB, Arizona, for storage by TSgt Steve Gelling, Lt Col Todd Lancaster, and MSgt Mark Mapel.

traditions, which . . . will carry far into the future."[57] Another unit pilot, Lt Col Brett Hauenstein, said of the Pave Low,

> The men made the machine what it is. The thing that is saddest for me is just the community of people that have been around and now are scattering off to do other things. Our community is really tight-knit. Those who've never flown the Pave might never understand. You have to wear the red scarf, its edges jauntily peeking out above the collar of the flight suit. Maybe you even have to sing Bon Jovi. But, mostly, you have to be part of a team that knows what happened to one happens to all.[58]

Six weeks later, MH-53J #66-14433 was enshrined in the 58th SOW's airpark near the Truman Gate. The venerable Black Knight, possessor of over 13,000 flying hours and veteran of combat in two wars, had found its last resting place, fittingly, at the very base where it had brought Pave Low to technological fruition. It had honorably trained uncounted Airmen to exploit its capabilities as only air commandos could and had well earned its final place of peace.[59]

21st Special Operations Squadron Inactivation

Facing the inevitable, Lt Col Kirk Smith resolved to keep his squadron as engaged as possible while steadily losing its personnel. As long as he could, he maintained his augmenting crews and support troops at Balad, Iraq, so that he could not only help the 20th with the continuing requirement there but also get the maximum number of his troops some combat experience. The squadron also deployed aircraft and crews on a final round of exercises to Norway, Albania, and Romania to participate with US and allied special forces units as long as flying hours were still available. On 29 June, Col Brad Webb relinquished command of the 352d SOG to Col Brian Cutts and departed for Hurlburt Field to take command of the 1st SOW and oversee the final inactivation of the Pave Lows.

The 21st SOS stopped its augmentation to Balad in June but flew operational sorties at home through August, averaging 23 local and 13 deployed sorties per month. In September the unit logged only 13, with five of those flown in one last formation over the coasts and fields of England on 13 September. On 9 October, Lt Col Kirk Smith presented the squadron guidon to Colonel Cutts for encasing, and the 21st SOS stood down. After the 21st closed, Colonel Smith went to AFSOC/A1 and worked to move Pave Low personnel throughout AFSOC. His purpose was straightforward, as he later explained,

> I considered it my responsibility to take that core competence of SOF culture and airmanship and push that out to other aspects of SOF, whether it's CV-22 or the blue airplanes that we are now flying at Cannon AFB. I had . . . gunners go back to the gunships [and] flight engineers go to CV-22s or the 6th SOS. The key was to take that core culture that we had. . . . Every community has its own culture, but the core air commando culture is what I wanted to send back out. . . . [I wanted to] populate the rest of AFSOC, as much as we could, with our small numbers from the 21st.[60]

The Pave Lows of the 21st SOS in formation along the cliffs of Dover

20th Special Operations Squadron/ Expeditionary Special Operations Squadron

Under the able leadership of Colonel Becklund, the 20th still maintained one-third of the unit on steady combat operations with the 20th ESOS at Balad, even as the unit was now beginning to lose aircraft and personnel in the fleet inactivation. Capt Derrick Stamos had transferred from the 21st to the 20th SOS in October 2006 and, within a month, was deployed to Balad on a 90-day tour as part of the steady crew rotation plan. He would ultimately complete six tours, remembering that going back over was like the movie *Groundhog Day*, where the main character was trapped in a time warp in which every day dawned as Groundhog Day, with the same set of situational experiences. However, in Iraq it was not benign daily events but "a mixture of direct action assaults and logistic runs" in support of US and allied special and conventional forces that framed the repetitive experiences.[61]

At the same time, the unit was also receiving the last crew members trained by the 551st. During the spring of 2007, the squadron received 18 pilots and flight engineers who needed mission readiness training. Colonel DeCaro was serving as an assistant DO and oversaw the training program. He worked with his instructors to provide the new crew members the mission readiness training they needed to deploy to Iraq, somewhat simpler now because all overwater training had been terminated. Additionally, the unit also needed to maintain the overall squadron upgrade program so that as the fleet of aircraft was drawn down, the 20th would still have the necessary first pilots, mission pilots, and instructors that it needed to carry out its last missions. One of his IPs was Capt Brian Roberts. Roberts had graduated from the Air Force Academy in 1998 and, like so many before him, went to Fort Rucker for his helicopter training and then did a tour in UH-1Ns before checking out in the Pave Low and reporting to the 20th SOS in January 2005. He subsequently served a series of three- to four-month tours at Balad, where he flew a variety of direct action missions and more mundane logistics missions in support of the US and allied special forces elements. He also steadily upgraded each time he came home—first to pilot, then to mission pilot and IP—a path facilitated and necessitated by the progressive departure of older, highly experienced pilots to CV-22s and other assignments.[62]

One of those last pilots from the 551st was 1st Lt Mark Hamilton. He had been commissioned in 2004 after graduating from the Virginia Military Institute. He attended pilot training at Vance AFB and selected the helicopter training track at Fort Rucker. Receiving his wings in February 2006, he proceeded to Kirtland for the Pave Low course. His experiences there were similar to the several generations of students that had preceded him. Arriving at the 20th in March 2007, he went directly through his mission readiness training in preparation for deployment to Iraq. Most flying was done with the squadron instructors and focused on specific tactical requirements such as mountain flying and AHHS qualification. However, his MH-53M conversion training was done mostly in the flight simulator with civilian instructors. He also received qualification training to conduct functional check flights. At Hurlburt the retired crews that worked for ARINC conducted these. However, since the ARINC contractors were not allowed to deploy to active theaters, the squadron needed a cadre of pilots and engineers to perform FCFs at deployed locations. To receive this training, Hamilton was able to fly with Tom Aldrich, Corby Martin, and Rick Simmon. These Pave Low veterans certainly qualified the young lieutenant to accomplish the FCFs. However, they were also training him on another level. Hamilton recalls of his encounter with these senior Pave Low Airmen, "I was a pretty green lieutenant, flying with some guys with serious Pave Low history to their names . . . flying with guys who . . . were some of the original authors of Pave Low. They were teaching me in a very quiet, experienced way. . . . [They] taught me a ton . . . from the second we briefed to the time we landed."[63]

Courtesy Rick Simmon

The ARINC Pave Low support team. *Left to right:* Frank Gray, Rick Dolby, Chris Prokosch (on aircraft), Darrel Carter, Joe Barnes, Jim Walters, Tom Aldrich, Rick Simmon, and Bill Smith.

In June Lt Col Gene Becker arrived from an assignment at USSOCOM to serve as the 20th SOS operations officer. Fortuitously, he was a highly experienced Pave Low pilot and able to requalify with the 20th SOS since there was now no other option. Becklund certainly needed him. CONUS exercise requirements were being curtailed as were collateral training requirements such as deck landing and night overwater qualifications, and the entire squadron training plan was in a high state of flux. Becklund was becoming concerned at the rate at which he was losing his more experienced pilots and engineers, the guys who had logged long years in Pave Low and had been to Desert Storm, Bosnia, and endless exercises with national assets across the United States. They were being replaced with new troops—determined and enthusiastic but inexperienced, nonetheless—such as Lieutenant Hamilton, who deployed to Iraq on his first tour in February 2008. There he was placed with an experienced crew that collectively introduced him to combat flying.[64]

However, Becklund was developing a solid cadre of younger officers and Airmen who had now logged a great deal of time operating in Iraq. Becklund explained of his crews, "All they knew was deploying back and forth, living in tents . . . and doing those direct action missions night after night. . . . Those guys' lives involved deploying forward for their 90-day rotation, coming home, taking leave, going right back into a train-up cycle 90 days before deployment, and then deploying again." Regardless of the changes now overtaking the 20th, the combat flying and conditions were no less dangerous, and Becklund had to make sure that the crews he was sending over were ready for combat and then closely monitor them, remembering the sage words of former USSOCOM commander Gen Peter Schoomaker, who always admonished his subordinate commanders to "never confuse enthusiasm for capability." More than once, Becklund had to tell his aircraft commanders, "I am not crazy about that. Let's change it this way."[65] He began requiring the crews to brief risk assessment specifically as part of every mission preparation and kept them focused almost exclusively on direct action missions.

Throughout 2007 the crews of the 20th flew 1,172 classified combat missions into insurgent-controlled locations and carried out 339 insurgent prisoners. On these and other support sorties, they carried 216,600 pounds of cargo and supplies to coalition troops. Additionally, they participated in uncounted missions to train thousands of Iraqi soldiers and special forces personnel to assume more and more of the fighting. And they were doing all of this with helicopters with an average age of 38.5 years.

With the cessation of 21st SOS augmentation in June, though, Becklund needed to change the way the 20th deployed crews to the 20th ESOS Balad. Until now, he had been rotating flights with four crews each on a 90-day cycle. Now he needed to supply six aircraft and crews. As the unit continued to lose aircraft and personnel at home, it was becoming increasing difficult to provide for deployment training for six crews at a time. Consequently, Becklund began to stagger his crews, swapping two crews every month on 90-day rotations so that he could maintain a range of experienced crews in-theater at any time. The flights and Airmen just had to adjust, and they did. Some Airmen ended up with shorter tours, some with longer tours; they could handle it. However, the rotations required constant management because the personnel situation was continually changing: training backing up because of maintenance or weather problems or crew members becoming sick, having family emergencies, and so forth. On one occasion, Becklund had to take a crew out of the rotation cycle because he just did not feel that it was ready to go. That was his job.

Colonel Becklund also started receiving levies from the USAF Personnel Center to dispatch his more senior NCOs to Iraq for 365-day tours as advisors to the Iraqi air force. That was a difficult challenge and heavily taxed the 20th SOS because they were exactly the same men whom he needed to work with his young Airmen and pilots.[66]

Several crews flew notable missions in Iraq. In May Maj Kevin Kozuch and his crew were leading a two-ship of Pave Lows to insert a special forces team into a landing zone to conduct a quick search for some missing Soldiers when both aircraft came under heavy and well-aimed enemy fire from several machine guns hidden in trucks. The gunners on both aircraft engaged the enemy while Kozuch's copilot contacted an orbiting AC-130 for supporting fire. Enemy fire damaged both Pave Lows, but the crews were then able to extract the special forces team that had collected critical information on the location of the missing Soldiers.

In August Maj Sean Hoyer commanded the lead aircraft in a five-ship formation of MH-53s and MH-60s on a direct action mission. During the infiltration, one of the MH-60s hit some wires with its tail rotor and crash-landed. Hoyer immediately shifted to a rescue operation and became the on-scene commander. He called in an orbiting AC-130 for top cover to hold back advancing enemy Soldiers and directed one of the other MH-53s to land and recover the crew and passengers of the MH-60. When all were safely retrieved, he extracted the remaining friendly forces and flew them to a medical facility for treatment. From a historical perspective, these were exactly the same kinds of missions that the 20th and 21st SOSs flew 35–40 years prior—and in some of the very same aircraft.

During this period, Capt Jonathan Graham was nominated for the Jabara Award for his sustained superior performance on his six combat tours as a Pave Low pilot. His nomination cited his constant selection to lead high-risk missions and his leadership of 23 joint and combined SOF air assault missions. While deployed, he developed detailed training programs for the increasingly inexperienced crews so that they could more quickly and thoroughly become combat ready and effective. He was selected for and received the award in 2008.[67]

At home the 20th remained busy as it slowly prepared for inactivation. The training load steadily decreased as the last Airmen trained at Kirtland arrived at the squadron, worked through their qualification on the MH-53M, and then prepared for combat. During the year, 68 percent of all squadron personnel deployed overseas, most to Iraq. The average length of deployment was 94 days, with over half of the squadron deploying for more than 180 days. During the year, too, 20th crews continued to test and perfect the AHHS system on the Pave Low. This was a task ready-made for the squadron's younger pilots, who had been raised on Xbox and Internet gaming technology and readily provided the critical human interface necessary for this system to work. The techniques they developed were then taught to all crews and exported to Balad. In the same vein, the squadron crews did some testing in conjunction with the 18th FLTS of a new landing system called the photographic landing augmentation system for helicopters (PhLASH). This was another attempt to deal with the dust-out problem. The system used an infrared camera to take a series of pictures of a landing zone just prior to the initiation of the brownout conditions. A computer would then combine those images with GPS navigational information, allowing the pilot to "fly the image" regardless of the dust. The system, developed by the Air Force Research Laboratory, showed great promise—if not so much for the retiring Pave Lows, then certainly for other helicopters or follow-on systems.

The 20th SOS was a dynamic place in a somewhat chaotic way. At one point, the 1st SOW Wing vice-commander, Col Tim Leahy, asked Becklund how it was going. His response was stoic: "Sir, it's like pushing a bus uphill, and every day the wheels fall off, and every day we put the wheels back on, and we keep pushing the bus uphill. [But] it's kind of hard . . . because you guys are asking me to dismantle something I love."[68]

The 20th SOS suffered another aircraft loss when MH-53M #69-5794 crashed on a night sortie on the ranges at Eglin AFB on 7 September 2007. Colonel Becklund was commanding the 20th ESOS at Balad at the time and working with the current CJSOAC commander, Col Greg Lengyel, when Becklund got the call from Colonel Becker that he and his crew of seven were practicing NVG insertions and extractions when the tail gunner sensed increasing vibrations during a landing approach and called for a "go-around." Becker took over from the copilot and initiated a right turn back to the landing zone for an immediate emergency landing. As he lined up for the approach, though, the aircraft went out of control and crashed. Fortunately, only two Airmen, A1C Bradley Jordan, a gunner, and Col William Nelson, a flight surgeon, were wounded seriously enough to require hospital care. Inspection determined that an intermediate gearbox in the tail pylon had failed, causing the vibrations and loss of control. The aircraft, a veteran of the *Mayaguez* rescue, where it was hit by 35 rounds of enemy fire, and of four combat rotations in Afghanistan/Iraq, was not recoverable. Now only 30 Pave Lows awaited retirement. Colonel Becklund could do little about the crash from Balad and relied on Becker to do all that needed to be done at Hurlburt to take care of those injured and the ensuing accident investigation. For his outstanding actions in handling the crash, Lt Col Gene Becker was nominated for the Koren Kolligian Jr. Trophy for 2007.[69]

A few days later, Colonel Lengyel stopped by Colonel Becklund's office at Balad to share the news that Becklund had been selected to attend the National War College in August 2008. While he was aware that this was a great opportunity, Becklund also knew this meant that he would not be the last commander of a Pave Low squadron. The 1st SOG commander, Col Dennis Pennell, informed Becklund that he would pass command of the squadron to Lt Col Gene Becker in June 2008.[70]

Air Force Special Operations Command

Within the Air Force Special Operations Command, Pave Low veterans steadily matriculated up through the ranks. On 1 October, AFSOC officially took control of Cannon AFB, and Col Tim Leahy assumed command of the 27th SOW. Since Leahy was a career Pave Low pilot, Pave Low officers now commanded both AFSOC wings. On 28 November 2007, newly promoted Lt Gen Donald Wurster assumed command of the AFSOC from General Wooley. This was another crowning event for the Pave Low community because Wurster was the first Pave Low pilot to be promoted to lieutenant general and also the first to command AFSOC.

Taking command, Wurster was swamped with a myriad of issues as AFSOC consolidated its finally achieved western base and worked through the strain of constant combat operations, aircraft acquisitions, and almost endless modifications. However, in one interview, he was able to share some thoughts about one particular group of air commandos that he especially admired. He said,

> Of all the people we have in our business today, most of us in AFSOC remain astounded at the skill and determination of the maintenance people who continue to spin gold from straw on the flight line and in the back shops to get these flying machines airborne every night. . . . The maintainers, who watch those big ugly birds go out and then greet them when they come back—those are the heroes of AFSOC. . . . Without those committed professionals, our command could not do what needs to be done.[71]

Anybody associated with Pave Low in any way would certainly second that accolade.

The general also had a soft spot in his heart for the venerable Pave Lows, and when asked to speak at the dedication ceremony for one of the aircraft at the Hurlburt Field Memorial Air Park, he could not refuse. The aircraft being dedicated was MH-53M #68-10928. This aircraft had started out as a CH-53C and had flown air commando operations in SEA with the 21st SOS at NKP, Thailand, and was in the *Mayaguez* rescue operation. After a long and distinguished operational history, its last flight in combat was with the 20th ESOS out of Balad, Iraq, on 29 July 2007 under the command of Maj Frank Cooper. Now it was cleaned up and ready to be enshrined in the airpark, right next to the main gate to Hurlburt Field, so that anybody entering the base would see it standing guard proudly. There is no full record of what General Wurster said to the crowd that day. However, he did point out that "this remarkable piece of equipment" belonged to two groups in the Pave Low community, "the crews who love and fear it and the crew chiefs who love and hate [it]." He was speaking to a sympathetic audience that day, many of its members wearing flight suits and red scarves. As 2007 ended, it was clear to all that over the next year, several more ceremonies like this would take place.[72]

Fini Pave Low

As 2008 began, the Pave Low fleet was in its twilight days. The 20th ESOS still operated at Balad, although meeting the tasking was progressively more difficult as personnel continued to leave the squadron. Colonel Becklund had to monitor his crews continually. In fact, both Col Brad Webb and Col Greg Lengyel served tours at Balad as the JSOAC commander and had begun to pull the Pave Lows back from the more demanding missions—a matter of risk assessment and operational necessity. As the calendar wound down, though, the rest of the year was just a series of "lasts."

One of the last 20th SOS pilots to deploy over to Balad was 1st Lt Dan Florence. A year earlier, he was the next-to-last pilot to complete the qualification course at the 551st SOS with 1st Lt Dave Hamilton and 1st Lt Bill Thompson. He had proceeded to Hurlburt but encountered numerous delays in his follow-on training. In May 2007, he went TDY to the 21st SOS and was able to fly several sorties with that unit in Europe before they stopped operations. Returning to Hurlburt, he received orders to Balad. However, he was not fully mission qualified and instead served a 45-day tour in one of the command centers there. Returning to Hurlburt in the fall, he was able to complete his aircraft mission qualification and, after volunteering several times to deploy, was finally dispatched in June 2008 to serve with the unit until it returned home. There he was assigned to a crew with Maj Brian Roberts, MSgt Mark Pryor, and TSgt Corey Fossbender. Initially, almost overwhelmed by all that was involved with combat flying, he learned quickly from this well-experienced crew and was soon flying his share of logistics sorties and direct action missions in which his crew assisted in the capture of al-Qaeda personnel and terrorists. Several of the missions were multiship formations with assaults directly into tight landing zones. Florence found the flying to be both challenging and rewarding. He had wanted to be a Pave Low pilot since he had first read about these aviators and the role they played in the Vega 31 rescue in 1999. He would log almost 70 hours of combat time in Iraq and return home with the rest of the unit in September.[73]

On 28 March, MH-53M #68-10357 was flown on its last career flight on a combat mission out of Balad. Flying it that night were pilots Lt Col Shawn Henrie and Capt Nathan Davidson, flight engineers MSgt Kevin James and TSgt Vince DePersio, and gunners MSgt Robert Strong and CMSgt John DeSalle. The mission involved an assault against an enemy position resulting in the capture of nine enemy combatants. The aircraft returned to home base mission ready. Instead, this last remaining veteran of the Son Tay raid into North Vietnam in 1970, call sign Apple 01, was dismantled for shipment by C-17 to Wright-Patterson AFB and permanent display in the US Air Force Museum. It arrived there still covered with the grit and grime of its last missions in Iraq. CMSgt John DeSalle sadly logged 357's *fini* flight as his last operational Pave Low sortie. Waxing nostalgic about the closeness and integration of the Pave Low crews, he said, "It's a closeness that other crews just don't have. . . . It's the same bond that connects all -53 crews and has created the 'Pave Low community.' Whether you were on a -53 in Vietnam or fly on a -53 today, you're part of that community. And it is more than that; it's a family."[74]

Courtesy CMSgt John DeSalle, USAF

CMSgt John DeSalle in Iraq

In May several of the aircraft were swapped out until only six were left with the 20th ESOS at Balad: 67-14995, 68-8284, 68-10924, 69-5785, 69-5790, and 70-1631. They would fly the last ever Pave Low sorties that would occur on combat missions—a most fitting end for such distinguished combat veterans and something that had never been accomplished by any other USAF aircraft.[75]

Maj Derrick Stamos was back at Hurlburt after his series of tours in Iraq. Now serving as an assistant operations officer, he began working on the dispersal of the remaining Pave Lows and coordinated his actions with Maj Fred Koegler, who was the project officer on the AFSOC staff. They tried to align the individual aircraft with locations with which they might have some personal history, similar to having MH-53J #66-14433 at Kirtland. Stamos coordinated with maintenance technicians to remove various classified equipment from the aircraft and began planning the delivery flights for the aircraft. To Stamos "it was a bittersweet thing to watch them go away."[76]

In May the 20th SOS held a grand combat dining-in at the main maintenance hangar on the east side of Hurlburt for USAF members only. The 20th SOS got all the necessary approvals and invited all the senior officers and NCOs on base. Brig Gen Tom Trask was asked to be the guest speaker. While playing the "Star-Spangled Banner," the audio equipment failed. Never one to miss the moment, Trask immediately began to sing, and all joined in. After dinner, he gave a great talk about Pave Low, rescue and special operations, and war and community. Retired major general Rich Comer was there, and General Wurster made a brief stop before leaving for another preplanned engagement. Then the games began, and the troops turned a bit rowdy. Colonel Webb checked with Colonel Becklund to ensure he had contingency plans so that the event would not get out of hand or that nobody would be arrested for drunk driving. As the combat obstacle course was opened and the dunking tank swung into high gear, Webb and several other more senior leaders departed. Regardless, the party went on for quite a while.[77]

In late May, back at Hurlburt, the 20th SOS deployed 90 operations and maintenance personnel and three helicopters to Roanoke, Virginia, for their last CONUS mountain deployment for TF/TA radar training. Colonel Becker led the team. A few days later, Colonel Becklund replaced him so that Becker could travel to Washington, DC, to receive the Koren Kolligian Jr. Trophy for his handling of the crash of MH-53M #69-5794 the previous September. Gen Duncan McNabb,

USAF vice chief of staff, presented him the award as family and friends watched.[78]

A week after they returned, Becker replaced Lt Col Vince Becklund as the last Pave Low commander of the 20th SOS. His operations officer was Lt Col Joe DeCaro, at the time deployed to Iraq as the 20th ESOS commander. At Hurlburt squadron members continued to fly local sorties through the summer. However, they also had to begin clearing out their squadron building and turning in vast quantities of equipment and Pave Low–unique items.

At the end of July, Becker deployed back to the 20th ESOS at Balad to serve as the commander with the last crews. They were still steadily flying their taskings. Becker could not help but marvel at his young crews. Flying missions as tough as any ever flown by earlier Pave Low crews, they were doing them night after night. He also agreed with General Comer's assessment that the Pave Low's greatest test and accomplishment came in the later years. He watched it happen every night as the last generation of young Pave Low crews maneuvered those still strong but tired Steel Horses in and out of one dangerous landing zone after another.[79]

At Hurlburt the squadron began ferrying the aircraft to their final destinations. On 5 September, Lt Col Sean Hoyer and crew flew MH-53M #73-1652, the last H-53 produced by Sikorsky for the USAF, the short distance to the Air Force Armament Museum at Eglin. This was a homecoming of sorts because that very aircraft had at one time been assigned to the 55th ARRSq when it was stationed at Eglin. It was one of the aircraft flown to Jonestown, Guyana, for the horrible recovery operation of over 900 bodies in the massacre that occurred there in November 1978.

On 12 September, the 20th received one last call to launch a Pave Low to support a domestic SAR operation. Hurricane Ike was sweeping through the Gulf of Mexico, heading for Texas. A disabled Cypriot-flagged freighter was in its path. The US Coast Guard wanted to evacuate the 22-man crew and called Hurlburt for help. Both a Pave Low and CV-22 launched to support the effort but had to turn back because of the strong and turbulent winds. Instead, a large tugboat was able to tow the ship to safety. It was a quiet but purposeful ending for Pave Low operations at Hurlburt.

That same day, Capt Mark Hamilton was ordered to fly MH-53 #73-1649 to the AMARC at Davis-Monthan. He had recently upgraded to first pilot on the Pave Low—the last one ever—and was the aircraft commander for the mission. It was his last Pave Low flight. In his relatively brief time in Pave Low, he logged almost 600 hours in the aircraft, a significant portion of which was in combat. He subsequently went on to fly the CV-22.[80]

Steadily, the aircraft disappeared. Colonel Becker also arranged to have senior contract pilots and engineers from the ARINC Corporation based in Fort Walton Beach fly the last Pave Low out. He did that for two reasons: first, he wanted to publicly acknowledge the enormous job the ARINC team had done over the years to help keep the Pave Low fleet as mission ready as possible while relieving 20th crews of FCF duties when at home station. Second, he also wanted to specifically honor the ARINC crew members (especially Rick Simmon) whose duty on CH/HH/MH-53 aircraft reached back 40 years. As a result, pilots Tom Aldrich and "Pappy" Walters, flight engineers Bill Smith and Simmon, and gunner SSgt Michael Tritt flew out the last Hurlburt aircraft, MH-53M #68-10369, on 16 September. Tritt was the only active duty person on board and remarked of his august crewmates, "They have about 150 years of experience between them." A large formation of 20th SOS troops were on the flight line to watch 68-10369 taxi out for takeoff, passing four new CV-22s of the 8th SOS and receiving a traditional washdown from the base fire trucks. As the aircraft lifted off, for the first time in 28 and a half years, there were no Pave Low helicopters on the ramp at Hurlburt. The ARINC crew ferried it to the Air Force Heritage Foundation Museum at Hill AFB, with a stop at the Air Force Academy in Colorado. To Simmon it was a poignant personal ending to his almost 30 years of flying the Steel Horse.[81]

Courtesy Jim Burns

The last Pave Low at Hurlburt, MH-53M #68-10369, departs on its retirement flight.

As intended, the 20th ESOS in Iraq would carry out the last flights. Crews flew their fragged sorties through the summer and into September. Colonel Becker worked with the CJSOAC to plan for one last mission that would include all of the remaining aircraft so that the detachment there could close out Pave Low as a unit. The mission was scheduled for 26 September. Maj Brian Roberts, now serving on his sixth combat rotation, was selected to serve as the flight lead. At the scheduled time, the crews were briefed and dispatched to their aircraft. They—well, we have already told that story.[82]

☆ ☆ ☆ ☆ ☆

Begun with such hope, the new millennium quickly fell prey to old and simmering conflicts that ripped asunder any hope of a benevolent age. After the horrific events of 9/11, the United States responded to the attacks with swift action as its military forces were dispatched to several areas of the globe. USSOCOM led that effort in most areas and supported theater commands in others. AFSOC elements were almost always involved, and the Pave Lows were in the thick of it. Reduced to just two operational squadrons because of the inexorable pressure of Initiative 17 and its persistent supporters, the remaining 20th and 21st SOSs were engaged in ongoing operations in Afghanistan, the Horn of Africa, and Iraq from right after 9/11 until fleet inactivation in September 2008. During that period, they did everything that the Pave Lows and even their predecessor HH- and CH-53s were designed to do: SAR, CSAR, direct action missions, NEOs, humanitarian-relief missions, civil disaster-relief missions, medevac, and so many other things divined on the spur of the moment by Airmen who were trained for and capable of thinking "outside the box." As ordered though, in September 2008 the Pave Lows were flown on their last sorties *ever* on combat taskings in Iraq. No other USAF aircraft has so ended its flying career.

While the aircraft may have departed, the Pave Low community itself remained. It had fully matured into that "unit of confidence," identified more than 30 years earlier by Joe Guilmartin in the aftermath of Koh Tang Island. That confidence had matured into a culture of professionalism, mentored to each succeeding generation and based upon high standards and a propensity to self-correct. General Trask explained that "one of the things that became part of our culture [was] you really got forced by your peers to focus on where you were and what you were doing. . . . 'Train like you fight.' . . . . Make sure that every day you are preparing and training . . . as realistically and thoroughly as possible." Echoing the words of General Comer, Trask added, "The great chapter of Pave Lows was written after 9/11, in my opinion. The amount of things they did and the amount of work they did . . . the days in Pakistan and Afghanistan, going well beyond their capabilities as far as power and altitude, just amazing things."[83]

Over its lifetime, the Pave Low community also spawned several generations of leaders who rose to high rank and responsibility in the AFSOC and USAF. An unofficial count conducted with the help of the AFSOC/A1 and several senior Pave Low individuals indicated that this community generated an estimated 60 squadron commanders, 18 group-level commanders, and 11 wing-level commanders. They came in all sizes and with all types of personalities. TSgt B. J. Jobling offered an enlisted troop's view of Pave Low leadership when he explained, "For a guy to be in charge of a group of that type of people took an exceptional leader. And we had exceptional leaders. I had six commanders, I think, starting with Jack Hester. For somebody to be able to stand up and say, 'All you cowboys and clowns and assholes and . . . whatever. . . .' To lead, and to lead unquestioningly, took a certain caliber of man. And we had them. My hat is off to the guy who could lead that rabble."[84]

For the larger enlisted Airman community, there is no way to determine the considerable number of individuals who rose to senior NCO leadership as did CMSgts Tom Green and John DeSalle. Their contributions and impact were just as immense, reflecting that "the enlisted troops provided the steadfast continuity of knowledge and experience which was a staple of Pave Low," as pointed out by CMSgt Jim Mecke.[85]

No doubt, there is among the younger generation another cohort just as capable, and it is now flowing out through the AFSOC and USAF and using what it so earnestly learned in its Pave Low days to perform other missions with other "tools," as Jobling highlighted.

Lt Col Scott Howell believed that mentoring and leadership development were two of the real strengths of the Pave Low community and, along with Lt Col Kirk Smith, worked to facilitate that flow of Pave Low guys into the CV-22, the newly developing U-28, and the RPV programs. He believed that "exporting the culture" of Pave Low was a useful and laudable goal and a way to further derive benefit from the heritage of Pave Low.

His successor commander at the 20th SOS, Lt Col Vince Becklund, took that thought a bit further when he remarked that "the heritage of the Pave Low community will not be the missions we did; it will be the continued leadership that [we] provide . . . throughout AFSOC."[86]

As the aircraft steadily disappeared, the sense of loss was palpable among the Pave Low veterans. After his last ferry flight, SMSgt Rick Simmon commented, "She was such a good bird and I think that she has a lot left to offer, so it is really sad to see her go." B. J. Jobling expressed, "Taking them to the boneyard is one of the saddest things ever." Lt Col Kent Landreth, now commanding the 18th Flight Test Squadron at Hurlburt, was a bit more blunt in his remarks and caustic in his tone when he pointed out that "the most capable helicopter on the planet now sits in the boneyard."[87]

From a longer historical perspective, though, the inactivation of the Pave Low fleet reflected the reality that Initiative 17, drafted 24 years earlier and directing the USAF to *"transfer the responsibility for providing rotary wing lift support for SOF to the Army,"* had ultimately come to a full and final conclusion.[88]

And so it was.

Courtesy USAF 309th Aerospace Maintenance and Regeneration Group

"The most capable helicopter on the planet now sits in the boneyard."
—Lt Col Kent Landreth

Notes

1. Wright and Reese, *On Point II*, 28, 36; and Williams, interview. Sijan Award data provided to author by Lt Col Joe Michalek.
2. Williams to the author, e-mail, 7 Aug 2010.
3. Wright and Reese, *On Point II*, 38–39.
4. Colannino, interview.
5. Berry, interview.
6. Mission narrative provided to author by Maj Steve Edwards.
7. West, *No True Glory*, 148–51.
8. History of 16th SOW, 1 Jan–31 Dec 2004, vol. 1, 34; and Air Force Instruction 36-2805, *Special Trophies and Awards*, para. 4.6.
9. Williams, interview.
10. Wright and Reese, *On Point II*, 172–73.
11. History of 352d SOG, 1 Jan 2004–31 Dec 2005, vol. 1, vi, 3; and Slife, interview.
12. Slife, interview.
13. Slife and Williams, interviews; and Wright and Reese, *On Point II*, 44.
14. History of 58th SOW, 1 Jan–31 Dec 2004, vol. 1, 7, 12, 15, 28, 36.
15. Holder, interview.
16. History of AFSOC, 1 Jan–31 Dec 2004, vol. 1, 20; and Slife to the author, e-mail, 25 July 2010.
17. History of AFSOC, 1 Jan–31 Dec 2004, vol. 1, 1, 37–38.
18. Ibid., 12–14.
19. Slife, interview; and Slife to the author, e-mail, review comments, 13 Sept 2010.
20. Howell, interview.
21. DeSalle, interview.
22. Ibid.
23. Berry, interview.
24. Williams and Howell, interviews.
25. Becklund, interview.
26. Kradel, interview.
27. Matlock to the author, e-mail.
28. Howell, interview; and History of 16th SOW, 1 Jan–31 Dec 2005, vol. 1, 32.
29. Jamie Haig, "Three Years Running: HMXS Named AF 'Best of Best,' " *Commando*, 6 May 2005, 6; and "HMXS 16th Helicopter Maintenance Squadron," *Commando*, 20 May 2005, 14.
30. History of AFSOC, 1 Jan–31 Dec 2005, vol. 1, 121–29; History of 16th SOW, 1 Jan–31 Dec 2005, vol. 1, 5, 32; and Howell, interview.
31. Becklund, interview.
32. Cardoso, interviews.
33. History of AFSOC, 1 Jan–31 Dec 2005, vol. 1, 66, 89, 96.
34. Ibid., 75.
35. Ibid., 76–77.
36. History of 58th SOW, 1 Jan–31 Dec 2005, vol. 1, 16–20, 39.
37. Ibid., ix, 3; and Trask and Holder, interviews.

38. History of 58th SOW, 1 Jan–31 Dec 2006, vol. 1, 3–4, 32–34.

39. History of AFSOC, 1 Jan–31 Dec 2006, vol. 1, 9.

40. Ibid., 7–10; and Davis, *31 Initiatives*, 110.

41. History of AFSOC, 1 Jan–31 Dec 2006, vol. 1, 12–15.

42. Ibid., 43; and Lt Gen Michael Wooley to CDRUSSOCOM, memorandum, 31 July 2006, received from Lt Col Vince Becklund.

43. History of 1st SOW, 1 Jan–31 Dec 2006, vol. 1, 2.

44. History of AFSOC, 1 Jan–31 Dec 2007, vol. 1, 22.

45. History of 58th SOW, 1 Jan–31 Dec 2006, vol. 1, 43–45, 59.

46. Smith, interview; and History of 352d SOG, 1 Jan–31 Dec 2006, vol. 1, vi, 2–3.

47. Stamos, interview.

48. History of 352d SOG, 1 Jan–31 Dec 2006, vol. 1, 7–12, 23; and Smith, interview.

49. History of 1st SOW, 1 Jan–31 Dec 2006, vol. 1, 37, and supplemental doc., 20th SOS Nomination for the Special Operations Squadron of the Year; and Becklund, interview.

50. Howell, interview.

51. History of 1st SOW, 1 Jan–31 Dec 2006, vol. 1, 37, and supplemental doc., 20th SOS Nomination for the Special Operations Squadron of the Year.

52. Howell, interview.

53. Becklund and Howell, interviews.

54. White House, "President's Address to the Nation," press release, 10 Jan 2007, http://georgewbush-whitehouse.archives.gov/news/releases/2007/01/20070110-7.html.

55. Daley to the author, e-mail, 10 Sept 2010.

56. History of AFSOC, 1 Jan–31 Dec 2007, vol. 1, 61–62; and History of 1st SOW, 1 Jan–31 Dec 2007, vol. 1, supplemental doc., AFSOC Aircraft Inventory, 2 Jan 2008, 6.

57. Maier, "551st Special Operations Squadron Deactivates."

58. Phil Casaus, "Pave Low, Sweet Chariot: The Choppers Fly Out of Kirtland for the Last Time," *Albuquerque Tribune*, 21 May 2007, n.p.

59. History of 58th SOW, 1 Jan 2007–31 Dec 2008, vol. 1, 6–8.

60. History of 352d SOG, 1 Jan–31 Dec 2007, vol. 1, 1, 3, 8, 64; and Smith, interview.

61. Stamos, interview.

62. DeCaro and Roberts, interviews.

63. Hamilton, interview.

64. Gene Becker and Hamilton, interviews.

65. Becklund, interview.

66. Becklund, interview; and History of 1st SOW, 1 Jan–31 Dec 2007, supplemental doc. 2103, 20th SOS Nomination for AFSOC Squadron of the Year, n.d.

67. History of 1st SOW, 1 Jan–31 Dec 2007, vol. 1, 18–20, and supplemental doc. 2103, 20th SOS Nomination for AFSOC Squadron of the Year, n.d.; and Citation for the 2008 Colonel James Jabara Award for Airmanship, presented to Capt Jonathan Graham, provided to the author by Captain Graham.

68. Becklund, interview.

69. Executive Summary, Aircraft Accident Investigation MH-53M S/N 69-05794, Hurlburt Field, Florida, 7 Sept 2007, USAF Safety Center, Kirtland AFB; Becklund, interview; and "Crash Crew Recovering," *Hurlburt Patriot*, 14 Sept 2007, 3.

70. Becklund, interview.

71. Gresham, "Interview: Lt Gen Donald C. Donny Wurster," 11.

72. History of AFSOC, 1 Jan–31 Dec 2007, vol. 1, 62.

73. Florence, interview.

74. Chapman, "AFSOC Retires a Legend, Hero," 32; and DeSalle, interview.

75. History of 1st SOW, 1 Jan–31 Dec 2008, vol. 1, 91; and History of AFSOC, 1 Jan–31 Dec 2008, vol. 1, 504.

76. Stamos, interview.

77. Becklund, interview.

78. Amy Oliver, "SOS Completes Final Training in Mountains," *Hurlburt Patriot*, 13 June 2008, 3; and Becker to the author, e-mail, 19 Sept 2010.

79. Gene Becker, interview; and History of 1st SOW, 1 Jan–31 Dec 2008, vol. 1, 72.

80. Hamilton, interview.

81. TSgt Kristina Newton, "Engineer Wraps Up 30 Years of Pave Low," *Hurlburt Patriot*, 31 Oct 2008, 2.

82. History of 1st SOW, 1 Jan–31 Dec 2008, vol. 1, 73; and Becker, interview.

83. Trask, interview.

84. Jobling, interview.

85. Mecke, interview.

86. Becklund, interview.

87. Newton, "Engineer Wraps Up 30 Years of Pave Low," 2; and Jobling and Landreth, interviews.

88. Davis, *31 Initiatives*, 111.

Chapter 18

Standing Down

The art of war is subject to many modifications by industrial and scientific progress. However, there is truly one constant, and that is the heart of man.

—Ardant du Picq

Enduring Heritage

Ardant du Picq was a French officer who fought and died in the 1870 Franco-Prussian War. A great student of the art of war, he wrote prolifically about the human element in battle. Living through that colossal time of change, du Picq developed a deep appreciation of the impact of technology on warfare but intuitively knew that the weapons were really only tools to be used by the man in the arena. He knew that man himself was the weapon, and at the core of this combination was the "heart of man."[1]

At du Picq's point in history, he could not have imagined anything as sophisticated as the Pave Low. However, he would have clearly understood that it would take highly spirited and solidly confident individuals to make those machines function to their full capacity. It was the synergy of the aircraft and crews that made Pave Low successful. Every crew was unique; Lt Col Brad Webb understood that when he said that "each crew had its own DNA" and that its cohesiveness and ability to function under intense pressure were key to safe and effective operations.

TSgt B. J. Jobling addressed this cohesion a bit differently but just as descriptively when he pointed out that the airplane "was almost the seventh crew member. But, at the end of the day, that airplane is just a tool. What made it all work was six guys who would not have gotten along stuck in an elevator together. For those six guys to work in concert as one unit was what made this airplane."[2] Corby Martin, ever the more direct individual, said in his own pithy way, "You get so that you are part of the machine. . . . I felt I was part of the helicopter. It was part of my body."[3]

These words speak powerfully to the bonds that were created between the men and their technologically advanced aircraft—a message that resonates throughout the entire history of Pave Low. Du Picq himself would surely have agreed.

Life, though, waits for no one. The veterans of Pave Low would have many more roads to travel and challenges to meet. The courage, devotion, dedication, and professionalism that they had developed in the community of Pave Low would now be applied to other units, specialties, and crises so surely to appear. It was Lt Col Vince Becklund who captured this reality when he asserted, "Those guys were all Pave Low aircrew members, and now they are the future leaders of AFSOC. That will be the heritage of Pave Low."[4]

Hurlburt Field

Ten days after those final sorties, Lt Col Gene Becker arrived back at Hurlburt with most of his Airmen. The combat flying was over, and the flight line at Hurlburt was empty; however, they had a great deal to do at home. Squadron troops were steadily departing, and those who remained had to go through their administrative processing. They had to clean and vacate the squadron building and turn in equipment. The remaining troops had to prepare for a final gala dinner and an inactivation ceremony on 16 and 17 October, respectively. Even in its last days, the sole Pave Low unit remained at a high ops tempo.

The dinner was held at the Soundside Club at Hurlburt. It had once been the Officers' Club and was a familiar setting for such occasions. Several hundred squadron members, veterans, and guests attended. The evening proceeded as expected, and after dinner, Becker made a few remarks. In an effort to honor all of the old veterans of the 20th SOS and Pave Low in attendance, he presented a special award to retired major John Grove for his 20-plus years of support to the squadron, both on active duty and in retirement. The audience watched a special DVD that SSgt Chris Curtis created to celebrate the distinguished career of the 20th SOS, shown, of course, to the sound of Bon Jovi playing its theme song "Wanted Dead or Alive."

The featured speaker for the evening was Lt Gen Donny Wurster. He had taken a direct interest in the inactivation of the Pave Lows. Additionally, he had been corresponding with Col Ron Thurlow, USAF, retired, an avid military historian who had developed a comprehensive knowledge of the history of those aircraft. Thurlow shared his work with Wurster, who then used a goodly portion of it at an earlier 20th SOS dining-in and at the enshrinement ceremony for MH-53M #68-10357 at the National Museum of the US Air Force at Wright-Patterson AFB three months earlier. At this last dinner, though, Wurster, as a Pave Low veteran, was among his own community of fellow veterans and could be much more personal and direct in his remarks.

Courtesy Col Darrel Whitcomb, USAF, Retired

Lt Gen Donny Wurster speaks at the inactivation dinner.

He began by talking about the aircraft. He reviewed the composition of the fleet as it was drawn from the USAF acquisition of the 52 HH-53s and the 20 CH-53s for duty in SEA. From that collection, 22 aircraft were lost in combat operations, and another 20 crashed and were destroyed. Of the remaining 30, 20 had also been in serious accidents but had been rebuilt which, incredibly, meant that of the 72 aircraft built, 62 had catastrophically impacted the ground—some more than once. Those numbers attest to the high-risk nature of the missions that the aircraft flew over their life span, the countless flight hours logged in almost every significant conflict in which the United States had participated in the last 40 years.

His remarks about the aircraft, though, were just a prelude to his key points. The general could no longer resist his enthusiasm to talk about the people who flew those machines. He referred back to the rescue crews that initially developed the early technology as precursor to Pave Low and the special operations crews that adapted the CH-53s to their mission set. He told of the development of Pave Low III by Frank Pehr, Steve Connelly, and Rick Simmon, and especially their initial missions across the Nellis AFB test ranges where nobody had detected them. He talked of the transfer of the Paves to Hurlburt that had moved Pave Low from rescue into special operations and the efforts to procure congressional support for more aircraft. At that point, he asked Gary Weikel and Ed Reed to stand as he explained their roles in these events, as well as that of their mentor, Bill Takacs, who provided the necessary leadership to integrate the Pave Low into the 20th SOS and special operations. Wurster spoke of the initial unsuccessful efforts to transfer the Pave Lows to the Army as part of Initiative 17 and the successful efforts to modify the aircraft—first to the J- and then the M-models—ever improving and equipping them with the latest navigational, communications, countermeasure, and safety equipment. He explained how the SLEP programs had enhanced the aircraft and kept them flying for over four decades, lauding the services of the unnamed specialists in the various logistics centers who had played a major role in that accomplishment. Many of them were still working on refinements to the aircraft's ability to land in brownout conditions even as it faced its final inactivation. He honored the maintainers—long-suffering and almost always in the background—but so critical to the success of Pave Low.

General Wurster also pointed out that this fleet of 72 aircraft had been flown on missions from Southeast Asia to Iraq, with so many places in between, leading to the awarding of 13 Air Force Crosses, 140 Silver Stars, and uncounted Distinguished Flying Crosses and Air Medals to its crew members. These numbers demonstrated that, ultimately, the success of Pave Low was due to its operators, those who had adopted its legacy of courage, each one hoping that his performance would prove him worthy to be counted as a brother in that very select community of Pave Low. He talked about that one true constant—the heart of man—that was at the center of the essence of Pave Low. The general concluded his talk with his personal vignette of the last flight in Iraq, just three weeks earlier. He told the audience,

After landing and shutdown, the mood was subdued but respectful. The early dawn showed the outlines of the big birds that would never fly again. Crews and maintainers traded hugs and signed their names on the machines as part of this worthy history. As I walked around the machines, I did not endure a sense of loss. It was the first time that I recognized that these machines looked war-worn and perhaps a bit tired, but proud of their service, faithful to their mission and calling, and committed to the end. Their stately elegance and now-silent repose reminded me of a verse from Paul the Apostle in the letter to Timothy that says, "I have fought the good fight, I have finished the race, I have kept the faith." And they have.[5]

The formal grand inactivation ceremony for both the Pave Low and the 20th SOS was the next day. Under a brilliant blue sky and a favoring gentle onshore breeze, a large mixed crowd of military and civilians gathered in the airpark next to Pave Low #68-10928 for the event. The 1st SOG commander, Col Dennis Pannell, officiated. He introduced retired colonel Steve Connelly, who provided the invocation and said,

> We gather in this airpark today . . . in this ceremony of remembrance and commemoration. We ask your blessings on us and on our nation, on these men and women among us still in uniform, on their families and ours.
>
> So ends the last chapter in the Pave Low MH-53 saga. Without question, the finest hour has been run, and a near-half-century long-distance race has been finished in a sprint. . . . The last men have built on all before them to make the close of this chapter the best in the book.
>
> We especially remember those few who yielded their lives in the line of duty, and we remember their families; they were the best of what we and the nation could offer in service. . . . Bless us Lord as we stand before you and remember.[6]

In his comments, Colonel Pannell stated, "The MH-53 has been a cornerstone in Special Operations airpower." He called upon the audience to bring to mind how the courage and resolve that the 20th SOS showed in Southeast Asia "continued through the 1980s . . . Desert Storm and the Balkans" and into the global war on terror, where its Airmen executed "thousands of missions after the 11 September 2001 attack." Pannell praised Colonel Becker for his leadership in the last difficult days, calling them "a leadership nightmare," which Becker handled in fine style.[7]

Colonel Becker spoke next. He thanked the crowd but, most importantly, thanked his troops for their admirable terminal efforts in Iraq and overall professionalism. When finished, he and Colonel Pannell cased the colors of the 20th SOS. Becker then presented a

Lt Col Gene Becker speaks at the Pave Low inactivation ceremony standing in front of MH-53M #68-10928 in the Hurlburt Field Memorial Air Park.

Pave Low commanders. *Left to right:* Col Joe Becker; Col Jim Slife; Col Gary Weikel, USAF, Retired; Col Steve Otto; Brig Gen Tom Trask; and Col Scott Howell.

memorial plaque to the wing commander, Col Brad Webb, which had inscribed upon it the names of the 12 Airmen who lost their lives while serving on Pave Lows. In accepting the plaque, Webb echoed the words of praise and remembrance of Pannell and Becker. He continued by saying, "This is the most brilliant helicopter and most brilliant helicopter force that have ever existed." Then, echoing the words of Lieutenant Colonels Howell, Smith, and Becklund, he added, "This culture is not going away. It lives on in the CV-22, U-28, AC-130H, AC-130U, Mi-17, UH-1, the Predator. The list goes on and on." It was exactly the right sentiment to conclude the bittersweet event.[8]

Later that evening, the 20th troops and guests gathered together at one of the local hotels for a more informal barbeque, celebration, and last hoorah. Several hundred attended, and as the evening progressed, they enjoyed the food, beer, and easy camaraderie. Some of the old veterans showed up, too. Steve Connelly was there, constantly surrounded by a clutch of younger officers eager to hear his stories of early Pave Low. John Grove was there, tending to the squadron "store" and attempting to sell off the last stocks of 20th SOS shirts, hats, and other memorabilia. Later in the evening, General Wurster stopped by; he was quickly and steadily engaged by a constant stream of former Pave Low mates and friends who wanted to pay their respects or just share a portion of his time. He stayed with them for a bit, enjoying their company, knowing that even though the Pave Lows were now gone, it was here, in these fine young officers and Airmen, that the heritage of this great community now resided.

Somewhere in the gathering, somebody turned on a CD player, and the music began to sweep over the crowd. Again, it was Bon Jovi playing the familiar tunes of its anthem, "I'm a cowboy, on a steel horse I ride. . . ." As the crowd began to sing along, one could not help but sense that as long as these Airmen were alive and still serving, Pave Low itself would survive in some form or manner—an indelible fact that gave another dimension to the oft-quoted mantra that "Pave Low leads."

Provocatively, too, it suggested that as phenomenal and enduring as the saga of the Pave Low machines and men was, perhaps some of its best chapters were yet to be written. And that is a comforting thought.

Official White House photo by Pete Souza

They still serve. Pave Low veteran Brig Gen Brad Webb, serving as the JSOC assistant commanding general, briefs Pres. Barack Obama, Vice Pres. Joe Biden, and other senior leaders and officers on the operation to capture Osama bin Laden on 1 May 2011.

Notes

1. Jacobs, "Human Element of Battle," 36.
2. Jobling, interview.
3. Martin, interview
4. Becklund, interview.
5. Prepared comments by Lt Gen Donny Wurster, induction ceremony, MH-53M #68-10357 to the National Museum of the US Air Force, in Burns, "Green Hornets Case Their Flag," USAF Rotorheads website; and Lt Gen Donny Wurster, comments, 20th SOS dining-out, 10 Nov 2007, recorded by the author.
6. Remarks by Col Steve Connelly, USAF, retired, provided to the author.
7. Kenneth Brook, "An Era Ends for MH-53, 20th SOS," *Hurlburt Patriot*, 24 Oct 2008, 1.
8. Ibid.

Epilogue

In Memoriam to Those Lost

*We especially remember those few who yielded their lives in
the line of duty, and we remember their families; they were
the best of what we and the nation could offer in service.*

—Col Steve Connelly, USAF, Retired

Pave Low Warriors Who Gave Their Lives While Flying MH-53s in Service to Their Nation

Maj James Prowell	Philippines	17 Oct 1984
Capt Michael Skeen		
TSgt Wayne Johnson		
TSgt Thomas Ortiz Jr.		
SSgt Robert Barker		
SSgt Max Lincks Jr.		
Maj Richard Brims	USA	21 May 1986
SSgt Kurt Upton	USA	3 June 1999
Maj Steven Plumhoff	Afghanistan	23 Nov 2003
MSgt William Kerwood		
TSgt Howard Walters		
SSgt Thomas Walkup Jr.[1]		

Pave Low Warriors Who Gave Their Lives While Flying CV-22s in Service to Their Nation

Maj Randall Voas	Afghanistan	8 Apr 2010
SMSgt James Lackey[2]		

Notes

1. Kenneth Brook, "An Era Ends for MH-53, 20th SOS," *Hurlburt Patriot,* 24 Oct 2008, 1.

2. "2 Hurlburt Airmen Die in CV-22 Crash," *Hurlburt Patriot,* 16 Apr 2010.

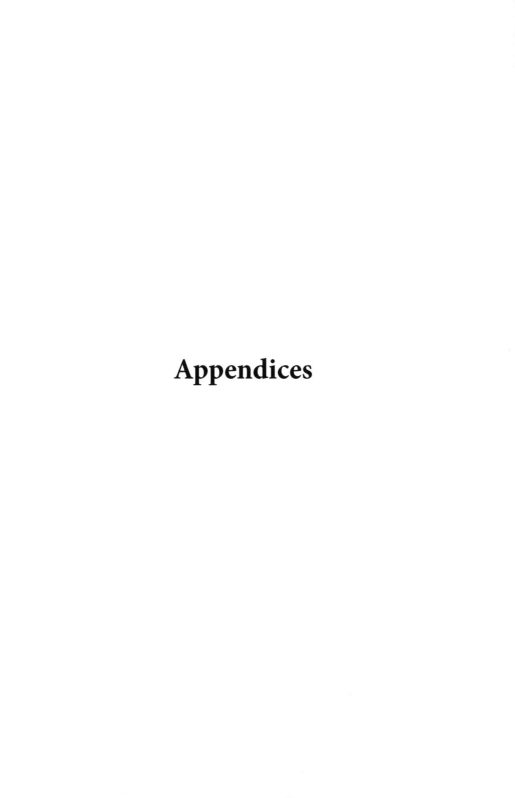

Appendices

Appendix A

Tail Number Listing of All USAF CH/HH/MH/NCH/TH-53 Aircraft

HH-53B (8 Aircraft)

66-

14428 Pave Low
14429 Pave Low
14430
14431 Pave Low
14432 Pave Low
14433 Pave Low (first prototype)
14434
14435

HH-53C (4 Aircraft)

67-

14993 Pave Low, MH-53M
14994 Pave Low, MH-53M
14995 Pave Low, MH-53M: Last mission 26–27 Sept 2008, Iraq
14996

HH-53C (20 Aircraft)

68-

8283
8284 Pave Low, MH-53M: Last mission 26–27 Sept 2008, Iraq
8285
8286 Pave Low, MH-53M
10354
10355
10356 Pave Low
10357 Pave Low, MH-53M
10358 Pave Low
10359
10360 Pave Low

10361
10362
10363 Pave Low
10364 Pave Low
10365
10366
10367 Pave Low
10368
10369 Pave Low, MH-53M: Last Pave Low at Hurlburt Field

CH-53C (12 Aircraft)

68-

10922
10923 Pave Low
10924 Pave Low, MH-53M: Last mission 26–27 Sept 2008, Iraq
10925
10926
10927
10928 Pave Low, MH-53M
10929
10930 Pave Low, MH-53M
10931
10932 Pave Low
10933

HH-53C (14 Aircraft)

69-

5784 Pave Low, MH-53M
5785 Pave Low, MH-53M: Last mission 26–27 Sept 2008, Iraq
5786
5787
5788
5789 Pave Low
5790 Pave Low, MH-53M: Last mission 26–27 Sept 2008, Iraq
5791 Pave Low, MH-53M
5792
5793 Pave Low, MH-53M
5794 Pave Low, MH-53M

5795 Pave Low, MH-53M
5796 Pave Low, MH-53M
5797 Pave Low, MH-53M

CH-53C (8 Aircraft)

70-

1625 Pave Low, MH-53M
1626 Pave Low, MH-53M
1627
1628
1629 Pave Low, MH-53M
1630 Pave Low, MH-53M
1631 Pave Low, MH-53M: Last mission 26–27 Sept 2008, Iraq
1632

HH-53C (6 Aircraft)

73-

1647 Pave Low
1648 Pave Low, MH-53M
1649 Pave Low, MH-53M
1650 Pave Low
1651 Pave Low
1652 Pave Low, MH-53M

USMC Aircraft Used as TH-53As

66-

14468
14469
14470
14471
14472
14473

67-30046

NCH-53A Aircraft Intermittently Listed as Part of the USAF H-53 Fleet

63-

13693
13694

These two aircraft were initially procured from the USMC to serve as testing platforms for the retrieval systems used by the "Crested Rooster" HH-53s based with the 6594th Test Group in Hawaii. When that program was inactivated, the aircraft were demodified and subsequently used as supplemental trainer aircraft.[1]

Notes

1. Air Force Special Operations Command (AFSOC)/A4MYH to Mr. Tim Brown, AFSOC History Office, e-mail, 2 Sept 2008; Sikorsky Aircraft Ship Number Master List, 8 June 2002, Sikorsky Archives, Stratford, CT; USAF H-53 Tail Number History, www.PaveCave.com; History of 542d Crew Training Wing, 1 Jan–30 Jun 1993, vol. 1, 55; and History of AFSOC, 1 Jan–31 Dec 1999, vol. 1, 154.

Appendix B

Pave Low Squadron Commanders

20th Special Operations Squadron

Lt Col

George Borinski Jr.	1 Jan 1980
William Takacs	18 Aug 1980
Wayne Corder	10 Aug 1982
Louis Grant	16 July 1984
Horace Johnson	2 July 1986
Gary Weikel	10 July 1988
Richard Comer	11 June 1990
Russell Rakip	8 June 1992
Donald Hoover	10 June 1994
Michael Homan	26 June 1995
Thomas Hull	30 Aug 1996
Jack Hester III	30 July 1998
Thomas Trask	16 July 1999
Michael Kingsley	1 Feb 2001
Marshall Webb	27 June 2002
R. K. Williams	1 July 2003
Scott Howell	1 June 2005
Vincent Becklund	11 Jan 2007
Eugene Becker	13 June 2008–
	17 Oct 2008[1]

21st Special Operations Squadron

Lt Col

Stephen Connelly	3 June 1988
Robert Zdenek	25 June 1990
Mike Russell	15 May 1992
Donald Wurster	9 July 1993
Jeffrey Walls	11 July 1994
Douglas Salmon	17 July 1996
Paul Harmon	17 July 1998
Timothy Minish	30 June 2000

Joseph Becker	26 June 2001
Greg Lengyel	9 July 2002
James Slife	21 June 2004
Kirk Smith	10 Feb 2006–
	9 Oct 2007[2]

31st Special Operations Squadron

Lt Col

Dale Cook	6 April 1989
Lee Massey	4 Aug 1990
Eugene Correll	18 Dec 1991
Craig Jensen	20 Dec 1993
Robert Hunt	13 Dec 1994
Lyle Koenig	7 July 1995
Clayton Spriet	26 July 1996
Steven Dreyer	4 Aug 1997
Tracey Goetz	3 Aug 1998
Steven Otto	16 July 1999
Brendan Clare	30 June 2000–
	31 March 2001[3]

1551st Flying Training Squadron
551st Flying Training Squadron
551st Special Operations Squadron

Lt Col

Paul Jacobs	1 Nov 1988
John Folkerts	28 June 1990
Michael Planert	1 July 1991
Michael Damron	11 June 1993
Robert Maldonado	26 July 1995
Thomas O'Boyle	2 June 1997
Dennis Jones	4 June 1999
Timothy Leahy	8 June 2001
Lance Bodine	20 June 2003
Charles Nussman	4 Feb 2005
Todd Lancaster	13 Feb 2006–
	8 Dec 2007[4]

Notes

1. Various 1st Special Operations Wing (SOW) and 16th SOW histories.
2. Various 39th SOW and 352d Special Operations Group histories.
3. Crawford, "Nomads of the Pacific," pamphlet, Air Force Special Operations Command History Office, Hurlburt Field, FL.
4. Various 1550th Combat Crew Training Wing, 542d Crew Training Wing, and 58th SOW histories.

Appendix C

Crews on the Last Flight,
26–27 Sept 2008

Cowboy 21 (MH-53M #69-5785)

Maj Brian Roberts
Capt Dan Florence
SMSgt Mark Pryor
SrA Justin Foster
TSgt Corey Fossbender
SSgt William Sell
Lt Col Gene Becker
Lt Gen Donald Wurster
Lt Col Larry Riddick

Cowboy 22 (MH-53M #70-1631)

Capt Eric Maddox
Capt Michael Blough
TSgt Shawn Watkins
SSgt Carl Smith
TSgt Michael Welles
SSgt Andrew Bickham

Cowboy 23 (MH-53M #67-14995)

Capt Brian Daniels
Capt Scott Dunning
TSgt Morris Jefferson
TSgt Terry Hobbs
TSgt Daniel Mann
SrA Justin Trumpower
Col John Hicks

Cowboy 24 (MH-53M #68-0924)

Capt Keith Snook
Capt Matthew Gidley
MSgt Kevin James
TSgt Jesse Kennedy
MSgt Robert Strong
SrA Brooks Sadilek

Cowboy 25 (MH-53M #69-5790)

Capt Ryan Vanveelen
Capt Andrew Billhartz
TSgt Vincent DePersio
TSgt James Rhodes
SSgt Matthew Garcia
TSgt Linwood Stull

Cowboy 26 (MH-53M #68-8284)

Maj Philip Cooper
Capt Peter Hettinger
TSgt Henry Woodie
A1C Joshua Lucas
SSgt Shawn Lewis
SrA Eric Harp
Col Scott Howell[1]

Notes

1. Flight crew lists, provided by Lt Col Gene Becker to the author.

Appendix D

Pave Low Distinguished Awards

Mr. Clarence Mackay Trophy

Sanctioned by the USAF, the Mackay Trophy recognizes the most meritorious flight of the year by an Air Force person, persons, or organization.

(1991) The Crew of Moccasin 04, 20th Special Operations Squadron (SOS):

Capt Thomas Trask
Maj Michael Homan
MSgt Tim Hadrych
TSgt Greg Vanhyning
TSgt James Peterson Jr.
SSgt Craig Dock
Sgt Thomas Bedard

Awarded for their rescue of the pilot of Slate 46 in Iraq during Operation Desert Storm.

(2001) The crew of Knife 04, 20th SOS:

1st Lt James Holder
Capt Jay Humphrey
SSgt Chad Ackman
TSgt Vince DePersio
SSgt Mark Wolcott
SSgt Alberto Aguinaldo Jr.

Awarded for the rescue of the crew and passengers of Knife 03, a fellow 20th SOS Pave Low that crashed in enemy territory in Afghanistan in November 2001.[1]

Aviator Valor Award

Sanctioned by the USAF, the Aviator Valor Award is given for a conspicuous act of valor or courage performed during aerial combat or noncombat flight by a rated Air Force officer.

(1996) Capt Steven Kelly
(2004) Capt Steven Edwards[2]

Cheney Award

The USAF presents this award yearly to aviators for bravery in a humanitarian venture in memory of 1st Lt William Cheney, killed in an air collision over Italy in 1918.

(1993) Lt Col Michael Russell and Maj John Brainerd, 21st SOS

(1995) Capt Charles (Mark) Harmon, 352d Special Operations Group, and Capt Charles Moncrief, 20th SOS

(1996) Maj Marshall Webb, 21st SOS

(2002) Maj Kevin Churchill and Capt Sean LeRoy, 21st SOS

(2003) Capt Randal Voas and Capt Craig Prather, 21st SOS

(2004) Maj Marshall Groves, 16th Special Operations Wing[3]

Col James Jabara Airmanship Award

The Jabara Award is awarded yearly to an Air Force Academy graduate who has demonstrated superior performance in fields directly involved with aerospace vehicles.

(1992) Capt Corby Martin
(2000) Maj James Cardoso
(2003) Maj Leighton Anderson
(2008) Capt Jonathan Graham[4]

Koren Kolligian Jr. Trophy

Supported by the USAF, the Kolligian Trophy is awarded annually for "outstanding feats of Airmanship by aircrew members who by extraordinary skill, exceptional alertness, ingenuity or proficiency, averted accidents or minimized the seriousness of accidents in terms of injury, loss of life, aircraft damage or property damage."

(1984) Capt Jack Kelly
> For saving his crew and passengers by successfully auto-rotating his aircraft into an open area when the tail rotor gearbox failed.

(2005) Capt Steven Edwards
> For the successful recovery of his aircraft when it was severely damaged by enemy fire in Iraq in April 2004.

(2007) Lt Col Gene Becker
> For actions that saved his crew when his MH-53M suffered catastrophic failure and crashed in September 2007.[5]

Lt Gen William H. Tunner Award

This award is presented by the Air Mobility Command (formerly Military Airlift Command) to the best airlift crew of the year.

(1988) An HH-53H crew from the 20th SOS for recovering its aircraft from a serious in-flight emergency.

> Capt Paul Schumacher
> Capt Jeff White
> TSgt Keith Moore
> SSgt Timothy Hill
> SSgt James Roth
> SSgt Michael Warren
> Sgt Harold Hinson Jr.
> SrA Thomas Brothers

(1997) Crew of Sealion 23 from the 21st SOS for evacuation flights in Operation Assured Response, Monrovia, Liberia.

> Maj Charles (Mark) Harmon
> Capt Gordon Moore
> MSgt Michael Nicholas
> SSgt Todd Buice
> SSgt Joseph Frank Jr.
> Amn Sean Burnett[6]

Lance P. Sijan USAF Leadership Award

Award named in honor of the late Captain Sijan, who was post-humously awarded the Medal of Honor for his intrepidity while held as a prisoner of war by North Vietnamese forces. It recognizes officers and enlisted leaders, assigned at wing level or below, who have demonstrated the highest qualities of leadership in the performance of their duties and the conduct of their lives.

> (1990) Maj Jeffrey Walls
> (1999) Maj Mark Daley
> (2004) Capt Joseph Michalek[7]

Notes

1. Air Force Instruction (AFI) 36-2805, *Special Trophies and Awards*, 6; and Mr. Kyle Rensler, USAF/A3O-ATF (Awards Office, Air Staff), Pentagon, Washington, DC.

2. Ibid.

3. Ibid.

4. Data supplied by Lt Col Steve Simon, USAF, retired, and Ms. Jean Bickford, Association of Graduates, Air Force Academy, Colorado.

5. *AFSOC Commando Safety Journal*, Winter 2009, 5; and www.jollygreen /research/RonThurlow/NotableH53s.htm.

6. History of the Twenty-Third Air Force, 1 Jan–31 Dec 1988, vol. 1, 47; and History of the Air Force Special Operations Command (AFSOC), 1 Jan–31 Dec 1997, vol. 1, 55.

7. History of AFSOC, 1 Jan–31 Dec 1990, vol. 1; ibid., 1 Jan–31 Dec 1999; AFI 36-2805, *Special Trophies and Awards*, para 3.9; and "Official List," provided by USAF/A1SOU (Uniforms and Recognition Branch).

Appendix E

Pave Low Chief Master Sergeants

Victor Allen
James Anderson
Richard Bobo
John DeSalle
Thomas Green
Scott Hedglin
Gregory Kebil
Jon Knox
James Kradel
James Mecke
Randy Patrick
John Selfridge
Leonard Sullivan
Kevin Thurman
Pete Zilink

Appendix F

Pave Low General Officers
(as of publication)

Lt Gen Donny Wurster
Maj Gen Mark Clark, USMC
Maj Gen Rich Comer
Maj Gen John Folkerts
Maj Gen Michael Kingsley
Maj Gen Tom Trask
Brig Gen Scott Howell
Brig Gen Lyle Koenig
Brig Gen Tim Leahy
Brig Gen Greg Lengyel
Brig Gen Michael Planert
Brig Gen Brad Webb

Abbreviations

AAA	antiaircraft artillery
AAW	aeromedical airlift wing
ABW	air base wing
ACC	Air Combat Command
AD	air division
AEF	air expeditionary force
AETC	Air Education and Training Command
AFHRA	Air Force Historical Research Agency
AFLC	Air Force Logistics Command
AFMC	Air Force Materiel Command
AFOTEC	Air Force Operational Test and Evaluation Center
AFR	Air Force regulation; Air Force Reserve
AFSC	Air Force Systems Command
AFSOC	Air Force Special Operations Command
AFSOCCENT	Air Force component of SOCCENT
AFSOD	Air Force special operations detachment
AGL	above ground level
AGSS	Aerial Gunner Scanner Simulator
AHHS	altitude hold and hover stabilization (system)
AIRSOUTH	Allied Air Forces Southern Europe
AMARC	Aerospace Maintenance and Regeneration Center
AMC	Air Mobility Command
ANG	Air National Guard
AOR	area of responsibility
AR	Atlas Response
ARINC	Aeronautical Radio, Incorporated
ARRG	Aerospace Rescue and Recovery Group
ARRS	Aerospace Rescue and Recovery Service
ARRSq	aerospace rescue and recovery squadron
ARRW	aerospace rescue and recovery wing
ARS	Air Rescue Service
ARSq	air rescue squadron
ASD-ISA	assistant secretary of defense for international security affairs

ASD/SDY	Aeronautical Systems Division Specialized System Program Office
ASD/SOLIC	assistant secretary of defense for special operations and low-intensity conflict
ATTW	Aircrew Training and Test Wing
AWACS	Airborne Warning and Control System
AWC	Air War College
BAT (Operation)	Bahamas, Antilles, and Turks
BIAP	Baghdad International Airport
BRAC	base realignment and closure
C4	command, control, communications, and computer systems
CAOC	combined air operations center
CARA	combat aircrew recovery aircraft
CBU	cluster bomb unit
CCT	combat control team
CCTW	combat crew training wing
CENTAF	US Air Forces, US Central Command
CFACC	combined forces air component commander
CHECO	Contemporary Historical Evaluation of Current Operations
CIA	Central Intelligence Agency
CJCS	chairman of the Joint Chiefs of Staff
CJSOAC	combined joint special operations air component
CJSOTF	combined joint special operations task force
CJSOTF-AP	Combined Joint Special Operations Task Force–Arabian Peninsula
CJTF	combined joint task force
COCOM	combatant command
CROC	combat required operational capability
CSAF	chief of staff of the Air Force
CSAR	combat search and rescue
CTJTF	counterterrorist joint task force
CTW	crew training wing
DCS	deputy chief of staff
DMZ	demilitarized zone

DO	director of operations
DOD	Department of Defense
DT&E	developmental testing and evaluation
EAPS	engine air particle separator
ECM	electronic countermeasures
ELF	electronic location finder
ESOS	expeditionary special operations squadron
FAA	Federal Aviation Administration
FAC	forward air control/forward air controller
FAD	force activity designator
FBI	Federal Bureau of Investigation
FCF	functional check flight
FEMA	Federal Emergency Management Agency
FLIR	forward-looking infrared
FLTS	flight test squadron
FOB	forward operating base
FOL	forward operating location
FOT&E	follow-on operational test and evaluation
FS	fighter squadron
FTS	flying training squadron
FW	fighter wing
FY	fiscal year
GAO	Government Accountability Office
GPS	Global Positioning System
GWOT	global war on terror
HCS	Helicopter Combat Support Special Squadron
HGS	Helicopter Generation Squadron
HM-16	Helicopter Mine Countermeasures Squadron 16
HMH	Marine heavy helicopter squadron
HMXS	helicopter maintenance squadron
HQ	headquarters
HS	helicopter squadron
HUD	head-up display

ID	infantry division
IDAS/MATT	Interactive Defense Avionics Systems/ Multi-Mission Advanced Tactical Terminal
IED	improvised explosive device
IFOR	Implementation Force
IFR	instrument flight rule
IG	inspector general
IHAS	integrated helicopter avionics system
IMC	instrument meteorological conditions
INS	inertial navigation system
IOT&E	initial operational test and evaluation
IP	instructor pilot
IR	infrared
IRCM	infrared countermeasure
J-3	operations directorate
J-CATCH	Joint Countering Attack Helicopter
JCET	joint combined exchange training
JCRC	Joint Casualty Resolution Center
JCS	Joint Chiefs of Staff
JDAM	Joint Direct Attack Munition
JFACC	joint forces air component commander
JOWG	joint organizational working group
JRCC	joint rescue coordination center
JSAR	joint search and rescue
JSOA	Joint Special Operations Agency
JSOAC	joint special operations air component; Joint Special Operations Aviation Command
JSOACC	joint special operations air component commander
JSOAD	joint special operations air detachment
JSOC	Joint Special Operations Command
JSOTF	joint special operations task force
JTF	joint task force
KFIA	King Fahd International Airport
KKMC	King Khalid Military City
KLA	Kosovo Liberation Army
LNRS	limited night recovery system

LORAN	long-range aid to navigation
LZ	landing zone
MAC	Military Airlift Command
MACV	Military Assistance Command, Vietnam
MACVSOG	Military Assistance Command, Vietnam, Studies and Observation Group
MATS	Military Air Transport Service
MCAS	Marine Corps air station
MDS	mission design series
MEF	Marine expeditionary force
MEI	management effectiveness inspection
METL	mission essential task list
MEU	Marine expeditionary unit
MFP	major force program
MiGCAP	MiG combat air patrol
mm	millimeter
MNC-I	Multi-National Corps–Iraq
MNF-I	Multi-National Force–Iraq
MOB	main operating base
MRS	Mission Rehearsal System
NADEP	naval aviation depot
NARF	Naval Air Rework Facility
NAS	naval air station
NASA	National Aeronautics and Space Administration
NATO	North Atlantic Treaty Organization
NAVSPECWARCOM	Naval Special Warfare Command
NCO	noncommissioned officer
NEO	noncombatant evacuation operation
NKP	Nakhon Phanom Air Base, Thailand
NOE	nap-of-the-earth
NOS	night operations system
NRS	night recovery system
NVA	North Vietnamese Army
NVG	night vision goggles
OAF	Operation Allied Force
ODA	Operational Detachment Alpha

OEF	Operating Enduring Freedom
OIF	Operation Iraqi Freedom
OPCON	operational control
OPLAN	operation plan
ORI	operational readiness inspection
OSD	Office of the Secretary of Defense
OT&E	operational testing and evaluation
PACAF	Pacific Air Forces
PCS	permanent change of station
PDASD-ISA	principal deputy assistant secretary of defense for international security affairs
PDF	Panama Defense Forces
PERSTEMPO	personnel tempo
PF	Prairie Fire (Operation)
PhLASH	photographic landing augmentation system for helicopters
PJ	pararescue jumper
PLS	precision locator system
PMD	program management directive
POM	program objective memorandum
PPBS	Planning, Programming, and Budgeting System
PSAB	Prince Sultan Air Base
QRF	quick reaction force
RAD	requirements action directive
RDJTF	Rapid Deployment Joint Task Force
RHAW	radar homing and warning
RMC	rescue mission commander
ROC	required operational capability
ROE	rule of engagement
ROTC	Reserve Officer Training Corps
RPG	rocket-propelled grenade
RPV	remotely piloted vehicle
RQS	rescue squadron
R-SOLL	rescue special operations low-level
RWR	radar warning receiver
RWRW	Rescue and Weather Reconnaissance Wing

SAAS	School of Advanced Airpower Studies
SAC	Strategic Air Command
SAM	surface-to-air missile
Sandy	call sign for rescue escort A-1s in Southeast Asia
SAR	search and rescue
SAS	Special Air Service (British); stability augmentation system
SATCOM	satellite communications
Scud	surface-to-surface missile
SEA	Southeast Asia
SEAOR	Southeast Asia operational requirement
SFG	special forces group
SFOD-Delta	Special Forces Operational Detachment–Delta
SGU	special guerilla unit
shp	shaft horsepower
SLEP	service life extension program
SMOTEC	Special Missions Operational Test and Evaluation Center
SO	special operations
SOA	special operations aviation
SOAR	Special Operations Aviation Regiment
SOC	special operations command
SOCCENT	Special Operations Component, US Central Command
SOCEUR	Special Operations Component, US European Command
SOCIFOR	Special Operations Command Implementation Force
SOCPAC	Special Operations Component, US Pacific Command
SOD	special operations division
SOF	special operations force
SOFC	Special Operations Forces Command
SOFNET	SOF Intersimulator Network
SOG	special operations group
SON	statement of operational need
SOPAG	Special Operations Policy Advisory Group

SOS	special operations squadron
SOW	special operations wing
SPO	system program office
stan/eval	standardization and evaluation
STS	special tactics squadron
STU	secure telephone unit
TAC	Tactical Air Command
TACAN	tactical air navigation
TACC	tactical air control center
TACON	tactical control
TACS	tactical air control system
TAF	tactical air force
TASS	tactical air support squadron
TCHTS	technical training squadron
TCW	Tactical Control Wing
TDY	temporary duty
TF	task force
TF/TA	terrain following/terrain avoidance
TFA	Task Force Alpha
TFR	terrain-following radar
TFS	tactical fighter squadron
TFW	tactical fighter wing
TRAP	tactical recovery of aircraft and personnel
TRSS	training support squadron
TSAR	theater search and rescue
TTP	tactics, techniques, and procedures
UHF	ultrahigh frequency
UHT	undergraduate helicopter training
UNPROFOR	United Nations Protection Force
USA	United States Army
USAAG/7AF	United States Army Advisory Group/ Seventh Air Force
USAFE	United States Air Forces in Europe
USASOC	United States Army Special Operations Command
USCENTCOM	United States Central Command
USEUCOM	United States European Command
USGS	United States Geological Survey

USLANTCOM	United States Atlantic Command
USMC	United States Marine Corps
USN	United States Navy
USPACOM	United States Pacific Command
USREDCOM	United States Readiness Command
USSAG/7AF	United States Support Activities Group/ Seventh Air Force
USSOCOM	United States Special Operations Command
USSOUTHCOM	United States Southern Command
UTM	universal transverse mercator
UW	unconventional warfare
VFR	visual flight rules
WIC	weapons instructor course
WMD	weapon of mass destruction
WR-ALC	Warner-Robins Air Logistics Center
WRSK	war readiness spares kit
WSO	weapons system operator
WST	weapons system trainer

Bibliography

The bibliography is divided into the following sections: archival collections of unit histories from the Air Force Historical Research Agency (AFHRA); articles; books; reports, papers, and studies; e-mails to the author; interviews by the author; messages, letters, and memorandums; and miscellaneous. The archival collections, particularly at the AFHRA, and the interviews I conducted were the sources I referred to the most in telling the Pave Low story. All documents are unclassified, declassified, or redacted for the author's use.

Air Force Historical Research Agency
Maxwell AFB, AL

Unit Histories

1st Special Operations Wing (SOW)
    1 Jan–31 Dec 2008, vol. 1
    1 Jan–31 Dec 2007, vol. 1
    1 Jan–31 Dec 2006, vol. 1
    1 Jan–31 Dec 1992, vol. 1
    1 Jan–31 Dec 1991, vols. 1, 3
    1 Jan–31 Dec 1990, vols. 1, 2, 3
    1 July–31 Dec 1989, vols. 1, 3
    1 Jan–30 June 1989, vols. 1, 3
    1 Jan–31 Dec 1988, vol. 1
    1 Jan–31 Dec 1987, vols. 1, 3
    1 Jan–31 Dec 1985, vol. 1
    1 Oct 1982–28 Feb 1983, vol. 1
    1 July–30 Sept 1982, vol. 1
    1 Apr–30 June 1982, vol. 1
    1 Jan–31 Mar 1982, vols. 1, 2
    1 Oct–31 Dec 1981, vols. 1, 2
    1 Apr–30 June 1981, vols. 1, 2
    1 Jan–31 Mar 1981, vols. 1, 2
    1 Oct–31 Dec 1980, vols. 1, 2
    1 Apr–30 June 1980, vol. 2
    1 Jan–31 Mar 1980, vol. 2
    1 Jan–30 June 1979, vol. 1

1 Oct–31 Dec 1978, vol. 1
1 Apr–30 June 1978, vol. 1
1 Jan–31 Mar 1978, vol. 1
1 Oct–31 Dec 1977, vol. 1
1 July–30 Sept 1977, vol. 1
1 Jan–31 Mar 1977, vol. 1
1 July–30 Sept 1976, vol. 1
1 Jan–31 Mar 1976, vol. 1
2d Air Division (AD) (Including the 1st SOW)
1 Jan–31 Dec 1986, vols. 1, 5
1 Jan–31 Dec 1984, vols. 1, 2
1 July–31 Dec 1983, vol. 1
1 Mar–30 June 1983, vols. 1, 2, 6
3d Aerospace Rescue and Recovery Group (ARRG)
1 Jan–31 Mar 1974
1 July–30 Sept 1973
1 Oct–31 Dec 1972
1 July–30 Sept 1972
1 Apr–30 June 1972
1 Oct–31 Dec 1971
1 July–30 Sept 1971
1 Apr–30 June 1971
1 Apr–30 June 1970
1 Jan–31 Mar 1970
16th SOW
1 Jan–31 Dec 2005, vol. 1
1 Jan–31 Dec 2004, vol. 1
1 Jan–31 Dec 2003, vol. 1
1 Jan–30 June 2002, vol. 1
1 Jan–30 June 2001, vol. 1
1 July–31 Dec 2000, vol. 1
1 Jan–30 June 2000, vol. 1
1 July–31 Dec 1999, vol. 1
1 July–31 Dec 1998, vol. 1
1 Jan–30 June 1998, vol. 1
1 Jan–31 Dec 1997, vol. 1
1 Jan–31 Dec 1996, vol. 1
1 July–31 Dec 1994, vol. 1
1 Jan–30 June 1994, vol. 1
1 July–31 Dec 1993, vol. 1

20th Special Operations Squadron (SOS)
See histories of 1st and 16th SOWs for the period specified.
21st Helicopter Squadron (HS) and 21st SOS
See histories of the 39th, 56th, and 656th SOWs; 56th Air Commando Wing (ACW); and 352d Special Operations Group (SOG) for the period specified.
Twenty-Third Air Force
1 Jan–31 Dec 1989, vols. 1, 6
1 Jan–31 Dec 1988, vols. 1, 3
1 Jan 1986–31 Dec 1987, vol. 1
1 Jan 1984–31 Dec 1985, vols. 1, 2
Twenty-Third Air Force and Aerospace Rescue and Recovery Service (ARRS)
1 Jan–31 Dec 1983, vols. 1, 5
23d Tactical Air Support Squadron (TASS)
1 July–30 Sept 1971
37th Aerospace Rescue and Recovery Squadron (ARRSq)
1 Apr–30 June 1972
1 Jan–31 Mar 1972
1 Oct–31 Dec 1971
1 Jul–30 Sept 1971
1 Apr–30 June 1971
39th SOW
1 Jan–31 Dec 1992, vol. 1
1 July 1990–31 Dec 1991, vols. 1, 3
1 Jan–30 June 1990, vol. 3
1 July–31 Dec 1989, vols. 1, 3
1 Jan–30 June 1989, vols. 1, 3
1 Jan–30 June 1988, vols. 1, 2
40th ARRSq
1 July 1975–31 Jan 1976
1 Jan–30 June 1975
1 July–31 Dec 1973
1 Apr–30 June 1973
1 Jan–31 Mar 1973
1 Apr–30 June 1972
1 Jan–31 Mar 1972
1 July–30 Sept 1971
1 Jan–31 Mar 1968 (Detachment 1)

56th ACW
    1 Apr–30 June 1968, vol. 1
    1 Jan–31 Mar 1968, vols. 1, 2
    1 Oct–31 Dec 1967
    8 Apr–30 June 1967
56th SOW
    1 July–30 Sept 1975, vol. 1
    1 Apr–30 June 1975, vols. 1, 2, 3
    1 Jan–31 Mar 1975, vols. 1, 2
    1 July–30 Sept 1974, vols. 1, 2
    1 Apr–30 June 1974, vol. 2
    1 Jan–31 Mar 1974, vol. 2
    1 Oct–31 Dec 1973, vol. 1
    1 July–30 Sept 1973, vols. 1, 2
    1 Apr–30 June 1973, vol. 1
    1 Jan–31 Mar 1973, vol. 1
    1 July–31 Dec 1972, vols. 1, 2, 3
    1 Apr–30 June 1972, vols. 1, 3
    1 Oct–31 Dec 1971, vols. 1, 2
    1 Jan–31 Mar 1971, vols. 1, 2
    1 Oct–31 Dec 1970, vols. 1, 2
    1 July–30 Sept 1970, vols. 1, 2
    1 Apr–30 June 1970, vol. 1
    1 Jan–31 Mar 1970, vol. 1
    1 Oct–31 Dec 1969, vols. 1, 2
    1 July–30 Sept 1969, vols. 1, 2
    1 Jan–31 Mar 1969, vols. 1, 2
    1 Oct–31 Dec 1968, vol. 2
    1 July–30 Sep 1968, vol. 1
58th SOW
    1 Jan 2007–31 Dec 2008, vol. 1
    1 Jan–31 Dec 2006, vol. 1
    1 Jan–31 Dec 2005, vol. 1
    1 Jan–31 Dec 2004, vol. 1
    1 Jan–31 Dec 2003, vol. 1
    1 Jan–31 Dec 2002, vol. 1
    1 July–31 Dec 2001, vol. 1
    1 Jan–30 June 2001, vol. 1
    1 July–31 Dec 2000, vol. 1
    1 Jan–30 June 2000, vol. 1

1 Jan–31 Dec 1999, vol. 1
1 July–31 Dec 1998, vol. 1
1 Jan–30 June 1998, vol. 1
1 July–31 Dec 1997, vol. 1
1 July 1996–30 June 1997, vol. 1
1 Jan–30 June 1996, vol. 1
1 July–31 Dec 1995, vol. 1
1 Jan–30 June 1995, vol. 1
1 Apr–31 Dec 1994, vol. 1

352d SOG
1 Jan–31 Dec 2007, vol. 1
1 Jan–31 Dec 2006, vol. 1
1 Jan 2004–31 Dec 2005, vol. 1
1 Jan–31 Dec 2003, vol. 1
1 July–31 Dec 2002, vol. 1
1 Jan–30 June 2002, vol. 1
1 July–31 Dec 2001, vol. 1
1 Jan–30 June 2001, vols. 1, 2
1 July–31 Dec 2000, vol. 1
1 July–31 Dec 1999, vol. 1
1 July–31 Dec 1998, vol. 1
1 Jan–30 June 1998, vol. 1
1 July–31 Dec 1997, vol. 1
1 Jan–30 June 1997, vol. 1
1 July–31 Dec 1996, vol. 1
1 Jan–30 June 1996, vol. 1
1 Jan–31 Dec 1995, vol. 1
1 July–31 Dec 1994, vol. 1
1 Jan–30 June 1994, vol. 1
1 Dec 1992–31 Dec 1993, vol. 1

353d SOG
1 July–31 Dec 2001, vol. 1
1 Jan–30 June 2001, vols. 1, 2
1 July–31 Dec 2000, vol. 1
1 Jan–31 Dec 1999, vol. 1
1 July–31 Dec 1998, vol. 1
1 Jan–30 June 1998, vol. 1
1 July–31 Dec 1997, vol. 1
1 Jan–30 June 1997, vol. 1
1 July–31 Dec 1995, vol. 1

1 Jan–30 June 1995, vol. 1
1 July–31 Dec 1993, vol. 1
1 Jan–30 June 1993, vol. 1
1 Jan–31 Dec 1992 (History of the 353d SOG, Formerly the 353d SOW), vols. 1, 2
353d SOW
1 July–31 Dec 1991, vols. 1, 5
1 Jan–30 June 1991, vols. 1, 3, 4, 5
1 July–31 Dec 1990, vol. 4
1 Jan–30 June 1990, vol. 3
1 July–31 Dec 1989, vol. 2
542d Crew Training Wing (CTW)
1 Jan–31 Mar 1994, vol. 1
1 July–31 Dec 1993, vol. 1
1 Jan–30 June 1993, vol. 1
1 Oct 1991–31 Dec 1992, vol. 1
1 July–30 Sept 1991, vol. 1
601st Tactical Control Wing (TCW)
1 Apr–30 June 1980, vol. 4
1 Apr–30 Sept 1975, vol. 1
1 Jan–31 Mar 1975, vol. 1
656th SOW
1 July–31 Oct 1975, vols. 1, 2
656th Security Police Squadron
1 Apr–30 June 1975
1550th Aircrew Training and Test Wing (ATTW)
1 Jan–30 June 1980, vol. 1
1 July–31 Dec 1979, vol. 1
1 Jan–30 June 1979
1 July–31 Dec 1978, vol. 1
1 July–31 Dec 1977, vols. 1, 2
1550th Combat Crew Training Wing (CCTW)
1 July–30 Sept 1991, vol. 1
1 Jan–30 June 1991, vol. 1
1 July–31 Dec 1990, vol. 1
1 Jan–30 June 1990, vol. 1
1 July–31 Dec 1989
1 Jan–30 June 1989
1 Jan–31 Dec 1988, vol. 1

Aerospace Rescue and Recovery Service
　1 Jan 1984–31 Dec 1985, vols. 1, 2
　1 Jan–31 Dec 1982, vol. 1
　1 Jan–31 Dec 1981, vol. 1
　1 Jan–31 Dec 1980, vols. 1, 2
　1 Jan–31 Dec 1979, vol. 1
　1 Jan–31 Dec 1978, vols. 1, 2
　1 Jan–31 Dec 1977, vols. 1, 2
　1 Jan–31 Dec 1976, vol. 1
　1 July 1974–31 Dec 1975, vol. 1
　1 July 1971–30 June 1972, vol. 1
　1 July 1970–30 June 1971, vols. 1, 2
Air Force Special Operations Command (AFSOC)
　1 Jan–31 Dec 2008, vol. 1
　1 Jan–31 Dec 2007, vol. 1
　1 Jan–31 Dec 2006, vol. 1
　1 Jan–31 Dec 2005, vol. 1
　1 Jan–31 Dec 2004, vol. 1
　1 Jan–31 Dec 2003, vol. 1
　1 Jan–31 Dec 2002, vol. 1
　1 Jan–31 Dec 2001, vol. 1
　1 Jan–31 Dec 2000, vol. 1
　1 Jan–31 Dec 1999, vol. 1
　1 Jan–31 Dec 1998, vol. 1
　1 Jan–31 Dec 1997, vol. 1
　1 Jan–31 Dec 1996, vol. 1
　1 Jan–31 Dec 1995, vols. 1, 2
　1 Jan–31 Dec 1994, vols. 1, 5
　1 Jan–31 Dec 1993, vol. 1
　1 Jan–31 Dec 1992, vols. 1, 2, 3, 4
　1 Jan 1990–31 Dec 1991, vol. 1
Air Rescue Service
　1 Jan 1991–2 July 1993
　1 Jan 1989–31 Dec 1990
Military Airlift Command
　1 July 1969–30 June 1970, vol. 12

Articles

"AFSOC to Acquire CV-22 Osprey Aircraft." *Night Flyer Magazine*, June 1995, 3.

"Air Force Special Operations Command." USAF fact sheet. AFSOC Public Affairs, 20 Sept 2011. http://www.af.mil/information/fact sheets/factsheet.asp?id=156.

Baker, Maj Brad. "Air Force Special Operations Forces (AFSOF): How Did We Decide What Was Enough?" *Airlift* 10 (Spring 1988): 14.

Berndt, Brig Gen Martin R., and Maj Michael C. Jordan. "The Recovery of Basher 52." *Proceedings* (US Naval Institute), Nov 1995, 41–47.

Chapman, TSgt Dorian. "AFSOC Retires a Legend, Hero." *Tip of the Spear*, United States Special Operations Command (USSOCOM), June 2008, 32.

Davenport, A1C Gregory. "A Leg to Stand On." *Airman* 42, no. 3 (Mar 1998): 2–5.

Dyhouse, Tim. "Coming Home to a Changed World." *VFW [Veterans of Foreign Wars] Magazine* 90, no. 2 (Oct 2002): n.p.

Ernest, Maj Kenneth. "The Craziest SAR I've Ever Seen." Jolly Green Association website. http://wwwjollygreen.org/Stories/Ashcan_01.htm.

Garamone, Jim. "Rumsfield Charges DoD to Vanquish Terror Enemies." American Forces Press Service, 12 Sept 2001. US Department of Defense website. http://www.defense.gov/news/newsarticle.aspx?id=44907.

Greeley, Jim. "Desert One: A Mission of Hope Turned Tragic: A Case of What Could've Been." *Airman* 45, no. 4 (Apr 2001): 2–9.

———. "The Search for Ebro 33." *Night Flyer Magazine*, May 1996, 6–7.

———. "They Lost Everything." *Night Flyer Magazine*, Sept 1996, 7. http://www.af.mil/news/airman/0401/hostage.html.

Gresham, John. "Interview: Lt Gen Donald C. Donny Wurster." *Special Operations Magazine*, 2008, 11.

Grier, Peter. "Last Days of Clark." *Air Force Magazine*, Feb 1992, 56–60.

Haig, Jamie. "Always Prepared: Hornets True to Motto for Past 30 Years." *Tip of the Spear*, USSOCOM, Apr 2006, 26.

Hebert, Adam. "CSAR, Under New Management." *Air Force Magazine* 86, no. 8 (Aug 2003): 84–86.

Hewson, Robert. "Operation Allied Force, Part 2: Overwhelming Air Power." *World Airpower Journal* 39 (Winter 1999): 96–123.

———. "Operation Allied Force: The First 30 Days." *World Air Power Journal* 38 (Fall 1999): 16–29.

Jacobs, Lt Col William M. "The Human Element of Battle: The Theories of Ardand du Picq." *Special Warfare Magazine*, May 1996, 36.

Lawrence, Thomas H. "Design and Development of the Sikorsky S-65 Helicopter." *Vertiflight*, Spring 2002, 2.

Maier, SSgt Markus. "551st Special Operations Squadron Deactivates While Pave Lows Continue Exodus." Fact sheet. 377th Air Base Wing Public Affairs, Kirtland AFB, 10 May 2007.

Manor, Lt Gen LeRoy J., USAF, retired. "The Son Tay Raid: 21 November 1970." *Daedalus Flyer* 35, no. 4 (Winter 1995): 8–16.

McConnell, Malcolm. "Rescue in Iraq!" *Reader's Digest* 138, no. 830 (June 1991): 75–82.

Meyer, Deborah. "Taft Makes 'Solomonic' Decision on SOF Transfer by Splitting Mission." *Armed Forces Journal International*, Oct 1985, 28.

Moore, Col Bernard II, USAF, retired. "The Lions in Winter." *Tip of the Spear*, USSOCOM, Jan 2009, 46.

Newman, Richard J. "Hunting War Criminals." World report, 6 July 1998. http://www.specialoperations.com/Army/Delta_Force/bosnia .html.

Pugh, Sgt Craig. "New Eyes for the Giant." *Airman*, Dec 1979, 30–33.

Reiter, Maj Thomas E. "Packing Rescue for Special Delivery." *Airlift Operations Review*, July 1981, 18–23.

Rhodes, SSgt Phil. "Commando Look." *Night Flyer Magazine*, 2d Quarter, 1993, 6–10.

———. "Wild Bill." Sidebar to "Commando Look." *Night Flyer Magazine*, 2d Quarter, 1993, 6–10.

Schemmer, Benjamin F. "December Was Not a Good Month for USAF Special Operations." *Armed Forces Journal International* 123 (Jan 1986): 46–47.

———. "No USAF Combat Rescue Aircraft in Gulf; It Took 72 Hours to Launch One Rescue." *Armed Forces Journal International* 128 (July 1991): 37–38.

———. "USAF MH-53J Pave Lows Led Army Apaches Knocking Out Iraqi Radars to Open Iraqi War." *Armed Forces Journal International* 128 (July 1991): 34.

"66th Rescue Squadron." Fact sheet. Nellis AFB Public Affairs, 15 Dec 2011. http://www.nellis.af.mil/library/factsheets/factsheet .asp?id=18481.

Thacker, SSgt Andrea. "MH-53s' Final Mission." *Tip of the Spear*, USSOCOM, Oct 2008.

Thigpen, Lt Col Jerry L. *AFSOC: The Air Force's Newest Command.* Carlisle Barracks, PA: US Army War College, 1991.

Waller, Douglas. "Secret Warriors." *Newsweek* 117 (17 June 1991): 20–28.

Whitcomb, Col Darrel D., USAF, retired. "The Night They Saved Vega 31." *Air Force Magazine* 89, no. 12 (Dec 2006): 70–74.

———. "The Nonrescue of Corvette 03." *Air and Space Power Journal* 18, no. 1 (Spring 2004): 101–14.

———. "Rescue Operations in the Second Gulf War." *Air and Space Power Journal* 19, no. 1 (Spring 2005): 95–102. http://www.airpower.af.mil/airchronicles/apj/apj05/whitcomb.html.

———. "Searching for Ebro 33." *Air Power History*, Fall 2002, 34–39.

Wright, TSgt Ken, and MSgt Pat McKenna. "To the Rescue." *Airman* 44, no. 2 (Feb 2000): 17–19.

Books

The Air War over Serbia: Aerospace Power in Operation Allied Force. Washington, DC: Headquarters USAF, 2000.

Anderegg, Col C. R., USAF, retired. *The Ash Warriors.* Hickam AFB, HI: Office of PACAF History, 2000.

Atkinson, Rick. *In the Company of Soldiers: A Chronicle of Combat.* New York: H. Holt, 2004.

Bahmanyar, Mir, and Chris Osman. *SEALs: The Navy's Elite Fighting Force.* Long Island City, NY: Osprey Publishing, 2008.

Beckwith, COL Charlie A., USA, retired, and Donald Knox. *Delta Force.* New York: Harcourt Brace Jovanovich, 1983.

Bergeron, TSgt Randy G. *Desert Shield / Desert Storm: Air Force Special Operations Command in the Gulf War.* Hurlburt Field, FL: AFSOC/History Office (HO), May 2001.

Blehm, Eric. *The Only Thing Worth Dying For.* New York: Harper Collins Publishers, 2010.

Bowden, Mark. *Guests of the Ayatollah.* New York: Atlantic Monthly Press, 2006.

Bowers, Col Ray L. *The United States Air Force in Southeast Asia: Tactical Airlift.* Washington, DC: Office of Air Force History, USAF, 1983.

Boykin, LTG William G., USA, retired, and Ms. Lynn Vincent. *Never Surrender: A Soldier's Journey to the Crossroads of Faith and Freedom.* New York: Faith Works, 2008.

Boyne, Col Walter J., USAF, retired. *Operation Iraqi Freedom: What Went Right, What Went Wrong, and Why*. New York: Doherty Associates, 2003.

Briscoe, Charles, Kenneth Finlayson, Robert Jones, Jr., Cherilyn Walley, Dwayne Aaron, Michael Mullins, and James Schroder. *All Roads Lead to Baghdad: Army Special Operations Forces in Iraq*. Fort Bragg, NC: USASOC/HO, 2006.

Briscoe, Charles H., Richard L. Kiper, James A. Schroder, and Kalev I. Sepp. *Weapon of Choice: ARSOF in Afghanistan*. Ft. Leavenworth, KS: Combat Studies Institute, 2003.

Budiansky, Stephen. *Airpower*. New York: Viking Press, 2004.

Chinnery, Philip D. *Any Time, Any Place: A History of USAF Air Commando and Special Operations Forces*. Annapolis, MD: Naval Institute Press, 1994.

Clancy, Tom. *Clear and Present Danger*. New York: Putnam, 1989.

Clancy, Tom, and Gen Chuck Horner, USAF, retired. *Every Man a Tiger*. New York: G. P. Putnam's Sons, 1999.

Clancy, Tom, Gen Carl Stiner, USA, retired, and Tony Koltz. *Shadow Warriors: Inside the Special Forces*. New York: G. P. Putnam's Sons, 2002.

Cole, Ronald H. *Operation Just Cause: The Planning and Execution of Joint Operations in Panama, February 1988–January 1990*. Washington, DC: Joint History Office, Office of the Chairman of the Joint Chiefs of Staff, USSOCOM/HO, MacDill AFB, FL, 1995.

Collins, John M. *Green Berets, Seals and Spetsnaz: U.S. and Soviet Special Military Operations*. McLean, VA: Pergamon-Brassey's, 1987.

Cross, Coy F., II. *The Birth of the Twenty-Third Air Force: MAC Becomes the Single Manager for Air Force Special Operations Assets: 1973–1983*. Scott AFB, IL: Office of History, Military Airlift Command, May 1990.

Davis, Richard G. *The 31 Initiatives: A Study in Air Force-Army Cooperation*. Washington, DC: Office of Air Force History, 1987.

Dunham, Maj George R., and Col David A. Quinlan. *U.S. Marines in Vietnam: The Bitter End, 1973–75*. Washington, DC: History and Museums Division, Headquarters, US Marine Corps, 1990.

Durant, CW3 Michael J., and Steve Hartov. *The Night Stalkers: Top Secret Missions of the U.S. Army's Special Operations Aviation Regiment*. New York: Putnam's Sons, 2006.

Fields, CDR Kenny W. *The Rescue of Streetcar 304: A Navy Pilot's Forty Hours on the Run in Laos*. Annapolis, MD: Naval Institute Press, 2007.

Fontenot, COL Gregory, USA, retired, LTC E. J. Degen, and LTC David Tohn. *On Point: The United States Army in Operation Iraqi Freedom*. Annapolis, MD: Naval Institute Press, 2005.

Galdorisi, CAPT George, USN, retired, and LCDR Thomas Phillips, USN, retired. *Leave No Man Behind: The Saga of Combat Search and Rescue*. Minneapolis, MN: Zenith Press, 2008.

Gambone, Leo A. *Pave Low III: That Others May Live*. Wright-Patterson AFB, OH: History Office, Aeronautical Systems Division, Air Force Systems Command, 1988. Vols. 1, 2, and 3.

Gordon, Michael R., and Lt Gen Bernard E. Trainor, US Marine Corps, retired. *Cobra II: The Inside Story of the Invasion and Occupation of Iraq*. New York: Pantheon Books, 2006.

———. *The Generals' War: The Inside Story of the Conflict in the Gulf*. New York: Little, Brown and Company, 1995.

Guilmartin, Lt Col John F., USAF, retired. *A Very Short War: The Mayaguez and the Battle of Koh Tang*. College Station, TX: Texas A&M University Press, 1995.

Haas, Col Michael E., USAF, retired. *Air Commando! 1950–1975: Twenty-Five Years at the Tip of the Spear*. Maxwell AFB, AL: Air University Press, 1994.

———. *Apollo's Warriors: US Air Force Special Operations during the Cold War*. Maxwell AFB, AL: Air University Press, 1997.

Hobson, Chris. *Vietnam Air Losses: United States Air Force, Navy and Marine Corps Fixed-Wing Aircraft Losses in Southeast Asia 1961–1973*. Hinckley, UK: Midland Publishing, 2001.

Hutto, Cong. Earl N. *Captain Supreme Goes to Washington: A Memoir*. Pensacola, FL: Enhutt Publishers, 1996.

Jane's All the World's Aircraft. Various editors. London: 1963–2008. Specific editions cited in notes.

Kelly, Orr. *From a Dark Sky: The Story of U.S. Air Force Special Operations*. New York: Pocket Books, 1997.

Koskinas, Lt Col Ioannis. *Black Hats and White Hats: The Effect of Organizational Culture and Institutional Identity on the Twenty-Third Air Force*. Maxwell AFB, AL: Air University Press, 2006.

Kyle, Col James H., USAF, retired. *The Guts to Try*. New York: Ballantine Books, 1995.

LaPointe, SMSgt Robert L., USAF, retired. *PJs in Vietnam: The Story of Air Rescue in Vietnam as Seen through the Eyes of Pararescuemen*. Anchorage, AK: Northern PJ Press, 2001.

Lenahan, Col Roderick, USAF, retired. *Confrontation Zone: The Story of the 1989 U.S. Intervention into Panama: Operation Just Cause*. Charleston, SC: Narwhall Press, 2002.

———. *Crippled Eagle: A Historical Perspective of U.S. Special Operations, 1976–1996*. Charleston, SC: Narwhall Press, 1998.

Locher, James R., III. *Victory on the Potomac*. College Station, TX: Texas A&M Press, 2002.

Marquis, Susan L. *Unconventional Warfare: Rebuilding U.S. Special Operations Forces*. Washington, DC: Brookings Institution Press, 1997.

McKinney, Lt Col Michael, and Michael Ryan. *Chariots of the Damned*. London, UK: Harper Collins Publishers, 2001.

McPeak, Gen Merrill A. *Selected Works, 1990–1994*. Maxwell AFB, AL: Air University Press, Aug 1995.

Moore, Robin. *The Hunt for Bin Laden*. New York: Random House Press, 2003.

Murphy, Michael J., and Lt Col William J. Northacker. *Response to Disaster: SOCEUR and the CT-43A Recovery Operation, Dubrovnik, Croatia, 3–6 April 1996*. MacDill AFB, FL: USSOCOM History and Research Office, 1998.

Murray, Williamson, and Dr. Wayne Thompson. *Air War in the Persian Gulf*. Baltimore, MD: The Nautical and Aviation Publishing Company of America, 1996.

Mutza, Wayne. *Green Hornets: The History of the U.S. Air Force 20th Special Operations Squadron*. Atglen, PA: Schiffer Military History, 2007.

Nalty, Bernard C., ed. *Winged Shield, Winged Sword: A History of the United States Air Force*. Vol. 2, *1950–1997*. Washington, DC: Air Force History and Museums Program, 1997.

Owen, Col Robert C. *Deliberate Force: A Case Study in Effective Air Campaigning*. Maxwell AFB, AL: Air University Press, 2000.

Partin, Dr. John W., and Capt Rob Rhoden. *Operation Assured Response: SOCEUR's NEO in Liberia*. MacDill AFB, FL: USSOCOM History and Research Office, 1997.

Partin, Dr. John W., CDR Linda Herlocker, and Michael J. Murphy. *Special Operation Forces in Operation Atlas Response: Flood Relief in Mozambique March 2000*. MacDill AFB, FL: USSOCOM History and Research Office, 2001.

Pushies, Fred J. *Deadly Blue: Battle Stories of the U.S. Air Force Special Operations Command*. New York: American Management Association, 2009.

——. *Night Stalkers: 160th Special Operations Aviation Regiment (Airborne)*. St. Paul, MN: Zenith Press, 2005.

Richardson, Lt Nick. *No Escape Zone*. London: Little, Brown and Company, 2000.

Rip, Michael R., and James M. Hasik. *The Precision Revolution, GPS and the Future of Aerial Warfare*. Annapolis, MD: Naval Institute Press, 2002. New York: Public Affairs, 2004.

Robinson, Linda. *Masters of Chaos: The Secret History of the Special Forces*. New York: Public Affairs, 2004.

Russo, Capt Lenny, USAF. *Flying Stories*. Bainbridge, OH: Russo Publishing, 2009.

Ryan, Paul B. *The Iranian Rescue Mission: Why It Failed*. Annapolis, MD: Naval Institute Press, 1985.

Secord, Richard V. *Honored and Betrayed: Irangate, Covert Affairs, and the Secret War in Laos*. New York: Wiley, 1992.

Stanton, Doug. *Horse Soldiers: The Extraordinary Story of a Band of U.S. Soldiers Who Rode to Victory in Afghanistan*. New York: Scribner Press, 2009.

Stewart, Richard W., Dr. Stanley Sandler, and Dr. Joseph R. Fischer. *Command History of the United States Army Special Operations Command, 1987–1992: Standing Up the MACOM*. Vol. 8. USASOC historical monographs. Fort Bragg, NC: United States Army Special Operations Command, Directorate of History and Museums, 1996.

Stewart, Richard W., ed. *American Military History*. Vol. 2, *The United States Army in a Global Era, 1917–2003*. Washington, DC: Center for Military History, 2005.

Taylor, John W. R., ed. *Jane's All the World's Aircraft 1969–70*. London: Jane's Yearbooks, 1969.

Thigpen, Col Jerry L., USAF, retired. *The Praetorian Starship: The Untold Story of the Combat Talon*. Maxwell AFB, AL: Air University Press, 2001.

Tilford, Earl H. *Search and Rescue in Southeast Asia*. Washington, DC: Center for Air Force History, 1992.

USSOCOM. *History of the United States Special Operations Command*. 6th ed. MacDill AFB, FL: USSOCOM/HO, 2008.

——. *United States Special Operations Command History, 1987–2007, 20th Anniversary Edition*. MacDill AFB, FL: USSOCOM/HO, 2007.

. *United States Special Operations Command 10th Anniversary History*. MacDill AFB, FL: USSOCOM/HO, 1997.

Vriesenga, Capt Michael P., ed. *From the Line in the Sand: Accounts of USAF Company Grade Officers in Support of Desert Shield / Desert Storm*. Maxwell AFB, AL: Air University Press, 1994.

Waller, Douglas C. *The Commandos: The Inside Story of America's Secret Soldiers*. New York: Simon & Schuster, 1994.

Webster's Encyclopedic Unabridged Dictionary of the English Language. New York: Gramercy Books, 1996.

West, Bing. *No True Glory: A Frontline Account of the Battle of Fallujah*. New York: Bantam Dell Publishers, 2006.

Wetterhahn, Col Ralph F., USAF, retired. *The Last Battle: The Mayaguez Incident and the End of the Vietnam War*. New York: Carroll & Graf Publishers, 2001.

Whitcomb, Col Darrel D., USAF, retired. *Combat Search and Rescue in Desert Storm*. Maxwell AFB, AL: Air University Press, 2006.

. *The Rescue of Bat 21*. Annapolis, MD: Naval Institute Press, 1998.

Woodward, Bob. *Bush at War*. New York: Simon & Schuster, 2005.

Wright, Dr. Donald P., and Col Timothy R. Reese. *On Point II: Transition to a New Campaign*. Fort Leavenworth, KS: Combat Studies Institute Press, 2008.

Yarsinske, Amy W. *No One Left Behind: The Lt. Comdr. Michael Scott Speicher Story*. New York: Dutton Books, 2002.

Reports, Papers, and Studies

AF Safety Report. Aircraft Accident Investigation MH-53M #68-10930, n.d. Judge Advocate General Office, Hurlburt Field, FL.

AFSOC. *Combat Rescue—Bridging the Gap*. White paper. Hurlburt Field, FL: AFSOC, Aug 1991.

After Action Report for CSAR for Vega 31, 5 April 1999. Operation Allied Force (OAF) file. 1st/16th SOW/HO, Hurlburt Field, FL.

Anderson, Capt B. Conn. *USAF Search and Rescue in Southeast Asia, 1961–66*. Project CHECO (Contemporary Historical Examination of Current Operations) Report. Hickam AFB, HI: HQ Pacific Air Forces, 1966. K717.0414-1. AFHRA, Maxwell AFB, AL.

Barich, Maj James D. "The History of Heavy Lift: Can the 1947 Vision of an All Heavy Helicopter Force Achieve Fruition in 2002?"

Master of Military Studies research paper, US Marine Corps Command and Staff College, 2002.

Boivin, R. H., J. Schmidt, and P. J. Balfe. *Pave Low—Evaluation of a Terrain Following Radar System for the HH-53 Helicopter.* Air Force Flight Test Center (AFFTC) Technical Report no. 73-11. Edwards AFB, CA: AFFTC, Mar 1973. Provided to the author by Lt Col Ray Dunn, USAF, retired.

Boykin, Col William G., USA. "The Origins of the United States Special Operations Command." MacDill AFB, FL: USSOCOM/HO, n.d. Originally published as *Special Operations and Low-Intensity Conflict Legislation: Why It Passed and Have the Voids Been Filled?* Military Studies Program paper. Carlisle Barracks, PA: US Army War College, 1991.

Brown, CMSgt Tim, USAF, retired. "AFSOC in the Balkans: Provide Promise to Noble Anvil 1992–1999," n.d. AFSOC/HO, Hurlburt Field, FL.

"Chronology of Desert Storm Missions," n.d., file 500.608. 1st/16th SOW/HO, Hurlburt Field, FL.

"Chronology of the 23d Air Force." Permanent file, box 5. AFSOC/HO, Hurlburt Field, FL.

CJTFEX 96/ORI After Action Report, 14 June 1996. 20th SOS, historical files. 1st/16th SOW/HO, Hurlburt Field, FL.

Comer, Maj Gen Richard L. "History of Desert Shield / Desert Storm, 20th SOS," n.d. 1st/16th SOW/HO, Hurlburt Field, FL.

Durkee, Maj Richard. *USAF Search and Rescue in Southeast Asia, July 1966–November 1967.* Project CHECO Report. Hickham AFB, HI: HQ Pacific Air Forces, 1968. K717.0414-1. AFHRA, Maxwell AFB, AL.

Exercise Krypton Vessel After Action Report Inputs, 30 Apr 1997. 20th SOS, historical files. 1st/16th SOW/HO, Hurlburt Field, FL.

Francis, Capt David G., and Maj David R. Nelson. *Search and Rescue Operations in SEA, 1 April 1972–30 June 1973.* Hickham AFB, HI: HQ Pacific Air Forces, 1974. K717.0414-1. AFHRA, Maxwell AFB, AL.

H-53 Major Aircraft Accident List, n.d. Safety Office, Hurlburt Field, FL.

HH-60G Class A Flight Mishap Report. AFSOC/HO, Hurlburt Field, FL.

Hilkert, Lt Col David E. "The History of SOCEUR 1954–2004: Fifty Years of Special Operations Forces in the European Command Theater." Unpublished report, Dec 2004. USSOCOM/HO, MacDill AFB, FL.

Holloway, James. *The Holloway Report*. Washington, DC: Joint Chiefs of Staff, 23 August 1980. http://www.gwu.edu/~nsarchiv/NSAEBB /NSAEBB63/doc8.pdf.

Lowe, Leroy W. *USAF Search and Rescue Operations in SEA, 1 January 1971–31 March 1972*. Hickham AFB, HI: HQ Pacific Air Forces. K717.0414-1. AFHRA, Maxwell AFB, AL.

Lynch, Walter F. *USAF Search and Rescue in Southeast Asia, 1 July 1969–31 December 1970*. Project CHECO Report. Hickam AFB, HI: HQ Pacific Air Forces, 1971. K717.0414-1. AFHRA, Maxwell AFB, AL.

Marion, Maj Forrest L. "Ash Warriors: The Relocation of the 353d Special Operations Wing, June–December 1991." Study. HQ AFSOC/ HO, Hurlburt Field, FL.

McLeaish, Maj John H., and Maj John W. Silvis. "Southeast Asia Combat Aircrew Recovery Requirements through FY 3/72." Study. 3d ARRG, 21 Mar 1967. K717.0414-1. AFHRA, Maxwell AFB, AL.

———. "Southeast Asia Operational Analysis of Required Performance Parameters for a Combat Aircrew Recovery Aircraft." Study. 3d ARRG, 22 May 1967. K717.0414-1. AFHRA, Maxwell AFB, AL.

MH-53J Interactive Defensive Avionics System / Multi-Mission Advanced Tactical Terminal Qualification Operational Test and Evaluation Final Report, June 1997. Air Force Operational Test and Evaluation Center (AFOTEC)/HO, Kirtland AFB, NM.

Morse, Lt Col John H. "Final Evaluation Pave Imp Operational Test Order 6-6-71, HH-53." Report, 9 July 1971. K318.2-448. AFHRA, Maxwell AFB, AL.

"Operational Test and Evaluation: Pave Low III." Unpublished report. Scott AFB, IL: DCS/Plans, HQ Military Airlift Command, Mar 1977. Procured from Lt Col Frank Pehr, USAF, retired.

Overton, Maj James B. *USAF Search and Rescue, November 1967– June 1969*. Project CHECO Report. Hickam AFB, HI: HQ Pacific Air Forces, 1969. K717.0414-1. AFHRA, Maxwell AFB, AL.

Pope AFB, Combat Search and Rescue Exercise After Action Report, 20 Nov 2000. 20th SOS, historical files. 1st/16th SOW HO, Hurlburt Field, FL.

Sikorsky, Igor I. "The Technical History of Sikorsky Aircraft and Its Predecessors (Since 1909)," May 1966. Sikorsky Aircraft Corporation, archival collections, Stratford, CT.

"The Son Tay Raid." In History of the ARRS, vol. 1, 1 July 1970. An-
nex. Permanent file, box 45, file 4M12. AFSOC/HO, Hurlburt
Field, FL.

"Statement by Mr. Richard Armitage, Asst. Secretary of Defense (International Security Affairs) before the Subcommittee on Seapower
and Force Projection, Committee on Armed Services, US Senate
Second Session, 99th Congress, Special Operations Forces Reorganization," 5 Aug 1986. AFSOC/HO, Hurlburt Field, FL.

Tyner, Lt Col Joe E. *AF Rescue and AFSOF: Overcoming Past Rivalries
for Combat Rescue Partnership Tomorrow.* Monterey, CA: US Navy
Postgraduate School, 1996.

20th SOS AFSOC Outstanding Squadron Nomination Package 1995.
20th SOS, historical files, Fort Walton Beach, FL. Maintained by
TSgt Vince DePersio.

"20th SOS History for 1993." Unpublished report. 20th SOS, historical
files, Fort Walton Beach, FL.

E-Mails to the Author

Beard, Capt Charles "Mike," 10 Jan 2011.
Becker, Lt Col Eugene, 6 Aug 2009, 19 Sept 2010.
Cardoso, Col James, 5 June 2010.
Connelly, Col Steve, USAF, retired, 9 Mar 2009.
Cooper, Maj Phil, 30 Apr 2010.
Daley, Lt Col Mark, 10 Sept, 16 Sept, and 19 Sept 2010.
Doty, Lt Col Pete, 6 Jan 2012.
Duffy, Dave, 19 July 2009.
Grub, Lt Col Mike, 9 Aug 2010.
Halcomb, MSgt Bill, USAF, retired, 11 Sept 2009.
Larsen, Dean, 17 May 2010.
Matlock, Capt Tim, 19 Dec 2011.
Michalek, Lt Col Joe, 26 July 2010.
Morse, Lt Col John, USAF, retired, 10 Jan 2009.
Owens, Lt Col Jonathan, USAF, retired, 23 Dec 2011.
Reed, Lt Col Ed, USAF, retired, 18 Sept and 18 Oct 2009, 3 Jan 2011.
Rouhier, SMSgt Chuck, USAF, retired, 20 Dec 2008.
Rowell, Lt Col Bill, 21 Aug 2010.
Schibler, Lt Col Mark, USAF, retired, 7 Jan 2009, 17 Sept 2010.
Slife, Col Jim, 25 July and 13 Sept 2010.

Stiles, Lt Col Rus, USAFR, retired, 12 May 2009.
Stricklin, SMSgt John, 22 and 23 Jan 2011.
Weikel, Col Gary, USAF, retired, 25 Mar 2009, 20 Aug 2010.
Williams, Col R. K., USAF, retired, 7 and 9 Aug 2010, 24 Jan 2011.

Interviews by the Author

Abernathy, Col Rob. Kirtland AFB, NM, 16 Sept 2009.
Aldrich, Capt Tom, USAF, retired, Fort Walton Beach (FWB), FL, 10 Feb 2009.
Bassett, Col Bill, Rosslyn, VA, 18 Dec 2008.
Becker, Col Joe, Fayetteville, NC, 25 July 2009.
Becker, Lt Col Eugene, FWB, FL, 13 Jan 2008.
Becklund, Col Vince, Fairfax, VA, 27 Mar 2010.
Berry, Maj Matt, Kirtland AFB, NM, 18 Sept 2009.
Blanchard, Maj James, US Air Force Academy, CO, 3 Nov 2009.
Borland, Maj Sean, phone interview, 18 July 2010.
Buice, MSgt Todd, Cannon AFB, NM, 22 Sept 2009.
Burkett, MSgt Art, USAF, retired, Kirtland AFB, NM, 16 Sept 2009.
Breck, Lt Col Jim, Kirtland AFB, NM, 17 Sept 2009.
Cardoso, Col Jim, Cannon AFB, NM, 21 Sept 2009, 5 June 2010.
Cessop, Brian, TSgt, USAF, retired, Kirtland AFB, NM, 18 Sept 2009.
Clem, Col J. D., FWB, FL, 19 May 2009.
Colannino, SMSgt Robert, FWB, FL, 15 Oct 2008.
Comer, Maj Gen Rich, USAF, retired, FWB, FL, 14 Jan 2008, 21 Aug 2009.
Connelly, Col Steve, USAF, retired, FWB, FL, 20 Oct 2008.
Correll, Col Gene, USAF, retired, phone interview, 29 Dec 2009.
DeCaro, Lt Col Joseph, FWB, FL, 15 Oct 2008.
DePersio, TSgt Vince, FWB, FL, 14 Oct 2008.
DeSalle, CMSgt John, Pope AFB, NC, 28 Aug 2009.
Dinsmore, MSgt Robert, Kirtland AFB, NM, 15 Sept 2009.
Edwards, Maj Steve, Maxwell AFB, AL, 10 Dec 2008.
Ezell, SSgt Erick, FWB, FL, 6 Aug 2010.
Florence, Capt Daniel, FWB, FL, 15 Oct 2008.
Folkerts, Maj Gen John, USAF, retired, phone interview, 4 Feb 2010.
Fremstad, SMSgt Paul, USAF, retired, Navarre, FL, 1 Apr 2009.
Gray, Brig Gen George, USAF, retired, phone interview, 2 Dec 2009.
Green, CMSgt Tom, USAF, retired, FWB, FL, 16 Oct 2009, 6 Aug 2010.
Grove, Maj John, USAF, retired, FWB, FL, 24 Oct 2008.

Groves, Maj Marshall, Kirtland AFB, NM, 18 Sept 2009.

Hamilton, Capt Mark, Kirtland AFB, NM, 23 Sept 2009.

Hammons, Lt Col Stewart, Cannon AFB, NM, 21 Sept 2009.

Harmon, Col Paul, FWB, FL, 13 Feb, 9 Apr, 15 Oct 2009.

Harris, Lt Col Dave, USAF, retired, FWB, FL, 1 Apr 2009.

Hester, Col Jack, USAF, retired, MacDill AFB, FL, 14 Aug 2009.

Holder, Maj Mike, Burke, VA, 6 Apr 2010.

Homan, Lt Col Mike, USAF, retired, Kirtland AFB, NM, 16 Sept 2009.

Hoover, Col Don, USAF, retired, phone interview, 1 Apr 2010.

Howell, Col Scott, Fairfax, VA, 12 Mar 2010.

Hull, Col Tom, USAF, retired, FWB, FL, 9 Feb 2009.

Hux, CMSgt Ed, USAF, retired, phone interview, 1 Feb 2010.

Jobling, MSgt B. J., Kirtland AFB, NM, 17 Sept 2009.

Johnson, Col Horace "Bo," USAF, retired, FWB, FL, 2 May 2010.

Jones, Col Dennis, USAF, retired, Maxwell AFB, AL, 22 July 2009.

Kelly, Capt Jack, retired (medically), phone interview, 23 Dec 2009.

Kingsley, Brig Gen Michael, Springfield, VA, 12 Dec 2009.

Kleve, Capt Jon, Cannon AFB, NM, 21 Sept 2009.

Koegler, Maj Fred, Kirtland AFB, NM, 15 Sept 2009.

Kradel, James, CMSgt, USAF, retired, phone interview, 20 July 2010.

Landreth, Lt Col Kent, FWB, FL, 15 Oct 2009.

Lawrence, Tom, Sikorsky Aircraft, Stratford, CT, 13 Nov 2008.

Lazzara, Maj Frank, FWB, FL, 9 Aug 2010.

Lengyel, Col Greg, FWB, FL, 16 Feb 2010.

Martin, Col Corby, FWB, FL, 17 Aug 2009.

McDonald, MSgt Robert D., Cannon AFB, NM, 22 Sept 2009.

McKinney, Lt Col Mike, Kirtland AFB, NM, 18 Sept 2009.

Mecke, CMSgt James, phone interview, 1 Apr 2010.

Oliver, Wayne, TSgt, USAF, retired, Kirtland AFB, NM, 16 Sept 2009.

Pehr, Lt Col Frank, USAF, retired, phone interview, 11 Mar 2009, and personal interview, Sandia, NM, 17 Sept 2009.

Piotrowski, Gen John, USAF, retired, phone interview, 17 Nov 2009.

Porter, SSgt Jeff, Cannon AFB, NM, 22 Sept 2009.

Prather, Maj Craig, Kirtland AFB, NM, 17 Sept 2009.

Pryor, SMSgt Mark, FWB, FL, 15 Oct 2008.

Pugmire, Col Scott, USAF, retired, Kirtland AFB, NM, 17 Sept 2009.

Reed, Lt Col Ed, USAF, retired, phone interview, 7 May 2009.

Roberts, Maj Brian, FWB, FL, 15 Oct 2008.

Russell, Col Mike, USAF, retired, phone interview, 24 Jan 2010.

Schibler, Lt Col Mark, USAF, retired, phone interview, 13 May 2009.

Schweim, Maj Marty, Kirtland AFB, NM, 24 Sept 2009.
Shipman, Col Jerry, USAF, retired, phone interview, 13 June 2002.
Simmon, MSgt Rick, USAF, retired, FWB, FL, 23 Oct 2008.
Slife, Col Jim Burke, VA, 26 Jan 2010.
Smith, Lt Col Kirk, FWB, FL, 11 Feb 2009.
Sosnowski, Maj Bill, Cannon AFB, NM, 22 Sept 2009.
Sprouse, MSgt John, USAF, retired, phone interview, 15 Sept 2010.
Stamos, Maj Derrick, Cannon AFB, NM, 21 Sept 2009.
Stankovich, Col Robert, USAF, retired, phone interview, 21 Dec 2009.
Stiles, Lt Col Rus, USAFR, retired, phone interview, 27 Dec 2008.
Stovall, Brig Gen Dale, USAF, retired, phone interview, 3 Sept 2001.
Strawbridge, Maj Steve, Pope AFB, NC, 28 Aug 2009.
Stringer, Scott, Warner-Robins Air Logistics Center/Special Operations/
    Personnel Recovery Division (GRUED), Robins AFB, GA, 3 Aug
    2010.
Strong, MSgt Robert, FWB, FL, 14 Oct 2008.
Stumpf, MSgt Brian, Cannon AFB, NM, 21 Sept 2009.
Teeple, Lt Col James, USAF, retired, phone interview, 24 Mar 2010.
Trask, Brig Gen Thomas, MacDill AFB, FL, 12 Aug 2009.
Walters, Capt Jim "Pappy," USAF, retired, FWB, FL, 10 Feb 2009.
Webb, Col Brad, FWB, FL, 15 Jan 2008, 9 July 2010.
Weikel, Col Gary, USAF, retired, FWB, FL, 13 Oct 2008.
Williams, Col R. K., US Air Force Academy, CO, 28 Sept 2009.
Wurster, Lt Gen Donny, FWB, FL, 16 Oct 2008, 11 Oct 2009.

Messages, Letters, and Memorandums

Becker, Capt Joe. To 1st SOW historian. Letter, 16 Sept 1993. File
    220.00, 1st/16th SOW HO, Hurlburt Field, FL.
1st SOW/CC. To 9AF/CC. Letter, 7 Mar 1980. Subject: Special Opera-
    tions Capability Requirements. In History of 1st SOW, 1 Jan–31
    Mar 1980, vol. 2.
Hess, Col Lee. To AFSOC operational flying units. Letter, 11 Dec
    1992. Subject: Duties and Responsibilities of the Aircraft Com-
    mander. AFSOC/HO, Hurlburt Field, FL.
Holder, 1st Lt James. Memorandum for record, 4 Nov 2001. Subject:
    Knife 04 CSAR Report. Provided to the author by Holder.
Hutto, Cong. Earl. To Adm William Crowe. Letter, 8 Dec 1987. 1988
    box 2: Directorates and Components, file: Rotary Aircraft. Hutto

Collection, John C. Pace Library, University of West Florida, Pensacola, FL.

Hutto, Cong. Earl. To Mrs. Richard Brims. Letter, 17 June 1986. Box 329-91-169, file 15 of 27. Hutto Collection, John C. Pace Library. University of West Florida, Pensacola, FL.

Message. USAF chief of plans and operations. To all commands, 20 Dec 1985. Subject: Update of SOF Rotary-Wing Issue. In History of ARRS, 1 Jan 1984–31 Dec 1985, vol. 2.

Message. 142310Z MAY 80. CSAF//CV (vice-commander). To MAC and TAC commanders et al. Subject: Pave Low III Beddown. In History of the Aerospace Rescue and Recovery Service, 1 Jan–31 Dec 1980, vol. 2.

Message. 130800Z SEP 71. HQ 7AF TSN AFLD RVN. To CINCPACAF/DO, 9 July 1971. Subject: Pave Imp. File K318.2-448. AFHRA, Maxwell AFB, AL.

Message. 120900Z AUG 71. HQ 7AF TSN AFLD RVN. To PACAF and various, 9 July 1971. Subject: Pave Imp. File K318.2-448. AFHRA, Maxwell AFB, AL.

Message. 251620Z AUG 71. MAC. To CINCPACAF et al. Subject: Pave Imp Combat Eval. K318.2-448. AFHRA, Maxwell AFB, AL.

Message. 251620Z AUG 71. MAC. To PACAF et al., 9 July 1971. Subject: Pave Imp Combat Eval. File K318.2-448. AFHRA, Maxwell AFB, AL.

Message. 191331Z MAY 70. CSAF. To MAC. Subject: Pave Star Night Recovery System. In History of Military Airlift Command, 1 July 1969–30 June 1970, vol. 12, supplemental docs. K300.01, FY 1970. AFHRA, Maxwell AFB, AL.

Message. 212209Z MAY 70. CSAF. To AFSC, MAC et al., 21 May 1970. Subject: Pave Star. K168.1621. AFHRA, Maxwell AFB, AL.

Message. 56SPOWG. To 7AF/DO and MACVSOG/Saigon. Subject: Prairie Fire Missions. In History of the 56th Special Operations Wing, 1 Jan–31 Mar 1969, vol. 2, History of the 21st Special Operations Squadron.

Robinson, Col Jack, 56 SOW commander. To 7AF/CC. Subject: Improvements in Search and Rescue (SAR) Capabilities. Letter, 30 Dec 1971. In History of the 56th Special Operations Wing, Oct–Dec 1971. Vol. 2. AFHRA, Maxwell AFB, AL.

To secretary of defense. Memorandum. Subject: Rotary-Wing Support for Special Operations, 10 July 1984. Establishment File, Assignment of Forces to SOCOM. SOCOM/HO, MacDill AFB, FL.

21 SOS/DO. To Lt Col Gregory Lengyel. Memorandum. Subject: Mission Commander AAA for 21–22 May 2002 Rescue Mission. Provided to the author by TSgt John Hickman.

Miscellaneous

Air Force Instruction 36-2805. *Special Trophies and Awards*, 29 June 2001.

Assistant Secretary of Defense/Public Affairs (ASD/PA), Wright-Patterson AFB, OH. News release. Public Affairs Memorandum (PAM) 80-126, n.d. In Gambone, *Pave Low III: That Others May Live*, supplemental docs.

Briefing books. Secretary of the Air Force. Directorate of Long-Range Power Projection, Special Operations Forces, Airlift and Training (SAF/AQQU). Pentagon, Washington, DC. Provided to the author by Col Bill Bassett.

Burns, James. "Green Hornets Case Their Flag . . . The End of an Era." Hurlburt Field, FL, 16–18 Oct 2008. A personal account. http://www.rotorheadsrus.us/documents/GREEN%20HORNETS%20CASE%20THEIR%20FLAG.pdf.

Cassidy, Gen Duane. Oral history interview. Transcript, 4 Aug and 17 Aug 1989. AFHRA, Maxwell AFB, AL.

Crawford, MSgt Robert. "Nomads of the Pacific: Chronology of the 31st SOS, 6 April 1989–31 December 2000." Pamphlet, n.d. AFSOC/HO, Hurlburt Field, FL.

Establishment File. Assignment of Forces to SOCOM. USSOCOM/HO, MacDill AFB, FL.

Executive Summary. Aircraft Accident Investigation MH–53M S/N 69–05794. Hurlburt Field, Florida, 7 Sept 2007. USAF Safety Center, Kirtland AFB, NM.

Executive Summary. Helicopter Accident Investigation MH-53M #70-1625, n.d. Office of the Judge Advocate General, Hurlburt Field, FL.

General Patterson's testimony to House Armed Services Committee panel on SOF forces. Point papers, 4 Dec 1985. Heritage File, box 51. AFSOC/HO, Hurlburt Field, FL.

Hutto, Cong. Earl. Special Collection. John C. Pace Library, University of West Florida, Pensacola, FL.

The National Defense Authorization Act for Fiscal Year 1987. Public Law 99-661, 99th Cong., 2d sess., 14 Nov 1986.

Nomination Package for Col Bill Takacs, USAF, retired, for the Air Commando Hall of Fame, n.d. Provided to the author by Col Gary Weikel, USAF, retired.

Operation Just Cause. File 220.00. Operation Allied Force (OAF) file. 1st/16th SOW HO, Hurlburt Field, FL.

Operations Desert Shield/Storm. File 500.600, Task Force (TF) Normandy. OAF file. 1st/16th SOW HO, Hurlburt Field, FL.

The Pave Cave. MH-53H/J/M Pave Low community website. http://www.thepavecave.com.

Pave Low file, Jan 1990. AFOTEC/HO, Kirtland AFB, NM.

Program Management Directive 5249 (2), 10 Jan 1986. In briefing books. Historical files, Secretary of the Air Force, Directorate of Long-Range Power Projection, Special Operations Forces, Airlift and Training (SAF/AQQU). Pentagon, Washington, DC. Provided to the author by Col Bill Bassett.

Program Management Directive for Class V Modification to Upgrade H-53 Aircraft to the MH-53 Pave Low "Enhanced" Configuration with SOF Improvements, 9 Mar 1989. Provided to the author by Lt Col Ed Reed, USAF, retired.

"Quotes." Permanent file, box 253. AFSOC/HO, Hurlburt Field, FL.

Sikorsky Aircraft Ship Number Master List, 8 June 2002, 37–38, 53–55. Sikorsky Aircraft Corporation, archival collections, Stratford, CT.

Staff Summary Sheet. Doctrinal Employment Concept of MH-53 and HC-130 Aircraft, 7 Dec 1987, and supplemental docs. File SOJ3 MC-130/MH 53 Basing Proposals. USSOCOM/HO, Hurlburt Field, FL.

USAF MH-53J Helicopter Requirements, point paper, n.d. In briefing books. Historical files, Secretary of the Air Force, Directorate of Long-Range Power Projection, Special Operations Forces, Airlift and Training (SAF/AQQU). Pentagon, Washington, DC. Provided to the author by Col Bill Bassett.

Vietnam Search and Rescue Database. Website hosted by PJs in Vietnam to provide pararescue and Air Rescue Service history. http://www.pjsinnam.com/Database1_interface/SARList.

Vogt, Gen John. Oral history interview. Transcript, 8–9 Aug 1978. AFHRA, Maxwell AFB, AL.

White House. "President Bush Delivers Graduation Speech at West Point." Press release, 1 June 2002. http://www.whitehouse.gov /news/releases/2002/06/20020601-3.html.

———."President's Address to the Nation." Press release, 10 Jan 2007. http:// georgewbush-whitehouse.archives.gov/news/releases/2007/01 /20070110-7.html.

Wurster, Lt Col Donny, SAF/AQQU. Point paper. Conversion of Additional MH–53Js, n.d. SAF/AQQU briefing book. Provided to the author by Col Bill Bassett.

Index

On a Steel Horse I Ride

A History of the MH-53 Pave Low Helicopters in War and Peace

Air University Press Team

Chief Editor
Jeanne K. Shamburger

Copy Editor
Sandi Davis

Cover Art, Book Design, and Illustrations
L. Susan Fair

Composition and Prepress Production
Nedra Looney

Print Preparation and Distribution
Diane Clark

MH-53M #68-10357 on display at the National Museum of the US Air Force

ABOUT THE BOOK

THE STEEL HORSES. Born of necessity in the long war in Southeast Asia, the US Air Force fleet of 52 HH-53s and 20 CH-53s was initially developed for search and rescue and special operations missions. After that conflict, US Air Force leaders recognized the need for a night, all-weather rescue capability, and nine of the aircraft were modified under a program called Pave Low, with evolutional radar and precision navigational capabilities to fulfill that requirement. However, when a place in Iran called Desert One clearly revealed the larger and more dramatic need for such a capability, these aircraft—and eventually the entire remaining US Air Force fleet of HH- and CH-53s—were reassigned specifically to support our growing special operations forces. Further modified and redesignated as MH-53Js and MH-53Ms, they subsequently flew and fought in every major US military action until their inactivation in Iraq in September 2008, when the last six of the 30 surviving aircraft flew their final sorties in combat.

BUT THE STORY is not just about the helicopters. It is also about the great Airmen—officers and enlisted members—who conceptualized, created, operated, maintained, loved, and, yes, sometimes cursed their Steel Horses. They and their great aircraft were the reality of Any Time, Any Place. This is their story, the men and machines, from first to last, presented with deepest appreciation and respect. Well done and hand salute!